Lippincott's
State Board Review
for NCLEX – PN

EDITION 3

Preface

Most people would agree that the best way to prepare for a state licensing examination is to use good study habits while enrolled in an educational program for nursing. This includes keeping up-to-date in both clinical and classroom work. However, many candidates feel more secure and at ease when they plan for a period of concentrated review before taking a state licensing examination.

Lippincott's State Board Review for NCLEX–PN, third edition, has been written to help candidates prepare for taking a state practical nurse licensing examination. Features that make this review book especially helpful for persons preparing for such an examination are summarized as follows:

- The Test Plan adopted by the National Council of State Boards of Nursing for preparing the licensing examination for practical nurses was used as a guide to prepare this book. Care was used so that the items in this book measure major abilities as described in the Test Plan. There is further discussion concerning the Test Plan and the preparation of the licensing examination in the Introduction of this book.

- There are four units containing review tests in this book, as follows:

Unit I.   The Nursing Care of Patients With Mental Illnesses (Unit I contains 1 review test)

Unit II.   The Nursing Care of Maternity Patients and of Newborns (Unit II has 2 review tests)

Unit III.   The Nursing Care of Children (Unit III has 2 review tests)

Unit IV.   The Nursing Care of Adults With Medical/Surgical Disorders (Unit IV has 9 review tests)

It is hoped that this method of organization, according to clinical areas, will simplify reviewing by grouping items dealing with each clinical area together.

- There is a two-part comprehensive examination following the 14 review tests in this book. This examination, beginning on page 557, is as like the state licensing examination as possible. It contains a total of 240 items, 120 items in each of two parts, just as the two-part state licensing examination does. Both parts of the examination contain items related to all clinical areas, that is, mental health nursing, maternity nursing and the care of the newborn, nursing care of children, and medical/surgical nursing (adults). The examination is integrated in the same manner as the licensing examination. The review tests in this book are integrated in like manner. This means that items are included that relate to all basic courses studied in nursing, such as anatomy and physiology, pharmacology, diet therapy and nutrition, fundamentals of nursing, and psychosocial sciences that deal with legal/ethical issues, interpersonal relationships, communication, professional adjustments, human development (physical and psychosocial), and the like.

- All of the items and patient situations in this book resemble to the greatest degree possible the items and patient situations used in the state licensing examination. The type of items and patient situations used are described in the Introduction of this book. Of course, it is unlikely that an item in this book will be identical to any appearing in the licensing examination. However, the licensing examination uses common situations in which practical nurses work, and items dealing with typical nursing measures required by patients described in situations.

- Principles of test construction were observed in the preparation of items for this book, just as they are by persons responsible for the final preparation of items used in licensing examinations. Observing these principles helps to prepare items that are reliable and valid and that realistically resemble items appearing in licensing examinations.

- Correct answers are given for all items in this book at the end of each review test and of the comprehensive examination. A rationale for the correct answer is also offered, that is, there are reasons given concerning why the correct answer is the best answer and why incorrect answers are wrong. Studying the rationales along with the items offers an excellent review of practical nursing. A textbook and a page in that textbook where correct answers can be verified are furnished for still further help in reviewing as necessary.

- Persons using this book may wish to determine in what area of nursing they need extra study because they have not done well in selecting correct answers for certain items. This review book has classified each item in one of six categories. By following directions for using this classification system, described on page xxiv in the Introduction of this book, it is easy to identify areas of weakness where further study is indicated.

- There are 1,603 items in the 14 review tests in this book and 240 items in the two-part comprehensive examination, for a total of 1,843 items. Many items new to this edition have been added, and outdated and questionable items from the previous edition have been discarded. No review book or licensing examination can cover all aspects of nursing. However, because of the generous sampling of knowledge in this book, an extensive review of an educational program to prepare students of practical nursing is offered.

- An experienced clinical nurse and faculty member was consulted on the items in this review book. Her expertise was helpful in assuring accuracy and relevancy in the practice of nursing today. Care was taken to avoid testing regional practices and policies.

- YOU ARE URGED TO READ THE INTRODUCTION OF THIS BOOK. The Introduction, which begins on page xix, offers many suggestions that will help candidates to use this book as well as how to prepare for and write a state licensing examination. To omit reading the Introduction may well diminish the value of reviewing when preparing to write a state licensing examination.

Although this book's primary purpose is to help candidates prepare for state licensing examinations, it can serve other purposes also. For example, the book can be used to prepare for various types of achievement tests in nursing. Inactive practical nurses who wish to return to nursing will find the book useful for review and self-appraisal. Persons who will write challenge examinations for advanced school credit are encouraged to use the book for review purposes. Faculty members may find the book helpful for developing ideas for teaching and evaluation.

The ultimate purpose of this book will have been reached when its use helps nurses offer high quality care to their patients.

The author wishes to take this opportunity to thank Rand Lyons, L.P.N. In most instances, Rand limits his practice of nursing to caring for patients in their homes. He offered helpful suggestions on situations dealing with home-care patients and shared ideas concerning their nursing-care needs.

LuVerne Wolff Lewis, R.N., M.A.

Acknowledgment

The author expresses sincere thanks for the expert review of test items presented in this book to

Bonnie Marie Ewald, R.N., B.S.N., M.S.
   Faculty, Department of Nursing
   Glendale Community College
   Glendale, Arizona

Contents

Introduction

What Is NCLEX – PN?

The acronym, NCLEX – PN, stands for the *N*ational *C*ouncil *L*icensure *E*xamination for *P*ractical *N*urses.

The National Council of State Boards of Nursing, whose Examination Committee is responsible for developing .NCLEX – PN, is made up of representatives from all state boards of nursing. The member boards of nursing consist of all of this country's states, the District of Columbia, and U.S. territories (Guam, American Samoa and the Virgin Islands). The word, state, is used to refer to all member boards for ease in reading.

All states use NCLEX – PN except California. However, the California licensing examination is similar to NCLEX – PN, and therefore, this book offers a review for all persons about to write an examination for licensure, including persons who will take California's licensure examination.

In some states, the terms, vocational nurses and vocational nursing, are used instead of practical nurses and practical nursing. Practical and vocational student nurses have similar educational programs, and all candidates for licensure take identical examinations. For ease in reading, the terms, practical nurse and practical nursing, are used in this book.

What Is the Purpose of NCLEX – PN?

Each of the state boards of nursing is given the responsibility by its legislature to regulate licensure for practical nurses and practical nursing within its jurisdiction. The responsibility includes determining an individual's competency to practice nursing in its state. A license issued by the state indicates that the holder of the license has been judged to be a safe practitioner in practical nursing.

NCLEX – PN helps state boards of nursing determine whether you are ready to give safe and effective nursing care. The examination tests your ability to apply knowledge in health care situations that require the services of a practical nurse.

How Is NCLEX – PN Prepared?

The National Council of State Boards of Nursing is responsible for developing NCLEX – PN. A test plan, discussed later, is prepared first, which must then be approved by representatives of the state boards of nursing. The states submit names of people to the National Council who write the examination items. Representative item writers are selected on the basis of their expertise, the area of the country in which they work, and the type of educational program in nursing or nursing service agency in which they work.

After items are reviewed and approved by the state boards of nursing, they are selected for use in NCLEX – PN. So-called try-out items are placed throughout the licensing examination. These items are then analyzed to determine whether they function well in helping to judge if a candidate knows nursing content sufficiently well to practice safe and effective nursing. Well-constructed items are used in later licensing examinations. Poorly constructed and ambiguous items are discarded. You will not know which items in NCLEX–PN are try-out items but these items do *not* count in your final NCLEX–PN score.

What Is the Test Plan Used to Prepare NCLEX–PN?

A specially-constructed Test Plan is used to guide persons responsible for constructing NCLEX–PN. The Plan describes categories of nursing content that are covered in the licensing examination, as well as practice settings in which practical nurses work and the age range of patients for whom practical nurses provide care. The Plan also contains categories that deal with changes in how a human functions during illness.

    The Test Plan used for NCLEX–PN was followed while preparing the review tests and the comprehensive examination presented in this book. Persons interested in more detailed information concerning the NCLEX–PN Test Plan are advised to write to the National Council of State Boards of Nursing, 625 North Michigan, Suite 1544, Chicago, Illinois 60611.

What Type of Item Is Used in NCLEX–PN?

The items in the licensing examinations change for each test. However, the items are of the same type, that is, all items in NCLEX–PN are objective and each one consists of two parts, as follows:

    The Stem. The stem presents a problem and is stated as a question or an incomplete sentence. The example below illustrates.

    The Options. The options present four alternatives from which you select one correct or best answer. The other three options are incorrect answers and are sometimes called distractors. The following examples illustrate:

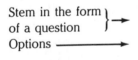 Which chamber of the heart normally receives oxygenated blood from the pulmonary veins?
1. The left atrium
2. The right atrium
3. The left ventricle
4. The right ventricle

Option 1 is the correct answer. Options 2, 3, and 4 are incorrect answers, or distractors.

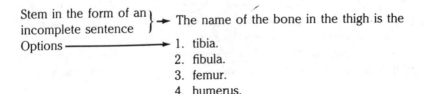 The name of the bone in the thigh is the
1. tibia.
2. fibula.
3. femur.
4. humerus.

Option 3 is the correct answer. Options 1, 2, and 4 are incorrect answers, or distractors.

There may be times when you believe the options do not offer the best possible response in a particular situation. Nevertheless, you are asked to select the best answer among the choices given.

How Are Patient Situations Used in NCLEX – PN?

With few exceptions, the test items in NCLEX – PN, as well as in this book, are given following a description of a patient. Here is an example of a patient situation:

> Two-year-old Christie Hawkins is hospitalized with croup. Christie is dyspneic and coughing.

> The items that follow this situation relate to Christie's nursing care.

How Do I Indicate my Choice for a Correct Answer in NCLEX – PN?

NCLEX – PN does *not* use answer sheets. You will be asked to blacken a circle with a pencil in your test booklet directly in front of the option you have chosen for the correct or best answer. This procedure helps eliminate errors because you may have lost your place on an answer sheet. Still, you should take care so that you correctly blacken the proper circle.

This review book offers you practice in indicating your choice for the answer in the same manner as you will when you take NCLEX – PN, that is, by blackening a circle with a pencil in this book directly in front of the option you have chosen as the correct answer. Additionally, perforated answer sheets for each test are provided, beginning on page 651, if you wish to avoid marking in this book.

Should I Make a Guess When Not Sure of the Correct Answer for an Item in NCLEX – PN?

NCLEX – PN does *not* correct scores for guessing. The total number of correct answers you chose in the licensing examination becomes your final raw score.* Therefore, it is to your advantage to guess when you are not sure of the correct answer because you have nothing to lose by doing so.

It is suggested that you make an educated guess rather than selecting your answer at random. After studying the item, if you are still unsure, read the four options again *carefully.* Rule out any option(s) you believe to be wrong. Then concentrate on the

---

*Raw scores are statistically treated to produce standardized scores, which are the final scores reported to each state board of nursing.

remaining options and try to select the correct answer. For example, if you believe two of the options are definitely wrong, you have a 50-50 chance of guessing which one of the remaining two options is correct. Even if you can find only one of the four options in the item that you believe is wrong, you still have a 1-in-3 chance of guessing the correct answer from the remaining three options. This is a better chance than randomly selecting one of the four options as your correct answer. Also, as you study an item's options to rule out the obviously incorrect answer(s), if you study the item carefully, you may well determine the correct answer by careful reasoning without having to guess.

How Long Is NCLEX-PN and When Is the Examination Offered?

NCLEX-PN consists of two parts, each one containing 120 items. You are allowed two hours to complete each part. Usual procedure is to take one part in the morning and one part in the afternoon on the day of the examination.

NCLEX-PN is offered twice a year, in April and October. All states offer NCLEX-PN on the same date in each of these two months. You can obtain the dates for taking NCLEX-PN from the office of the board of nursing in the state in which you plan to write the examination.

Who Decides the Pass/Fail Score for NCLEX-PN?

Each state has the responsibility of determining a passing score in its own jurisdiction. The pass/fail score is not necessarily the same for all states. However, most states use the same pass/fail score, which is arrived at from a statistical analysis of all scores, as prepared by the National Council of State Boards of Nursing.

What Happens if I Fail NCLEX-PN?

Each state notifies candidates in its jurisdiction whether they failed or passed NCLEX-PN. Those candidates who have failed are provided with a diagnostic profile so that they know their particular areas of weaknesses in nursing competency as measured by NCLEX-PN. The primary purpose of the diagnostic profile is to help candidates who fail so that they can better prepare for taking the licensing examination again.

Can Foreign-educated Nurses Take NCLEX-PN?

Yes, foreign-educated nurses can take NCLEX-PN. However, before they can take the examination, they must first meet requirements set up in the state where they take the licensing examination. An example of such a requirement is that in most states, foreign-educated nurses are asked to present credentials describing the course of study in the country where they studied. When foreign-educated nurses are eligible for taking NCLEX–PN, this review book offers an excellent review for them, just as it does for American-educated persons.

How Can I Best Use this Book While Preparing for NCLEX–PN?

• Plan your review for the licensing examination well in advance. Use whatever techniques suit you best. This may include reviewing your texts and classroom notes. Then take the review tests in this book. Whichever way you choose to review, give yourself sufficient time.

• Blacken the circle in front of the option you choose for your correct answer. This same procedure for indicating your choice for the correct answer is used in NCLEX–PN, as described earlier.

• Avoid looking at the correct answers at the end of the test before completing each test. You will defeat your reason for reviewing if you begin by looking at the answers.

• Do not look for clues to correct answers among the items in this book. Spend your time on understanding the information being tested. The correct answers are randomized, that is, they do not follow a pattern.

• Read *carefully*, think logically, and use only the information you are given. You can easily select a wrong answer when you have missed such words as "best," "least," "contraindicated," and the like, when you have not thought out what knowledge the item is testing, or when you make assumptions.

• Concentrate on understanding knowledge upon which each item is based and on understanding why wrong options are incorrect. Trying to memorize information is futile in helping you review.

• Ask questions concerning each item, such as those that follow, for still further review. Do you understand the knowledge upon which the item was based? Do you understand why each wrong option is incorrect? Could you have answered the item correctly if the answer had been the stem and the stem had been stated as an option? Is there additional information about the patient that was not sampled in these tests but which is important, in your opinion, and in need of further review?

• Apply basic principles to new or unfamiliar health care situations when you have had little or no experience with the situation you are given. Unfamiliar situations will help call your attention to areas in which further study may be indicated.

• Be prepared to find that some patients described in this book may have health problems not directly related to their present reason for seeking health care. For example, a patient who requires the surgical removal of a diseased organ may have diabetes mellitus. This book, like NCLEX–PN, is based on a philosophy that patients—not diseases—require care. It is hoped that the manner in which situations are presented will help you focus on a patient in need of care that will help him maintain health, cope with health problems, recover from the effects of illnesses or trauma, or meet death with comfort and dignity.

- Pace yourself occasionally. For example, plan to complete each test in approximately two hours. If you are falling behind, practice working faster. If you are ahead, be sure you are proceeding carefully and consider slowing your pace somewhat.
- Refer to the section on Correct Answers and Rationales *after* you have completed a test. Make a check mark next to the items that you answered incorrectly and return to them for more study. Consider if you answered incorrectly because you did not know the information. In that case, plan for a review of the subject matter. If you answered incorrectly because you did not read the item carefully or because you carelessly blackened the wrong circle when choosing the answer, plan to practice reading and answering the items with greater care.
- Study the rationales given for each item. They often contain information in addition to the specific knowledge being tested, and hence, will help you complete a more thorough review. Also, use the texts referred to at the end of each rationale for further study, as indicated.
- Seriously practice taking the tests in this book, as though you were writing the licensing examination. This type of practice will familiarize you with taking a test that resembles NCLEX – PN, which may be as important as reviewing the subject content.
- After you have completed the 14 review tests, plan to take Part I and Part II of the Comprehensive Examination, beginning on page 557. This two-part test will serve as a final review to determine how well you do when confronted with an examination most nearly resembling NCLEX – PN.

After Taking the Tests in this Book, How Can I Learn in Which Areas I Need Additional Review in Preparation for NCLEX – PN?

Suggestions given in the previous section on how to use this review book to your greatest advantage will often help you identify areas where you believe you need further review.

Also, following each of the review tests in this book, there is a table that classifies items. You can use these tables to determine which items you answered correctly according to clinical area and subject matter.

After completing the 14 review tests, turn to pages 553 – 556 to enter information on classification tables for each test in the one summary-type table.

Directions are given with all tables on how to use them properly. By completing these tables as directed, you can easily determine in which clinical areas and in which subject-matter areas you most probably need further review before writing NCLEX – PN.

How Can I Best Prepare for the Day on Which I Shall Take NCLEX – PN?

The following suggestions, some of which resemble those offered earlier on how to use this book, will help you prepare for taking NCLEX – PN:
- Follow instructions concerning the licensing examination in your state for completing application forms, submitting fees, and the like. Allow sufficient time for such requirements.

- Know the location of the room in which the examination is offered. Become familiar with transportation, parking, and eating facilities. Many persons recommend that you do a "dry run" so that you are thoroughly acquainted with how you will travel to where you must go and how much time it takes. You may wish to bring your lunch if eating facilities are inconvenient or unsatisfactory.

- Review as you feel necessary over a period of time. Cramming is not recommended. Last-minute, hurried study actually may interfere with your understanding of the total body of knowledge being tested.

- Use relaxation exercises or meditation techniques when you feel anxious as you prepare for the examination. The method you choose to use to relax is an individual matter, but reducing anxiety will permit you to be better prepared to take NCLEX–PN.

- Plan some leisure-time activity each day before the examination. This is healthful and also helps relieve tension and worry.

- Have sufficient rest and a good night's sleep before the examination. A tired person has more difficulty concentrating and tends to become more tense and confused than a rested person.

- Eat a nourishing breakfast before the examination. Having only a cup of coffee or a glass of juice prepares you poorly for a day of concentrated work.

- Try some exercise, such as a brisk walk, immediately before the examination. This often helps one to relax.

- Wear comfortable clothing that is suitable for the season. It is a good idea to bring a sweater, which can be worn or removed during the examination.

- Do not plan to take books or notes to the licensing examination. You will not be allowed to take them into the examining room. Scrap paper and pencils are provided.

Are There Ways in Which I Can Help Myself While Taking NCLEX–PN?

- Approach the examination with a feeling of confidence and a positive mental attitude. Worrying about the examination or having a negative attitude can stand in the way of sound thinking.

- Listen carefully and follow all instructions given to you at the time of the examination. Be sure to give all identifying information accurately — your name, address, and school of nursing, for example.

- Be aware of exactly how much time you have for the examination. Pace yourself properly; avoid the stress of running out of time. Skip items when you are unsure and come back to them later for more thorough consideration. If at all possible, the examination should be completed in order to obtain the best possible score.

- Read each item carefully. Be aware of such words as "most," "best," and "contraindicated." Overlooking key words can result in giving a wrong answer, even when you know the information being tested.

- Eliminate the obviously incorrect responses and then focus your attention on the other options. This avoids unnecessary and time-consuming reading as you concentrate on the best possible choice for the correct answer.

- Use an educated, well thought-out guess if you are unsure of the correct answer. You will not be penalized for guessing.

- Do not read inferences into an item. Use only the information you are given without making assumptions or asking yourself, "What if . . ." Do not look for tricky interpretations and then proceed to miss the obvious.
- Assume the nurses described in NCLEX–PN are practical nurses. You will be informed if a care-taker being described in an item is not a practical nurse.
- Remember that correct answers are randomized throughout NCLEX–PN and do not follow a pattern.

What Editorial Policies Are Observed in this Book and in the State Licensing Examination?

Certain policies are observed for consistency, clarity, and ease of reading, as follows:
- The word *patient* is used to refer to persons receiving services from health-care personnel, although it is recognized that the term client may be used in some health agencies.
- Feminine pronouns are used when referring to a nurse. Male pronouns are used when referring to a physician. This was done with no slight intended to the increasing ranks of male nurses and female physicians.
- The title *Mr.* is used when referring to men. The title *Ms.* is used when referring to women. Given names are used for children and teenagers.
- Generic names of drugs are used. Common brand, or trade, names are given in parentheses following the generic names when they first appear in a situation.

Lippincott's
State Board Review
for NCLEX-PN

EDITION 3

UNIT I

Review Test 1

The Nursing Care of Patients with Mental Illnesses

Review Test 1

The Nursing Care of Patients Attending the Clinic of a Community Mental Health Center

Attending a Conference for New Employees
Caring for a Patient With Agoraphobia
Caring for a Patient With an Obsessive–Compulsive Disorder
Caring for a Patient With Hypochondriasis
Caring for a Patient Having Group Therapy
Caring for a Patient Having Amitriptyline Therapy
Caring for a Patient Suffering With Loneliness
Caring for a Patient With Infantile Autism
Caring for a Patient With Anorexia Nervosa

The Nursing Care of Patients in Mental Health Hospitals

Caring for a Patient With Regression
Caring for a Patient With a Bipolar Disorder
Caring for a Patient With Chronic Alcoholism
Caring for a Patient With Problems Due to Substance Abuse
Caring for a Patient With Schizophrenia
Caring for a Patient With Depression

The Nursing Care of Patients in the Dayroom of a Mental Health Hospital

Caring for a Patient With Abusive Behavior
Caring for a Patient With Numerous Physical Complaints
Caring for a Patient With an Inability to Recognize Reality
Caring for a Hyperactive Patient
Caring for a Patient With Impaired Sensory Perception
Caring for a Patient With Catatonia

Individual Items
Correct Answers and Rationales
Classification of Test Items

Directions: *With a pencil, blacken the circle in front of the option you have chosen for your correct answer.*

A Nurse Helps in the Care of Patients Attending the Clinic of a Community Health Center.

A nurse is recently employed to work in the clinic and attends confer-ences, conducted by a nursing supervisor, for new employees.

1 It is generally agreed that a nurse can best understand and accept the behavior of her patients when she first
   ⊘ 1. learns to understand her own behavior.
   ○ 2. analyzes what motivates patients' behaviors.
   ○ 3. is familiar with common abnormal behaviors.
   ○ 4. helps to counsel persons with behavior problems.

2 The supervisor describes a mental illness as a disorder characterized by the person's having
   ○ 1. organic abnormalities.
   ○ 2. moral and ethical weaknesses.
   ○ 3. maladaptive behavior to relieve anxiety.
   ○ 4. inclinations toward violent and aggressive behavior.

3 The nursing supervisor discusses with the new employees the psychosocial needs of patients. Of the following needs, it is usually believed that the one with the highest priority in life is the need for
   ○ 1. love.
   ○ 2. status.
   ○ 3. creativity.
   ○ 4. acquiring knowledge.

4 Anxiety disorders are discussed. A typical physical sign of anxiety is
   ○ 1. nausea.
   ○ 2. dizziness.
   ⊘ 3. heart palpitations.
   ○ 4. sensations of chillness.

5 Anxiety is also expressed through emotional feelings. Which of the following subjective signs is *least* likely to be described by an anxious person?
   ○ 1. Regretfulness
   ○ 2. Hostility
   ○ 3. Phobia
   ○ 4. Fear

6 Many authorities believe that some anxiety is a normal part of everyday living and that it is necessary to help persons develop skills to handle it. Healthy persons have been noted to handle anxiety by learning to
   ○ 1. resist it.
   ○ 2. ignore it.
   ○ 3. suppress it.
   ○ 4. cope with it.

7 A nurse asks, during the conference, about the incidence of alcoholism in the general population. The nursing supervisor is correct when she explains that during the last few decades, demographics indicate that the incidence of alcoholism has increased most among
   O 1. the elderly.
   O 2. people living in slums.
   O 3. single men and women.
   ⊙ 4. children and teenagers.

8 Various common forms of therapy being used to treat the mentally ill are discussed. Which of the following forms of therapy has had the greatest impact on the care of the mentally ill within the last 20 to 30 years?
   ⊙ 1. Group therapy
   O 2. Electroshock therapy
   O 3. Psychoanalytical therapy
   O 4. Psychopharmacological therapy

9 The nursing supervisor states that several patients attending the clinic have conduct disorders. The most typical behavior of a person with a conduct disorder is characterized by
   O 1. ideas of grandeur.
   O 2. a lack of respect for others' rights.
   O 3. feelings of contrition for his acts.
   O 4. an obsessive fear of being reprimanded for his acts.

10 A question arises concerning paranoid disorders. The nurse can anticipate that a patient with a paranoid disorder is most likely to demonstrate feelings of
   O 1. anger and aggression.
   O 2. suspicion and distrust.
   O 3. self-pity and self-centeredness.
   O 4. simultaneous hero-worship and hero-hating.

11 Behavior modification, used for several clinic patients, is discussed. Which of the following techniques is often used in behavior modification?
   O 1. A listing of behaviors that need modifying
   O 2. A token economy that rewards desired behaviors
   O 3. A type of hydrotherapy that promotes complete relaxation
   O 4. A purposeful exploration of why the patient behaves as he does

12 The subject of stress and the Social Readjustment Rating Scale is discussed. If a patient experiences the following events, which one is likely causing her the greatest stress?
   O 1. The person is about to retire.
   O 2. The person has recently divorced her husband.
   O 3. The person's daughter is about to leave home to marry.
   O 4. The person recently experienced the death of a close friend.

13 Documentation is discussed. The nursing supervisor uses the following example of an entry in a patient's record: "Patient says, 'I feel unwanted.' Appears to be confused." Which of the following statements best describes why this entry is unsatisfactory?

O 1. The nurse fails to define the word "confused."
O 2. The nurse fails to indicate why the patient's statement is important.
O 3. The nurse fails to substantiate that the words in quotes are what the patient said.
O 4. The nurse fails to describe behavior which led her to believe that the patient is confused.

14 A nurse asks the supervisor to explain how a nurse empathizes with a patient. The supervisor explains correctly when she says a nurse is empathizing with a patient when the nurse

O 1. offers the patient encouragement.
O 2. helps the patient describe his feelings.
O 3. describes the patient's feelings about his illness.
O 4. tries to understand the patient's feelings by placing herself in the patient's situation.

15 The nursing supervisor discusses the concept of milieu therapy. Which of the following statements is *least* characteristic of a therapeutic milieu?

O 1. A therapeutic milieu allows a patient to help make decisions about his care.
O 2. A therapeutic milieu encourages a patient to be responsible for his behavior.
O 3. A therapeutic milieu encourages a patient to expect improvement in his behavior.
O 4. A therapeutic milieu eliminates psychopharmacological agents from the patient's plan of care.

16 Some of Freud's theories are discussed. Ego is the aspect of the personality that, according to Freud, influences behavior by

O 1. helping a person to decide which types of behavior are right and wrong.
O 2. allowing a person to develop appropriate feelings of guilt and anxiety.
O 3. developing an unconscious code of behavior that is consistent with a person's cultural background.
O 4. assessing the environment so that a person's needs may be met in ways that coincide with reality.

17 According to Freud, superego is the aspect of the mind that influences behavior by

O 1. functioning as a person's sense of conscience.
O 2. enabling a person to develop appropriate defenses for anxiety.
O 3. enabling a person to satisfy his instinct for seeking pleasure and avoiding pain.
O 4. allowing the person to postpone immediate gratification in favor of future goals.

Ms. Davis seeks help at the clinic because of agoraphobia.

18 Ms. Davis has a fear of
  ○ 1. germs.
  ○ 2. flying.
  ○ 3. open spaces.
  ○ 4. confined areas.

19 Nursing care efforts for Ms. Davis are best directed toward helping the patient understand her phobia and further exploring with her
  ○ 1. where she could turn for in-depth psychiatric therapy.
  ○ 2. why her coping efforts are failing to relieve the phobia.
  ○ 3. what experiences in her past may have contributed to her phobia.
  ⊗ 4. how she can best make adjustments so that her phobia will not interfere with her activities of daily living.

Mr. Garcia has an obsessive–compulsive disorder.

20 Which of the following types of behavior would be most typical for Mr. Garcia?
  ◐ 1. Having a need to brush his teeth repeatedly
  ○ 2. Having a need to leave groups of people repeatedly
  ○ 3. Having intermittent but regularly occurring bouts of amnesia
  ○ 4. Having intermittent but regularly occurring periods of partial paralysis

21 Mr. Garcia's obsessive–compulsive behavior is a result of Mr. Garcia's attempt to
  ○ 1. reduce anxiety.
  ○ 2. manipulate others.
  ○ 3. pretend to have a mental illness.
  ○ 4. avoid a necessity to deal with others.

22 The members of Mr. Garcia's nuclear family are listed in the patient's record. Who makes up the members of Mr. Garcia's nuclear family?
  ○ 1. The patient and his spouse
  ○ 2. The patient and his parents
  ○ 3. The patient, his spouse, and their children
  ○ 4. The patient, his spouse, their children and a relative who lives with them

The nurse interviews Ms. Baker, a clinical patient with a diagnosis of hypochondriasis.

23 After completing the admission interview with Ms. Baker, the nurse tells a co-worker, "Ms. Baker sounds just like any other hypochondriac to me." Such a statement, which stereotypes a patient, is likely to distort the nurse's judgment because stereotyping tends to

- ○ 1. disallow each patient's uniqueness.
- ○ 2. support the patient's inappropriate behavior.
- ○ 3. violate the confidentiality between the nurse and patient.
- ○ 4. diminish the seriousness of the patient's health problem and prognosis.

24 Ms. Baker has been coming to the clinic for several months. One day she says to the nurse, "Do you think I'll ever be able to stop these visits?" In this situation, it would be best for the nurse to say

- ○ 1. "That is something you should discuss with your doctor."
- ○ 2. "It sounds as though you are discouraged with your progress."
- ○ 3. "Let us worry about that while you concentrate on getting well."
- ○ 4. "You are fine, but you will need to practice a little more patience."

Six patients meet regularly at the clinic for group therapy.

25 If the following goals are developed by the patients in the group, the one that is *least* likely to be met through group therapy is

- ○ 1. changing socially unacceptable behavior.
- ○ 2. understanding their own behaviors more fully.
- ○ 3. developing satisfactory relationships with others in the group.
- ○ 4. learning skills to help others who are in need of counseling.

26 Mr. Jeffry becomes angry one day during a group session and says, "You people certainly aren't helping me feel better!" In this situation, it is best for the nurse to acknowledge the patient's anger and then

- ○ 1. listen to what the patient says.
- ○ 2. divert the patient's attention to other things.
- ○ 3. leave the patient alone to work out his emotions.
- ○ 4. help the patient understand that his behavior is not helping him.

Ms. Fowler, a clinic patient, takes amitriptyline hydrochloride (Elavil).

27 The nurse should understand that amitriptyline hydrochloride is most likely prescribed for Ms. Fowler because she is experiencing signs of

- ○ 1. anxiety.
- ○ 2. paranoia.
- ○ 3. depression.
- ○ 4. hyperactivity.

28 The nurse should also understand that amitriptyline hydrochloride is contraindicated for Ms. Fowler if she has a medical diagnosis of

- ○ 1. glaucoma.
- ○ 2. psoriasis.
- ○ 3. diabetes mellitus.
- ○ 4. pernicious anemia.

The nurse is caring for Ms. Jarvis, who is having emotional problems because of loneliness.

29 Ms. Jarvis says she feels "down and worthless." In what age range is loneliness most often observed as an important emotional problem?
  ○ 1. During adolescent years
  ○ 2. During the fourth decade of life
  ○ 3. During the fifth decade of life
  ○ 4. After about age 65

30 When interviewing Ms. Jarvis, the nurse wishes to obtain information about the patient's family. Of the following questions and statements, which one is likely to elicit the most information for the nurse?
  ○ 1. "Tell me about your family."
  ○ 2. "Have you been married more than once?"
  ○ 3. "Give me the ages of your family members."
  ○ 4. "Would you describe your marriage as a good one?"

Mr. and Ms. Gaynor have been bringing their 3-year-old child, Brent, who has infantile autism, to the clinic.

31 How is Brent most likely to react when the nurse attempts to touch and hug him?
  ○ 1. The child is likely to push the nurse aside.
  ○ 2. The child is likely to babble incoherently at the nurse.
  ○ 3. The child is likely to direct profane language at the nurse.
  ○ 4. The child is likely to return the nurse's show of affection for him.

32 The Gaynors say that Brent started to take finger foods but then reverted and refused to eat anything unless he was fed. In this situation, it is best for the nurse to teach the parents to
  ○ 1. feed the child while ignoring his behavior.
  ○ 2. put a spoon in the child's hand, fill it with food, and guide the spoon to his mouth.
  ○ 3. remove the food while explaining to the child that he will be hungrier by the next mealtime.
  ○ 4. pretend to taste the food, comment about how good it is, and offer the child a spoon to feed himself.

33 The nurse explains to Brent's parents how important it is to have a therapeutic milieu for Brent. The word *milieu* is used to refer to a
  ○ 1. health team.
  ○ 2. medical program.
  ○ 3. total environment.
  ○ 4. health care facility.

34 The nurse should teach Brent's parents that the surroundings that will be best for Brent are those that are
  ○ 1. interesting, with a variety of stimuli.

○ 2. consistent, with a minimum amount of change.
○ 3. creative, with activities that bring out artistic talents.
○ 4. social, with frequent opportunities to be with others.

Three patients are attending the clinic because of the eating disorder, anorexia nervosa.

35 In which of the following age groups can the nurse predict these patients will most likely fall?
○ 1. In late childhood, 9 to 12 years of age
○ 2. In adolescence, between 12 and 18 years of age
○ 3. In middle adulthood, between 30 and 50 years of age
○ 4. In late adulthood, between 50 and 65 years of age

36 The three patients with anorexia nervosa require that the nurse pay particular attention to their nutritional needs because death from this disorder usually results from cardiovascular failure due to
○ 1. anemia.
○ 2. renal failure.
○ 3. liver necrosis.
○ 4. electrolyte imbalances.

37 It is generally agreed that patients with anorexia nervosa are suffering from
○ 1. a hormonal imbalance.
○ 2. a distorted body image.
○ 3. a hereditary tendency to lose weight.
○ 4. an inability to resist peer pressures.

Mr. Shorham is hospitalized because of regression from normal activities of daily living. Among the nurse's goals of care are helping Mr. Shorham attend to his personal hygienic and dietary needs.

38 Mr. Shorham spends most of his time in bed and neglects his personal hygiene. To encourage the patient to participate in his care, the best course of action for the nurse to take would be to prepare articles for personal grooming and then
○ 1. help the patient to bathe and shave.
○ 2. give the patient a bath and shave him.
○ 3. explain to the patient that he must bathe and shave himself.
○ 4. tell the patient he will feel better after he has bathed and shaved himself.

39 To encourage Mr. Shorham to eat an adequate diet, which of the following courses of action is best for the nurse to follow?
○ 1. Serve the patient his food at his bedside.
○ 2. Tell the patient it will make his wife happy if he eats.
○ 3. Serve small portions of food and stay with the patient while he eats.

   ○ 4. Tell the patient that he must eat and point out the dangers of excess weight loss.

Mr. Shorham tells the nurse, "Everyone would be better off if I were dead. I could jump out of that window and it would be all over."

40 Of the following responses the nurse could make, it would be best for her to say to Mr. Shorham,
   ○ 1. "What would the doctor say if he heard you talking that way?"
   ○ 2. "If you continue to say things like that, we will have to restrain you."
   ○ 3. "You should not talk that way. It's such a beautiful day and your family will visit soon."
   ○ 4. "You must be feeling very sad today. I will stay with you and we'll go for a walk while we talk."

Mr. Zorn, who is brought to a hospital by his wife, has a bipolar disorder (mixed).

41 The nurse should expect that a characteristic behavior pattern Mr. Zorn is most likely to display due to his bipolar disorder is
   ○ 1. ritualistic behavior.
   ○ 2. symbolic aggressiveness.
   ○ 3. exaggerated mood swings.
   ○ 4. intermittent periods of amnesia.

42 The admitting nurse takes Mr. Zorn to his room. He says to the nurse, "My goodness, you are even more charming than the lady who admitted me. I see I have a private room. How about spending the night with me?" Of the following possible responses the nurse could make, which one would be best in this situation?
   ○ 1. "Don't say that. Someone may hear you."
   ○ 2. "I am uncomfortable. Please stop speaking that way."
   ○ 3. "I think this is something we should discuss together with your doctor."
   ○ 4. "Let's find another patient and the three of us can go for a walk. We need the exercise."

43 While the admitting nurse converses with him, Mr. Zorn talks quickly and excitedly. Within a short time, he speaks of his car, the length of the nurse's hair, the color of his socks, the name of a friend, and his wife's cooking ability. This type of verbal expression is called
   ○ 1. word salad.
   ○ 2. ambivalence.
   ○ 3. confabulation.
   ○ 4. flight of ideas.

The nurse is required to deal with Mr. Zorn's frenzied and sometimes aggressive behavior.

44 Which of the following nursing activities would most probably be therapeutic for Mr. Zorn when he becomes very active?
- O 1. Interesting the patient in a jigsaw puzzle
- O 2. Tossing a ball back and forth with the patient
- O 3. Having the patient join others who are quietly watching television
- O 4. Starting the patient on reading a book that includes descriptions of one of his interests

45 Because of Mr. Zorn's behavior, the nurse should be especially alert that his nursing care includes giving him
- O 1. oral hygiene.
- O 2. special skin care.
- O 3. adequate nutrition.
- O 4. recreational activities.

46 Mr. Zorn argues with another patient and threatens to "beat up on" him. Which of the following courses of action is most therapeutic for the nurse to use in this situation?
- O 1. Medicate and seclude Mr. Zorn.
- O 2. Distract both patients with a puzzle.
- O 3. Take Mr. Zorn for a walk without the other patient.
- O 4. Ask both patients to describe their disagreement in a quiet manner.

Mr. Zorn is receiving lithium carbonate (Lithane).

47 Of the following methods, the one which the nurse should anticipate will be used to monitor lithium levels in Mr. Zorn's body is
- O 1. carefully observing changes in the patient's behavior.
- O 2. carefully observing changes in the patient's eye grounds.
- O 3. regularly analyzing urine specimens obtained from the patient.
- O 4. regularly analyzing blood specimens obtained from the patient.

48 Monitoring lithium carbonate levels in Mr. Zorn's body is especially important because a characteristic of lithium is that it has
- O 1. a relatively rapid onset.
- O 2. an unusually long duration of action.
- O 3. a high potential for abuse and addiction.
- O 4. a relatively narrow range between therapeutic and toxic doses.

49 When Mr. Zorn has a bout of diarrhea and complains of drowsiness following lithium use, the nurse is correct when she judges that the patient very likely is developing
- O 1. a tolerance for the drug.
- O 2. a toxic reaction to the drug.
- O 3. an allergic reaction to the drug.

○ 4. an interaction with other drugs that the patient receives.

The nurse reads Mr. Zorn's record and notes that he was a patient the previous year, when he was depressed and dejected and spoke often of how he deserved torture for the many wrongs he had committed.

50 At the time when Mr. Zorn was depressed, Mr. Zorn needed to be watched especially carefully for signs of
○ 1. wanting to destroy himself.
○ 2. planning to escape the health agency.
○ 3. taking out hostility on other patients.
○ 4. becoming abusive of authority figures.

Thirty-five-year-old Mr. Blander, a chronic alcoholic, is admitted to the hospital with delirium tremens (DTs).

51 On admission, Mr. Blander is very restless and shouts that he must "kill all of those bugs" in his room. In this situation, it is of primary importance for the nurse to
○ 1. place restraints on the patient.
○ 2. remain with the patient at his bedside.
○ 3. help the patient take generous amounts of fluid.
○ 4. explain quietly but firmly to the patient that there are no bugs in the room.

52 Which of the following perceptual disorders is Mr. Blander exhibiting when he wants to "kill all of those bugs" in his room?
○ 1. Paranoia
○ 2. Illusions
○ 3. Delusions
○ 4. Hallucinations

53 After his delirium tremens subside, Mr. Blander makes the following comments to the nurse. In the nurse's judgment, which comment should be considered *least* typical of alcoholism?
○ 1. "There were times when I did not drink for 3 or 4 months."
○ 2. "I could drink a lot of liquor without even getting drunk."
○ 3. "I didn't drink while I was working but I did drink every evening."
○ 4. "I knew I was an alcoholic when I could no longer afford my habit."

The nurse learns that Mr. Blander has abused alcohol since he was a student in high school.

54 Mr. Blander is very likely to be at risk for developing pellagra due to chronic alcoholism, which is caused by a deficiency in the diet of the vitamin

  ○ 1. B$_{12}$.
  ○ 2. folacin (folic acid).
  ○ 3. niacin (nicotinic acid).
  ○ 4. ascorbic acid (vitamin C).

55 Because of chronic alcohol abuse, Mr. Blander is most likely to show evidence of having exaggerated feelings of
  ○ 1. fear.
  ○ 2. euphoria.
  ○ 3. self-pity.
  ○ 4. worthlessness.

Mr. Blander agrees to therapy that includes the use of disulfiram (Antabuse).

56 Mr. Blander should be taught that if he drinks alcohol while taking disulfiram he is most likely to experience
  ○ 1. ringing in the ears.
  ○ 2. cardiac arrhythmias.
  ○ 3. tremors and seizure activity.
  ○ 4. nausea and severe vomiting.

A Nurse Works in a Substance Abuse Center That Includes Facilities for Emergency Care.

Mr. Kamp is brought by a friend to the emergency facility in a life-threatening condition. The friend says Mr. Kamp may have taken an overdose of heroin.

57 How should the nurse begin her care of Mr. Kamp?
  ○ 1. By administering oxygen by mask
  ○ 2. By seeing to it that the patient's airway is open
  ○ 3. By connecting the patient to a cardiac monitoring system
  ○ 4. By making preparations to start the patient on intravenous therapy

58 After his condition stabilizes and Mr. Kamp is alert, he tells the nurse that the overdose of heroin he took happened because he finds that he is using ever-larger doses to obtain the desired effect. This phenomenon in the use of drugs is called
  ○ 1. tolerance.
  ○ 2. dependency.
  ○ 3. habituation.
  ○ 4. idiosyncrasy.

59 Mr. Kamp uses "street jargon" when referring to the route he uses to

administer heroin to himself. Which of the following words refers to the intravenous injection of heroin into the body?
- ○ 1. "Blowing"
- ○ 2. "Crashing"
- ○ 3. "Mainlining"
- ○ 4. "Speedballing"

60 For which of the following illnesses is Mr. Kamp at high risk?
- ○ 1. Osteoarthritis
- ○ 2. Epileptic seizures
- ○ 3. Cerebral vascular accidents (CVA)
- ○ 4. Acquired immune deficiency syndrome (AIDS)

61 Mr. Kamp becomes a candidate for drug replacement therapy. Which of the following drugs is most likely to be used to treat his abuse of heroin?
- ○ 1. Methadone (Dolophine)
- ○ 2. Phenobarbital (Luminal)
- ○ 3. Methaqualone (Quaalude)
- ○ 4. Hydromorphone (Dilaudid)

62 While Mr. Kamp is on drug replacement therapy, he must return to the clinic regularly to determine whether he has taken heroin or other drugs. On these visits, the nurse should be prepared to assist by helping to collect a specimen of Mr. Kamp's
- ○ 1. urine.
- ○ 2. blood.
- ○ 3. saliva.
- ○ 4. cerebrospinal fluid.

Ms. Heller comes to the clinic for help in overcoming her abuse of cocaine.

63 The nurse believes Ms. Heller is in a state of euphoria when she arrives at the clinic. The word, euphoria, is best defined as
- ○ 1. an unfounded fear.
- ○ 2. an exaggerated sense of well-being.
- ○ 3. an illogical mixture of words and phrases.
- ○ 4. a rapid swing in periods of elation and depression.

64 Ms. Heller presents a common physical sign of using cocaine when the nurse observes that the patient has
- ○ 1. dilated pupils.
- ○ 2. a hacking cough.
- ○ 3. excessive salivation.
- ○ 4. a subnormal temperature.

65 The nurse notes another sign of Ms. Heller's cocaine abuse when she observes that the patient has inflammation of the mucous membranes in her
- ○ 1. nose.

    ○ 2. eyes.
    ○ 3. mouth.
    ○ 4. throat.

66 Ms. Heller is a possible candidate for hospitalization. A relatively common physical complication of cocaine (and also heroin) abuse that may require hospitalization to correct is
    ○ 1. diarrhea.
    ○ 2. tachycardia.
    ○ 3. malnutrition.
    ○ 4. hypertension.

Mr. Hatty attends the clinic because he has been abusing dextroamphetamine sulfate (Dexedrine).

67 In "street jargon," Mr. Hatty refers to this drug as
    ○ 1. "speed."
    ○ 2. "a red."
    ○ 3. "a joint."
    ○ 4. "angel dust."

68 Mr. Hatty's drug abuse started when dextroamphetamine sulfate was prescribed for him. Amphetamines, of which dextroamphetamines are an example, are prescribed legitimately in health care to help control
    ○ 1. nausea.
    ○ 2. narcolepsy.
    ○ 3. sleeplessness.
    ○ 4. blood pressure.

Ms. Leniti has been abusing methaqualone (Quaalude).

69 Ms. Leniti is very uncomfortable with a withdrawal symptom when she discontinues using methaqualone. Because this drug interferes with rapid eye movement (REM) during sleep, Ms. Leniti is most probably complaining of having
    ○ 1. enuresis.
    ○ 2. nightmares.
    ○ 3. depression.
    ○ 4. sleepwalking.

70 Ms. Leniti asks the nurse, "Why are Quaaludes made? Do they have any good use?" The nurse should explain to Ms. Leniti that the drug is prescribed legitimately in health care to help control
    ○ 1. edema.
    ○ 2. depression.
    ○ 3. inflammation.
    ○ 4. sleeplessness.

Seventeen-year-old Jimmy Dodd comes to the clinic because, he says, his mother caught him smoking marijuana and she wants him to stop using it.

71 What physical sign is Jimmy most likely to present to the nurse if he has smoked marijuana within the last few hours before admission?
- ○ 1. A headache
- ○ 2. Inflamed eyes
- ○ 3. A staggering gait
- ○ 4. A slow pulse rate

Ms. Ashton, who has a schizophrenic disorder, is brought to a hospital by members of her family.

72 A nurse is interviewing Ms. Ashton upon admission. Of the following questions or statements the nurse could use when interviewing Ms. Ashton, which one would be best?
- ○ 1. "Why did your family decide you should come to the hospital?"
- ○ 2. "Explain to me, if you can, how you feel about being hospitalized?"
- ○ 3. "Tell me about what was happening that caused you to come to the hospital?"
- ○ 4. "Let's discuss what stresses you have been having that may have led to your illness."

73 The nurse reads Ms. Ashton's health history. A finding that is typical in the childhood of a patient with a schizophrenic disorder is having
- ○ 1. strong feelings of being unwanted.
- ○ 2. marked fears of being a social misfit.
- ○ 3. exaggerated concern for other people.
- ○ 4. firm beliefs of being very capable intellectually.

74 Ms. Ashton's health history uses the term, psychotic behavior, several times. A characteristic of psychotic behavior that typically differentiates it from neurotic behavior is that psychotic behavior is
- ○ 1. chronic in nature.
- ○ 2. without motivation.
- ○ 3. unrelated to what is real in life.
- ○ 4. unresponsive to most therapeutic regimes.

Planning Ms. Ashton's nursing care begins.

75 The nurses who are responsible for Ms. Ashton's care identify goals of care. Determining short-term goals, along with long-term goals, is recommended primarily because short-term goals have been found to
- ○ 1. increase the patient's participation in his own care.
- ○ 2. increase the family's interest in the patient's progress.

○ 3. lessen frustration when the patient's progress toward recovery is slow.

○ 4. lessen the need for collecting additional information from the patient.

76 While carrying out nursing measures as described in Ms. Ashton's care plan, the nurse should follow a basic guideline of care which is best described as

○ 1. accepting the patient as she is.

○ 2. ignoring the patient's unacceptable behavior.

○ 3. indicating approval of the patient's behavior.

○ 4. helping the patient recognize her faulty behavior.

The nurse encounters Ms. Ashton several times when Ms. Ashton's behavior is inappropriate.

77 When the nurse enters Ms. Ashton's room one time, the nurse finds the patient throwing food and dishes from her tray onto her bed. The nurse says, "You are being very naughty! If you don't stop throwing things around, I shall have to take your dinner from you." She then leaves the room to obtain clean linens. The nurse's actions will probably not help because the patient is likely to believe that she is being treated as though she is

○ 1. unworthy.

○ 2. unreliable.

○ 3. untrusting.

○ 4. unintelligent.

78 Ms. Ashton is very suspicious. She says to the nurse, "I've got to get out of here. Those FBI agents have lost their minds!" She then points to a group of patients and says, "Look! They are talking about me right now." The disorder of thinking that the patient is demonstrating is called

○ 1. a delusion.

○ 2. incoherence.

○ 3. an obsession.

○ 4. displacement.

79 The nurse tells Ms. Ashton, "You are invited to a holiday party in the solarium this afternoon." Of the following possible responses to the invitation, which one should the nurse judge correctly as being typical of a patient with a schizophrenic disorder?

○ 1. "Great!"

○ 2. "Thank you! I appreciate it."

○ 3. "Singing. I want to lead the singing."

○ 4. "Nonsense! And a batch of rats to you too!"

Chlorpromazine (thorazine) is prescribed for Ms. Ashton.

80 Chlorpromazine is classified as
   ○ 1. an antianxiety agent.
   ○ 2. a parkinsonian agent.
   ○ 3. an antipsychotic agent.
   ○ 4. an antidepressant agent.

81 Chlorpromazine should be withheld and the nurse-in-charge notified promptly if Ms. Ashton complains to the nurse of
   ○ 1. anorexia.
   ○ 2. a backache.
   ○ 3. a sore throat.
   ○ 4. extreme thirst.

82 While using chlorpromazine therapy, Ms. Ashton is very likely when out-of-doors to be especially sensitive to
   ○ 1. cold.
   ○ 2. wind.
   ○ 3. sunlight.
   ○ 4. humidity.

83 The nurse should observe Ms. Ashton for extrapyramidal signs while taking chlorpromazine. These signs most nearly resemble signs of the neurological disorder called
   ○ 1. meningitis.
   ○ 2. herpes zoster.
   ○ 3. multiple sclerosis.
   ○ 4. Parkinson's disease.

Ms. Cordova, a 49-year-old woman, is admitted to a hospital with a mental disorder characterized by major depression.

84 If the following rooms are available for Ms. Cordova upon admission, in which one would it be best for the nurse to place her?
   ○ 1. In a room that is sunny and bright
   ○ 2. In a room with a cheerful and talkative roommate
   ○ 3. In a room as far from the nurse's station as possible
   ○ 4. In a room as near areas for patient-socializing as possible

85 According to her health record, Ms. Cordova's illness appears to have been precipitated by a sense of disappointment in her life. If Ms. Cordova had been mentally healthy, she would most probably have handled the problem that caused the disappointment by
   ○ 1. avoiding the problem.
   ○ 2. coping with the problem.
   ○ 3. putting the problem out of her mind.
   ○ 4. substituting fear for the anxiety created by the problem.

86 The nurse reads in the patient's record that Ms. Cordova has threatened to commit suicide several times in the past. In what stage of Ms.

Cordova's illness is she at highest risk and most likely to carry out suicide?

   ○ 1. When the patient becomes ill
   ○ 2. When the patient begins therapy
   ○ 3. When the patient feels the most depressed
   ○ 4. When the patient's depression is beginning to lift

87 The nurse observes on Ms. Cordova's record that in addition to depression, she has been suffering with hypochondriasis, which means that the patient is preoccupied with thoughts of having

   ○ 1. wronged her God.
   ○ 2. harmed a pet or friend.
   ○ 3. committed an immoral act.
   ○ 4. acquired an uncurable disease.

88 Beginning at the time of admission, the nurse works to develop a therapeutic relationship with Ms. Cordova. Such a relationship is best promoted when the nurse's behavior demonstrates

   ○ 1. authority.
   ○ 2. sympathy.
   ○ 3. friendliness.
   ○ 4. consistency.

Three days after admission, Ms. Cordova has a body temperature of 39° C (102.2° F). It is determined that the patient's throat is inflamed and swollen.

89 What is the primary reason why the nurse should be ever-so-alert for signs of physical illnesses, especially infections, when caring for Ms. Cordova?

   ○ 1. A very depressed person rarely complains of pain.
   ○ 2. A very depressed person rarely has an elevated temperature.
   ○ 3. A very depressed person usually fears he will be isolated if he complains.
   ○ 4. A very depressed person usually fears he will be punished if he complains.

When Ms. Cordova fails to respond favorably to psychopharmacological therapy, she is to have electroshock therapy (EST).

90 Which of the following procedures is essential and to be carried out before Ms. Cordova receives EST?

   ○ 1. Seeing to it that the patient has received an analgesic drug
   ○ 2. Seeing to it that the patient has signed an informed consent form
   ○ 3. Seeing to it that the patient's identification bracelet is removed
   ○ 4. Seeing to it that the temporal areas of the patient's head are shaven

91 The nurse can expect that after receiving EST, Ms. Cordova's behavior
will temporarily demonstrate that the patient is
O 1. angry.
O 2. hostile.
O 3. confused.
O 4. hallucinating.

After working with Ms. Cordova on a one-to-one basis, the nurses dis-
cuss the possibility of using therapy that involves patients helping each
other.

92 The type of therapy when patients help each other is best illustrated by
O 1. milieu therapy.
O 2. group therapy.
O 3. gestalt therapy.
O 4. behavior modification therapy.

A Nurse Is Assigned To Care for Patients Who Are in the Dayroom of a Mental Health Hospital.

Mr. Lemay starts calling other patients in the dayroom derogatory names
and uses profane language.

93 When dealing with Mr. Lemay, it is best for the nurse first to
O 1. ignore the patient's comments; calling attention to his behavior
is likely to make it worse.
O 2. explain to the patient that name-calling is unacceptable; the
patient needs to know limits of his behavior.
O 3. discuss, with the nurse-in-charge, moving the patient to another
unit; the patient is unable to relate to persons he dislikes.
O 4. tell the patient that his behavior will be reported to his physician;
the patient is helped when he knows he must accept authority.

94 Mr. Lemay's inappropriate behavior in the dayroom becomes worse,
and he is bothering other patients. The nurse concludes that it is
necessary to place the patient in seclusion. Which of the following
guidelines should the nurse be especially careful to follow before
placing Mr. Lemay in seclusion?
O 1. Seclusion should be carried out only if 2 patients can be
secluded together.
O 2. Seclusion should be carried out only after the patient has
received a sedative.
O 3. Seclusion should be carried out only if the attending physician
has ordered it.

  ○ 4. Seclusion should be carried out only if the patient has signed an informed consent.

95 Mr. Lemay has been committed to the hospital involuntarily by court order and he objects. Which of the following courses of action would be most legitimate for this patient to take?
  ○ 1. Apply for a writ of habeus corpus
  ○ 2. Engage an attorney to sue the hospital
  ○ 3. Refuse therapy except on an out-patient basis
  ○ 4. Leave the hospital against his physician's consent

Ms. Finch has an almost endless list of physical symptoms that she describes in detail to the nurse and to other patients in the dayroom.

96 In the situation described, it is best for the nurse to listen to Ms. Finch and to
  ○ 1. offer the patient sympathy for her many physical discomforts.
  ○ 2. give her reading material that deals with ways to stay healthy.
  ○ 3. suggest that she write a list of her symptoms for her physician's consideration.
  ○ 4. help the patient join recreational activities with other patients in the dayroom.

97 Ms. Finch tells the nurse while they visit in the dayroom, "I had an affair with my husband's brother 5 years ago before I became sick." Then she quickly adds, "Oh! I never should have said that. Don't you dare tell anyone." The nurse is unable to decide whether or not she should document this information. In this situation, it would be best for the nurse to
  ○ 1. discuss the information with the nurse-in-charge before documenting it.
  ○ 2. discuss the information with the patient's physician before documenting it.
  ○ 3. document the information but carefully note in her entry that the information is confidential.
  ○ 4. document the information as she would other information she has received from the patient.

Mr. Sosha, who is 71 years old, approaches the nurse in the dayroom and says, "Please let me out. I have to go to work. The store opens at eight o'clock."

98 In this situation, it would be best for the nurse to say to Mr. Sosha,
  ○ 1. "You don't have to go to work today. This is a holiday."
  ○ 2. "You used to own a store, didn't you? What kind of a store was it?"
  ○ 3. "You don't own a store now. Sit on the porch and rest for a while."

○ 4. "Don't you worry about the store. Someone is taking care of it
for you."

99 It is recommended that when speaking to Mr. Sosha, it is best for the
nurse to talk to him by calling him by his
○ 1. title: Gramps.
○ 2. nickname: Dick.
○ 3. given name: Richard.
○ 4. surname: Mr. Sosha.

*The nurse cares for Ms. Williams, who has become hyperactive in the
dayroom.*

100 Which of the following nursing measures is most often recommended
when caring for hyperactive patients, such as Ms. Williams?
○ 1. Restraining the patient so that she will not exhaust herself
○ 2. Isolating the patient so that she will not be stimulated by other
patients
○ 3. Providing the patient with activities so that she will channel her
energy into safe pursuits
○ 4. Explaining to the patient that her behavior is unacceptable, so
that she learns to control her activity

101 Ms. Williams remains in almost constant motion in the dayroom. She is
at risk for weight loss and dehydration because she is too busy to eat
or drink. In this situation, it would be best for the nurse to help the
patient meet her nutritional and fluid needs by
○ 1. staying with the patient at mealtimes and reminding her to eat.
○ 2. serving the patient generous quantities of high-calorie foods and
beverages.
○ 3. insisting that the patient sit down for at least 20 minutes in the
dining room, whether she eats or not.
○ 4. providing the patient with nutritious snacks and finger-foods that
she can eat while moving about.

102 Ms. Williams has removed her clothing and is dancing in the dayroom.
The nurse's most helpful comment in this situation would be to say,
○ 1. "Put your clothes on. Everyone is looking at you."
○ 2. "Put your clothes on right away before you catch a cold."
○ 3. "Let me help you to get dressed. Then we can play a game
together."
○ 4. "Don't you see that everyone else here has clothes on? You
don't want to be different, do you?"

Mr. Kroski is demonstrating impaired sensory perceptions.

103 Mr. Kroski tells the nurse that he could not sleep the night before

because the sun was shining in his room all night. In this situation, it would be best for the nurse to respond to the patient's comment by
- ☑ 1. explaining that he is mistaken because the sun shines during the day.
- ○ 2. offering to pull his window shades so that the sun will not bother his sleep.
- ○ 3. telling him that he should look outside at night because he is confusing the moon and sun.
- ○ 4. suggesting that he sleep during the day because the sun shines into his room at night.

104 When the nurse observes Mr. Kroski speaking to an imaginary person in the dayroom, the nurse should judge that the patient is most probably responding to
- ○ 1. illusions.
- ○ 2. delusions.
- ○ 3. hallucinations.
- ○ 4. ideas of reference.

105 One day, Mr. Kroski is withdrawn and moves in the dayroom in a sluggish manner. Of the following ways for the nurse to engage Mr. Kroski in activity, which one would be most therapeutic for him?
- ○ 1. Drawing the patient into a game of cards with the nurse
- ○ 2. Planning for the patient to go for a walk with a group of patients
- ○ 3. Arranging for another withdrawn person to have lunch with the patient
- ○ 4. Allowing the patient to watch television in the dayroom with a group of patients

106 During a conversation with Mr. Kroski, he describes growing up in a home with 4 sisters and brothers. His grandparents lived next door and were close to the family. There were numerous children with whom he played in the neighborhood. During personality development, the persons in Mr. Kroski's childhood environment who could normally be expected to play the most important role in the process of identification are Mr. Kroski's
- ○ 1. grandparents.
- ○ 2. mother and father.
- ○ 3. sisters and brothers.
- ○ 4. childhood playmates.

The nurse notes that Ms. Keim is in a state of catatonic stupor.

107 Which of the following phenomena can the nurse most likely expect when the nurse places one of Ms. Keim's hands on the patient's shoulder?
- ○ 1. The patient will strike out at the nurse.
- ○ 2. The patient will question the nurse's action.
- ○ 3. The patient will maintain the position indefinitely.

○ 4. The patient will allow her hand to fall from her shoulder almost immediately.

The Remaining Items Are Individual Items Dealing with Mental Health Care.

108 Ms. Gunther is 78 years old. When caring for this elderly patient, the nurse should be aware that the patient's most important emotional need usually is to help her feel that she is
○ 1. safe in the hospital and will be cared for there.
○ 2. an important person and has the ability to contribute to life.
○ 3. now dependent on the hospital staff and should follow instructions.
○ 4. capable of caring for her own needs but in need of help to make decisions.

109 Mr. Tarkington is failing college courses because he becomes "sick to my stomach" at every examination time. The defense mechanism Mr. Tarkington is most probably using is called
○ 1. projection.
○ 2. conversion.
○ 3. displacement.
○ 4. compensation.

110 The nurse interviews a patient who expresses great pride in his being a member of a "gang." This person's age is most probably between about
○ 1. 8 and 10 years.
○ 2. 12 and 15 years.
○ 3. 18 and 21 years.
○ 4. 22 and 25 years.

111 The major tranquilizer, fluphenazine hydrochloride (Proloxin), is prescribed for Mr. Dunbar. One advantage this drug has over most other drugs offering the same type of benefit is that fluphenazine
○ 1. rarely causes untoward side-effects.
○ 2. relieves symptoms especially rapidly.
○ 3. is excreted from the body through the urinary system.
○ 4. needs to be administered only once every 10 to 14 days.

112 Aversion therapy (conditioned avoidance) is used to help Mr. Hall overcome alcoholism. Which of the following therapies is an example of aversion therapy?
○ 1. Using group therapy that assists alcoholics to help each other
○ 2. Using hydrotherapy to relax an alcoholic and overcome anxiety
○ 3. Using a drug that causes nausea and vomiting when an alcoholic drinks alcohol
○ 4. Using psychoanalysis to help the alcoholic see the uselessness of his drinking

113 The nurse assigned to care for Ms. Graham assesses the patient's suicidal potential. Of the following findings concerning Ms. Graham's behavior, which one is considered to pose the *lowest* potential as a suicidal risk?
- O 1. The patient describes feelings of hopelessness and is withdrawn.
- O 2. The patient describes moderate use of alcohol several times a week.
- O 3. The patient is unable to participate in normal activities of daily living.
- O 4. The patient is critical of past health care she has received and is pessimistic of care she is presently receiving.

114 Mr. Johnson becomes combative and attacks a nurse by striking out at her. In addition to calling for assistance, which of the following precautions should the nurse take?
- O 1. Push the patient onto his bed, not into a chair.
- O 2. Keep the patient in front of the nurse, not behind her back.
- O 3. Close the door to an adjoining bathroom, but not the room's exit door.
- O 4. Slap the patient on his cheek, but not with sufficient force to hurt him.

115 In terms of psychological needs, when compared with a person with normal intellectual capacity, a mentally retarded person has
- O 1. the same basic needs.
- O 2. a greater need for love.
- O 3. a lesser need for security.
- O 4. a lesser need for intellectual stimulation.

116 The defense mechanism for relieving anxiety that generally is most constructive is the mechanism of
- O 1. projection.
- O 2. repression.
- O 3. sublimation.
- O 4. rationalization.

117 A mental disorder characterized by severe personality changes and the inability to evaluate external reality is called a
- O 1. neurosis.
- O 2. psychosis.
- O 3. hypochondriasis.
- O 4. antisocial personality disorder.

Correct Answers and Rationales

Two numbers appear in parentheses following each rationale. The first number identifies the textbook listed in the references, page 649, and the second number identifies the page(s) in that textbook on which the correct answer can be verified. Occasionally, two textbooks are given for verifying the correct answer.

Caring for Patients Attending the Clinic of a Community Mental Health Center

Attending a conference for new employees

1 1. A nurse can understand and accept the behavior of patients better if she first takes the time to analyze and understand her own behavior and the reasons for it. Group discussions have been found especially helpful to develop self-understanding. (1:89)

2 3. The term, mental illness, is often described today as maladaptive behavior that is used to relieve anxiety. Mental health is described as the ability to adapt to new situations and problems without marked distress. There is overlapping in these descriptions. Everyone ordinarily has distress when coping with anxiety at times. However, the person who is mentally ill demonstrates inappropriate behavior to a degree that results in disorganization of the self. Moral and ethical weaknesses and inclinations toward violence and aggression more accurately describe mental illness as it was defined in the past. Organic disorders may play a role in certain mental illnesses but do not in all. (1:70–71)

3 1. Under usual conditions, and ordinarily after such basic needs as having food and water, being able to eliminate wastes from the body, and experiencing safety, the psychosocial need for love takes highest priority in life. Love as defined here includes feelings of warmth, trust, and understanding. The need begins at birth and continues in various forms throughout life. (1:12)

4 3. Typical physical signs of anxiety include palpitations, sweating, pacing, diarrhea, and general restlessness. The signs of anxiety mimic those when there is stimulation of the sympathetic nervous system of the body. (1:205)

5 2. Hostility is an uncommon sign of anxiety. Common emotional feelings associated with anxiety include fear, regretfulness, feelings of inadequacy, apprehension, uncertainty, and various phobias. (1:205)

6 4. Many authorities believe that anxiety is a normal part of everyday living. The healthy person learns how to cope with anxiety and thereby overcomes excessive distress from anxiety that leads to mental illnesses.

Persons with excessive anxiety have not learned these skills that normally help one to cope.   (1:204–208)

7 4.   Alcoholism is seen in all age categories and socioeconomic groups and among men and women. In recent years, the incidence of alcoholism has increased most among teenagers and children.   (12:851; 15:90)

8 4.   Of all therapies that have been used in the care and treatment of the mentally ill, psychopharmacological therapy has had the greatest impact. The use of this therapy has reduced markedly the number of patients requiring hospitalization and has helped large numbers of people to return to society as responsible and active citizens.   (1:235; 12:89)

9 2.   A person with a conduct disorder typically shows no interest in or concern for the rights of others. He seems unaware of society's codes of behavior. There are 4 main types of conduct disorders: undersocialized, socialized, aggressive, and nonaggressive. Conduct disorders are usually found among children and adolescents, but they may also be present in adults.   (1:144–145)

10 2.   Paranoid thinking is characterized by feelings of suspicion, distrust, secrecy, dissatisfaction, and resentfulness.   (1:297)

11 2.   A common technique of behavior modification is using a token economy. As rewards for desired behavior, the patient is given tokens that he can "spend" on things he wishes. Behavior modification focuses on what a patient does, and through a learning process, the patient learns to change what he does. A more traditional approach has been to help a patient learn how to relieve internal psychological conflicts that are responsible for his signs and symptoms, rather than to modify behavior in a purposeful manner.   (1:255)

12 2.   Various life events were researched by R. Holmes and R. H. Rohe to determine levels of stress the events caused. From findings, the Social Readjustment Rating Scale was prepared. Common life events were assigned point values. According to findings, the death of a spouse was the most stressful event in a person's life and was assigned 100 points. The least stressful of the events studied was given 11 points (minor law violation). Life events described in this item were assigned the following point values:

> Divorce — 73 points
> Retirement — 45 points
> Death of a close friend — 37 points
> Child leaving home — 29 points

The patient described in this item has a total score on the stress scale of 184. The researchers found that when stress levels exceed 300 points, physical or mental illness commonly occurs. The study was done about 20 years ago and has been questioned by some. Nevertheless, many persons use the scale as a guide in evaluating patients under stress and find it helpful to identify potential problems among persons under stress. (1:56–57)

13 4. One of the basic principles of documentation is to describe exactly what the nurse observes. In the entry cited in this item, the nurse should describe what the patient said and did that made her think the patient was confused. The nurse should avoid using her opinions and interpretations when documenting. (12:221)

14 4. To emphasize means attempting to understand by placing oneself in the patient's place. A person has developed empathy when he has the ability to sense the feeling tones of others while still maintaining objectivity. To sympathize means to suffer along with the patient. Offering encouragement is one way to give a patient emotional support. (1:90)

15 4. A therapeutic milieu focuses on the concept that a patient's environment can be therapeutic. The discovery and use of psychopharmacological agents, not their elimination from use, contribute greatly to the development of this concept because they are capable of making an enormous impact on patient behavior by lowering anxiety levels and thus relieving the patient of many untoward symptoms. A therapeutic milieu has several characteristics, some of which are as follows: it concentrates on the patient's needs; it promotes co-worker behavior that indicates acceptance of the patient; it protects the patient's rights; it allows the patient to assist in planning his own care to the extent possible; it promotes self-government to the extent possible in patient groups; it encourages and helps the patient to be responsible for his behavior; and it encourages the patient to expect improvement in his behavior. (1:250–254)

16 4. The ego is the aspect of the mind that appraises the environment so that a person is able to behave appropriately. The ego part of the personality is most nearly in touch with reality. Determining right from wrong, having feelings of guilt and anxiety, and developing a code of behavior consistent with cultural expectations most nearly describe functions of the superego. (1:34)

17 1. The superego is believed primarily responsible for helping a person develop his sense of conscience. Developing appropriate defenses for anxiety and delaying immediate gratification for future goals describe functions of the ego. Seeking pleasure and avoiding pain describe functions of the id. (1:34)

Caring for a patient with agoraphobia

18 3. Agoraphobia means a fear of open spaces. The phobia may become so severe that a patient is unable to leave his home. Claustrophobia is a fear of confined spaces. Mysophobia, or rupophobia, is a fear of dirt. The names of phobias originate in Greek words. Many people prefer to refer to the fear itself, rather than use technical terms. This practice eliminates danger of misunderstandings concerning correct definitions of terms. (1:207)

19   3. Phobic disorders characteristically increase a person's anxiety when the person experiences situations or objects that cause the phobia. It is generally beneficial for caretakers to help the patient explore experiences he has had that contribute to the phobia. The unpleasant feelings associated with phobias are not likely to be relieved until the person changes activities of daily living to the point, eventually, that mental health is threatened. Experts believe that, in general, psychological counseling and possibly attending phobia clinics help when the phobia has not reached major disabling proportions. Psychopharmaceutical agents are occasionally used, but some experts believe medications delay recovery. (1:206)

Caring for a patient with an obsessive–compulsive disorder

20   1. Having to perform an act repeatedly is typical behavior of a patient with an obsessive–compulsive disorder. The patient is unable to stop his stereotype, or repetitive, actions or thoughts. (1:207)

21   1. Persons who perform typical obsessive–compulsive ritualistic acts do so to relieve anxiety. If the persons, or others, try to stop these acts, persons suffering with the disorder experience extreme anxiety. (1:207)

22   3. Members of the nuclear family include the mother, the father, and their children. The nuclear family is also sometimes called the family of origin. The extended family includes the members of the nuclear family and all relatives of the nuclear family. (1:101)

Caring for a patient with hypochondriasis

23   1. Stereotyping is described as giving certain characteristics to an individual which are typical of a standardized group. This type of generalizing from a group to an individual tends to stand in the way of the nurse's thinking of each individual as a unique person. It very often results in errors of observation and judgment. (9:21)

24   2. The nurse should allow and encourage a patient to express feelings. The nurse is doing this best when she makes statements that describe what the patient has just expressed. Asking the patient to describe a problem with the physician may become necessary, but the nurse should attempt first to explore the patient's feelings. (1:64; 9:21)

Caring for patients having group therapy

25   4. Group therapy ordinarily does not include as a goal helping persons to develop counseling skills. Typical goals of group therapy include changing socially unacceptable behavior, understanding one's own behavior more fully, and developing good relations with others. (1:260)

26 1. The best action when a patient is expressing feelings is to listen very carefully to the patient and give him an opportunity to talk about his feelings. Diverting attention, leaving the patient, and trying to make him understand that anger does not help are unlikely to assist the patient who needs to express his anger. (1:64)

Caring for a patient having amitriptyline therapy

27 3. Amitriptyline hydrochloride (Elavil) is a tricyclic, and it is used primarily for its antidepressant effects. (1:240; 14:219)

28 1. Amitriptyline hydrochloride has an atropine-like side-effect which tends to aggravate glaucoma. The drug is not necessarily contraindicated for patients with psoriasis, pernicious anemia, or diabetes mellitus. (1:241; 14:219)

Caring for a patient suffering with loneliness

29 4. Loneliness can be a problem at any age but is more often seen among elderly persons. Many older persons have lost mates and friends. They often live alone, find it difficult to make new friends, and the like. These circumstances often lead to major problems related to feeling dejected, unwanted, and depressed. (1:267)

30 1. When gathering information during an interview, it is best to pose questions that cannot be answered with a word or two, or a "yes" or "no." More information will be gathered by keeping questions general and open. (1:62–65)

Caring for a patient with infantile autism

31 1. Autistic children, whose interpersonal relationships are typically very poor and whose responsiveness to others is also poor, are apt to dislike being touched, hugged, and so on, and will push the person aside when the person tries to show caring. These children seem most comfortable when left alone. Only about a third of these children grow up to function normally, and even they usually find it difficult to develop satisfactory relations with others. (1:150; 12:553)

32 1. When the autistic child reverts to old behavior, it is best to ignore it. The child is probably testing his mother or a nurse, and after his confidence is built up again, he then may progress to more acceptable behavior. Building up confidence takes time and patience; the autistic child develops trust slowly. (1:150; 12:553)

33 3. *Milieu* is a French word meaning the total environment. A therapeutic milieu is established when the patient's total environment acts to help improve behavior, develop self-confidence, and socialize with others. The term is used when one is speaking of caring for any patient, but persons working in the field of mental health first introduced the word for therapy that takes the person's total environment into account.   (1:250–255)

34   2.   The best way to describe a therapeutic environment for a child with autism is that it should be one that is consistent. The autistic child does not tolerate change and does best when consistence is maintained.   (1:150; 12:553)

Caring for patients with anorexia nervosa

35   2.   Patients suffering with anorexia nervosa are most often adolescents, usually females, between the ages of 12 and 18 years. Bulimia, another eating disorder, is usually seen in young females in their late teens and early twenties.   (1:147; 12:559)

36   4.   Special attention needs to be paid to the nutritional needs of patients suffering with eating disorders, such as anorexia nervosa and bulimia. Death among these patients is between about 5% and 15% and is usually the result of circulatory and cardiac failure due to electrolyte imbalances. A deficit in potassium, which is essential for electrical impulse transmission in heart muscle cells, is common.   (11:48–49; 12:726–727)

37   2.   Persons with anorexia nervosa have a distorted sense of their body image. Even though they may not be obese, they believe they are fat and continue to believe this even when they reach a state of emaciation.   (1:147)

The Nursing Care of Patients in Mental Health Hospitals

Caring for a patient with regression

38   1.   The nurse should not promote dependency but should encourage a patient to care for himself. To begin developing independence, the nurse starts by helping the patient to bathe and shave while still not doing everything for the patient. This is especially true with inactive patients. To give entire care when the patient can physically carry out these tasks encourages dependency. A directive that a patient is unable to follow decreases self-esteem. The patient is not likely to feel better emotionally if he takes care of hygienic needs for himself, and telling him he will feel better offers false assurance.   (12:847)

39   3.   Small portions of food are not as overwhelming as large portions to the patient who is uninterested in eating. The nurse's presence is important in the care of the patient described in this item. If the patient is left alone, he is unlikely to eat. Telling the patient that his wife will be happy if he eats or that he will lose weight if he does not is unsuitable because the patient is so absorbed in his feelings that concern for his wife or his weight are unimportant to him.   (12:847)

40   4.   The nurse is showing that she is accepting the patient's feelings and is taking steps to channel his behavior into acceptable activities by staying with a suicidal patient and talking with him as they walk. Telling a patient that his doctor would disapprove of his behavior or threatening restraints tends to increase a patient's feelings of guilt and worthlessness. The nurse avoids the problem when she tells the patient not to talk as he has been.   (1:87-88)

Caring for a patient with a bipolar disorder

41   3.   Normal behavior demonstrates mood swings, but a characteristic behavior pattern of the patient with a bipolar disorder, mixed, is exaggerated mood swings. The patient swings from exaggerated moods of elation to normal behavior and then to depression, and back again to normal and elated behavior. This type of mood swing is often referred to as circular type.   (1:195)

42   2.   The best response in a situation in which a patient makes advances to the nurse is to tell the patient you are uncomfortable with his comment and to ask him to stop such behavior. By so doing, the nurse strengthens the nurse-patient relationship by setting limits for the patient. To tell the patient that someone may overhear his comments suggests that the nurse's concern is not the patient's health status but only with fear of being overheard. Suggesting that the patient's comments be discussed with the physician or suggesting another type of activity avoids the problem at hand. The patient should be helped to see that his behavior is expected to fall within certain limits.   (1:91; 12:845)

43   4.   Moving rapidly from one idea to another is called flight of ideas and is commonly observed in a patient in the hyperactive, or manic, phase of bipolar disorder. Word salad is a mixture of words and ideas that are usually illogical and have no particular meaning. Ambivalence means the person has two opposing feelings toward the same object or person. Confabulation occurs when the person fills in details on the subject under discussion.   (1:196)

44   2.   A patient who is hyperactive needs to discharge his energies into his environment. Of the activities described in this item, tossing a ball back and forth with the patient seems best. He is unable to sit still long enough to read, watch television, or put a puzzle together. Also, when hyperactivity is present, it is better to use large muscles rather than the small muscles that would be necessary, for example, to work a jigsaw puzzle.   (1:198; 12:845)

45   3.   Oral hygiene, special skin care, adequate nutrition, and appropriate recreation are important for the care of a very active patient. However, he must be observed especially carefully so that he is not at risk for malnutrition, dehydration, and exhaustion from lack of rest.   (1:198)

46   3.   A patient who threatens others must be distracted and given a physical outlet for his anger. Medications, seclusion, being put to work on a puzzle, and asking a distraught patient to discuss his disagreement do not allow the patient an opportunity to discharge aggressive and over-abundant energy.   (1:198; 12:845)

47   4.   A patient receiving lithium carbonate (Lithane) is carefully monitored to determine the level of the drug in the body. The method of choice is analyzing blood serum levels and therefore, regular specimens of blood are obtained from the patient.   (1:244; 14:220)

48   4.   A safe dosage of lithium carbonate has a fairly narrow range between therapeutic and toxic doses. For this reason, determining serum blood levels in the patient's blood is very important.   (1:244)

49   2.   Signs of lithium carbonate intoxication include diarrhea, drowsiness, vomiting, and muscular weakness, and represent a toxic reaction to the drug. Untoward signs and symptoms should be reported promptly so that dosage levels can be adjusted or the drug's use may have to be discontinued.   (1:244; 14:216)

50   1.   A depressed patient must be watched especially carefully because he often has strong desires to commit suicide. He is more likely to attempt to carry out the act just before or just after he has reached the depth of depression, when he has sufficient energy to do so. At the lowest ebb of depression, he ordinarily does not have sufficient energy to carry out an act of suicide.   (1:199)

Caring for a patient suffering with chronic alcoholism

51   2.   For the restless patient with delirium tremens (DTs), it is best for the nurse to remain with the patient at his bedside and help to prevent him from harming himself with his excessive restlessness. The use of restraints usually makes the patient more restless as he fights them. The patient is in no condition to accept explanations. He may have generous amounts of fluid but in the presence of DTs, of primary importance is remaining with the patient and seeing that he does himself no harm.   (15:92)

52   4.   A perceptual disorder frequently associated with chronic alcoholism is hallucinations. Any of the five senses may be involved when a person hallucinates, but visual and auditory hallucinations are most common. The hallucinations experienced by the alcoholic during withdrawal are believed to be due to the depression of the central nervous system causing perceptual impairment. Withdrawal is associated with excitation. Excitation is the opposite of alcohol's effect in the body, which is depression of the central nervous system.   (1:160; 12:853)

53   4.   An alcoholic craves liquor with very little regard for cost, so that indicating that he cannot afford his habit is an unlikely comment. Many alcoholics can drink large amounts of liquor without acting or appearing drunk, they may not drink during working hours but will drink when away from work, and they may well stop drinking for as long as 3 or 4 months, only to return to drinking again.   (15:91)

54 3.   Malnutrition, often associated with chronic alcoholism, places an alcoholic at risk for pellagra, which is caused by a lack of sufficient niacin in the diet. Niacin is also known as vitamin B_3 or nicotinic acid. Vitamin B-complex is a group of water-soluble substances that includes niacin and folacin, but a deficiency in folacin is not a cause of pellagra. Vitamin B_{12} is not present in vitamin B-complex. Pellagra is characterized by a type of pigment dermatitis with scaling of the skin, especially in areas exposed to the sun. Foods rich in niacin include meat, poultry, fish, nuts, milk, and whole-grain cereals and bread.   (14:250; 15:92)

55 4.   Some behaviors, including feelings, have been found typical of many alcoholics: inability to relate well with others, dissatisfaction with life in general; and low frustration levels. Very common among alcoholics is low self-esteem that makes them feel worthless, guilty, depressed, and angry. The feelings and behaviors described above are important to keep in mind by persons caring for or living with alcoholics. Chronic alcoholics tend to be at high risk for suicide and should be kept under careful observation. Mention will be made of the Hatton, Valente, and Rink scale to assess suicide potential in another item later in this book. One factor considered to be cause for high risk for suicide is continual abuse of alcohol over a period of time.   (1:173, 200; 12:851–852)

56 4.   Typical effects if alcohol is used during disulfiram (Antabuse) therapy is that the patient will experience nausea and severe vomiting. Other symptoms include diarrhea, hypotension, throbbing headaches, sweating, thirst, chest pains, dizziness, blurred vision, and mental confusion.   (15:92)

Caring for patients at a substance abuse center

57 2.   In any life-threatening situation, it is important for the nurse first to see to it that the patient has an open airway and then to maintain its patency. No other therapy can be effective if the patient is not breathing.   (12:859)

58 1.   Needing increasingly larger doses of any drug to obtain the desired effect is called tolerance. Dependence, or addiction, is described as a condition that results in the appearance of physical symptoms when the use of the drug is delayed or stopped. Habituation is a desire to use a drug with little or no tendency to increase the dosage. Idiosyncrasy is an unusual or abnormal reaction to a drug.   (1:169–170; 176; 14:27, 77)

59 3.   Administering heroin intravenously, in "street jargon," is called "mainlining." "Blowing" refers to smoking marijuana. "Crashing" refers to the depression when the effects of a drug wear off. "Speedballing" refers to the administration of heroin in combination with cocaine; the drugs are ordinarily given intravenously when an abuser uses "speedballing."   (12:855; 14:77–78)

60   4.   Acquired immune deficiency syndrome (AIDS) is spread among persons with contaminated needles, contaminated blood and blood products, and sexual contact. It may also be spread from an infected woman to her fetus. Persons who use needles to inject drugs they are abusing are at high risk for AIDS. If the needles are used by a person infected with the organism causing AIDS and are then not sterilized, which is common practice, the contaminated needles can easily spread the disease.   (12:576)

61   1.   The drug of choice in replacement therapy for persons with heroin addiction is methadone (Dolophine). The drug is addictive but it helps keep the patient comfortable without producing euphoria while heroin is gradually withdrawn. The way in which methadone achieves this is called cross-tolerance; certain drug tolerances can be transferred to another drug in the same chemical category. When the patient has replaced heroin with methadone, a plan for methadone withdrawal then starts. In some cases, the patient remains on a methadone regime indefinitely.   (12:858–859)

62   1.   Urine specimens are obtained on a regular basis from patients on drug replacement therapy. Analysis of the urine indicates whether the patient is abusing drugs. In some programs, repeated use of drugs may result in the patient's dismissal from a drug replacement program.   (12:859)

63   2.   Euphoria is defined as an exaggerated sense of well-being. Lability is defined as rapid changes in emotions or as mood swings. A phobia is an unfounded fear. Word salad is defined as a mixture of words and phrases that do not make sense.   (1:294)

64   1.   Persons using cocaine experience dilated pupils of the eyes. They often wear dark glasses to hide the symptom. They also may use a cholinergic preparation to constrict the pupils; an example is pilocarpine eye drops.   (12:854; 14:49)

65   1.   Cocaine is ordinarily taken into the body in powder form by inhalation through the nose. This method of inhaling cocaine is called "snorting." As a result of "snorting," the cocaine user very often develops chronic inflammation of the nasal mucosa. The nasal septum may erode also as a result of "snorting" cocaine.   (12:856)

66   3.   Persons abusing heroin and cocaine have no appetite and usually eat very poorly, which often results in malnutrition. Hospitalization may become necessary to correct malnutrition and its accompanying adverse effects on the body.   (1:177)

67   1.   Amphetamines are referred to in "street jargon" as "speed" because of the exhilarating effect they have on the body. A "red" is seconal, called this because of the color of its capsule. A "joint" is a marijuana cigarette. "Angel dust" is a hallucinogenic stimulant made from phencyclidine.   (12:855)

68   2.   Amphetamines sometimes are prescribed to help control narcolepsy, which is a sleeping disorder. They have also been used in the treatment of obesity because they help suppress the appetite. Persons who abuse these drugs do so for the euphoria they produce. Because amphetamines have a high abuse potential, their use in health care has declined.   (1:177–178)

69 2.   Methaqualone (Quaalude) interferes with REM sleep, when the person normally dreams. When the drug is withdrawn, the person appears to try to make up for lost REM sleep, begins to dream excessively, and is then likely to have nightmares.   (1:175)

70 4.   Methaqualone is a nonbarbiturate sedative–hypnotic. Unfortunately, methaqualone has a high abuse potential and as a result, its use in health care to control sleeplessness has decreased.   (12:397)

71 2.   Inflammation of the eyes is almost always present after smoking marijuana. The pulse rate is likely to be rapid. Other signs include euphoria, drowsiness, light-headedness, and hunger.   (14:79)

Caring for a patient with a schizophrenic disorder

72 2.   An interview with a patient should be nonthreatening and the nurse's questions should make no assumptions. When interviewing, the nurse is likely to gather the most useful data when her questions are open and encourage discussion. Especially in the case of a patient who is mentally ill, it is usually very helpful to obtain the patient's perceptions of his problems rather than only perceptions of others. This item illustrates assessment, that is, data- or information-gathering, which is the first step in the nursing process.   (1:107)

73 1.   Typically, patients with schizophrenic disorders have felt unloved and unwanted during childhood. Most patients seem not to have had good interpersonal relations with members of their families, and they usually feel very rejected. These findings describe functional factors in the history of schizophrenia. However, recent research suggests that it is likely that there are chemical, or physiological, factors that predispose to schizophrenia also. It is very possible that both functional and chemical factors play a role in causing schizophrenia.   (1:182)

74 3.   Although certain people with neuroses may be incapacitated, the neurotic person still is in touch with reality. The psychotic person is out of touch with reality and cannot distinguish between what is real and what is unreal.   (1:70)

75 3.   Planning nursing care is an important step in the nursing process. Planning starts by stating short- and long-term goals that describe expected outcomes of nursing care. While long-term goals are recommended, developing short-term goals as well has several important advantages: small increments in the patient's progress can be observed readily; the patient and nurse can enjoy satisfaction in seeing progress readily rather than feeling frustration and discouragement when progress toward long-term goals can barely be seen; and necessary modifications in nursing care can be made quickly as indicated and, as a result, nursing care that is ineffective is not reinforced. Short-term goals are especially helpful when caring for a patient with a chronic long-term illness, such as the illness of the patient described in this item. Both short- and long-term goals should include a timetable for their implementation.   (1:189–190, 279; 17:211)

76   1.   A basic guideline when working with a mentally ill patient is to demonstrate acceptance of the patient as he is. The nurse does not judge or punish him for his behavior. This item illustrates implementation of nursing care, an important step in the nursing process.   (1:88)

77   1.   It is important for the nurse to set limits on a patient's behavior and help him to behave appropriately. She should support him as he tries to improve so that he will feel worthy and accepted. Scolding and threatening a patient are most likely to make him feel unacceptable. The nurse's role is to help patients meet psychosocial needs. Acceptance as a person is a need of everyone, regardless of behavior, even when behavior is inappropriate.   (1:88)

78   1.   A delusion is a false belief or opinion. The patient who has delusions thinks that others are talking about him or acting against him, even though the remarks or actions have nothing to do with him. Incoherence means speaking without proper sequence. Sentences are disjointed and ideas drift into each other. Obsession consists of having persistent and recurring thoughts or acts, usually against the person's wishes. Displacement refers to shifting unacceptable feelings about one set of ideas to another person or object.   (1:81–82)

79   4.   Typical behavior of a person with schizophrenia is an emotional response that is inappropriate for the occasion. This is best illustrated by the response, "Nonsense! And a batch of rats to you too!" Such responses to an invitation as "Great," "Thank you," and "I want to lead the singing," are appropriate responses to an invitation to a holiday party.   (1:183)

80   3.   Chlorpromazine (Thorazine) is classified as an antipsychotic agent. It may also be classified as a major tranquilizer. It is a phenothiazine and, although its exact manner of action is not clearly understood, it appears to affect the cerebral cortex, hypothalamus, and certain subcortical areas.   (1:237; 14:281–282)

81   3.   Side-effects to chlorpromazine include blood, liver, and skin reactions. A blood reaction is agranulocytosis, a serious drop in the level of white blood cells. This predisposes the patient to serious and possibly life-threatening infections. Therefore, if the patient complains of a sore throat, or shows any symptoms of an infection, the drug should be withheld and the nurse-in-charge notified promptly. Although this complication does not occur often, it carries a very high mortality rate. Adverse effects *may* include a dry mouth and anorexia, but these effects do not pose a life-threatening situation. Another adverse effect to chlorpromazine is the appearance of tardive dyskinesia, characterized by abnormal and bizarre movements, usually in the area of the mouth, which are slow to develop and *may* be irreversible.   (1:239)

82 3. An untoward side-effect of chlorpromazine is extreme sensitivity to the sun. Photophobia may also develop. (14:220)

83 4. Extrapyramidal signs most nearly resemble signs of the neurological disorder called Parkinson's disease. Signs include muscular rigidity, tremors, drooling, and a shuffling gait. The condition is often called pseudoparkinsonism. The symptoms of this condition are sometimes controlled with anticholinergic drugs. (1:239, 247)

Caring for a patient with depression

84 1. It is best, when possible, to place a depressed patient in a sunny and bright room. Depressed patients usually do not respond well to cheerful and talkative patients; they may even become more depressed by being reminded of their own problems. Depressed persons require careful and frequent observation and, therefore, it is best to place them in rooms convenient for caretakers to do so. (12:847)

85 2. The mentally healthy person handles problems by coping with them without marked distress and while still being able to function as a member of society. He adjusts to change and recognizes people and objects in realistic terms. He may at times use such defense mechanisms as denial, repression, substitution, and the like, to ease tension and anxiety temporarily. Only if defense mechanisms are used to excess is the behavior considered pathological. (1:58-59)

86 4. A person is most likely to carry out suicide when he has had some therapy, and the therapy shows evidence of helping the patient when depression begins to abate. At this time, activity levels start to increase. The person still ordinarily feels depressed but now has enough energy and motivation to carry out a suicide threat. A person rarely has enough energy to carry out self-destruction at the depth of depression. (12:847)

87 4. Hypochondriasis means that the patient is abnormally concerned with his own body and is preoccupied with thoughts of an incurable disease. The patient often will recite symptoms that he is sure indicate the seriousness of the condition. (1:51, 211)

88 4. The nurse should demonstrate consistent behavior when working to develop a therapeutic relationship with a mentally ill person. Other components of a therapeutic relationship between a patient and a nurse include accepting the patient as a unique and worthwhile person, developing trust, and using effective skills of communication. Behavior that demonstrates sympathy and authority does not promote a helping relationship. A therapeutic relationship does not necessarily require that the patient and nurse become friends. (1:90)

89 1. Very depressed persons with physical illnesses that can be expected to cause pain rarely complain of it. Therefore, depressed persons should be observed carefully for evidence of physical illnesses. The thought processes of the very depressed are not sufficiently well organized to cause fear of punishment. Generally depressed persons prefer being away from and isolated from others. Depressed persons respond to illnesses with elevated temperatures in the same manner as the mentally healthy do.   (12:847)

90 2.   It is essential that the person who is to receive electroshock therapy (EST) sign an informed consent form. Shaving part of the head and having the patient receive an analgesic drug prior to therapy is unnecessary. The identification bracelet should not be removed from a person about to receive EST. Having the person in loose-fitting clothes is recommended. Hairpins and dentures should be removed. EST is also called electroconvulsive therapy (ECT)   (1:234–235)

91 3.   Following EST, it is typical for a patient to be confused and dazed. This state ordinarily lasts only for a short time. However, the experience of having had EST is unlikely to be remembered for quite some time after therapy.   (1:235)

92 2.   Group therapy is a situation in which patients help to administer therapy to each other. A professional person ordinarily is present during group therapy to assist. Milieu therapy means using the total environment to help a patient function more effectively. Gestalt psychology refers to the "whole person," rather than thinking in terms of a mental entity separate from a physical person. Behavior modification refers to techniques that help persons to change present behavior to behavior that is more socially acceptable or healthful.   (1:258–263)

The Nursing Care of Patients in the Dayroom of a Mental Health Hospital

Caring for a patient with abusive behavior

93 2.   A patient needs to be accepted, but he also needs to know that there are limits to what he can and cannot do. The patient has a reason for feeling as he does, but setting limits that are enforced objectively and consistently can help the patient change his behavior. Whatever limits are set should be agreed upon by all caretakers.   (1:91)

94 3.   Patients should not be secluded unless the attending physician has ordered seclusion. An informed consent to use seclusion is not required. A patient in seclusion should be in the room alone and not with other patients. However, the patient should be kept under careful observation by nursing personnel during seclusion. Its use, including the length of time, should be documented. Sedatives are not ordinarily used for secluded patients.   (12:841)

95 1.   Involuntary commitment to a hospital requires a court order. Laws vary among the states but each state is empowered to protect the patient and others when endangerment is feared. Strong supporting evidence of endangerment to self and others is ordinarily required before involuntary commitment is ordered. If the patient objects, he can apply for a writ of habeus corpus. A court hearing is then held to determine the person's mental status. If the patient is declared legally sane, the hospital must release the patient. (1:282)

Caring for a patient with numerous physical complaints

96 4. It is best to refrain from commenting, as much as possible, if a patient has many physical complaints when examinations indicate the patient appears in good health. If the nurse says anything, it is best to repeat feelings the patient expresses. The nurse should try to divert the attention of a patient who describes endless physical symptoms when no pathology is present from what the patient perceives as health problems by involving him in activities with others. (1:209, 211)

97 1. It is not uncommon for patients to share sensitive information with nurses. When in doubt about documenting the information, it is best for the nurse to discuss it with the nurse-in-charge before documenting information of this nature. Health agencies vary in their policies concerning documentation. The nurse should be aware of these policies but still consult the nurse-in-charge when in doubt. (1:279)

Caring for a patient with an inability to recognize reality

98 2. A comment that acknowledges what the patient has said and asks for more information implies to the patient that he is important and that the nurse is listening to him. This type of response helps contribute to his sense of self-worth and integrity. (1:13, 64, 87)

99 4. Unless the patient requests otherwise, it is recommended that patients be addressed by their surnames. Addressing persons properly shows respect for the patient. (9:25)

Caring for a hyperactive patient

100 3. It is best to try to channel the energies of an aggressive or hyperactive patient so that he will carry out acceptable pursuits. Restraining a patient is not advised unless other measures fail and the patient must be protected from harming himself or others. Isolating an aggressive or hyperactive patient avoids the problem, and he is rarely able to accept explanations. (1:198)

101 4. An overactive patient is unable to stay in one place for long and needs to be able to eat while moving about. Other measures usually will be useless because the overactive patient cannot control his behavior. (1:198)

102 3. A patient who disrobes in the presence of others is behaving in an unacceptable manner. The patient needs to be removed from others in a nonjudgmental manner and given an acceptable channel for discharging feelings. Such a patient is unlikely to be influenced by comments about a cold, being seen by others, or acting differently from others.   (1:87, 91)

Caring for a patient with impaired sensory perception

103 2.   The nurse is accepting the patient and his problem and offering him help when she offers to pull a shade so that the patient is not bothered by the sun, even though the nurse knows the sun does not shine at night. The patient is likely to challenge the nurse and nothing will be accomplished if the nurse tries to explain to the patient that his thinking is wrong. The patient's behavior is not changed by reasoning with him, nor is he helped to comprehend reality when the nurse suggests that the patient sleep during the day because the sun shines at night.   (1:87–88)

104 3.   Imaginary perceptions are called hallucinations. Hallucinations have meaning to the patient and usually represent needs, wishes, daydreams, or rejected impulses. Misinterpreting a sensory stimulus is an illusion. A false belief or opinion is a delusion. The patient's thinking that remarks he overhears are directed toward him or thinking that others are talking about him is called ideas of reference.   (1:81–83)

105 1.   The withdrawn patient is fearful of others and has isolated himself from painful situations, such as those that require him to relate to others. The best action in a situation in which the patient is withdrawn is to help the patient to learn to trust the nurse, starting gradually with such activities as walking with the patient or playing cards with him. The patient most probably will continue withdrawal behavior if thrown into the company of other persons or left with another withdrawn patient.   (1:846)

106 2.   Through the process of identification, a youngster molds himself to be like his parents, especially the parent of the same sex.   (1:5)

Caring for a patient with catatonia

107 3.   The phenomenon of indefinitely maintaining a position in which someone placed a patient is called waxy flexibility. It is characteristic of a patient suffering with catatonic stupor, in which the patient is withdrawn and shows no interest in his environment. Two additional mannerisms patients with catatonic stupor sometimes demonstrate are echolalia, which occurs when the patient repeats words and phrases spoken by another person, and echopraxia, which occurs when the patient mimics actions or gestures of another person.   (1:186–187)

Individual Items

108 2.   The elderly person's most important possession is his sense of dignity and integrity. His emotional care should be directed toward preserving and fostering these feelings. All patients, including the mentally ill, should be helped to maintain as much independence as the patient's condition permits. (1:209)

109 2. Conversion is a defense mechanism by which an emotional problem is expressed as a physical one. The symptoms the patient experiences are very real even though a physiological basis cannot be found. Projection is blaming someone else for one's own faults. Displacement is transferring an emotional feeling from one object or situation to another. Compensation is using extra efforts to overcome a real or imagined deficit in another area. (1:53)

110 2. During adolescence, between about 12 and 15 years of age, a youngster is seeking self-identity, according to Erik Erikson, and is striving to begin making breaks from parents. He often finds that identifying with a "gang" of his peers gives him confidence and a sense of belonging. Typically, he will dress, speak, and behave as do the other "gang" members. Gang activity can be destructive but when used appropriately, it can also help a young person through the emotionally difficult years of adolescence. (1:31)

111 4. An advantage of fluphenazine hydrochloride (Proloxin) is that it needs to be administered only once every 10 to 14 days. It is very potent, about 20 times as potent as chlorpromazine, and has sustained and prolonged action. Because the medication need not be given as often as other antipsychotic drugs, it is especially useful when caring for patients on an out-patient basis. Like most drugs, it too has untoward side-effects. (1:239)

112 3. Aversion therapy is a technique used in behavior modification. The objective is for the person to associate inappropriate behavior with an unpleasant experience and, as a result, avoid both the inappropriate behavior and the unpleasant stimulus. The technique is also called conditioned avoidance. Using aversion therapy (conditioned avoidance) for alcoholics uses drugs that cause nausea and vomiting when the person drinks alcohol. Such drugs are intended to associate discomfort with the use of alcohol so that the person will avoid his drinking to stay comfortable and well. (1:256)

113 2. A tool that rates the degree of suicide risk when selected behaviors or symptoms of patients are present has been developed by Hatton, Valente, and Rink. According to these researchers, feelings of helplessness, hopelessness, and being withdrawn, holding to negative views of care received, and being unable to participate in normal activities of daily living are ranked high when the degree of suicide risk is being considered. Other behaviors and symptoms that place a person at great risk for suicide include demonstrating high amounts of anxiety, being severely depressed, having destructive coping abilities, having one or no "significant others," living an unstable life-style, having marked disorganization, and having frequent thoughts of suicide with a specific plan on how to carry out suicide. Using alcohol moderately is not considered a high-risk suicidal factor. However, continual and chronic abuse of alcohol is a high-risk factor.   (1:200)

114   2.   When a patient becomes hostile and combative and attacks a caretaker, in addition to calling for assistance, the person should keep the patient in front of her and in full sight, not behind her where she would be unable to observe the patient. This technique helps keep the nurse in a safer position. The nurse should do nothing to cause possible harm to the patient, such as pushing the patient onto his bed or chair, nor should she retaliate, such as slapping the patient. The nurse should concern herself with her own and the patient's safety, and opening and closing doors does nothing to accomplish this goal.   (12:846)

115   1.   A retarded person has the same basic psychological needs as a person with normal intellectual capacity. He needs to feel loved, accepted, secure, and significant. He also needs a variety of stimuli in his environment, including intellectual stimulation, to help reach the goals of normal psychological development.   (12:562)

116   3.   Defense mechanisms are used to resolve conflicts and to help relieve anxiety. Sublimation is the defense mechanism that is most often constructive in nature. The mechanism is used to channel socially unacceptable behavior to acceptable, constructive behavior. An example of an act of sublimation is using masturbation when other types of sexual activity are not satisfactory at a particular time. Most healthy persons at one time or another use any of the defense mechanisms described in the literature. These mechanisms can serve a useful purpose, giving a person time to deal with a conflict. However, mental health is threatened when a defense mechanism is overused and becomes a normal part of behavior.   (1:52)

117   2.   A psychosis is present when the person's behavior interferes severely with effective functioning and is not related to reality. A neurosis is characterized by severe anxiety and the resulting abnormal behavior represents the person's ineffective attempts to relieve his anxiety. An antisocial personality disorder is characterized by the individual's acting out against society in general. Hypochondriasis is a neurotic illness characterized by a pathological preoccupation with various physical symptoms.   (1:298)

Classification of Test Items

Directions: *Each item in the previous review test is classified here according to the subject area it tests. Place a check mark after each item you answered **correctly** by referring to your answers. Total the number of items you answered correctly in each area and enter the numbers in the correct places on pages 553–556.*

Clinical: Mental Health Nursing

2 _____	17 _____	35 _____	53 _____	85 _____	102 _____
4 _____	18 _____	36 _____	55 _____	86 _____	103 _____
5 _____	19 _____	37 _____	59 _____	87 _____	104 _____
6 _____	20 _____	38 _____	60 _____	89 _____	105 _____
7 _____	21 _____	39 _____	63 _____	90 _____	107 _____
8 _____	22 _____	41 _____	66 _____	91 _____	109 _____
9 _____	25 _____	43 _____	67 _____	92 _____	110 _____
10 _____	26 _____	44 _____	73 _____	93 _____	112 _____
11 _____	29 _____	45 _____	74 _____	94 _____	113 _____
12 _____	31 _____	46 _____	76 _____	96 _____	114 _____
14 _____	32 _____	50 _____	78 _____	98 _____	116 _____
15 _____	33 _____	51 _____	79 _____	100 _____	117 _____
16 _____	34 _____	52 _____	84 _____	101 _____	

TOTAL _____

Fundamentals of Nursing

13 _____   57 _____   75 _____

TOTAL _____

Diet Therapy/Nutrition

54 _____

TOTAL _____

Pharmacology

27 _____	48 _____	58 _____	64 _____	69 _____	81 _____
28 _____	49 _____	61 _____	65 _____	70 _____	82 _____
47 _____	56 _____	62 _____	68 _____	71 _____	83 _____
				80 _____	111 _____

TOTAL _____

Psychosocial Sciences

1 _____	24 _____	42 _____	88 _____	99 _____	105 _____
3 _____	30 _____	72 _____	95 _____	106 _____	
23 _____	40 _____	77 _____	97 _____	108 _____	

TOTAL _____

UNIT II

Review Tests 2 and 3

The Nursing Care of Maternity Patients and of Newborns

Review Test 2

The Nursing Care of Women Attending a Prenatal Clinic

Directions: *With a pencil, blacken the circle in front of the option you have chosen for your correct answer.*

A Nurse Works in a Community Health Clinic Where She is Assigned Duty in the Unit that Offers Prenatal Care.

Ms. Rush comes to the clinic because she thinks she is pregnant. An immunological test is to be done.

1 The specimen the nurse should collect from Ms. Rush for the immunological test is a specimen of
  ○ 1. urine.
  ○ 2. stool.
  ○ 3. blood.
  ○ 4. vaginal secretions.

2 No agglutination occurs when the immunological test is performed on Ms. Rush, which means that the test result is
  ○ 1. false.
  ○ 2. positive.
  ○ 3. negative.
  ○ 4. uncertain.

Shortly after Ms. Rush's clinic visit, the nurse learns that Ms. Rush is admitted to a hospital because she has an ectopic pregnancy.

3 An ectopic pregnancy, such as Ms. Rush has, is best defined as a pregnancy that
  ○ 1. occurs outside of the uterus.
  ○ 2. causes the rupture of a fallopian tube.
  ○ 3. results in some form of fetal malformation.
  ○ 4. progresses even though the woman continues to menstruate.

4 When Ms. Rush is hospitalized, the highest priority for nurses caring for her should be to observe Ms. Rush for signs of
  ○ 1. infection.
  ○ 2. hemorrhage.
  ○ 3. uterine relaxation.
  ○ 4. premature delivery.

Ms. Renotti makes her first visit to the clinic. She is pregnant for the first time.

5 The term used to describe Ms. Renotti (pregnant for the first time) is
  ○ 1. multipara.
  ○ 2. primipara.
  ○ 3. primigravida.
  ○ 4. multigravida.

6 Using Nägele's rule, when is Ms. Renotti expected to deliver if her last menstrual period began on March 13?
  ○ 1. November 13
  ○ 2. November 23
  ○ 3. December 3
  ○ 4. December 20

7 Ms. Renotti is estimated to be between 9 and 10 weeks pregnant. She says she feels "something moving" in her abdomen. It is most probable that what she is feeling is due to

○ 1. peristaltic movements.
○ 2. early fetal movements.
○ 3. shifting of the uterus out of the pelvis.
○ 4. palpitations from large abdominal blood vessels.

8 Ms. Renotti's pelvic measurements are to be obtained. The equipment the nurse should have ready for measuring Ms. Renotti's diagonal conjugate includes

○ 1. a speculum.
○ 2. a pelvimeter.
○ 3. an x-ray plate.
○ 4. a waterproof glove.

9 When Ms. Renotti's blood specimen is examined, she is found to be Rh negative. In this situation, the nurse should be prepared next to

○ 1. assist with an intrauterine transfusion.
○ 2. request that the father's blood be examined.
○ 3. prepare to assist with a desensitization program.
○ 4. notify the hospital that the baby is likely to have erythroblastosis.

10 Ms. Renotti asks how the sex of the baby is determined. The nurse explains correctly when she says that the sex of a fetus is determined by a sex

○ 1. gene in the sperm.
○ 2. gene in the ovum.
○ 3. chromosome in the sperm.
○ 4. chromosome in the ovum.

11 Unless complications develop, the nurse should plan that during the first 7 months of pregnancy, Ms. Renotti should plan to visit the clinic for an examination every

○ 1. 1 to 2 weeks.
○ 2. 2 to 3 weeks.
○ 3. 3 to 4 weeks.
○ 4. 6 to 8 weeks.

Ms. Teloni, who is 41 years old, calls the clinic to say she has been vomiting several times a day for almost 4 days.

12 The nurse urges Ms. Teloni to come to the clinic promptly, recognizing that the mother has a typical sign of

○ 1. reflex emesis.
○ 2. neurotic emesis.
○ 3. cyclic vomiting.
○ 4. pernicious vomiting.

13 Because of her age, Ms. Teloni is considered at risk for having an infant that has

○ 1. cerebral palsy.
○ 2. Down's syndrome.
○ 3. phenylketonuria (PKU).
○ 4. respiratory distress syndrome.

14 Ms. Teloni tells the nurse that she and her husband have chosen to use the Lamaze method of childbirth. During a labor contraction, Ms. Teloni should be taught to focus her entire attention on
○ 1. a name for the baby.
○ 2. an object in the room.
○ 3. the length of the contraction.
○ 4. the predicted time of delivery.

15 The Telonis should also be taught that during labor, Ms. Teloni should avoid rapid, panting-type breathing because such breathing predisposes her to
○ 1. alkalosis.
○ 2. exhaustion.
○ 3. uterine atony.
○ 4. muscular stress.

Ms. North is pregnant and comes to the clinic because of a vaginal discharge. It is determined that Ms. North has trichomoniasis.

16 The drug usually used to treat trichomoniasis is metronidazole (Flagyl) but this drug is not used for Ms. North because it is thought that it may be teratogenic. The term teratogen refers to an agent or factor that is likely to cause
○ 1. premature labor.
○ 2. physical defects in the fetus.
○ 3. pregnancy-induced hypertension.
○ 4. premature separation of the placenta.

17 The nurse places a fetoscope on Ms. North's abdomen to listen for fetal heart sounds. For how many weeks can Ms. North be expected to be pregnant when the nurse can *first* hear fetal heart sounds?
○ 1. 7 to 8 weeks
○ 2. 10 to 12 weeks
○ 3. 13 to 15 weeks
○ 4. 18 to 20 weeks

18 Which of the following procedures should the nurse use while she listens with the fetoscope on Ms. North's abdomen for fetal heart sounds?
○ 1. Having the mother lie on her left side
○ 2. Obtaining the mother's respiratory rate
○ 3. Feeling for the mother's radial pulse rate
○ 4. Encouraging the mother to use very deep breaths

19 Ms. North asks about the yellowish fluid discharge from her nipples. The nurse should recognize that the discharge is most probably

    ◯ 1. abnormal; the secretion is due to an inability of the breasts to produce milk.

    ◯ 2. abnormal; the secretion indicates that the patient likely has a breast infection.

    ◯ 3. normal; the secretion is replaced by milk after delivery.

    ◯ 4. normal; the secretion indicates the patient will have large amounts of milk for her baby.

Ms. Schall comes to the clinic because, she says, "I don't feel good." It is believed she is threatening to abort spontaneously.

20   The two symptoms that Ms. Schall reports that should indicate to the nurse that the patient is very likely threatening to abort are having vaginal bleeding and having

    ◯ 1. ankle swelling.

    ◯ 2. severe headaches.

    ◯ 3. persistent nausea.

    ◯ 4. abdominal cramping.

21   Ms. Schall tells the nurse, "My aunt took DES when she threatened to abort and all went well. Because I seem to be aborting, can't I have DES too?" A response to the patient's question should be based on knowledge that diethylstilbestrol (DES) is rarely used for threatened abortions today because a pregnant mother who takes the drug is likely to predispose a female offspring to

    ◯ 1. cancer.

    ◯ 2. infertility.

    ◯ 3. Rh-incompatability disease.

    ◯ 4. malformed reproductive organs.

22   Ms. Schall aborts spontaneously. A characteristic of a spontaneous abortion that differentiates it from other types is that a spontaneous abortion

    ◯ 1. rarely is associated with physical discomforts.

    ◯ 2. occurs during the first trimester of pregnancy.

    ◯ 3. is the result of conditions that are not related to pregnancy.

    ◯ 4. occurs without the patient's having done anything to cause it.

Ms. Mitchell visits the clinic when she is about 7 or 8 weeks pregnant. She is to have an amniocentesis.

23   Ms. Mitchell complains of having to urinate at frequent intervals. The nurse should explain that frequent urinating early in pregnancy usually subsides when the

    ◯ 1. placenta is fully developed.

    ◯ 2. fetal kidneys begin to function.

    ◯ 3. uterus rises into the abdominal cavity.

    ○ 4. Mother's kidneys adjust to the added load of fetal wastes.

24 Ms. Mitchell is scheduled to have an amniocentesis when she is about 15 weeks pregnant. The amniocentesis is most probably performed to help determine

    ○ 1. the sex of the fetus.
    ○ 2. the maturity of the fetus.
    ○ 3. whether the amniotic fluid is excessive.
    ○ 4. whether a genetic abnormality is present.

25 The nurse should anticipate that preparation for Ms. Mitchell's amniocentesis is very likely to include

    ○ 1. giving the patient an enema.
    ○ 2. restricting the patient's fluid intake.
    ○ 3. having the patient in a state of fasting.
    ○ 4. seeing that the patient's urinary bladder is empty.

It is determined that Ms. Wickes is pregnant with twins.

26 Types of twins are described to Ms. Wickes. A term often used to describe dizygotic twins is

    ○ 1. true twins.
    ○ 2. identical twins.
    ○ 3. fraternal twins.
    ○ 4. conjoined twins.

27 A problem for which Ms. Wickes and her caretakers should be alert, because she has a multiple pregnancy, is that the patient is likely to

    ○ 1. deliver prematurely.
    ○ 2. have placenta previa.
    ○ 3. develop hyperemesis gravidarum.
    ○ 4. manufacture scant amounts of amniotic fluid.

28 When Ms. Wickes delivers, nurses giving her postpartum care should observe her especially carefully because a woman with a multiple pregnancy is at risk for the postpartum complication of

    ○ 1. infection.
    ○ 2. hemorrhaging.
    ○ 3. kidney shutdown.
    ○ 4. respiratory distress.

Mr. Glick brings Ms. Glick to the clinic because they believe Ms. Glick may be starting labor.

29 When Ms. Glick is examined, it is determined that she has false labor pains. Which of the following statements concerning false labor is most accurate?

    ○ 1. Uterine contractions usually occur at regular intervals.
    ○ 2. The cervix usually dilates slowly with uterine contractions.

    ◯ 3. Uterine contractions fail to decrease and stop with ambulation.

    ◯ 4. The discomfort of uterine contractions is usually felt primarily in the back and left side.

30 About 10 days after the clinic visit, Ms. Glick delivers. When she returns to the clinic about 6 weeks after delivery, she says to the nurse, "I'm nursing the baby and not menstruating so I can't become pregnant, can I?" The nurse should base her response on knowledge that during lactation, ovulation

    ◯ 1. can occur and a woman can become pregnant.

    ◯ 2. does not occur and a woman cannot become pregnant.

    ◯ 3. can occur but a fertilized ovum is promptly discharged.

    ◯ 4. can occur but a fertilized ovum cannot implant in the uterus.

Ms. Gant believes she is pregnant and comes to the clinic for her first visit.

31 If Ms. Gant presents the following signs on her clinic visit, the one that is classified as a probable sign of pregnancy is

    ◯ 1. quickening.

    ◯ 2. morning sickness.

    ◯ 3. enlargement of the uterus.

    ◯ 4. tingling sensations in the breasts.

32 It is determined that Ms. Gant is pregnant. Ms. Gant has 3 children, a son and twin daughters. She has no history of having had an abortion or a stillborn infant. In terms of gravida and para, Ms. Gant is correctly described by the nurse as being

    ◯ 1. gravida III, para II.

    ◯ 2. gravida III, para III.

    ◯ 3. gravida II, para II.

    ◯ 4. gravida II, para III.

33 Ms. Gant reports that she recently had rubella (German measles). The primary danger of having had rubella early in her pregnancy is that the causative virus is likely to cause

    ◯ 1. premature labor.

    ◯ 2. fetal deformities.

    ◯ 3. severe preeclampsia.

    ◯ 4. hydatidiform mole formation.

Ms. Taski comes to the clinic for a roll-over test.

34 Which of the following equipment should the nurse have in readiness when Ms. Taski has her roll-over test?

    ◯ 1. Equipment to monitor the fetal heart beats

    ◯ 2. Equipment to obtain the patient's blood pressure

    ◯ 3. Equipment to obtain the patient's external pelvic measurements

    ○ 4. Equipment to obtain clean-catch urine specimens from the patient

35 When Ms. Taski's roll-over test proves to be positive, the nurse should understand that Ms. Taski requires especially careful observations for signs and symptoms of

    ○ 1. a heart disease.
    ○ 2. diabetes mellitus.
    ○ 3. a blood abnormality.
    ○ 4. pregnancy-induced hypertension.

36 Because her roll-over test is positive, which of the following positions should Ms. Taski be taught to assume as much as possible while she rests in bed?

    ○ 1. On her back
    ○ 2. On her abdomen
    ○ 3. On her left side
    ○ 4. On her right side

37 Ms. Taski is to have an intramuscular injection. If Ms. Taski is in a sitting position, which one of the following muscles should the nurse *avoid* using for injecting the medication?

    ○ 1. A gluteal muscle
    ○ 2. A deltoid muscle
    ○ 3. A rectus femoris muscle
    ○ 4. A vastus lateralis muscle

Ms. Enos, who has diabetes mellitus, attends the clinic on a regular basis.

38 The manner in which the placenta is affected if Ms. Enos's diabetes is poorly controlled is that the placenta tends to

    ○ 1. become oversized.
    ○ 2. function ineffectively.
    ○ 3. be retained after delivery.
    ○ 4. separate from the uterine wall prematurely.

39 An oxytocin challenge test (OCT) is scheduled for Ms. Enos, the primary purpose being to help

    ○ 1. detect genetic defects in the fetus.
    ○ 2. estimate the size of the fetal skull.
    ○ 3. locate the area of placental attachment in the uterus.
    ○ 4. determine how well the placenta functions under the stress of labor.

Ms. Smith is being followed carefully at the clinic and then is hospitalized because of having pregnancy-induced hypertension (PIH).

40 Ms. Smith asks the nurse what caused her pregnancy-induced

hypertension (PIH). The nurse should base her response to Ms. Smith's question on knowledge that the cause of PIH is

- ○ 1. unknown.
- ○ 2. toxemia.
- ○ 3. an infection.
- ○ 4. poor nutrition.

41 Ms. Smith demonstrates typical signs and symptoms of preeclampsia. Of the following signs and symptoms, the one *least* characteristic of preeclampsia is

- ○ 1. retention of fluid.
- ○ 2. albumin in the urine.
- ○ 3. an irregular pulse rate.
- ○ 4. an elevated blood pressure.

42 When Ms. Smith is hospitalized, her caretakers observe her carefully for eclampsia. Ms. Smith will be considered to have developed eclampsia if she has

- ○ 1. convulsions.
- ○ 2. a dead fetus.
- ○ 3. renal failure.
- ○ 4. a sudden worsening of preeclamptic signs.

Ms. Jackson is pregnant and attends the clinic.

43 During the nurse's assessment of Ms. Jackson, she suspects that Ms. Jackson may have placenta previa because she notes that the patient has

- ○ 1. sudden sharp abdominal pain.
- ○ 2. painless bleeding from the vagina.
- ○ 3. a marked elevation in blood pressure.
- ○ 4. continuous, painless uterine contractions.

44 Diagnostic studies confirm that Ms. Jackson has placenta previa. When during pregnancy does placenta previa usually first become apparent?

- ○ 1. During the first month of pregnancy
- ○ 2. During the second or third month of pregnancy
- ○ 3. During the second trimester of pregnancy
- ○ 4. During the third trimester of pregnancy

45 The health problem that Ms. Jackson is experiencing with placenta previa is due to a condition in which the placenta is

- ○ 1. being invaded by polyps or myomas.
- ○ 2. degenerating on either the maternal or on the fetal side.
- ○ 3. covering the cervical os or is implanted low in the uterus.
- ○ 4. failing in its ability to produce hormones or enzymes that act to maintain pregnancy.

Ms. Dorter comes to the clinic unit that performs abortions for women wishing one.

46 Ms. Dorter's caretaker recommends using hypertonic saline solution for the procedure of abortion. Before beginning the procedure, it is particularly important for the nurse to see that the patient has
- O 1. been fasting.
- O 2. had an enema.
- O 3. emptied her bladder.
- O 4. been shaven at the injection site.

47 According to a 1989 US Supreme Court decision, the state cannot interfere with Ms. Dorter's right to have an abortion if she wants one and if she
- O 1. is not married.
- O 2. has had previous children.
- O 3. has the consent of the father.
- O 4. is not in violation of permissable state restrictions.

The remaining items in this situation are individual items related to prenatal care.

48 Ms. France, who is within a short time of delivery, has herpesvirus hominis type II (genital herpes). For which of the following measures related to Ms. France's delivery should the nurse begin to prepare Ms. France?
- O 1. A forceps delivery
- O 2. A cesarean delivery
- O 3. A precipitate delivery
- O 4. An artificial rupturing of the membranes

49 Mr. and Ms. Mitchell have chosen to use the Bradley method of childbirth. The nurse should teach the parents that of the following positions, the one recommended for Ms. Mitchell during labor when she is not walking about is the
- O 1. tailor position.
- O 2. Fowler's position.
- O 3. squatting position.
- O 4. face-lying position.

50 Ms. Warner has chloasma, which is best described as
- O 1. brown spots on the face.
- O 2. dark rings around the nipples.
- O 3. stretch marks on the abdomen.
- O 4. a dark vertical line on the abdomen.

51 Of the following 4 women for whom the nurse is helping to care, which one is *most* likely to deliver an infant that is larger-than-average in size?
- O 1. Ms. Lang, who has preeclampsia
- O 2. Ms. West, who has heart disease
- O 3. Ms. Zigler, who has placenta previa

    ○ 4. Ms. Kamps, who has diabetes mellitus

52 Of the following 4 women for whom the nurse is helping to care, the one who is *least* likely to be considered a high-risk mother is

    ○ 1. Ms. Curtis, who is unmarried.

    ○ 2. Ms. James, who is in her eighth pregnancy.

    ○ 3. Ms. Marin, who is in a low socioeconomic group.

    ○ 4. Ms. Sklar, who had an infant born with pyloric stenosis.

53 The nurse overhears several patients, for whom she has cared, in the clinic waiting room gossiping and saying untruths about her. One patient says, "Would you believe it? They say she is in love with a married man who works here." The best guide for the nurse to follow in a situation involving gossip is to

    ○ 1. avoid saying anything to the patients about the gossip and go on with her work.

    ○ 2. discuss the gossip with the patients and ask them who the persons referred to as "they" are.

    ○ 3. explain the erroneousness of the gossip to the patients and ask for their apologies.

    ○ 4. tell the nurse-in-charge about the gossip and ask not to be assigned to care for these patients.

The nurse is responsible for the sterilization and disinfection of certain equipment and for handling various types of electrical equipment in the clinic.

54 The nurse should know that of the following methods of sterilization and disinfection, the one best suited to destroying spores is using

    ○ 1. a germicide.

    ○ 2. a disinfectant.

    ○ 3. free-flowing steam.

    ○ 4. steam under pressure.

55 The nurse should understand that of the following practices, the one that will help most to reduce accidents from electrical shock is

    ○ 1. using retractable electrical cords.

    ○ 2. using three-pronged electrical plugs.

    ○ 3. having 2 receivers at each electrical outlet.

    ○ 4. having electrical outlets well above the baseboard level.

A Nurse Meets with Small Groups of Women at a Prenatal Clinic to Teach Them About Common Discomforts of Pregnancy.

56 Ms. Warren, who has been in good health during pregnancy, says she urinates frequently, ". . . just as I did early in pregnancy." The nurse should explain that the most probable cause of frequent urination late in pregnancy is that the

- ○ 1. mother has alkaline urine.
- ○ 2. mother is developing a urinary infection.
- ○ 3. enlarging uterus is causing pressure on the bladder.
- ○ 4. growing fetus is excreting increased amounts of wastes.

57 Ms. Volez complains of difficulty with breathing. At what time during pregnancy is dyspnea ordinarily a normal discomfort?

- ○ 1. Early in the first trimester
- ○ 2. Late in the first trimester
- ○ 3. During the second trimester
- ○ 4. During the third trimester

58 Ms. Curtis has a complaint for which the nurse recommends using the pelvic rock (pelvic tilt). For which of the following discomforts of pregnancy is the pelvic rock most often recommended?

- ○ 1. For backaches
- ○ 2. For heartburn
- ○ 3. For varicosities
- ○ 4. For constipation

59 Ms. Young says, "My skin itches so much. What can I do about it?" The nurse should teach that this discomfort of pregnancy is often relieved by taking a bath in water to which has been added

- ○ 1. milk.
- ○ 2. mineral oil.
- ○ 3. sodium bicarbonate.
- ○ 4. nonperfumed liquid soap.

60 Ms. McGrew is uncomfortable because of varicose veins of the vulva. To help lessen the discomfort, the nurse should suggest that Ms. McGrew

- ○ 1. decrease exercising to several times a week.
- ○ 2. apply warm compresses to the area several times a day.
- ○ 3. sleep in a low-Fowler's position several nights a week.
- ○ 4. lie in bed with the buttocks elevated several times a day.

61 Ms. Morton complains of increased flatulence since being pregnant. Of the following measures, which one should the nurse teach as the one most likely to help overcome flatulence?

- ○ 1. Avoiding the use of antacids
- ○ 2. Moderating daily fluid intake
- ○ 3. Maintaining regular bowel elimination
- ○ 4. Decreasing the amount of raw vegetables in the diet

62 Several women tell the nurse that they have a problem affecting their mouths. What effect does the increased amount of estrogen in the body sometimes have on a pregnant woman's mouth?

- ○ 1. Saliva becomes sticky.
- ○ 2. The tongue becomes smooth.
- ○ 3. The gums tend to bleed easily.

○ 4. Plaque deposits itself readily on the teeth.

63 Ms. Nu complains of heartburn. Heartburn is most probably due to
○ 1. an increase in the secretion of bile.
○ 2. an increase in the secretion of stomach acids.
○ 3. a decrease in peristaltic action in the gastrointestinal tract.
○ 4. a decrease in the size of the chest cavity as the uterus enlarges.

64 Ms. Nu says she has relief from heartburn when she uses baking soda in water. The nurse should caution her that one disadvantage of this remedy is that the baking soda may cause
○ 1. constipation.
○ 2. poor absorption of nutrients.
○ 3. fluid retention of body fluids.
○ 4. irritation of gastrointestinal mucosa.

65 Ms. Godwin, who has had no complications and is now about 9 months pregnant, has edema in her feet. The nurse should explain to Ms. Godwin that this edema is believed to be caused primarily by
○ 1. an increase in blood pressure.
○ 2. the pressure of an enlarged uterus on pelvic veins.
○ 3. the pressure of a full bladder on the kidney tubules.
○ 4. an increase in blood volume in the circulatory system.

66 The nurse teaches Ms. Godwin that a measure very likely to help decrease edema in her feet is to decrease her daily intake of
○ 1. fat.
○ 2. salt.
○ 3. fluids.
○ 4. sweets.

67 Ms. Bach, who is early in her pregnancy, asks the nurse for suggestions to help relieve nausea and vomiting she has upon awakening in the morning. The nurse should teach Ms. Bach that her nausea and vomiting can often be relieved if, about one half hour before arising in the morning, she eats/drinks a
○ 1. glass of milk.
○ 2. piece of fruit.
○ 3. cup of hot tea.
○ 4. piece of dry toast.

68 The nurse teaches that nausea and vomiting, as well as heartburn, are often relieved when pregnant women alter their diets by reducing the intake of
○ 1. fats.
○ 2. proteins.
○ 3. minerals.
○ 4. carbohydrates.

69 Several women complain of constipation. The nurse should teach that constipation can often be controlled when women increase their
○ 1. rest.

○ 2. exercise.
○ 3. caloric intake.
○ 4. vitamin intake.

70   Ms. Long says she takes mineral oil for occasional constipation. Ms. Long should be taught *not* to take the oil at or near mealtimes because it interferes with the absorption of vitamin
○ 1. A.
○ 2. B_2.
○ 3. B_{12}.
○ 4. C.

71   Ms. Won complains of leg cramps. The nurse should teach Ms. Won that leg cramps are frequently relieved by straightening the leg and then placing the ankle in a position of
○ 1. rotation, by moving the foot so that the toes outline a large circle.
○ 2. dorsiflexion, by moving the foot so that the toes point toward the kneecap.
○ 3. extension, by moving the foot so that the toes point straight up toward the ceiling.
○ 4. plantar flexion, by moving the foot so that the toes point downward toward the floor.

72   The nurse should understand that if Ms. Won's leg cramps are caused by a mineral imbalance, the two minerals involved are phosphorus and
○ 1. iron.
○ 2. sodium.
○ 3. calcium.
○ 4. potassium.

73   Several women complain of various muscle "aches and pains." The nurse should teach the importance of using good body mechanics to help prevent and relieve discomforts related to the musculoskeletal system. The term, body mechanics, is best defined as
○ 1. maintaining good body posture.
○ 2. using the body effectively as a machine.
○ 3. observing healthful habits of daily living.
○ 4. keeping the body in good physical condition.

74   The nurse should teach the women that, when in the standing position, it is recommended that the knees be flexed slightly because this helps
○ 1. absorb shocks to the body.
○ 2. improve circulation in the legs.
○ 3. keep the spine in a straight position.
○ 4. relieve tension in the arches of the feet.

75   The nurse teaches the women that good posture includes extending or stretching the waist, primarily because this technique helps to
○ 1. overcome the effects of gravity.
○ 2. prevent strain on abdominal muscles.
○ 3. supplement the work of muscles in the legs.

  ○ 4. give the lungs the most amount of room to work.

A Nurse Helps in Teaching a Group of Pregnant Women How to Promote Health During Pregnancy.

76 While discussing smoking during pregnancy, the nurse should explain that when compared with babies of nonsmokers, babies born of women who smoke tend to

  ○ 1. be lighter in weight.
  ○ 2. have more birth defects.
  ○ 3. be born post-term more often.
  ○ 4. have a lower white blood count.

77 One woman asks the nurse if she can swim during pregnancy. Of the following possible responses, it would be best for the nurse to say

  ○ 1. "Swimming is good exercise, but swim in moderation so that you do not become too tired."
  ○ 2. "Swimming is not recommended because it requires energy needed for fetal development."
  ○ 3. "Swimming is all right, but it is better to limit your activity to light housework and walking."
  ○ 4. "Swimming is not recommended because it causes too much stretching of muscles in the legs and arm."

78 Ms. Fitzer says her physician advises against having sexual intercourse during the last month of pregnancy and her sister's physician does not. The nurse should explain that opinions vary, but those who recommend avoiding intercourse late in pregnancy do so because they believe it may cause infection as well as

  ○ 1. fetal distress.
  ○ 2. premature labor.
  ○ 3. prolapse of the cord.
  ○ 4. displacement of the placenta.

The nurse discusses dietary needs during pregnancy with the women.

79 It is important that the diet of a pregnant woman contains larger-than-average quantities of the minerals calcium, phosphorus, and

  ○ 1. iron.
  ○ 2. sodium.
  ○ 3. potassium.
  ○ 4. magnesium.

80 When the nurse discusses the need for a diet rich in calcium, she should teach that of the following foods, the two that are richest in calcium are

  ○ 1. apples and pears.

    ◯ 2. potatoes and carrots.
    ◯ 3. oranges and grapefruit.
    ◯ 4. cheddar cheese and sardines.

81 The nurse teaches the women in the class that their diets should include adequate amounts of calcium and phosphorus because these minerals are especially important for the proper development of the baby's
    ◯ 1. bones and teeth.
    ◯ 2. kidneys and liver.
    ◯ 3. gray and white matter.
    ◯ 4. heart and blood vessels.

82 The nurse teaches the women to cook vegetables quickly with the least amount of water possible in a covered container. The nurse's rationale is that cooking vegetables in this manner is done primarily to help avoid destroying the vegetables'
    ◯ 1. fiber.
    ◯ 2. color.
    ◯ 3. vitamins.
    ◯ 4. minerals.

83 The nurse is correct when she teaches that the vitamin that is important for the proper absorption and utilization of calcium in the body is the vitamin
    ◯ 1. A.
    ◯ 2. B.
    ◯ 3. C.
    ◯ 4. D.

84 While teaching about the importance of an adequate intake of vitamin C, the nurse should teach the mothers that of the following vegetables, the one richest in this vitamin is
    ◯ 1. corn.
    ◯ 2. carrots.
    ◯ 3. tomatoes.
    ◯ 4. lima beans.

85 The nurse goes on to explain that phosphorus is found in the same foods as those containing generous amounts of the mineral
    ◯ 1. iron.
    ◯ 2. sodium.
    ◯ 3. calcium.
    ◯ 4. magnesium.

86 The importance of milk in the diet of pregnant women is discussed in class. The daily minimum amount of milk that a pregnant woman should have is
    ◯ 1. 2 cups.
    ◯ 2. 4 cups.
    ◯ 3. 6 cups.
    ◯ 4. 8 cups.

87 Ms. Foster says she cannot drink the amount of milk recommended for pregnant women. The nurse should teach Ms. Foster that the recommended daily intake of milk can be reduced in volume if she fortifies her regular milk with

- ○ 1. molasses.
- ○ 2. fruit puree.
- ○ 3. unflavored gelatin.
- ○ 4. powdered nonfat milk.

88 Ms. Brown asks, "Is it all right to drink alcoholic beverages during pregnancy?" The nurse should base her response on knowledge that using alcohol during pregnancy is likely to predispose the fetus to having an

- ○ 1. increased heart rate.
- ○ 2. impaired intellectual capacity.
- ○ 3. excessive fatty deposits in the liver.
- ○ 4. accelerated long bone development.

89 Ms. Engle says, "I love coffee. Don't tell me I have to give it up during pregnancy!" Which of the following statements should guide the nurse when she responds to Ms. Engle's comment?

- ○ 1. Coffee should be used sparingly or avoided during pregnancy.
- ○ 2. Coffee should be prepared by the drip method during pregnancy.
- ○ 3. Coffee should be drunk with generous amounts of milk during pregnancy.
- ○ 4. Coffee has not been demonstrated to have ill effects when used during pregnancy.

90 The question arises concerning how much weight one should gain during pregnancy. Which of the following statements best describes current opinion concerning how much weight a woman should gain during pregnancy?

- ○ 1. The amount of weight that a woman gains during pregnancy is no longer considered to be important.
- ○ 2. The amount of weight that a woman gains during pregnancy is best when it does not exceed 10 to 12 pounds.
- ○ 3. The amount of weight that a woman gains during pregnancy is considered less important than having a nutritious diet.
- ○ 4. The amount of weight that a woman gains during pregnancy is important only if the woman is underweight or overweight before becoming pregnant.

The nurse discusses articles of clothing with the women attending the classes.

91 Of the following articles of clothing, the nurse should teach the mothers to *avoid* wearing

- ○ 1. foot Peds.

○ 2. panty hose.
○ 3. garter belts.
○ 4. knee-length stockings.

92 Several women attending the classes are observed to be wearing high-heeled shoes. They ordinarily are *not* recommended to be worn during pregnancy because they tend to cause or aggravate
○ 1. backaches.
○ 2. hemorrhoids.
○ 3. varicose veins.
○ 4. edema in the feet.

Ms. Cort, who is about 5 months pregnant, wishes to take a 6-hour motor trip.

93 Unless she has complications, the trip Ms. Cort wishes to take is ordinarily permissible but she should be encouraged to
○ 1. plan to take 2 days to make the trip.
○ 2. stop for short walks about every 2 hours.
○ 3. avoid sharing the driving with her husband.
○ 4. spend about half of the time lying on the back seat of the car.

94 Which of the following statements most accurately describes how Ms. Cort should be taught to secure herself in the seat of the car in which she travels?
○ 1. The pregnant woman should wear shoulder straps.
○ 2. The pregnant woman should place a seat belt under her abdomen.
○ 3. The pregnant woman should place a seat belt over the top of her abdomen.
○ 4. The pregnant woman should refrain from wearing shoulder straps or seat belts.

Several women raise questions about cleaning secretions from the nipples

95 The nurse should explain that it is best to keep the nipples clean by sponging them carefully and regularly with a soft cloth and warm
○ 1. water.
○ 2. alcohol.
○ 3. soap solution.
○ 4. soda bicarbonate solution.

96 The nurse continues the discussion on the care of nipples during pregnancy. Grasping the nipples with a thumb and forefinger and massaging them with an emollient is sometimes recommended primarily to help
○ 1. stimulate milk production.
○ 2. enlarge the size of the nipples.

○ 3. prepare the nipples for nursing.
○ 4. prevent organisms from entering the milk ducts.

The Remaining Items Relate to a Variety of Questions the Pregnant Women Ask the Nurse During a Class That Deals with the Anatomy and Physiology of the Reproductive Process and an Understanding of Common Terms Used by Their Caretakers.

97 The women are taught that the inner lining of the uterus is called the
○ 1. peritoneum.
○ 2. perimetrium.
○ 3. myometrium.
○ 4. endometrium.

98 In response to a question about how sperm travel, the nurse teaches that after ejaculation of sperm into the vagina, sperm are propelled by
○ 1. cilia on their body.
○ 2. movements of their tail-like portion.
○ 3. peristaltic-like cervical and uterine contractions.
○ 4. pressure differences in the uterus and fallopian tubes.

99 The total number of chromosomes in each *mature* germ cell (ovum or sperm) is
○ 1. 23.
○ 2. 24.
○ 3. 46.
○ 4. 48.

100 The women are taught that sperm are manufactured in the body in the
○ 1. testes.
○ 2. epididymis.
○ 3. ductus deferens.
○ 4. seminal vesicles.

101 The anatomical structure, the nurse explains, where the egg (ovum) normally unites with the sperm is called the
○ 1. ovary.
○ 2. cervix.
○ 3. uterus.
○ 4. fallopian tubes.

102 Which of the following hormones plays the most important role in preparing the uterus for pregnancy?
○ 1. Prosecretin
○ 2. Progesterone
○ 3. Human growth hormone (HGH)
○ 4. Follicle-stimulating hormone (FSH)

103 When the subject of signs of pregnancy began, the nurse teaches that as a sign of pregnancy, amenorrhea is classified as a
○ 1. positive sign.
○ 2. negative sign.
○ 3. probable sign.
○ 4. presumptive sign.

104 A probable sign of pregnancy is present when an examiner can determine
○ 1. a fetal heart rate.
○ 2. softening of the cervix.
○ 3. movements of the fetus.
○ 4. an increase in skin pigmentation.

105 The nurse explains that the term used to describe the first time fetal movements are felt by a pregnant woman is called
○ 1. lightening.
○ 2. quickening.
○ 3. engagement.
○ 4. engorgement.

106 A discoloration of the vulva and vagina during pregnancy is called
○ 1. Braxton Hicks' sign.
○ 2. Hegar's sign.
○ 3. Goodell's sign.
○ 4. Chadwick's sign.

107 Several women asked about the function of the placenta. In addition to carrying nourishment to the fetus and wastes from it, the nurse should teach that the placenta functions to
○ 1. store nutrients for the fetus.
○ 2. prevent certain fetal malformations.
○ 3. provide the body with several hormones.
○ 4. remove organisms from the maternal blood.

108 The nurse went on to explain that amniotic fluid has all of the following purposes *except*
○ 1. protecting the fetus from external injury.
○ 2. allowing the fetus to move about in the mother's uterus.
○ 3. preventing the fetus from acquiring organisms from the mother's body.
○ 4. keeping the fetus in an environment that has a constant temperature.

109 A hormone in the body that stimulates the production of milk in the breasts is
○ 1. estrogen.
○ 2. oxytocin.
○ 3. prolactin.
○ 4. parathormone.

110 During a discussion of the fetal circulation, the nurse explains that the foramen ovale allows considerable blood to bypass the lungs of a fetus by allowing blood to move in the heart from the right atrium directly into the

○ 1. aorta.
○ 2. left atrium.
○ 3. left ventricle.
○ 4. inferior vena cava.

111 When compared with the level of oxygen concentration in the blood of a normal infant, the level of oxygen concentration in the blood of a normal fetus is

○ 1. lower.
○ 2. slightly higher.
○ 3. much higher.
○ 4. about the same.

112 Oxytocin is a hormone produced by the

○ 1. ovaries.
○ 2. placenta.
○ 3. adrenal glands.
○ 4. pituitary gland.

113 When discussing delivery, the nurse teaches that the cervix prepares for delivery by becoming thinner and shorter. This phenomenon is called

○ 1. dilatation.
○ 2. effacement.
○ 3. engagement.
○ 4. ballottement.

Correct Answers and Rationales

Two numbers appear in parentheses following each rationale. The first number identifies the textbook listed in the references, page 649, and the second number identifies the page(s) in that textbook on which the correct answer can be verified. Occasionally, two textbooks are given for verifying the correct answer.

The Nursing Care of Women Attending a Prenatal Clinic

Caring for a woman having an immunological test

1   1.   An immunological test uses a urine specimen to determine whether a woman is pregnant. The test depends on the presence of human chorionic gonadotropin (HCG) in the urine. Examples of immunological tests include the Gravindex, the UCG-Slide, and the Pregnosticon Accuspheres tests.   (2:48–49)

2   2.   Urine from a pregnant woman contains human chorionic gonadotropin (HCG). An antiserum and then an antigen are added to the urine. The test is positive when no agglutination occurs.   (2:49)

3   1.   An ectopic pregnancy is one that occurs somewhere outside the uterus. Most often, an ectopic pregnancy occurs in the fallopian tube but it may occur in the abdomen, ovary, or cervix. If it occurs in the fallopian tube, the tube will eventually rupture or tear due to distention of the growing results of conception.   (2:161)

4   2.   An ectopic pregnancy often is associated with extremely serious hemorrhaging. If a fallopian tube ruptures, severe pain in the lower abdomen is generally present. Infection, uterine relaxation, and premature delivery are not associated with an ectopic pregnancy.   (2:161–162)

Caring for a woman during her first visit to the clinic

5   3.   Primigravida describes a woman pregnant for the first time. A primipara describes a woman who has delivered her first viable infant. Multipara describes a woman who has delivered more than one viable infant. Multigravida describes a woman who has been pregnant before this pregnancy.   (2:466)

6   4.   Nägele's rule requires adding 7 days to the first day of the woman's last menstrual period and then count back 3 months. This means the patient described in this item is due to deliver on December 20.   (2:44; 12:442)

7   1.   It is unusual for a pregnant woman to feel the fetus move before 16 to 18 weeks of pregnancy. Peristaltic movements and the movement of gas in the intestines often cause a pregnant woman to feel something that she is likely to confuse with fetal movements. Fetal movement is called quickening. Because movement related to gastrointestinal activity is easily confused early in pregnancy for fetal movement, quickening described by the mother is a presumptive sign of pregnancy. Later in pregnancy, when an experienced caretaker feels movement of the fetus, the sign is considered a positive sign of pregnancy. (2:47)

8 4. The diagonal conjugate is obtained by measuring the distance from the bottom of the sacral promontory to the lower border of the symphysis pubis. This is done by performing a vaginal examination. Waterproof gloves are needed. An x-ray is necessary if the true conjugate (conjugata vera) is obtained. Most often, however, the true conjugate measurement is done indirectly by subtracting 1½ cm to 2 cm from the diagonal conjugate. The transverse diameter of the pelvic outlet is measured with a pelvimeter. (2:93–94)

9 2. When a mother is pregnant for the first time and found to be Rh negative, the next step is to examine the father's blood. If he is also Rh negative, the infant is not ordinarily at risk, unless the mother has a history of being exposed to blood that was Rh positive. If the infant is Rh positive, the physician may use a desensitization program on the mother. (2:172–174)

10 3. Each ovum contains an X sex chromosome. Some sperm contain an X chromosome and some contain a Y chromosome. If an X chromosome sperm unites with the ovum, the result is a female child (XX). If a Y chromosome sperm unites with the ovum, the result is a male child (XY). (10:326; 12:438)

11 3. If there are no complications, it is generally recommended that a pregnant woman see her physician every 3 to 4 weeks until about the seventh month of pregnancy and then every 2 weeks until the last month of pregnancy. During the last month, it is recommended that a pregnant woman see her physician every week. (2:98)

Caring for a woman with excessive vomiting

12 4. Persistent vomiting that occurs several times a day is a typical sign of pernicious vomiting. It is also called hyperemesis gravidarum. Such patients should be examined and cared for promptly. Most require hospitalization with intravenous fluid and electrolyte therapy; psychological counseling may be indicated for some patients. (2:168)

13 2. Women over age 35 to 40 years are at risk for having an infant with Down's syndrome. (2:417)

14 2. The Lamaze method is based on replacing restlessness and fear during labor with another type of behavior. A woman using this method is taught to focus her attention on an object in the room during a labor contraction. The object may be something the woman has brought with her, such as a family picture. The Lamaze method is described as being psychoprophylactic, that is, the method uses a mental prevention of pain. (2:118–119)

15 1. The Lamaze method of childbirth, as well as the Bradley method, encourages slow and deep breathing during labor. Rapid, panting-type breathing predisposes a woman in labor to respiratory alkalosis and subsequently, to acidosis in the baby. (2:177–119)

Caring for a woman with trichomoniasis

16 2. The term teratogen refers to an agent or factor that predisposes the fetus or embryo to physical defects. A variety of drugs, infections, and other miscellaneous conditions have been found to be teratogenic. Metronidazole (Flagyl) is possibly one such drug, although it has not been definitely proven that it is. Aspirin may also be teratogenic because it may cause prothrombin problems in the fetus. Even such medications as diet pills, diuretics, and cold remedies may cause difficulties. These findings form the basis for teaching pregnant women not to use any medications without first consulting a physician. (12:446)

17 4. Fetal heart tones ordinarily are heard first with a fetoscope after 18 to 20 weeks of pregnancy. They may be heard as early as 10 to 12 weeks by using ultrasound. (12:442)

18 3. When using a fetoscope to auscultate for fetal heart sounds, the nurse must be careful not to confuse fetal sounds with pulsations in the mother's aorta. This can be avoided when the nurse feels for the mother's radial pulse while listening for fetal heart sounds. The fetal pulse is considerably faster than the mother's heartbeat. (2:51)

19 3. During pregnancy, a yellowish discharge from the nipples is normal. It is called colostrum and is replaced by milk soon after the birth of the baby. (2:62)

Caring for a woman who is threatening to abort

20 4. Vaginal bleeding and abdominal cramping or backaches are typical symptoms patients report when a spontaneous abortion threatens. (2:154; 12:481)

21 1. Women who use diethylstilbestrol (DES) during pregnancy, especially during the first part of pregnancy, predispose female offspring to vaginal or cervical cancer. Because of this, its use has been largely discontinued in prenatal care. The use of DES is not associated with infertility in the female, Rh-incompatibility disease, or malformed reproductive organs. DES also affects male off-spring; it causes changes in the sperm that may lead to infertility. (2:154)

22 4. A spontaneous abortion is best defined as one that occurs without having done anything to cause it. Most spontaneous abortions, about 75%, occur before the twelfth week of gestation, but this is not what differentiates a spontaneous abortion from other types. (12:481)

Caring for a woman having an amniocentesis

23 3. Early in pregnancy, urinary frequency is common because the uterus causes pressure on the urinary bladder. When the uterus rises into the abdominal cavity, urinary frequency usually subsides. Frequency recurs later in pregnancy when the fetus drops low into the abdomen and its presenting part causes pressure on the bladder.   (12:447)

24 4. Early in pregnancy, an amniocentesis is usually done to help determine whether the fetus has a genetic abnormality. When one exists, the parents may choose whether to terminate the pregnancy. The fetal sex can be determined by amniocentesis but is not done primarily for this reason. Late in pregnancy, an amniocentesis may be done to evaluate the maturity of the fetus. In about 75% of cases, amniocentesis is performed to detect Down's syndrome.   (2:331–332; 12:481)

25 4. Seeing to it that the patient's bladder is empty is an important part of preparing a patient for amniocentesis. However, this practice of having an empty bladder is not observed by all physicians; local policy should be observed. Most amniocenteses are preceded by ultrasonography to help locate intrauterine structures before the needle for an amniocentesis is inserted.   (2:332)

Caring for a woman who is pregnant with twins

26 3. The terms fraternal twins, dizygotic twins, and biovular twins are synonymous. These twins are the result of two ova being fertilized by two sperm. The terms true twins, identical twins, uniovular twins, and monozygotic twins are synonymous. These twins result when one ovum, fertilized by one sperm, divides into two parts after conception.   (2:83)

27 1. Women with multiple pregnancies, which means that there is more than one fetus, are at risk for such problems as having premature labor and delivery, hydramnios (excessive amniotic fluid), abnormal presentation of the fetuses, hypertension disorders, and uterine dysfunctioning. Cord compression and entanglement, retarded growth of the fetuses, and an operative delivery also are associated with multiple pregnancies.   (2:84)

28 2. A woman having a multiple pregnancy is at risk for postpartum hemorrhaging when the uterus tends to fail to contract and firm up after delivery because the uterus has been overstretched. Steps should be taken to help prevent hemorrhaging, and the patient must be observed with care.   (2:84)

Caring for a woman who has false labor pains

29 4. Uterine contractions of false labor are usually felt only in the abdomen whereas true labor uterine contractions are felt in the back and abdomen. Ambulation often stops false labor pains. The cervix does not dilate when a patient is experiencing false labor, which is an exaggeration of Braxton Hick's contractions. The cervix dilates when the patient is in true labor. False labor is also characterized by having uterine contractions at irregular intervals. (2:199)

30 1. Ovulation can occur during lactation and, although the lactating woman may not be menstruating, she can become pregnant. The presence of lactation is a very unreliable method to use for contraceptive purposes. (2:315)

Caring for a woman who is pregnant for the third time

31 3. An enlargement of the uterus is classified as a probable sign of pregnancy. Morning sickness, quickening, and tingling sensations in the breasts are classified as presumptive signs of pregnancy because these signs can be due to conditions other than pregnancy. (2:46)

32 1. Gravida is the term used to indicate that a woman is pregnant. The first time she is pregnant, she is gravida I. On subsequent pregnancies, she is gravida II, III, and so forth. The patient described in this item is gravida III because she is pregnant for the third time. Para is the term used to indicate the number of pregnancies a woman has had in the past that resulted in the delivery of a viable infant, or infants. Multiple births, such as twins, are counted as one para. The patient described in this item is para 2. It should be remembered that para and gravida are terms that describe pregnancies, not fetuses. (2:43)

33 2. The virus causing rubella (German measles) is believed responsible for many fetal deformities when a mother contracts the disease early in pregnancy, usually during the first trimester. The *time* during pregnancy when the mother has rubella is critical. The fetus is most susceptible during the first 2 months of pregnancy when cell differentiation is taking place, which is a time when some women do not even know they are pregnant. (2:178)

Caring for a woman having a roll-over test

34 2. The roll-over test involves taking the patient's blood pressure at approximately 5-minute intervals, first while the patient lies on her left side. When the pressure stabilizes, the patient is then turned onto her back and her blood pressure is taken 2 more times at 5-minute intervals. (2:100–101)

35 4. A positive roll-over test means that a pregnant woman is at risk for developing pregnancy-induced hypertension. (2:101)

36 3. Lying in bed on the left side is recommended for a patient whose roll-over test is positive because it removes pressure on the vena cava. This position promotes placental circulation and hence, assures the fetus of the best possible benefits of adequate circulation. (12:484)

37   1.   No attempt should be made to inject a gluteal muscle when a patient is sitting because it is too difficult to locate a safe site. A sitting position may be used when injecting a deltoid muscle in the arm and the rectus femoris and vastus lateralis muscles in the thigh.   (9:564)

Caring for a woman with diabetes mellitus

38   2.   The blood vessels, especially the small vessels, in the placenta are often affected when a pregnant woman has diabetes that is poorly controlled. This results in placenta insufficiency. If the insufficiency is severe, the fetus may die in utero because of poor nourishment and poor removal of wastes.   (2:176)

39   4.   An oxytocin challenge test (OCT) helps determine how well the placenta is functioning in its ability to exchange nutrients, including oxygen, and wastes under the stress of labor. An oxytocin infusion is used to produce uterine contractions while the fetal heart is monitored. Abnormal deceleration of the fetal heart rate during the test is interpreted to mean that the fetus is at risk because of diminished placental efficiency. Placental insufficiency can lead to the death of the fetus while under the stress of true labor. An amniocentesis most frequently is used to detect genetic defects. Ultrasound frequently is used to determine the size of the fetal skull and to help locate the placental attachment.   (2:177)

Caring for a woman with pregnancy-induced hypertension

40   1.   The cause of pregnancy-induced hypertension (PIH) is unknown. Although PIH was once thought to be caused by a toxin, none has been identified. Poor nutrition has often been associated with PIH but no direct causal relationship has been established. Infections are not believed to be the cause of PIH.   (2:169; 4:201)

41   3.   An irregular heart beat is not associated with preeclampsia. The 3 classical signs and symptoms of the condition are an elevated blood pressure, albuminuria, and fluid-retention edema. Preeclampsia is considered a very serious complication of pregnancy. It is one of the chief causes of maternal mortality, and a surviving infant often suffers with intrauterine growth retardation.   (2:169)

42   1.   The patient who is preeclamptic is diagnosed as having eclampsia when she has convulsions and coma. Eclampsia may occur during the antepartal period, labor, delivery, or postpartal period. When eclampsia occurs, precautions should continue after delivery for at least 48 hours because there is danger of convulsions occurring as long as irritability of the central nervous system exists.   (2:170)

Caring for a woman with placenta previa

43   2.   The most characteristic sign of placenta previa is painless bleeding from the vagina. It occurs late in pregnancy, usually after the 28th week of pregnancy, and is the most common cause of bleeding during the third trimester. Sharp abdominal pain, an elevated blood pressure, and continuous and painless contractions are not associated with placenta previa. (2:162–163)

44 4. Placenta previa becomes apparent during the last trimester of pregnancy. (2:162–163)

45 3. Placenta previa is a condition in which the placenta totally (complete or total placenta previa) or partially (partial placenta previa) covers the cervical os. Or, the placenta may be implanted low in the uterus (marginal placenta previa) without covering any part of the os. The painless bleeding associated with placenta previa is due to a separation of the placenta from the uterus in the area that is near or covers the cervical os. The separation is caused by normal changes in the cervix that are occurring in preparation for labor. Placenta previa is unrelated to the development of polyps or myomas, degeneration of the placenta, or failure in the proper functioning of the placenta. (2:162–163)

Caring for a woman who requests an abortion

46 3. It is important to have a patient empty her bladder before hypertonic saline is injected for an abortion. A full bladder may make it difficult to enter the uterus and it could be punctured. (2:157)

47 4. In 1989 the United States Supreme Court upheld its 1973 decision that an abortion can be performed legally, but ruled that states may set certain restriction on abortions. An example is that a state may deny certain personnel from performing abortions and some agencies from being used for performing abortions. Another example is that a state may require that a test to determine fetal viability be done before an abortion is performed. If the fetus is not viable, an abortion may be performed, provided no other of the state's restrictions are violated.

Caring for women with miscellaneous prenatal needs

48 2. When a pregnant woman has herpesvirus hominis type II (genital herpes), a cesarean delivery is most often done to prevent infecting the infant during vaginal delivery. The infant mortality rate is high, and surviving infants often have neurological damage when the virus is passed on to the newborn during delivery. However, if the membranes are no longer intact when delivery nears, the fetus is most probably infected and therefore, a cesarean delivery would no longer be a good preventive measure. (2:179)

49 1. When using the Bradley method during childbirth, mothers are taught to assume the tailor position during labor when they are not walking about. The mother sits on a flat surface, flexes her knees sharply, and crosses her lower legs. The Bradley method is described as a physiological approach to childbirth that emphasizes that labor is a normal process.   (2:117–118)

50   1.   Chloasma is best described as brown blotchy areas on the face. It is often called the mask of pregnancy. Pigmentation of the nipples and areolae also is typical during pregnancy. The dark vertical line on the abdomen is called linea nigra. Stretch marks on the abdomen, thighs, and breasts are called striae gravidarum.   (12:462)

51   4.   In general, diabetics tend to have babies that are larger-than-average in size at birth, especially those who have had diabetes for a long time and whose disease is not under good control. This is due to the mother's high blood glucose level that causes fat and often edematous infants. The exception is the diabetic woman with vascular complications, whose baby may be smaller-than-average in size. Having preeclampsia, placenta previa, or heart disease does not necessarily predispose to delivering an infant that is larger-than-average in size.   (2:427–428)

52   4.   Of the 4 women described in this item, the pregnant mother who had an infant with pyloric stenosis is least likely to be considered at risk. Unmarried women, women who have had multiple pregnancies, and women from low socioeconomic groups are at risk because they tend to have more complications during pregnancy than the average patient. So also are women who have had inadequate prenatal care, are heavy smokers, abuse chemicals, and have emotional problems in the home.   (2:185–187)

53   1.   It is generally best to handle gossip by ignoring it, going on with one's work, and avoiding attacking the "gossipers." Confronting gossip often draws more attention, rather than less, to the gossip. Most people admire the person who carries on well despite gossip. Demonstrating behavior that shows the falseness of gossip appears better than explanations and confrontations. These general principles to deal with gossip were explored and described by the psychologist, Dr. Hadley Cantril.   (13:75)

The care of selected clinic equipment

54   4.   Using steam under pressure is best suited for destroying spores. Spores are very resistant and can survive under adverse conditions. The high temperature generated in autoclaves that place steam under pressure is responsible for spore destruction.   (9:284)

55   2.   Using three-prong electrical plugs best helps to prevent accidents from electrical shocks because the third prong grounds electrical currents that could cause shock. Placing electrical outlets above baseboards and providing for two receivers at each electrical outlet will not help to prevent accidents from electrical shock. Retractable cords are convenient and help prevent people from tripping over cords, but they do not necessarily reduce accidents from electrical shock.   (9:176)

Teaching Women About Common Discomforts of Pregnancy

56   3.   Frequent urination is common late in pregnancy, especially after lightening occurs, because the enlarged uterus causes pressure on the bladder. Frequency is unrelated to having alkaline urine or increasing wastes from the fetus. A urinary tract infection could cause frequency but this is not the most probable cause late in pregnancy and it would likely cause additional symptoms, such as burning and painful urination.   (2:122)

57   4.   Dyspnea is a normal discomfort of pregnancy during the third trimester, when the uterus tends to crowd the chest cavity. Many women relieve this discomfort by lying on their side while placing a small pillow under the abdomen. Good posture also relieves dyspnea by allowing more room for the lungs to function normally.   (2:123)

58   1.   The pelvic rock (pelvic tilt), which involves moving the hips and pelvis back and forth, often helps relieve a backache. The exercise can be carried out while the woman is on her hands and knees, standing up, or lying down. The knee–chest position is also recommended for relieving lower backaches.   (2:124–125)

59   3.   Itching of the skin is not uncommon and is a very annoying discomfort of pregnancy. There are several ways to help promote relief. A sodium bicarbonate, starch, or oatmeal bath may be used. Oiling the skin after bathing and increasing fluid intake may offer some relief. Soap should probably not be used but if it is, it should be used sparingly; the soap should be very mild.   (2:128)

60   4.   Varicose veins (varicosities) are veins distended with blood. They are usually uncomfortable and can lead to complications. Varicose veins in the rectum are called hemorrhoids. When varicosities are present in the vulva, distention of the affected veins and the discomfort can often be relieved by having the woman position herself so that blood can leave the area more readily. This can be done by having the woman lie in bed with her buttocks elevated several times a day. Applying compresses may add to comfort but does not help promote blood flow from the varicosities. Sleeping in the low-Fowler's position and decreasing exercise are unlikely to relieve pressure and discomfort associated with varicose veins.   (2:125)

61   3.   During pregnancy, the gastrointestinal tract relaxes and bacterial action on waste products in the intestine occurs to produce flatulence. The best measure to overcome flatulence is to maintain regular bowel elimination. Increasing daily fluid intake and exercising are two common measures to help overcome constipation. Other measures to prevent flatulence include chewing food well, eliminating foods from the diet that tend to form gas, such as beans and cabbage, and eating small but more frequent meals.   (2:123)

62   3.   Some pregnant women note bleeding from the gums during pregnancy. It is believed due to an increase in the amount of estrogen in the body. This causes softening of the gums. Irritation, such as tooth brushing, is likely to cause bleeding. Salivation is often increased during pregnancy. Pregnancy is not known to predispose to plaque being deposited on the teeth in increased amounts. Nor is there a change in the normal roughness of the tongue during pregnancy.   (2:64)

63   3.   During pregnancy, peristalsis slows down due to the relaxing effects of progesterone. This is believed to cause heartburn, constipation, flatulence, and belching in some pregnant women. The enlarging uterus can also contribute to hiatal hernia formation with the production of heartburn as a symptom.   (2:122)

64   3.   Baking soda contains sodium and therefore, predisposes to the retention of body fluids. The indiscriminate use of baking soda also can upset the body's acid–base balance and can have a rebound effect to cause an increase in secretions of acid in the stomach. The use of baking soda is not associated with constipation, poor absorption of nutrients, and irritation of gastrointestinal mucosa.   (2:122)

65   2.   Edema of the feet late in pregnancy is believed to be caused primarily by the pressure of an enlarging uterus on pelvic veins, which causes less than optimal return of blood from the extremities. Fluids seep through the walls of the distended veins to cause the edema.   (2:122)

66   2.   Salt tends to hold excess fluid in the body. Restricting salt intake will usually help relieve edema in the legs and feet that often appears during pregnancy. However, any patient with edema should be observed carefully; generalized edema is a symptom of preeclampsia, a serious complication of pregnancy.   (2:169)

67   4.   Early in pregnancy, many women experience early morning nausea and vomiting, which can often be relieved by eating a piece of dry toast or dry crackers about a half hour before arising in the morning. Other measures that tend to relieve nausea and vomiting early in pregnancy are eating small but more frequent meals, eating unbuttered popcorn before arising in the morning, taking fluids between meals, and obtaining sufficient rest and fresh air. Although nausea and vomiting may have a physiological basis, emotional factors may contribute and, therefore, a healthy and happy outlook also may help to prevent or relieve the condition.   (2:122; 4:202)

68   1.   Reducing fats in the diet often helps to relieve heartburn and vomiting during pregnancy. Restricted intake of proteins, minerals, and carbohydrates are not recommended.   (2:122; 4:202)

69   2.   Constipation can often be controlled during pregnancy when women observe an appropriate exercise program. Other measures that often relieve constipation include increasing roughage in the diet, increasing fluid intake, and observing regular habits of elimination. Pregnant women should be taught to avoid laxatives and enemas to relieve constipation, unless prescribed for them. In some obstinate cases, taking a stool softener may be prescribed.   (2:122)

70 1. Mineral oil interferes with the absorption of vitamin A, one of the fat-soluble vitamins. It also interferes with the absorption of other fat-soluble vitamins, such as vitamins D, E, and K.   (4:149)

71 2. The pain of leg cramps can often be relieved by moving the foot so that the toes point toward the kneecap, in a position of dorsiflexion. Standing up, massaging the leg, and applying heat also often help to relieve leg cramps, which are among the most annoying discomforts of pregnancy. If the woman has varicosities or a history of blood clots, the legs should not be massaged nor should heat be applied to them.   (2:125–126)

72 3. An imbalance in the body's calcium–phosphorus ratio is likely to cause leg cramps. Aluminum hydroxide gel may be prescribed to absorb some of the phosphorus present in milk to restore the calcium–phosphorus balance. The gel stops the action of phosphorus on calcium by absorbing the phosphorus and eliminating it through the large intestine. Leg cramps may be due to pressure of the enlarging uterus on nerves leading to the legs. Exercise has not been found helpful in relieving leg cramps.   (4:132; 12:447)

73 2. Body mechanics is best defined as using the body effectively as a machine. While using good body mechanics helps to prevent and relieve discomfort related to the musculoskeletal system, it also promotes better functioning of other systems in the body, such as the respiratory system.   (9:116)

74 1. Flexing the knees slightly while standing helps to absorb shocks to the body. The flexed knees do not necessarily help improve circulation in the legs, keep the spine straight, or relieve tension in the arches of the feet.   (9:116)

75 4. The primary reason for extending or stretching the waist is to give the lungs the most amount of space to function in the body. This technique is often called "putting on a long midriff."   (9–116)

Teaching Women How to Promote Health During Pregnancy

76 1. The most striking difference between babies born of smoking and nonsmoking mothers is that babies born to smokers tend to be lighter in weight. The carbon monoxide blood levels increase in smoking mothers and the carbon monoxide attaches to hemoglobin before oxygen does, thereby causing intrauterine hypoxemia. Also, vasoconstriction caused by nicotine decreases the diffusion of nutrients to the fetus, which contributes to a low birth weight. When comparisons are made with nonsmokers, the rates of fetal and newborn deaths are higher when pregnant women smoke.   (2:107–108)

77 1. Exercises, such as swimming, bowling, and golfing, will improve the mother's circulation and increase oxygen supply to the fetus. However, the pregnant woman should stop exercising before reaching fatigue. Two sports that authorities generally advise avoiding are horseback riding and competitive tennis, especially singles tennis. In general, exercise during pregnancy should be consistent with what the woman did before she became pregnant, and exercise should be done in moderation.   (2:105–106; 12:445)

78   2.   Physicians who advise against having sexual intercourse late in pregnancy believe that it may cause infection, premature labor, and rupture of the amniotic sac. Other physicians believe that intercourse may be continued throughout pregnancy without ill effects and need not be discontinued unless complications occur.   (2:107; 12:445–446)

79   1.   A diet rich in iron is needed for a pregnant woman for the formation of hemoglobin and for transporting oxygen and carbon dioxide for the growing fetus. Anemia is relatively common during pregnancy because many women are not likely to include sufficient amounts in their diets and as a result, iron may need to be prescribed as a dietary supplement.   (4:202)

80   4.   Of the foods described in this item, cheddar cheese and sardines are richest in calcium.   (4:133)

81   1.   Calcium and phosphorus are especially important for the development of the fetus's bones and teeth.   (4:130, 133–134)

82   3.   Many vitamins lack stability to withstand heat and contact with air while being cooked. Vitamin C is especially fragile. Preferably, vegetables should be eaten raw whenever possible to preserve vitamin content. Cooking does not destroy minerals and fiber. Color may be affected by cooking but this is not the primary reason for cooking quickly with the least amount of water in a covered container.   (16:58–67)

83   4.   Vitamin D is necessary for the absorption and utilization of calcium, and its intake should be increased during pregnancy. Vitamin A and C also should be increased in a pregnant woman's diet. Vitamin A is important for vision, tooth formation, and reduced susceptibility to infection. However, vitamin A is more important to the mother and for the preservation of her pregnancy because the vitamin does not cross the placenta. Vitamin C plays an important role in blood vessel development, and the development and maintenance of normal connective tissues in bones, muscles, and cartilage.   (4:131)

84   3.   Tomatoes are a rich source of Vitamin C, as are citrus fruits, cabbage, and other raw leafy vegetables, melons, broccoli, collards, and strawberries.   (4:158)

85   3.   Foods rich in calcium also have generous amounts of phosphorous. Therefore, a pregnant woman who is receiving adequate amounts of calcium in her diet is simultaneously receiving adequate amounts of phosphorus.   (2:103; 4:134)

86   2.   A daily intake of a quart of milk (4 cups) is recommended for pregnant women because milk is an excellent source of calcium and protein, both of which are essential for the proper growth of the fetus. Pregnant teen-agers may require even larger amounts of milk, up to 5 to 6 cups a day, because the teenager requires calcium and protein for her own growth as well as for that of the fetus.   (4:199)

87 4.   When ⅓ cup of powdered nonfat milk is added to 8 ounces of regular milk, the mixture will have the nutritional value of 2 glasses of milk. Molasses and pureed fruit will flavor milk for those who dislike the taste but will not decrease the volume of milk recommended for pregnant women. Gelatin has little nutritional value.   (4:199)

88 2.   Using alcohol during pregnancy is likely to influence the fetus in the following ways: intellect may be impaired, fetal growth may be retarded, and congenital malformations are likely to occur. Even in minimal-to-mod-erate amounts, alcohol may be harmful to the fetus. The best and safest policy is to avoid alcohol during pregnancy.   (2:108; 4:203)

89 1.   The culprit in coffee is the caffeine, a central nervous system stimu-lant. It can cross the placenta to reach the fetus and appears to play a part in causing mastitis in pregnant women. The Food and Drug Administration recommends using coffee sparingly or avoiding it entirely. Cola drinks and chocolate should also be used sparingly or avoided during pregnancy because of their caffeine content.   (4:203; 12:446)

90 3.   Current opinion is that the amount of weight a woman gains during pregnancy is less important than having a nutritious, or high-quality, diet. However, weight is still significant, especially because a rapid loss or gain may signal a complication. Some authors consider a normal weight gain during pregnancy to be between 22 or 24 and 27 pounds.   (2:65; 4:198)

91 4.   Knee-length stockings and round garters are contraindicated because they tend to decrease circulation in the lower extremities. Garter belts, panty hose, and foot Peds are not necessarily contraindicated because they do not interfere with circulation in the lower extremities.   (2:104–105; 12:446)

92 1.   During pregnancy, a woman's posture changes to accommodate the growing fetus. This change can cause backaches. Wearing high-heeled shoes tends to cause or aggravate backaches because the shoes shift the center of gravity, which puts extra strain on the back. Also, high-heeled shoes tend to make women more prone to falls than low-heeled shoes. Wearing high-heeled shoes does not predispose to hemorrhoids, varicose veins, and edema in the feet.   (2:105; 12:446)

93 2.   When there are no complications, traveling by car is usually permissi-ble. But pregnant women should be advised to stop about every 2 hours during a motor trip and take short walks to improve circulation and to avoid becoming tired. Emptying the bladder about every 2 hours helps prevent cystitis.   (2:106; 12:446)

94 2.   It is recommended that a pregnant woman wear a seat belt under her abdomen. She should not wear shoulder straps. Placing a seat belt over the abdomen is likely to interfere with proper breathing.   (12:446)

95 1. Cleansing the nipples regularly with a soft cloth and warm water ordinarily keeps the nipples clean of secretions. Other preparations, especially alcohol and soap solution, are likely to cause drying and cracking of nipples by removing normal protective oils from their surfaces. (2:107; 12:445)

96 3. Grasping the nipples and massaging them with an emollient helps to prepare the nipples for nursing. Massaging should be gentle to avoid tissue injury. The nipples may also be rubbed with a terry cloth towel to help toughen them. Teasing out inverted nipples to help them assume an erect position also assists in preparing for nursing. Grasping and massaging the nipples will not stimulate milk production, enlarge the size of the nipples, or prevent organisms from entering milk ducts. (12:445)

Teaching Women About the Anatomy and Physiology of the Reproductive Process

97 4. The endometrium is the inner lining of the uterus. The myometrium is the middle muscular layer. The perimetrium is the outer layer and is continuous with the peritoneum, which lines the abdominal cavity. (2:20; 10:306)

98 2. Sperm are propelled by movements of their tail-like portion, called the flagellum. Sperm do not have cilia. They do not move in the female by contractions of the cervix or uterus, or by pressure differences in the uterus and fallopian tubes. (10:302)

99 1. Each cell in the human body contains 46 chromosomes. So also do immature germ cells. By the process of meiosis, the number of chromosomes decreases in each germ cell so that by maturity, each ovum and each sperm contains 23 chromosomes. When the sperm and ovum unite, the new cell contains 46 chromosomes. (10:326–327)

100 1. Sperm are continuously manufactured in the body in the testes. The epididymis is a tube that conducts sperm from the testes to the vas, or ductus deferens. The seminal vesicles produce fluid in which sperm are carried during ejaculation. Sperm are exceedingly small. It has been estimated that at least 200 million are present in an average ejaculation. (10:302)

101 4. Conception normally takes place in the outer half of a fallopian tube. The fertilized ovum then divides and subdivides many times (mitosis) while it journeys down the tube to the uterus, where it will implant. (2:72)

102 2. Progesterone helps to prepare the uterus for pregnancy. It is produced by the corpus luteum. Prosecretin is a precursor of secretin, which is a hormone secreted by mucous membranes of the duodenum and jejunum. The human growth hormone (HGH), also called somatotropin, is concerned primarily with the growth of bones, muscles, and other organs. It is secreted by the anterior pituitary gland. Follicle-stimulating hormone (FSH) stimulates the development of ovarian follicles, the secretion of estrogen, the development of seminiferous tubules, and the maturation of spermatozoa.   (10:309)

103   4.   Presumptive signs of pregnancy include amenorrhea, nausea and vomiting, frequent urination, breast changes, color changes in the skin and mucous membranes, and fatigue. There are no signs called negative signs of pregnancy.   (2:46–53)

104   2.   A softening of the cervix (Goodell's sign) is a probable sign of pregnancy. Observing an increase in pigmentation is a presumptive sign of pregnancy. Pigmentation may remain from one pregnancy to the next and therefore, is called a presumptive sign because it is not reliable for diagnosing pregnancy. Hearing a fetal heart rate and feeling fetal movements are positive signs of pregnancy when they are noted by an examiner.   (2:46–53)

105   2.   Quickening refers to the first movements of the fetus felt by a pregnant woman. This generally occurs after about 16 weeks in mothers who previously have had babies, and after about 18 weeks in women pregnant for the first time. Quickening is a presumptive sign of pregnancy because gas within the bowel and peristalsis are sometimes mistaken for fetal movements. Engagement is present when the largest diameter of the presenting part of the fetus passes through the pelvic inlet. Lightening refers to a drop of the fetus and uterus downward into the pelvic cavity and ordinarily occurs about 2 weeks before delivery.   (2:47)

106   4.   The discoloration of the vulva and vagina during pregnancy is Chadwick's sign. A softening of the lower segment of the uterus is Hegar's sign. A softening of the cervix, one of the first observable signs of pregnancy, is Goodell's sign. These 3 signs are probable signs of pregnancy. Braxton Hicks' contractions are painless uterine contractions that usually occur throughout pregnancy. They are believed to facilitate placental circulation. Ordinarily, Braxton Hick's contractions are not felt by a woman until late in her pregnancy.   (10:48, 59)

107   3.   The placenta provides the body with several hormones, including human chorionic gonadotropin (HCG), estrogen, progesterone, and various other hormones and enzymes. Organisms can cross the placenta from maternal blood to the blood stream of the fetus. The placenta does not store nutrients, nor does it function to prevent fetal malformations.   (2:76)

108   3.   The amniotic fluid protects the fetus, permits the fetus to move, keeps the environment for the fetus at a constant temperature, provides some nourishment for the fetus, serves as a reservoir for fetal urine, and prevents the amnion from adhering to the fetus. Keeping the fetus free of microorganisms from the mother is not a function of the amniotic fluid.   (2:15)

109   3.   Prolactin is responsible for stimulating the production of milk in the

breasts. It is produced by the anterior lobe of the pituitary gland. Estrogen suppresses lactation, among other things. Oxytocin, secreted by the posterior lobe of the pituitary gland, stimulates the contraction of the uterus and stimulates the "letdown" reflex to bring milk to the nipples. Parathormone regulates the amount of calcium in the blood.   (10:17)

110   2.   A good deal of blood bypasses the lungs of a fetus by moving directly from the right atrium to the left atrium of the heart through the foramen ovale. At birth, the foramen ovale normally closes when respirations of the newborn are established.   (2:82)

111   1.   The blood of the fetus in the uterus has a lower level of oxygen concentration than the blood of a normal infant. This low level of oxygen in the blood of the fetus is due to the mixing of oxygenated blood from the ductus venosis and of used blood in the interior vena cava. The fetus survives this state of hypoxemia well, but the situation changes as soon as the respiratory system begins to function at birth. Blood oxygen levels then increase.   (2:82)

112   4.   Oxytocin plays an important role in starting labor. It is produced by the posterior lobe of the pituitary gland. Because of its action on uterine muscles, oxytocin is administered following delivery to prevent or to help stop hemorrhaging. It causes the muscles of the uterus to contract.   (10:155, 161)

113   2.   A shortening and thinning of the cervix, which help prepare for delivery, is called effacement. Engagement is the settling of the presenting part of the fetus into the true pelvis. Dilatation is an opening of the cervix that takes place during the first stage of labor before the baby is born. Ballottement describes being able to move the fetus about in the uterus.   (10:204)

Classification of Test Items

Directions: *Each item in the previous review test is classified here according to the subject area it tests. Place a check mark after each item you answered* **correctly** *by referring to your answers. Total the number of items you answered correctly in each area and enter the numbers in the correct places on pages 553–556.*

Clinical: Maternity Nursing and the Care of Newborns

1 ___	14 ___	27 ___	40 ___	56 ___	77 ___
2 ___	15 ___	28 ___	41 ___	57 ___	78 ___
3 ___	16 ___	29 ___	42 ___	58 ___	91 ___
4 ___	17 ___	30 ___	43 ___	59 ___	92 ___
5 ___	18 ___	31 ___	44 ___	60 ___	93 ___
6 ___	19 ___	32 ___	45 ___	61 ___	94 ___
7 ___	20 ___	33 ___	46 ___	62 ___	95 ___
8 ___	21 ___	34 ___	48 ___	63 ___	96 ___
9 ___	22 ___	35 ___	49 ___	65 ___	103 ___
11 ___	23 ___	36 ___	50 ___	69 ___	105 ___
12 ___	24 ___	38 ___	51 ___	71 ___	113 ___
13 ___	25 ___	39 ___	52 ___	76 ___	

TOTAL ___

Biological/Physical Sciences

10 ___	55 ___	97 ___	100 ___	104 ___	109 ___
26 ___	64 ___	98 ___	101 ___	106 ___	110 ___
54 ___	72 ___	99 ___	102 ___	107 ___	111 ___
				108 ___	112 ___

TOTAL ___

Fundamentals of Nursing

37 ___	73 ___	74 ___	75 ___

TOTAL ___

Diet Therapy/Nutrition

66 ✓	68 ____	80 ✓	82 ✓	84 ✓	87 ✓
67 ✓	79 ✓	81 ✓	83 ✓	85 ✓	89 ✓
				86 ✓	90 ✓

TOTAL 13

Pharmacology

70 ____   88 ✓

TOTAL 1

Psychosocial Sciences

47 ✓   53 ✓

TOTAL 2

Review Test 3

The Nursing Care of Women During Labor and Delivery, the Care of Their Newborns, and Their Postpartal Care

    Caring for a Woman During Labor and Assisting With a Delivery
    Caring for a Newborn
    Caring for a Woman During the Postpartal Period
    Caring for a Woman Who Has a Cesarean Delivery
    Caring for a Woman During an Emergency Delivery

Teaching a Woman About Family Planning
Individual Items
Correct Answers and Rationales
Classification of Test Items

Directions: *With a pencil, blacken the circle in front of the option you have chosen for your correct answer.*

The Nursing Care of Women During Labor and Delivery, the Care of Their Newborns, and Their Postpartal Care

Ms. Carson is having her first baby and is at term. She is having uterine contractions when admitted to the hospital.

1 Which of the following questions that the nurse asks Ms. Carson upon admission is *least* pertinent?
    ○ 1. "When did you last eat?"
    ○ 2. "Have you ever had an enema?"
    ○ 3. "Have your membranes ruptured?"
    ○ 4. "When did your contractions start?"

2 Ms. Carson thinks her membranes have ruptured but she is not sure. The nurse-in-charge performs a Nitrazine test. The primary purpose of this test is to
    ○ 1. differentiate between urine and amniotic fluid.
    ○ 2. differentiate between amniotic fluid and vaginal mucus.
    ○ 3. determine whether there is blood in the amniotic fluid.
    ○ 4. determine whether there is meconium in the amniotic fluid.

3 Ms. Carson's urinary bladder should *not* be allowed to become distended primarily because a full bladder during labor tends to
   ○ 1. increase the risk of urinary incontinence.
   ○ 2. predispose to a prolapse of the umbilical cord.
   ○ 3. interfere with observations of uterine contractions.
   ○ 4. prevent the descent of the infant into the birth canal.

4 It is determined that Ms. Carson requires a cleansing enema. One reason for administering an enema to Ms. Carson is to help
   ○ 1. provide a clean delivery.
   ○ 2. ease the discomfort of contractions.
   ○ 3. prevent constipation after delivery.
   ○ 4. relieve pressure in an area where an episiotomy may be performed.

The nurse times Ms. Carson's contractions.

5 The term used to describe the period when Ms. Carson's uterus begins a contraction until the contraction ends is called its
   ○ 1. interval.
   ○ 2. duration.
   ○ 3. intensity.
   ○ 4. frequency.

6 Where on Ms. Carson's abdomen should the nurse rest her hand when feeling a contraction?
   ○ 1. Just above the patient's pubis
   ○ 2. Just above the patient's umbilicus
   ○ 3. In the middle of the patient's abdomen, halfway between the umbilicus and the pubis
   ○ 4. On either side of the patient's abdomen, halfway between the umbilicus and the pubis

The nurse uses a manual fetoscope to check the fetal heart rate.

7 The nurse should check the fetal heart rate during the time when Ms. Carson has a contraction and again
   ○ 1. midway between contractions.
   ○ 2. immediately after the contraction.
   ○ 3. immediately before the next contraction.
   ○ 4. as near to the end of the contraction as possible.

8 The nurse judges the fetal heart rate to be normal when she notes that the rate per minute is between
   ○ 1. 80 and 100 beats.
   ○ 2. 100 and 120 beats.
   ○ 3. 120 and 160 beats.
   ○ 4. 160 and 200 beats.

Ms. Carson is to have a vaginal examination.

9 The nurse should help prepare for Ms. Carson's vaginal examination by
  ○ 1. having clean gloves in readiness.
  ○ 2. teaching the patient to bear down slightly.
  ○ 3. placing the patient in a lithotomy position.
  ○ 4. cleaning the area well at the patient's vulva.

10 The nurse-in-charge who performs the vaginal examination on Ms. Carson tells the nurse that Ms. Carson's cervix is dilated 4 centimeters. The nurse's interpretation of this finding is correct when the nurse judges that in terms of cervical dilatation, the patient is
  ○ 1. at a very early stage of dilatation.
  ○ 2. approaching half of the total amount of dilatation.
  ○ 3. nearing total dilatation.
  ○ 4. in labor but an interpretation of dilatation cannot be made with available information.

It is judged that Ms. Carson is in early true labor.

11 It will be correct to state that Ms. Carson is in true labor when her
  ○ 1. uterine contractions are regular.
  ○ 2. membranes rupture spontaneously.
  ○ 3. fetus drops into the brim of the pelvis.
  ○ 4. mucus plug in the cervical canal is expelled.

12 Early in labor, the preferred position for Ms. Carson while resting in bed is the
  ○ 1. back-lying position.
  ○ 2. semi-sitting position.
  ○ 3. left side-lying position.
  ○ 4. right side-lying position.

13 During which of the following stages of labor should the nurse anticipate that Ms. Carson will ordinarily need the most encouragement and support?
  ○ 1. During the early part of stage one
  ○ 2. During the transition part of stage one
  ○ 3. During stage two
  ○ 4. During stage three

14 Ms. Carson is nearing the end of the first stage of labor. Which of the following nursing measures is *least* appropriate at this time?
  ○ 1. Encouraging the patient to void
  ○ 2. Urging the patient to breathe deeply
  ○ 3. Helping the patient to lie on her left side
  ○ 4. Having the patient push with each contraction

The nurse prepares to transfer Ms. Carson to the delivery room.

15 The time to transfer the patient to the delivery room is when Ms. Carson's labor has progressed to the point that Ms. Carson
- O 1. is crowning.
- O 2. is fully dilated.
- O 3. has an absence of vaginal show.
- O 4. has a desire to push with contractions.

16 After transferring her to the delivery room, Ms. Carson has saddle block anesthetic for delivery. The anesthetic will be injected into the
- O 1. tissues of the perineum.
- O 2. areas next to the cervix.
- O 3. area of the pudental nerves.
- O 4. lower part of the spinal canal.

17 Ms. Carson has an episiotomy. The primary reason for the episiotomy is to help prevent
- O 1. uterine rupture.
- O 2. postpartum infection.
- O 3. prolonged pressure on the fetal head.
- O 4. undue trauma to the urinary bladder.

Ms. Carson delivers a baby boy.

18 Before Baby Boy Carson takes his first breath, the physician ordinarily will first need equipment to
- O 1. repair the episiotomy.
- O 2. clamp and cut the umbilical cord.
- O 3. do an Apgar evaluation on the infant.
- O 4. clean the infant's airway of mucus and debris.

19 The umbilical cord is examined after Ms. Carson delivers. It has been observed that when there is an abnormal number of blood vessels in the cord, the infant is likely to have
- O 1. Erb's palsy.
- O 2. a congenital defect.
- O 4. erythroblastosis fetalis.
- O 4. respiratory distress syndrome.

20 Ms. Carson is given an oxytocic agent soon after the delivery of the placenta, primarily to help
- O 1. hasten the process of involution.
- O 2. prevent the uterus from inverting.
- O 3. strengthen contractions of the uterus.
- O 4. decrease the likelihood of uterine spasms.

21 Which of the following procedures should the nurse use when she removes Ms. Carson's legs from the stirrups following delivery?
- O 1. Both legs should be removed at the same time.
- O 2. The right leg should be removed first and then the left leg.
- O 3. The left leg should be removed first and then the right leg.

    ○ 4. Any one of the described procedures is satisfactory as long as the legs are moved slowly.

22 If the nurse notes the height of the top of Ms. Carson's uterus to be level with the patient's umbilicus, the nurse should judge the height of the uterus to be
    ○ 1. normal.
    ○ 2. abnormally low.
    ○ 3. slightly higher than normal.
    ○ 4. markedly higher than normal.

23 When after birth is it believed best to begin a bonding relationship between Baby Boy Carson and his parents?
    ○ 1. During the first hour after delivery
    ○ 2. Immediately after initial care is given to the newborn in the nursery
    ○ 3. Immediately after the mother is permitted to ambulate after delivery
    ○ 4. During the day when the mother and infant are discharged from the hospital

The Nurse Cares for Newborn Baby Boy Carson.

Baby Boy Carson is given vitamin K shortly after birth.

24 Baby Boy Carson is given vitamin K primarily to help
    ○ 1. stimulate respirations.
    ○ 2. start peristaltic movements.
    ○ 3. improve blood coagulation.
    ○ 4. increase calcium absorption.

25 When giving Baby Boy Carson vitamin K intramuscularly, of the following muscles, it is best for the nurse to inject into the
    ○ 1. biceps brachii muscle.
    ○ 2. biceps femoris muscle.
    ○ 3. rectus femoris muscle.
    ○ 4. gluteus maximus muscle.

The nurse evaluates Baby Boy Carson by using the traditional Apgar scoring system.

26 After the nurse has scored Baby Boy Carson's color, respiratory effort, reflex irritability, and heart rate, she should next score the infant's
    ○ 1. length.
    ○ 2. weight.
    ○ 3. muscle tone.
    ○ 4. blood pressure.

27   The best possible score that Baby Boy Carson can obtain when using
the Apgar scoring system is
  O 1. 5.
  O 2. 10.
  O 3. 15.
  O 4. 20.

28   The nurse dries Baby Boy Carson as soon after birth as possible,
primarily to help
  O 1. stimulate the infant's circulatory system.
  O 2. avoid excess heat loss from the infant's body.
  O 3. remove the white cheesy substance on the infant's skin.
  O 4. remove organisms from the infant's skin acquired during delivery.

29   Baby Boy Carson's temperature is obtained. The primary reason for
obtaining a newborn's first temperature rectally is to
  O 1. break up a meconium plug.
  O 2. determine whether the anus is open.
  O 3. provide a stimulus to start peristalsis.
  O 4. obtain the most accurate temperature possible.

30   Identification bracelets are placed on Baby Boy Carson. In addition to
this, which of the following identification methods is being used
increasingly, and is considered the safest method of identification?
  O 1. Footprinting the baby and thumbprinting the mother
  O 2. Obtaining an x-ray of one of the mother's and infant's wrists
  O 3. Taking the mother's and infant's photo within 24 hours after birth
  O 4. Placing identification on the mother's and infant's wrist with
        invisible ink that is seen in ultraviolet light

31   Although the instillation of silver nitrate solution or an antibiotic
ointment may be postponed temporarily after Baby Boy Carson's birth,
the *maximum* time to delay instillation is
  O 1. ½ hour.
  O 2. 1 hour.
  O 3. 1½ hours.
  O 4. 2 hours.

32   The nurse weighs Baby Boy Carson. If the nurse uses the following
techniques in the order given below, which one is in *error*?
  O 1. The nurse places a clean paper on the scale.
  O 2. The nurse balances the scale.
  O 3. The nurse places the nude infant on the scale.
  O 4. The nurse holds the infant's hands to protect him from falling.

*Baby Boy Carson is transferred to the newborn nursery where the nurse
continues with various observations.*

33   Baby Boy Carson's umbilical cord should be checked frequently during
the first few hours after birth for signs of

○ 1. infection.
○ 2. herniation.
○ 3. prolonged pulsation.
○ 4. excessive bleeding.

34 When observing Baby Boy Carson's skin, the nurse notes a white
cheesy substance on the newborn's body which is called
○ 1. lanugo.
○ 2. petechiae.
○ 3. miliaria rubra.
○ 4. vernix caseosa.

35 Which of the following signs, if Baby Boy Carson develops it, should
the nurse report promptly to the nurse-in-charge?
○ 1. The infant's scrotum appears swollen.
○ 2. The infant appears jaundiced a few hours after birth.
○ 3. The infant does not void until about 8 hours after birth.
○ 4. The infant spits up mucus shortly after being admitted to the
nursery.

36 If Baby Boy Carson has the following signs several hours after birth,
which one should the nurse report promptly?
○ 1. The infant's hands are bluish.
○ 2. The infant's pulse rate is 140 per minute.
○ 3. The infant's regurgitates after his last feeding.
○ 4. The infant's sternum moves inward with inspirations.

37 Within how many hours/days after birth can the nurse expect Baby Boy
Carson's body temperature to stabilize?
○ 1. Within about 4 hours
○ 2. Within about 8 hours
○ 3. Within about 1 day
○ 4. Within about 2 days

38 Baby Boy Carson has a swelling caused by a ruptured blood vessel in
the periosteum. The accumulation of blood between the periosteum
and the skull, which produced the swelling, is called
○ 1. caput.
○ 2. cephaledema.
○ 3. cephalhematoma.
○ 4. caput succedaneum.

39 Where in the body does an *abnormal* condition exist if Baby Boy
Carson develops respiratory distress syndrome?
○ 1. In the lungs
○ 2. In the bronchi
○ 3. In the pleural spaces
○ 4. In the respiratory center

*Baby Boy Carson has physiological jaundice on his second day after
birth.*

40   What should the nurse do first when she notes Baby Boy Carson's skin
      is jaundiced?
      ○ 1. Weigh the infant.
      ○ 2. Withhold the infant's next feeding.
      ○ 3. Report the observation to the nurse-in-charge.
      ○ 4. Do nothing; jaundice at 2 days of age is insignificant.

41   The blood constituents that are being destroyed in excessive amounts
      and believed responsible for Baby Boy Carson's jaundice are
      ○ 1. blood lipids.
      ○ 2. blood platelets.
      ○ 3. red blood cells.
      ○ 4. white blood cells.

42   The organ in Baby Boy Carson's body that does not handle excessive
      amounts of bilirubin well is the
      ○ 1. liver.
      ○ 2. brain.
      ○ 3. heart.
      ○ 4. spleen.

The nurse takes Baby Boy Carson to Ms. Carson to breast-feed her infant.

43   When the nurse places the infant next to Ms. Carson, she touches her
      infant's cheek affectionately with her finger and exclaims, "Look! He
      turns his head toward my finger." The nurse should explain that the
      reason Baby Boy Carson responds to his mother's touch on his cheek
      is that the infant is
      ○ 1. reacting to fear.
      ○ 2. looking for food.
      ○ 3. demonstrating a need for love.
      ○ 4. startled for being disturbed.

44   The nurse goes on to tell Ms. Carson that her infant's response to
      touch on his cheek is a reflex called the
      ○ 1. grasp reflex.
      ○ 2. startle reflex.
      ○ 3. sucking reflex.
      ○ 4. rooting reflex.

45   The nurse should teach Ms. Carson that while nursing the baby, Ms.
      Carson's body normally releases oxytocin. What effect will oxytocin
      have on Ms. Carson?
      ○ 1. The patient will feel faint.
      ○ 2. The patient will have a desire to void.
      ○ 3. The patient will have abdominal discomfort.
      ○ 4. The patient will feel the nipples become erect.

46   The nurse explains to Ms. Carson that the first secretion from the

breasts after the birth of her baby is called colostrum and is especially
beneficial for the infant because colostrum contains

- O 1. vitamins.
- O 2. antibodies.
- O 3. predigested fat.
- O 4. digestive enzymes.

47 The nurse observes Ms. Carson place her nipple and all of the dark
area immediately around the nipple (areola) into the infant's mouth
when she nurses her baby. Which of the following comments is most
appropriate for the nurse to make to Ms. Carson about her breast-
feeding technique?

- O 1. "It is better that none of the dark area around the nipple enters
your baby's mouth."
- O 2. "Your baby knows how much of the nipple and dark area
around it he needs for nursing."
- O 3. "Try not to allow more than about one half of the dark area
around the nipple to enter your baby's mouth."
- O 4. "You are nursing correctly when you place the nipple and dark
area around it into your baby's mouth as you are doing."

48 The nurse should teach Ms. Carson that when she wishes to remove
her baby from the nipple, she should put gentle downward pressure on
her baby's

- O 1. lip.
- O 2. nose.
- O 3. chin.
- O 4. forehead.

49 After Baby Boy Carson is finished nursing, the best measure to help
him get rid of air he has swallowed while nursing is to

- O 1. give the infant water and hold him on his side.
- O 2. hold the infant over the shoulder and rub his back.
- O 3. give the infant a pacifier and hold him in the face-down position.
- O 4. hold the infant with his head slightly elevated and rub his stomach.

50 The nurse should teach Ms. Carson that the best way to ensure her
baby of an adequate milk supply from her breasts is for the mother to

- O 1. follow a daily exercise program.
- O 2. have a diet high in protein content.
- O 3. empty the breasts with each feeding.
- O 4. drink generous amounts of milk each day.

51 Which of the following factors has the *least* effect on the quantity and
quality of milk that Ms. Carson produces?

- O 1. The type of diet the patient has.
- O 2. The amount of fluid intake the patient has.
- O 3. The size and shape of the patient's breasts.
- O 4. The amount of rest and relaxation the patient has.

52 Because Ms. Carson is breast-feeding her infant, she should be taught that during lactation, her daily milk intake should be a *minimum* of
   ○ 1. 3 cups.
   ○ 2. 4 cups.
   ○ 3. 6 cups.
   ○ 4. 8 cups.

53 Which of the following procedures will best help to toughen Ms. Carson's nipples during the first 2 or 3 days after delivery?
   ○ 1. Wearing a waterproof, supportive bra
   ○ 2. Exposing the nipples to air after each nursing
   ○ 3. Nursing the infant only 12 to 15 minutes at one time
   ○ 4. Swab the nipples with boric acid solution after each nursing

54 After several days of breast-feeding, Baby Boy Carson's stools will be considered normal in color if they are
   ○ 1. brownish.
   ○ 2. dull orange.
   ○ 3. light green.
   ○ 4. golden yellow.

55 During a breast examination, the nurse notes that Ms. Carson's nipples are cracked. In this situation, it would be best for the nurse to
   ○ 1. apply petrolatum to the patient's nipples.
   ○ 2. sponge the patient's nipples with alcohol.
   ○ 3. apply warm compresses to the patient's nipples.
   ○ 4. inform the nurse-in-charge of the patient's cracked nipples.

Baby Boy Carson will be circumcised.

56 If Mr. and Ms. Carson plan a religious ceremony for the circumcision, which of the following religions do the parents practice?
   ○ 1. Judaism
   ○ 2. Islamism
   ○ 3. Buddhism
   ○ 4. Mormonism

57 Following the circumcision, Baby Boy Carson should most certainly be observed for signs of
   ○ 1. blood in the urine.
   ○ 2. swelling of the scrotum.
   ○ 3. profuse urine production.
   ○ 4. bleeding at the site of excision.

Ms. Carson asks the nurse various questions concerning her infant and his care.

58 Ms. Carson asks the nurse when her baby's umbilical cord will drop off.

The nurse answers that the cord will normally drop off when the baby's age is between
○ 1. 3 and 4 days.
○ 2. 6 and 10 days.
○ 3. 12 and 14 days.
○ 4. 15 and 20 days.

59 Ms. Carson feels the soft spot on her infant's head and asks when it will close. The nurse responds correctly that the anterior fontanel normally is closed by the time the infant reaches the age of about
○ 1. 3 months.
○ 2. 6 months.
○ 3. 12 months.
○ 4. 18 months.

60 Ms. Carson asks the nurse about a bluish area on her infant's buttocks. The nurse's response should be based on knowledge that this discoloration
○ 1. may need to be removed surgically.
○ 2. is a birthmark that the infant will have for life.
○ 3. will normally disappear in about one's year time.
○ 4. should be checked about twice a year for precancerous cells.

61 The bluish area on Baby Boy Carson's buttocks is called
○ 1. milia.
○ 2. nevi.
○ 3. stork bite.
○ 4. mongolian spot.

62 Ms. Carson asks whether to use reusable or disposable diapers for her baby. The nurse should explain that most people are of the opinion that
○ 1. reusable diapers are better because they are more absorbent.
○ 2. disposable diapers are better because they are less irritating to an infant's skin.
○ 3. reusable diapers are better for daytime use, and disposable diapers are better for nighttime use.
○ 4. reusable and disposable diapers have both been found satisfactory, and the choice is a personal one.

63 While teaching Ms. Carson care of her baby, the nurse uses Erikson's concept of personality development. She explains that the infant's primary psychosocial need is to develop feelings of
○ 1. trust.
○ 2. identity.
○ 3. intimacy.
○ 4. autonomy.

64 According to Freud's theory of personality structure, Baby Boy Carson's personality development is guided primarily by the
○ 1. id.

○ 2. ego.
○ 3. superego.
○ 4. reality principle.

A Nurse is Assigned to Give Ms. Carson Her Postpartal Care.

Shortly after delivery, Ms. Carson complains of chilliness and says she is hungry.

65 Several reasons have been given to explain why Ms. Carson complains of extreme chilliness after delivery. One reason is that the
○ 1. patient is reacting unfavorably to an analgesic used during labor.
○ 2. patient's hormonal system is in a period of adjustment after delivery.
○ 3. patient has experienced a rapid cooling of her body immediately after delivery.
○ 4. patient's temperature control center is temporarily very sensitive to environmental coolness after delivery.

66 Ms. Carson, who is alert and free of nausea, is about 3 hours post-delivery when she complains of hunger. The nurse offers her a sandwich and a glass of milk. How should the nurse's action be judged in this situation?
○ 1. The nurse's action cannot be judged. Because the situation does not describe when the patient last ate, judgment cannot be made about giving her food at this time.
○ 2. The nurse's action is questionable. It is believed that the fatigue of labor causes poor digestion and absorption of food and therefore, it is better to offer the patient clear liquids at this time.
○ 3. The nurse's action is inappropriate. Because the patient is less than 8 hours postpartum, eating solid food and drinking beverages predispose her to abdominal distention.
○ 4. The nurse's action is appropriate. Because the patient is alert and free of nausea, she may be served some solid food and a beverage shortly after delivery.

The remaining items in this situation are individual items related to Ms. Carson's postpartal care.

67 Several hours after delivery, the nurse notes that Ms. Carson's uterus lies to the right side of her abdomen. The most likely reason for this position is that the patient's
○ 1. urinary bladder is full.
○ 2. stomach is overdistended.

○ 3. uterus is filling with blood.

○ 4. uterus is returning to a normal position.

68 Ms. Carson begins ambulation about 6 hours after delivery. This type of activity is especially beneficial to help prevent problems associated with the patient's

○ 1. circulatory system.

○ 2. process of involution.

○ 3. milk-producing ability.

○ 4. return to sexual activity.

69 Ms. Carson has a temperature of 100°F (37.8°C) on her first postpartum day. The most likely reason for this elevated temperature is that Ms. Carson is

○ 1. experiencing dehydration.

○ 2. experiencing subinvolution.

○ 3. developing a breast infection.

○ 4. developing a urinary infection.

70 Two days after delivery, the nurse notes that Ms. Carson is crying. Up until now, the patient has appeared happy and excited. In this situation, it would be best for the nurse to

○ 1. ask the patient why she is crying.

○ 2. offer the patient any help she may need.

○ 3. volunteer to telephone the patient's husband.

○ 4. explain to the patient that crying delays recovery.

71 A common measure to relieve discomfort from an episiotomy is to have Ms. Carson

○ 1. take sitz baths.

○ 2. ambulate frequently.

○ 3. lie on her abdomen in bed.

○ 4. elevate her hips while in bed.

72 Propoxyphene hydrochloride (Darvon) is prescribed for Ms. Carson. The nurse judges that the desired effect has been met after administering this medication when Ms. Carson

○ 1. has a firm uterus.

○ 2. is producing more milk.

○ 3. has been relieved of nausea.

○ 4. no longer complains of discomfort.

73 Ms. Carson asks the nurse when she may resume sexual activity. It is common practice to recommend that sexual activity be *avoided* after delivery for a period of approximately

○ 1. 1 to 2 weeks.

○ 2. 3 to 4 weeks.

○ 3. about 8 weeks.

○ 4. about 12 weeks.

74 If Ms. Carson had hemorrhaged after delivery, when would excessive bleeding most likely have occurred?

○ 1. During the first few hours after delivery
○ 2. About 6 to 8 hours after delivery
○ 3. About 12 to 24 hours after delivery
○ 4. About 24 to 48 hours after delivery

75 Ms. Carson's lochia has clots and saturates the perineal pad quickly. The nurse should document that the amount of Ms. Carson's lochia is
○ 1. scant.
○ 2. moderate.
○ 3. heavy.
○ 4. gross.

76 Ms. Carson's lochia is classified as lochia serosa, lochia rubra, or lochia alba. In which order does the lochia normally appear during the postpartum period?
○ 1. Lochia alba, lochia serosa, lochia rubra
○ 2. Lochia serosa, lochia rubra, lochia alba
○ 3. Lochia rubra, lochia alba, lochia serosa
○ 4. Lochia rubra, lochia serosa, lochia alba

77 The nurse uses measures to help Ms. Carson void after delivery. If Ms. Carson is allowed to have an overdistended bladder, she is at risk for developing
○ 1. a hematoma.
○ 2. thrombophlebitis.
○ 3. bladder herniation.
○ 4. a bladder infection.

78 Ms. Carson is unable to void and is to be catheterized. When compared with techniques used to catheterize other women, what technique, if any, is different when catheterizing a postpartum patient.
○ 1. The nurse should clean the postpartum patient's meatal area with normal saline rather than with an antiseptic as she uses for other women.
○ 2. The nurse should avoid lubricating the catheter for the postpartum patient as she does for other women.
○ 3. The nurse should insert the catheter farther for the postpartum patient than she does for other women.
○ 4. The nurse should use essentially the same techniques for the postpartum patient that she uses for other women.

79 While catheterizing Ms. Carson, the nurse checks Ms. Carson's perineum for a hematoma, the most common signs of which are
○ 1. heavy and foul lochia.
○ 2. swelling and discolored perineal skin.
○ 3. irritated perineum and bloody vaginal discharge.
○ 4. separation of and purulent drainage from the episiotomy.

80 If Ms. Carson develops a hematoma, she is most likely to complain of
○ 1. discomfort when voiding.
○ 2. pain in the perineal area.

○ 3. itching of the vaginal meatus.
○ 4. a feeling of fullness in the vagina.

Ms. Kopper Is Admitted to a Hospital for a Cesarean Delivery. She Has Placenta Previa.

81 The admitting nurse notes that Ms. Kopper is passing some blood from the vagina when she arrives. Which of the following nursing measures is *contraindicated* for Ms. Kopper?
○ 1. Performing a vaginal examination
○ 2. Positioning the patient on her left side
○ 3. Obtaining a urine specimen from the patient
○ 4. Checking the fetal heart rate with a fetoscope

Ms. Kopper is to have external electronic monitoring.

82 The nurse should prepare Ms. Kopper for monitoring by
○ 1. giving the patient an enema.
○ 2. having the patient empty her bladder.
○ 3. explaining to the patient that she will need intravenous therapy.
○ 4. placing the patient in a high-Fowler's position in bed.

83 Before placing the fetal transducer on Ms. Kopper's abdomen, a gel is applied to the transducer's surface primarily to
○ 1. improve the conduction of sound.
○ 2. prevent the transducer from sliding.
○ 3. prevent electrical shock from reaching the patient.
○ 4. decrease the irritating effect of the transducer on the patient's skin.

84 Ms. Kopper is aware of some uterine contractions. For most effective monitoring of uterine contractions, where over Ms. Kopper's uterus should the tokodynamometer be placed?
○ 1. At the top of the uterus
○ 2. At the bottom of the uterus
○ 3. On the left side of the uterus
○ 4. On the right side of the uterus

85 Baseline information is obtained by monitoring the heartbeat of Ms. Kopper's fetus. A few hours later, the nurse notes baseline variability. After making this observation, the nurse' course of action should be to
○ 1. report the finding to the nurse-in-charge.
○ 2. position the patient on her left side.
○ 3. move the transducer to another area on the patient's abdomen.
○ 4. do nothing because baseline variability is normal.

Ms. Kopper is prepared for a cesarean delivery.

86 An indwelling catheter is placed in Ms. Kopper's bladder before surgery primarily in order to
   ○ 1. help prevent urinary retention postoperatively.
   ○ 2. keep the bladder empty during the surgical procedure.
   ○ 3. avoid contamination if the patient has incontinence during surgery.
   ○ 4. provide for a convenient way to collect urine specimens as needed.

87 While preparing Ms. Kopper for surgery, the nurse notes that an informed consent form has not been signed. In this situation, the nurse should
   ○ 1. tell the nurse-in-charge that an informed consent has not been signed.
   ○ 2. ask the patient and her husband if either one has signed an informed consent that the nurse has not seen.
   ○ 3. obtain an informed consent form and have the patient sign it in the presence of the nurse.
   ○ 4. do nothing because an informed consent is unnecessary for a cesarean delivery.

88 While preparing Ms. Kopper for surgery, she says to the nurse, "I am so worried because I am still several weeks from term. Whatever will I do if my baby doesn't make it?" Which of the following responses would be best for the nurse to make in this situation?
   ○ 1. "You are concerned. Tell me more about how you feel."
   ○ 2. "Nearly everyone is worried in your situation. You are not alone."
   ○ 3. "Technology is now so advanced that your baby will make it, I am sure."
   ○ 4. "I think it is a good idea for you to discuss your worries with your doctor."

Ms. Kopper returns from surgery after the cesarean delivery.

89 Ms. Kopper is receiving intravenous therapy. An oxytocic agent is to be administered intravenously. The nurse should prepare necessary equipment while anticipating that the drug is most likely to be administered by
   ○ 1. using a 2-bottle setup.
   ○ 2. adding the drug to the intravenous solution.
   ○ 3. introducing the drug through a heparin lock.
   ○ 4. injecting the drug directly into the patient's vein.

90 Below are 4 nursing measures ordinarily carried out in the postpartal care of patients. Which measure is usually *omitted* when caring for a patient who has had a cesarean delivery, such as Ms. Kopper has had?
   ○ 1. Observing for urinary retention.
   ○ 2. Checking for postpartum bleeding.
   ○ 3. Palpating the fundus of the uterus for muscle tone.

    ○ 4. Providing opportunities for maternal–infant bonding.

91 Ms. Kopper's care following the cesarean delivery will most nearly resemble the care of a patient who has undergone the procedure of
    ○ 1. cystoscopy.
    ○ 2. chest surgery.
    ○ 3. abdominal surgery.
    ○ 4. a dilatation and curettage.

92 Assume Ms. Kopper had abruptio placentae, rather than placenta previa. The complaint that would have most likely caused Ms. Kopper to seek health care would have been
    ○ 1. abdominal pain.
    ○ 2. sudden weight gain.
    ○ 3. unrelenting headaches.
    ○ 4. severe nausea with vomiting.

Ms. Kopper's infant is tested for phenylketonuria (PKU).

93 If Ms. Kopper's infant is positive for phenylketonuria (PKU), a sample of the infant's blood will contain abnormal amounts of
    ○ 1. tyrosine.
    ○ 2. phenylalanine.
    ○ 3. phenylpyruvic acid.
    ○ 4. phenylalanine hydroxylase.

94 If Baby Kopper is found to have phenylketonuria, his diet therapy will be based on knowledge that the offending nutrients for the infant are
    ○ 1. fats.
    ○ 2. minerals.
    ○ 3. proteins.
    ○ 4. carbohydrates.

95 If the diet of an infant with phenylketonuria contains contraindicated foods, the child is likely to suffer from improper nervous system development that will cause
    ○ 1. epileptic seizures.
    ○ 2. mental retardation.
    ○ 3. cerebral aneurysms.
    ○ 4. Parkinsonian syndrome.

Ms. Barker Calls Loudly from Her Hospital Room, "Nurse! Hurry! The Baby is Coming." The Nurse Examines the Patient and Notes that the Infant's Head is Clearly Visible and No Help is Readily Available.

96 If possible, the nurse's first course of action when Ms. Barker's delivery appears imminent should be to

○ 1. take the fetal heart rate.
○ 2. instruct the mother not to bear down.
○ 3. provide for a clean field for delivery.
○ 4. assure the mother that help will arrive in time.

97 The nurse notes that the baby's head continues to crown at Ms. Barker's vaginal opening. In this situation, it would be best for the nurse to

○ 1. allow the head to emerge slowly and deliver it between contractions.

○ 2. push back firmly on the head and place pressure on the vaginal meatus.

○ 3. place a sterile towel over the perineal area and have the patient bring her legs closely together.

○ 4. slide her finger into the vagina and enlarge its exit while delivering the head during a contraction.

No help arrives to assist with Ms. Barker's delivery.

98 When the infant's head emerges, the nurse notes that the infant's airway is clear and therefore, she should *next*

○ 1. place pressure against the mother's perineum.
○ 2. raise the infant's head to deliver the posterior shoulder.
○ 3. check to see whether the cord encircles the infant's head.
○ 4. reach into the axilla of the infant to help deliver the trunk.

99 The nurse can expect that normally, the largest part of the Barker infant's body at birth is the

○ 1. pelvis.
○ 2. head.
○ 3. chest.

100 Which of the following signs should indicate to the nurse that Ms. Barker is about to deliver the placenta?

○ 1. The uterus becomes soft.
○ 2. Bleeding from the vagina stops.
○ 3. The patient has an urge to void.
○ 4. The cord lengthens outside the vulva.

101 After delivery of the placenta, the nurse notes that Ms. Barker's uterus is not as firm as it should be. In order to stimulate uterine contractions, the nurse should massage the uterus and also

○ 1. lower the head of the mother's bed.
○ 2. turn the mother onto her left side.
○ 3. put the infant to the mother's breast.
○ 4. place the infant on the mother's abdomen.

102 Ms. Barker's delivery, which occurred with such speed that proper preparation could not be made and medical supervision was unavailable, is most often called

○ 1. an artificial delivery.
○ 2. a precipitate delivery.
○ 3. an automatic delivery.
○ 4. a spontaneous delivery.

Ms. Barker's postpartum care begins.

103 One common postpartum complication following a rapid delivery for
which the nurse should be especially watchful of Ms. Barker is
○ 1. vaginal tearing and bleeding.
○ 2. retained placenta and infection.
○ 3. inversion of the uterus and shock.
○ 4. relaxation of the uterus and hemorrhage.

104 Two days after delivery, the nurse is requested to carry out the
procedures on Ms. Barker that are given below. Which procedure
should cause the nurse to tell the nurse-in-charge that she is *not*
qualified to do so?
○ 1. Catheterize the patient.
○ 2. Start intravenous therapy.
○ 3. Obtain the patient's apical–radial pulse.
○ 4. Administer oxygen therapy by nasal cannula.

Ms. George Comes to a Clinic for Information
Concerning Family Planning. A Nurse Discusses
Various Contraceptive Methods with Her.

105 Ms. George asks how "the pill" prevents pregnancy. The nurse should
explain that the estrogen in an oral contraceptive ("the pill") will
prevent a woman from becoming pregnant by
○ 1. preventing ovulation.
○ 2. depressing progesterone secretion.
○ 3. depressing corpus luteum formation.
○ 4. preventing sperm from reaching the ovum.

106 If adverse side-effects occur when Ms. George uses an oral
contraceptive, the system of the body most likely to be affected
is the
○ 1. urinary system.
○ 2. respiratory system.
○ 3. cardiovascular system.
○ 4. musculoskeletal system.

107 An intrauterine device (IUD) is discussed with Ms. George. The nurse

should explain that some women cannot tolerate an IUD, most commonly because the device may cause
- O 1. frequent headaches with nausea.
- O 2. discomfort during sexual intercourse.
- O 3. marked pain when the device is inserted.
- O 4. excessive bleeding when the device is in place.

108 Ms. George says she does not like using a diaphragm. Women who object to wearing a diaphragm for contraception usually complain that it is
- O 1. not particularly reliable.
- O 2. irritating to vaginal mucosa.
- O 3. unpleasant to put into place.
- O 4. not very comfortable during sexual intercourse.

109 Ms. George asks about the rhythm method for family planning. The nurse should teach Ms. George that the most effective way for her to determine when she is *unlikely* to become pregnant when using the rhythm method is to keep a record of her
- O 1. weight.
- O 2. pulse rate.
- O 3. blood pressure.
- O 4. body temperature.

110 Ms. George asks, "What do men do if they wish to be sterilized?" The nurse should respond that a commonly used procedure involves clamping or cutting the anatomical structure called the
- O 1. epididymis.
- O 2. seminal vesicles.
- O 3. ejaculatory duct.
- O 4. ductus deferens.

111 Ms. George says she is easily stimulated during sexual activity when a fold of tissue at the upper end of her labia is touched and asks the nurse if this tissue has a name. The nurse correctly identifies the tissue as the
- O 1. clitoris.
- O 2. hymen.
- O 3. mons pubis.
- O 4. labia minora.

112 Ms. George tells the nurse that she has some whitish vaginal discharge about midway between menstrual periods. She asks the nurse what to do about it. It is best for the nurse to answer Ms. George's question by telling her to
- O 1. see her physician for evaluation and diagnosis.
- O 2. avoid sexual intercourse when the discharge occurs.
- O 3. consider the discharge as normal and part of her sexuality.
- O 4. give herself a douche with a mild antiseptic when the discharge occurs.

The Remaining Items Are Individual Items Dealing with Maternity Nursing.

113 It is believed that bonding between parents and their newborn occurs through various sense organs. The strongest of the following senses for developing bonding is believed to be the sense of
O 1. taste.
O 2. smell.
O 3. sight.
O 4. hearing.

114 About 3 weeks after delivery, an infant develops a typical sign of pyloric stenosis, which is
O 1. jaundice.
O 2. diarrhea.
O 3. projectile vomiting.
O 4. gagging with cyanosis.

115 A nurse should understand that the longer a pregnancy continues beyond term, the greater is the risk that the fetus will
O 1. be stillborn.
O 2. be malformed.
O 3. have a hereditary disease.
O 4. have physiological jaundice.

116 The age of women that carries the *least* risk to life for becoming pregnant and giving birth is between
O 1. 17 and 19 years.
O 2. 20 and 24 years.
O 3. 26 and 30 years.
O 4. 30 and 32 years.

117 Of the following factors, the one generally believed to be most helpful in decreasing maternal and neonatal death rates in this country is
O 1. utilization of proper antepartal care.
O 2. general acceptance of genetic counseling.
O 3. widespread practice in the use of contraceptives for family planning.
O 4. increased use of immunization for preventable communicable diseases.

118 Authorities believe that one reason women in upper socioeconomic groups tend to have fewer problems during pregnancy and delivery is that, in contrast to women in lower socioeconomic groups, they are most likely to
O 1. be older.
O 2. have more prenatal care.
O 3. be more willing to have children.
O 4. have fewer work-related responsibilities.

119   When a death is classified as a neonatal death, the infant dies between
      the age of birth and
      ○ 1. 1 day.
      ○ 2. 10 days.
      ○ 3. 2 weeks.
      ○ 4. 4 weeks.

120   The birth rate in this country is described by the National Office of
      Vital Statistics as the number of live births per
      ○ 1. 1,000 population
      ○ 2. 10,000 population.
      ○ 3. 100,000 population.
      ○ 4. 1,000,000 population.

Correct Answers and Rationales

Two numbers appear in parentheses following each rationale. The first number identifies the textbook listed in the references, page 649, and the second number identifies the page(s) in the textbook in which the correct answer can be verified. Occasionally two textbooks are given for verification.

The Nursing Care of Women During Labor and Delivery, the Care of Their Newborns, and Their Postpartal Care

Caring for a woman during labor and assisting with a delivery

1 2. Pertinent questions to ask a woman having uterine contractions when she is being admitted to the hospital include questions related to whether membranes have ruptured, when contractions started, and when the patient last ate. The anesthesiologist is especially interested in knowing when the patient last ate. Least pertinent of the questions given in this item deals with the administration of an enema. Not all patients have enemas. The appropriate time to ask a patient if she has ever had one is before administering the enema. (2:224–225)

2 1. When there is question concerning whether membranes have ruptured, a Nitrazine test helps to determine if the patient has amniotic fluid leaving the vagina or if the patient is leaking urine. The test strips used in this examination determine alkalinity/acidity. Urine is normally acid and amniotic fluid is alkaline. If the Nitrazine strips turn blue, the patient is probably leaking amniotic fluid. If the urine remains yellow, the patient is probably leaking urine and the membranes are likely intact. (12:457)

3 4. A full urinary bladder during labor tends to prevent the descent of the infant into the birth canal by imposing on the canal. Also, it interferes with uterine contractions, but not necessarily on the observations of contractions. It predisposes the bladder to injury and, also, a full bladder is uncomfortable for the mother. (2:235)

4 1. A cleansing enema prior to delivery serves several purposes: to provide for a clean delivery and reduce the possibility of infection, to stimulate contractions, and to provide maximum room in the birth canal. Frequently, an enema is omitted when a patient has had a bowel movement very recently. An enema is also omitted when a patient is in advanced labor because of the danger of expelling it during delivery or of delivering the infant into the bedpan while expelling the enema. An enema prior to delivery does not prevent constipation during the postpartal period, ease the discomfort of contractions, or relieve pressure in the area where an episiotomy may be performed. (2:228–229)

5 2. The length of a contraction from its beginning to its end is called its duration. The degree of hardness or firmness when the uterus contracts is called intensity. The time from the beginning of one contraction to the beginning of the next contraction is called the frequency. Frequency refers to how often contractions occur, and is described in minutes and seconds. (2:201)

6 2. The nurse should place her hand just above the patient's umbilicus on the fundus, or top, of the uterus. This is where the stongest muscular contractions can be felt most easily. (12:456)

7 2. It is recommended that the fetal heart rate be checked immediately after a contraction as well as during a contraction. This procedure helps to detect late deceleration of the heartbeat that may be due to fetal distress. Fetal distress is very likely to be caused by placental insufficiency. Continuous, recorded monitoring of the fetal heart rate is preferred by many, but equipment to monitor is not available in all agencies. Also, there is still some controversy concerning the use of continuous monitoring for all patients in labor. (2:236; 12:456)

8 3. The normal fetal heart rate is between 120 and 160 beats per minute. Some authors extend the range to between 110 and 160 beats per minute. (2:350; 12:459)

9 4. A vaginal examination to determine how much cervical dilatation has occurred is done under conditions of strictest cleanliness. The nurse should clean the patient's vulva well before the examination. The examiner should wash hands well and then don a sterile glove. A sterile lubricant is used. In some agencies, a disinfectant may be poured over the gloved hand and the vulva. Vaginal examinations of women in labor are ordinarily performed by a registered nurse, a midwife, or a physician. (2:227; 12:456)

10 2. When a patient's cervix is dilated between 0 and 4 centimeters, the woman is considered to be active in the beginning of the first stage of labor. At about 4 centimeters, the patient is approaching half of the total amount of cervical dilatation. During the transition stage, the patient's cervix is normally dilated between 8 and 10 centimeters. The end of the first stage of labor occurs when the cervix is fully dilated, that is, 10 centimeters, and the cervix is fully effaced, that is, 100%. (2:225–226)

11 1. True labor is best described as starting when uterine contractions occur regularly. During true labor, there is complete effacement of the cervical canal and the cervix dilates. Expelling the mucus plug from the cervical canal, called show (due to a softening of the cervix and effacement), is a sign that labor is about to start. Ordinarily, the fetus drops into the brim of the pelvis about a week or two before delivery in mothers having their first baby. The phenomenon is called lightening. (2:204)

12 3. Early in labor while not ambulating, the patient is encouraged to rest in bed in the left side-lying position. This position interferes least with circulation in the mother and baby, and promotes urinary functioning and uterine efficiency. During assessments, the patient temporarily uses the back-lying position for the convenience of the examiner. Later in labor, especially during transition and while the mother is pushing, a low-Fowler's position is ordinarily used.   (12:457)

13 2.   The transition part of stage one is ordinarily the most difficult period of labor. It is a time when the mother often loses control of herself. The patient requires the most encouragement and support from the nurse during this stage. This is a time when the nurse should certainly stay with the patient. The mother often suffers fatigue, may be nauseated, and has very forceful contractions.   (12:453)

14 4.   It is inappropriate to have the patient push with contractions until she is in the second stage of labor. Until then, pushing will be ineffective and tiring. Helping the patient onto her left side, urging her to void, and encouraging her to breathe deeply are appropriate nursing measures late in the first stage of labor.   (2:234, 237; 12:457)

15 1.   It is generally recommended that a primigravida be moved to the delivery room when she is crowning. A multigravida should be moved earlier, about the time when she has dilated to about 6 to 8 centimeters.   (12:459)

16 4.   Anesthetic for a saddle block is injected into the lower part of the spinal canal. Contractions are not felt when saddle block (also called low spinal) anesthesia is used. Anesthetic is injected into the areas next to the cervix for a paracervical block. Anesthetic is injected into the area of pudental nerves for a pudental block. Local infiltration is used to inject anesthetic into the perineum.   (2:213–215; 12:459)

17 3.   An important reason for doing an episiotomy is to help prevent prolonged pressure on the fetal head. The incision also helps prevent undue stretching of perineal muscles and lacerations of the perineum. However, episiotomies are no longer being done as frequently as in the past. Mothers prepared for labor and delivery in childbirth classes are less likely to require an episiotomy than mothers who have not had this type of preparation.   (2:212)

18 4.   Before the infant takes its first breath, the physician will ordinarily clear the airway of mucus and debris so that the infant will not inhale the material. A bulb syringe is usually used. The physician also ordinarily first clears the airway after the birth of the baby's head, before the body is delivered. Repairing an episiotomy, cutting the umbilical cord, and evaluating the infant's condition are done after the infant's breathing is established.   (2:243)

19 2.   It has been observed that when only two blood vessels are found in the umbilical cord, the incidence of congenital defects, such as malformed kidney or heart, is higher than when there are the normal three blood vessels in the cord. An abnormal number of cord blood vessels is not

associated with erythroblastosis fetalis or respiratory distress syndrome. Erb's palsy is a condition due to a birth injury to the brachial plexus in the arm.   (2:77)

20   3.   An oxytocic is administered after the birth of the placenta to help strengthen contractions of the uterus and, thereby, prevent excessive bleeding. The agent is not used to hasten involution, prevent uterine inversion, or decrease uterine spasms. Some physicians do not use oxytocics when a mother starts breast-feeding in the delivery room because breast-feeding increases the mother's production of oxytocin.   (2:243; 12:461)

21   1.   When removing a patient's legs from stirrups, it is recommended that both legs be removed at the same time. This technique is less likely to cause stretching of muscles and ligaments.   (2:246)

22   1.   The uterus is ordinarily level with, slightly below, or slightly above the patient's umbilicus shortly after delivery.   (2:246)

23   1.   It is best when parent–infant bonding can be started within one hour after the birth of an infant. Bonding means developing an attachment between the infant and the parents. The senses are the means through which bonding develops and therefore, opportunities to allow the parents to see, touch, hear, and smell their infant should be provided.   (2:378)

Caring for a newborn

24   3.   A newborn has a very low level of blood prothrombin and therefore, is prone to bleeding. Vitamin K is needed by the liver to manufacture prothrombin and various other factors involved with blood clotting. Vitamin K is given to many newborns to help improve blood clotting. After a newborn begins to take food, normal bacteria will grow in the intestinal tract and vitamin K will be manufactured normally by the second week of life. Vitamin K does not stimulate respirations, start peristalsis, or increase calcium absorption.   (12:469; 14:252)

25   3.   It is recommended that intramuscular injections be given to the newborn in the rectus femoris, vastus lateralis, or deltoid muscle. Gluteus muscles should not be used because of the danger of injuring the sciatic nerve. The biceps brachii muscle, located in the arm, and the biceps femoris muscle, located in the back of the leg, are unsuitable sites.   (9:564)

26   3.   The five areas on the Apgar scoring system are muscle tone, color, respiratory effort, reflex irritability, and heart rate. Some new terms for the Apgar scoring system may be used in certain agencies, as follows:

Appearance, rather than color
Pulse, rather than heart rate
Grimace, rather than reflex response

*A*ctivity, rather than muscle tone
*R*espiratory effort

It will be noted that the first letter of the five terms given above form the acronym, APGAR.   (2:376)

27 2.   The best possible score on the Apgar scoring system is 10. Each of the five areas evaluated is scored 0, 1, or 2. The evaluating is ordinarily done one minute after delivery and then again in five minutes. Some persons routinely score a third time 10 minutes after delivery.   (2:376)

28 2.   Drying the infant promptly after birth is done primarily to prevent excess heat loss from evaporation of moisture. This technique prevents cold stress that predisposes to respiratory distress, apnea, hypoglycemia, and acidosis.   (2:376)

29 2.   The primary reason for obtaining a newborn's first temperature rectally is to determine whether the anus is open. Studies have shown that an axillary temperature also is very accurate when the procedure is carried out properly, but this method will not test the patency of the anus.   (12:470)

30 1.   Footprinting the infant and thumbprinting the mother is considered the safest method of identification and is used increasingly in hospitals today. Such methods as x-raying the mother's and infant's wrist bones, using photographs, and using so-called invisible ink are not considered safe methods of identification.   (2:245)

31 2.   It is recommended that the eyes be protected from gonorrhea ophthalmia neonatorum within one hour after birth. Within this time limit, the baby has an opportunity to look around and the mother has an opportunity to establish eye contact for promoting bonding before the eyedrops or ointment interferes with the infant's vision.   (2:245)

32 4.   The nurse should have her hand over the baby and be ready to hold him if the infant needs protection from injury while being weighed. But the nurse's hand should be free of the infant so that her hand does not interfere with an accurate weight. Placing a clean protective paper (a fresh one for each infant) on the scale, balancing the scale, and weighing the infant without clothing describe proper techniques.   (2:379)

33 4.   The umbilical cord should be checked frequently during the first few hours after birth for signs of bleeding. If an infection develops, it will appear later. Pulsation ceases soon after the cord is cut after delivery, and herniation appears later after birth if it occurs.   (2:382)

34 4.   The white substance on a newborn's skin is called vernix caseosa. It consists of old cutaneous cells and secretions from the skin's oil glands. Lanugo is the soft fine hair on the newborn's body. Petechiae are small blue or purple dots on the skin caused by capillary bleeding. Miliaria rubra is heat rash.   (2:361)

35 2.   Jaundice appearing within a few hours after birth may be a sign of a pathological condition and should be reported promptly. Newborns void and pass stool within about 12 hours after birth; if these excretory functions do not occur until later after birth, the nurse-in-charge should be notified. It is normal for an infant to spit up mucus shortly after birth. The scrotum of the male infant and the labia of the female infant are likely to be swollen shortly after birth due to pressure on them during the birthing process.   (2:364, 382)

36   4.   Normally, a newborn's abdomen rises and falls with respirations while the chest barely moves. This type of breathing is often called abdominal breathing. Sternal respirations are present when the sternum moves in (retracts) on inspiration; it is abnormal and should be reported promptly. Costal respirations and a respiratory rate of more than 50 per minute over a period of time are also abnormal. The hands and feet and an area around the mouth may appear cyanotic for several hours after birth owing to poor circulation to these areas. However, the remainder of the body should be pink shortly after birth. A pulse rate of 140 per minute is normal in a newborn. Regurgitating the first feeding or two after birth is also normal.   (2:366)

37   2.   Normally, a newborn's temperature will stabilize within about 8 hours after birth. The heat-regulating mechanism of a newborn is still immature and, therefore, a newborn responds readily to environmental temperatures.   (2:380)

38   3.   An accumulation of blood between the periosteum and the skull is called a cephalhematoma. A cephalhematoma may be seen a few hours after birth but it may take as long as several weeks to disappear, depending on its size. Caput succedaneum is caused by pressure on the head during delivery, which causes swelling of the head. It is present at birth and usually disappears within about 48 hours after birth. Caput refers to the head. Cephaledema describes swelling of the head.   (2:361)

39   1.   When an infant has respiratory distress syndrome, a hyaline membrane forms in the lining of the lungs' aveoli, which causes an improper exchange of carbon dioxide and oxygen. As a result, parts of the lung collapse and respiratory functioning may become seriously impaired. It is not known exactly what causes the hyaline membrane to develop but it is known that there is a lack of surfactant produced in the body, a substance that normally helps maintain patency of the alveoli.   (2:406)

40   3.   When a nurse observes that a newborn has jaundice, even when it is physiological jaundice, she should report the observation to the nurse-in-charge. The nurse should not allow herself to be lulled into a false sense of security when an infant has jaundice because the sign may be a symptom of a serious complication.   (3:26; 12:366)

41   3.   During fetal development, the blood contains a higher number of red blood cells than is typical later in life because fetal oxygen concentration is lower before birth than after birth. As a result, higher blood levels of red blood cells are needed by the fetus for adequate oxygenation. After birth, when the respiratory system functions, excessive red blood cells are destroyed. Because the liver is immature, it cannot handle all of the bilirubin. The excess spills into body tissues and causes the skin to have a yellowish (jaundiced) appearance. Physiological jaundice usually presents no threat to an infant, but it should be watched closely because jaundice due to other causes can be very serious.   (2:366)

42 1.   The destruction of excess red blood cells that occurs shortly after birth causes increased amounts of bilirubin in the body. The bilirubin cannot be taken care of adequately by the newborn's immature liver, and he develops physiological jaundice as a result.   (2:366)

43 2.   An infant is in search of food when he turns his head toward an object that touches his cheek. The response is entirely normal.   (2:368)

44 4.   The rooting reflex is demonstrated when the infant is touched on the cheek and then turns his head toward food. The sucking reflex is demonstrated when the infant sucks when his lips are touched. The grasp reflex is demonstrated when the baby takes hold of an object placed in his hand. The startle or Moro reflex is demonstrated when the infant draws up the legs and brings his arms forward and upward, when he hears a loud noise, or feels sudden movement.   (2:368-369)

45 3.   Oxytocin released by the body during nursing has two main effects: it stimulates the uterus to contract which sometimes causes the mother to complain of abdominal discomfort; and it stimulates the letdown reflex, which causes the milk to move from the milk ducts into sinuses near the nipples.   (2:475)

46 2.   Colostrum contains antibodies. It is also rich in protein and acts as a mild laxative. Colostrum is replaced by breast milk on about the third or fourth day after birth.   (4:208-209; 12:462)

47 4.   It is best to place the entire nipple and the dark area around it (areola) into the infant's mouth when nursing him. This technique is easier on the nipple and helps bring milk from the nearby area in the breast down to the end of the nipple. A newborn does not automatically know how to grasp the nipple when he starts breast feedings.   (12:474)

48 3.   Gentle downward pressure on the infant's chin or at the corner of his mouth on the cheek will usually cause the baby to release the nipple. Also, the mother can carefully insert her finger into the infant's mouth to break the suction if the infant is reluctant to let go. The nipples should *not* be pulled from the infant's mouth, because this is likely to injure the nipples.   (12:474)

49 2.   The best way to help an infant get rid of air he has swallowed while nursing is to hold him over the shoulder and rub his back. This technique is called burping the infant.   (2:391; 12:476)

50 3.   It has been found that emptying the breasts completely is the best way to ensure a good milk supply. If the infant does not empty the breasts, the mother should empty them manually. A nourishing diet and a generous intake of milk are important, but to best ensure a good milk supply, the breasts should be emptied regularly.   (2:275)

51   3.   The size and shape of the breasts have nothing to do with the quality and quantity of milk a woman produces. Such factors as type of diet, fluid intake, rest, and relaxation tend to influence milk production.   (12:474–475)

52   3.   During lactation, a mother's daily milk intake should be a minimum of 6 cups. A lactating mother's diet should be high in protein and her fluid intake should be generous.   (4:203)

53   2.   It is recommended that the nipples be exposed to air frequently during the first few days after delivery to help toughen the nipples. Keeping the nipples dry helps prevent breakdown of the skin on the nipples. Swabbing the nipples with boric acid solution is not recommended and may injure the nipples. If a bra is worn, it should be absorbent and without waterproofing so that the nipples will be kept dry. A newborn should nurse no more than about 5 to 10 minutes for the first few days after delivery. Prolonging the nursing period unnecessarily may injure the nipples. The LaLeche League, an organization that promotes breast-feeding, states that maintaining poor positioning and that improper "latching onto" the nipples are also responsible for sore nipples.   (2:391; 12:475)

54   4.   The normal stools of a breast-fed infant are best described as golden yellow. They tend to be softer and more frequent for the first few weeks than stools of infants receiving milk formulas.   (2:399)

55   4.   The nurse should inform the nurse-in-charge when she notes that the patient's nipples are cracked. Cracked or fissured nipples offer a good entrance for organisms that could cause a breast infection. Measures to treat cracked nipples are ordinarily prescribed by a physician.   (2:290)

56   1.   Persons practicing Judaism observe a religious ceremony when an infant is circumcised.   (12:473)

57   4.   After circumcision, the baby should be observed for signs of bleeding, and if it occurs, the condition should be reported. Urinary output should be observed because occasionally, there is retention of urine following a circumcision due to excessive swelling of the penis near the urinary meatus. Swelling of the scrotum is not associated with circumcision.   (12:473)

58   2.   Normally, the cord drops off and the place where it was attached heals when the infant is between about 6 and 10 days old. However, this time interval may vary somewhat without cause for concern. The size of the cord may influence time required for healing.   (2:363)

59   4.   The anterior fontanel normally closes by the time an infant is 18 months old. The posterior fontanel is normally closed when an infant reaches about 3 months of age. Some variations exist without abnormalities being present.   (2:362)

60   3.   Bluish areas on the buttocks fade away normally in about one year's time and require no treatment.   (2:365)

61   4.   A bluish area on a newborn's buttock is called a mongolian spot. Mongolian spots are in no way associated with Down's syndrome, which has often been referred to in the past as mongolism.   (2:365)

62   4.   In most instances, the decision to use reusable or disposable diapers is a personal one. Both have been found to be satisfactory. However, some women find that reusable diapers generally are cheaper to use than disposable ones when reusable diapers are laundered at home.   (2:145, 388)

63   1.   The basic need in the psychosocial development of the infant is to develop feelings of trust. When this need is not met, the infant develops distrust. An infant develops trust when he is wanted, loved, and warmly accepted. A need to develop feelings of autonomy is present in toddlers. A need to develop identity is present during adolescence. A need to develop intimate interpersonal relationships is present during adulthood.   (1:29; 17:61)

64   1.   According to Freud, a newborn's personality is guided only by the id, which is governed by the pleasure principle. The pleasure principle states that man seeks to avoid discomfort and pain and strives for pleasure and gratification instinctively. The ego, also sometimes called the reality principle, develops next, and finally, the superego.   (1:33)

Caring for a woman during the postpartal period

65   3.   Patients often perspire during labor and delivery. This causes rapid cooling of the body from evaporation of moisture, making the patient feel chilly. Other reasons for chilliness include fatigue, nervousness, rapid cooling of the body in an air-conditioned room, and loss of weight that occurs with delivery of the infant and placenta.   (2:284)

66   4.   The nurse's action is appropriate in the situation described in this item. The postpartum patient who is alert and free of nausea may be served some solid food soon after delivery. It also would be appropriate to offer fluids, especially because the mother loses considerable fluid during the course of labor and delivery. Many times, patients who have prepared for labor and delivery and use natural childbirth eat and take fluids even sooner than 3 hours after delivery.   (2:279, 285)

67   1.   A full urinary bladder causes the uterus to lie to one side instead of being centrally located in the abdomen. An overdistended stomach and a uterus filling with blood are unlikely reasons for the uterus being to one side of the abdomen. The uterus normally is located centrally in the abdomen.   (2:285)

68   1.   Early ambulation helps to prevent problems with the circulatory, respiratory, gastrointestinal, urinary, and musculoskeletal systems. It is unlikely to help improve milk-producing ability, the process of involution, or returning to sexual activity. However, early ambulation should be done with moderation to prevent the mother's becoming fatigued.   (2:287)

69   1.   The most common reason for an increase in body temperature during the first postpartum day is that the mother is dehydrated. *After* the first day, an elevated temperature is likely to be caused by an infection somewhere in the body.   (2:289)

70   2.   The "postpartum blues" are fairly common. Most often, the patient cannot explain why she feels "down." In this situation, it is best to stay with the patient and offer her any help she may need. If the patient wishes to talk about her crying, the nurse should listen quietly and avoid trying to give advice. For some women, it is helpful to explain that a "down" feeling *may* possibly be related to the sudden drop in body hormones after delivery.   (2:327)

71   1.   Sitz baths are often used to decrease the discomfort associated with an episiotomy. Anesthetic sprays also are usually helpful.   (2:293)

72   4.   Propoxyphene hydrochloride (Darvon) is classified as a non-narcotic analgesic and is often prescribed to be given every 3 to 4 hours as necessary for the relief of discomfort from afterpains, pain from stitches when an episiotomy has been done, and breast engorgement. The drug does not act as an antiemetic or hypnotic, nor is it used to firm the uterus. The drug is a controlled substance, which means it cannot be obtained without a prescription.   (2:294)

73   2.   It is common practice to recommend that sexual intercourse can be safely resumed in about 3 to 4 weeks after delivery, if no complications are present. Some physicians may prefer that patients wait as long as 6 weeks before resuming sexual activity after delivery.   (2:304)

74   1.   Most postpartum hemorrhages occur during the first few hours after delivery, although hemorrhaging *can* occur later. During these first few hours after delivery, hemorrhaging is most often due to uterine atony or lacerations in the genital tract. After the first few hours, excessive bleeding is usually due to debris retained in the uterus or to subnormal or abnormal involution of the placental site.   (2:283, 322; 12:461)

75   3.   The amount of lochia is described as being scant, moderate, or heavy. Lochia is considered to be heavy when perineal pads are quickly saturated and the discharge contains blood clots.   (2:285)

76   4.   During the first 2 to 3 days postpartum, the lochia is red and contains blood. It is called lochia rubra. Beginning on about the third or fourth day, the lochia decreases, becomes serous, and is called lochia serosa. About the ninth or tenth day, the lochia becomes scant, is yellow white in color, and is called lochia alba. Lochia usually terminates about three weeks postpartum.   (2:277)

77   4.   An overdistended urinary bladder is especially likely to predispose to the development of a bladder infection. Also, bladder muscle tonus decreases with overdistention. A full bladder also predisposes to increased uterine bleeding because it prevents the uterus from contracting properly.   (2:295; 12:463)

78 4.   The nurse should use essentially the same techniques for catheterizing a postpartum patient as she uses for other women. The meatal area is cleansed, the catheter is lubricated, and the catheter is introduced in the same manner as when catheterizing other women.   (9:462)

79 2.   A hematoma will cause a swelling on the perineum, and the skin will become bluish or purple in color. A hematoma generally develops during the first few hours after delivery.   (2:285)

80 2.   A patient who develops a hematoma generally complains of a great deal of pain in the perineal area, especially when there are stitches following an episiotomy. The pain may also be felt in the rectum. The condition should be reported promptly. A hematoma is not associated with dysuria, itching in the perineal area, or a feeling of fullness in the vagina.   (2:286)

Caring for a woman who has a cesarean delivery

81 1.   A vaginal examination is contraindicated when a patient has vaginal bleeding. Vaginal bleeding is usually present when a patient with placenta previa is admitted for delivery. Obtaining urine specimens, positioning the patient on her left side, and checking the fetal heart rate are not contraindicated when a patient has vaginal bleeding. An enema should also not be administered to a woman who has vaginal bleeding.   (2:167)

82 2.   The bladder should be emptied prior to starting external electronic fetal monitoring. Certain monitoring equipment is likely to cause pressure with discomfort on a full bladder. Also, it is easier to detect fetal heartbeats when the bladder is empty. An enema and intravenous therapy are not a necessary part of monitoring. When the monitor is being placed, the patient needs to be on her back. Preferably, the patient should lie on her side during monitoring but can be on her back if this position is more comfortable. In this case, the head of the bed should be elevated slightly to help prevent supine hypotension.   (2:347)

83 1.   A gel is placed on the transducer primarily to improve the conduction of sound. The gel is not used to prevent the transducer from slipping or to decrease irritating effects of the transducer on the skin. No electrical current passes through the transducer to the patient.   (2:346–347)

84 1.   The tokodynamometer, which monitors uterine contractions, should be placed where uterine contractions are strongest. This is normally at the top of the uterus.   (2:347)

85 4.   When a woman has external electronic fetal monitoring, baseline information, defined as the fetal heart rate between contractions over a period of about 10 minutes, is obtained. Baseline variability means that the fetal heart rate demonstrates normal irregularity or fluctuations. *Loss* of baseline variability is abnormal. The nurse needs to do nothing when baseline variability is present but should report loss of baseline variability to the nurse-in-charge. (2:350–351)

86 2. The primary reason for placing an indwelling catheter in the patient's bladder prior to abdominal surgery is to keep the bladder empty during the surgical procedure. A full bladder makes handling abdominal contents more difficult for the surgeon. The indwelling catheter is not in place to prevent contamination in case of incontinence, prevent postoperative retention, or provide easy access for obtaining urine specimens. (2:260)

87 1. If a nurse notes that a signed consent form has not been signed prior to a surgical procedure, such as a cesarean delivery, the nurse should report this to the nurse-in-charge immediately. It is the physician's responsibility to see to it that an informed consent form has been signed, although, in many instances, a registered nurse may assist with the procedure. Every patient has a right to be informed about a surgical procedure, including the attending risks, benefits, and likely outcome. It is a nursing procedure to determine that one is signed before the patient is transferred to an operating room. (9:47, 374)

88 1. When caring for a patient who is worried, it is best for the nurse to give the patient a chance to discuss her feelings while the nurse attentively listens. Cliches, telling people not to worry, and saying they are like others are not helpful comments. The nurse is shirking her duty by turning a responsibility that is hers over to someone else. (17:230)

89 1. An oxytocic agent given intravenously is ordinarily administered by using the 2-bottle setup, which is also called the piggyback method. The agent also may be administered with an infusion pump. It is not given by bolus through a heparin lock or directly into a vein. Practical nurses do *not* administer drugs intravenously, but they often are asked to help with the administration of intravenous drugs and to monitor the patients receiving them. (2:263)

90 3. Ordinarily, the fundus is not palpated following a cesarean delivery because of the dressings and the surgical incision. The height of the fundus can be determined with slight gentle pressure. Following a cesarean delivery, it is appropriate to observe the patient for urinary retention, check for postpartum bleeding, and provide opportunities for maternal–infant bonding. (2:262)

91 3. The care of a patient who has had a cesarean delivery most nearly resembles the care of a patient who has had abdominal surgery. The patient is likely to develop complications and experience discomforts similar to those of any other patient having abdominal surgery. In addition, the patient is subject to develop most complications and discomforts that other postpartal patients do. (2:262; 12:494)

92 1. Abruptio placentae is best defined as the early separation of a normally implanted placenta from the uterine wall. All of the placenta may separate or only a part of it. Unlike placenta previa in which painless bleeding is present, abruptio placentae is characterized by abdominal pain. The great danger when this complication is present is loss of blood due to hemorrhaging. Abruptio placentae is a leading cause of maternal and fetal death.   (2:163; 12:487)

93 2.   The blood of an infant with phenylketonuria (PKU) contains abnormal amounts of phenylalanine. The blood test is called the Guthrie test. Tyrosine results when phenylalanine is properly digested. Phenylpyruvic acid is a derivative of phenylalanine and is found in the urine of a child with PKU. Phenylalanine hydroxylase is an enzyme that converts phenylalanine into tyrosine.   (2:418–419; 3:204)

94 3.   The offending nutrients in the diet of a child with PKU are animal and vegetable proteins. The liver fails to secrete an enzyme critical for the final digestion and absorption of proteins. A low protein diet is prescribed.   (3:204; 12:477)

95 2.   Interference with proper nervous system development in the child with PKU results in mental retardation in most affected infants.   (2:419; 3:204)

Caring for a woman during an emergency delivery

96 3.   When a delivery appears imminent and the nurse is without help, if it is possible, it is best for the nurse to prepare for a clean field for delivery. This precaution helps prevent infection. Sometimes there is not time for this, but an attempt should be made without sacrificing efforts to control the birth. Assuring the mother that help will arrive offers false hope when the delivery is obviously imminent. A mother late in the first stage of labor and entering the second stage of labor is unable to avoid bearing down. Taking the fetal heart rate is less important in the situation described in this item — there simply does not appear to be time for this unless controlling the birth, which should take precedence, is neglected.   (2:249)

97 1.   When birth is imminent and no help is available, the nurse should gently control the delivery of the head, allow it to emerge, and deliver it between contractions. The nurse should *not* hold back the baby's head to prevent birth, nor should the nurse enter the vagina with her fingers.   (2:249–250; 12:494)

98 3.   After the head is delivered, the nurse should next check to see whether the cord encircles the neck. The infant can strangle if it does. She should try to bring it over the infant's head or shoulder gently, and if this is not possible, the cord should be cut and clamped to free it so that the rest of the body can be delivered.   (2:250)

99 2.   The largest part of the infant's body at birth is the head. The average circumference is normally between about 13½ and 14½ inches (34 and 36 cm). The chest is the next largest part of the infant's body.   (2:382)

100 4.   Signs that indicate the placenta is about to be delivered include a lengthening of the cord outside of the vulva, an increase in bleeding while the uterus rises in the abdomen and becomes firm, and an awareness by the patient that the uterus is contracting.   (12:454, 460)

101   3.   Putting an infant to breast following delivery helps to cause the uterus to contract and become firm. This technique and massaging the uterus help to prevent excessive bleeding following delivery.   (12:494)

102   2.   A delivery that is rapid and that occurs with such speed that proper precautions cannot be made and medical supervision is unavailable is called a precipitate delivery. Sometimes, it may be called an emergency delivery. Some persons define a precipitate delivery as one in which labor lasts less than 3 hours or one in which there is no time to provide sterile facilities for delivery. This type of delivery occurs most often among women who have had previous pregnancies.   (2:249)

103   4.   Following a precipitate delivery, the uterus often remains relaxed. Then, unless measures are taken, the patient is prone to excessive bleeding.   (2:251)

104   2.   Nursing Practice Standards indicate that practical/vocational nurses may assist with intravenous therapy but are not qualified to start such therapy. When asked to start intravenous therapy, the nurse should explain to the nurse-in-charge that she cannot do so without risk of legal problems. Practical/vocational nurses are qualified to obtain apical–radial pulses, catheterize a patient, and administer oxygen therapy.   (13:43, 169)

Teaching a Woman about Family Planning

105   1.   Oral contraceptives contain estrogen or progesterone or both. It is theorized that estrogen in "the pill" suppresses ovulation to prevent pregnancy. Progesterone acts to create a hostile environment detrimental to the survival of the sperm and to implantation if a fertilized ovum is present.   (2:311; 12:700)

106   3.   Adverse effects of the use of oral contraceptives very often strike the cardiovascular system with such complications as thrombophlebitis, strokes, heart attacks, and hypertension. Gastrointestinal symptoms, such as abdominal cramps, nausea, and vomiting, also are reported. However, "the pill" is a very reliable (99%) contraceptive and is used by many without untoward effects.   (2:312; 12:760)

107   4.   Intrauterine devices (IUDs) cause cramping and bleeding in some women. IUDs may be intolerable for these women. Some women tend to expel IUDs and therefore cannot use them. An IUD functions by preventing implantation of the fertilized ovum. It is second only to "the pill" in terms of reliability.   (2:313–314)

108   3.   Most women who object to using a diaphragm for contraception complain that it is unpleasant and inconvenient to put into place. The diaphragm tends to interfere with the spontaneity of sexual activity. If used properly, diaphragms are effective, comfortable to wear, and nonirritating.   (2:314; 12:760)

109 4.   To be effective, the rhythm method for family planning depends on knowing when a woman ovulates, at which time sexual intercourse should be avoided. One way to determine when a woman ovulates is to keep careful records of body temperature, because the temperature normally increases when ovulation occurs. Another sign of ovulation is the presence of cervical mucus, which is necessary for the mobility and viability of sperm. Women can learn to recognize that, when cervical mucus is present, they should avoid intercourse to prevent pregnancy. Symptoms usually occurring simultaneously with cervical mucus production include breast tenderness, *mittelschmerz* (midcycle abdominal cramps), and possible bloody spotting.   (2:314–315; 12:759)

110 4.   A common surgical procedure for sterilizing a man is to cut or clamp the ductus deferens (vas deferens). The procedure is called a vasectomy.   (2:317)

111 1.   The clitoris is erectile tissue especially sensitive to sexual activity. The hymen is a membrane at the vaginal orifice. The labia minora consists of folds of tissue along the area where the vaginal and urinary meatuses are located. The labia minora is sensitive to manipulation too, but does not contain erectile tissue. The mons pubis is the fatty tissue located over the pubis.   (2:17; 10:307)

112 1.   A woman who reports having a whitish discharge about midway between menstrual periods may be describing leukorrhea, the mucus produced by cervical glands that is usually most profuse at the time of ovulation. However, the discharge can be due to an infection and the patient is well advised to see a physician for diagnosis.   (10:309)

Individual Items

113 3.   It is believed that sight is the strongest sense in developing parent–infant bonding. This is why eye-to-eye contact between mother and father and the baby is encouraged. Touch is also important to promote bonding.   (2:378)

114 3.   A typical sign of pyloric stenosis is projectile vomiting. Because of an abnormal condition at the pyloric valve, food cannot leave the stomach properly and vomiting in a projectile, or forceful, manner is typical.   (2:544; 12:414–415)

115 1.   The longer that pregnancy continues beyond term, the higher the risk that the fetus will be stillborn. The risk to the life of the fetus is due to degeneration of the placenta, which is essentially a 9-month organ. Malformed fetuses are often aborted. Hereditary diseases are determined at the time of conception, and the length of the pregnancy will not influence whether one is present. Physiological jaundice is due to an immaturely functioning liver and may be seen in babies delivered early, at term, or beyond term.   (2:442)

116   2.   Statistics illustrate that a woman between about 20 and 24 years of age who becomes pregnant and has a baby bears less risk than either women younger than 20 or older than 24. Perinatal deaths are highest in women between 15 and 19 years of age and over 35 years of age. Nevertheless, there are many women who become pregnant and deliver before age 20 and after age 35 without difficulty, especially when they have good health supervision.   (2:185)

117   1.   It is generally agreed that proper antepartal care plays the most important role in helping to decrease maternal and neonatal mortality rates. Interestingly, antepartal care was started very early in this century by nurses who began making one home visit to mothers who planned to deliver in a particular hospital in Boston. The value of even one visit became apparent and antepartal care gradually grew to be recognized as an integral part of maternity care and important to decrease maternal and neonatal death rates.   (2:11)

118   2.   Women in upper socioeconomic groups tend to have more and better prenatal care than women in lower socioeconomic groups. It is believed that this is one reason that women from upper socioeconomic groups have fewer problems during pregnancy and delivery.   (2:12)

119   4.   A neonatal death occurs between the age of birth and 4 weeks.   (2:8)

120   1.   The National Office of Vital Statistics describes the birth rate as being the number of live births per 1,000 population.   (2:8)

Classification of Test Items

Directions: *Each item in the previous review test is classified here according to the subject area it tests. Place a check mark after each item you answered **correctly** by referring to your answers. Total the number of items you answered correctly in each area and enter the numbers in the correct places on pages 553–556.*

Clinical: Maternity Nursing and the Care of Newborns

1 ✓	17 ✓	37 ____	61 ____	82 ✓	103 ____
2 ____	18 ✓	38 ✓	62 ✓	83 ✓	107 ✓
3 ____	19 ____	39 ✓	65 ✓	84 ____	108 ____
4 ✓	20 ____	40 ✓	66 ✓	85 ✓	109 ✓
5 ✓	22 ____	41 ✓	67 ✓	86 ✓	112 ____
6 ____	23 ✓	42 ✓	68 ✓	90 ____	114 ✓
7 ____	26 ✓	47 ✓	69 ✓	91 ✓	115 ✓
8 ✓	27 ✓	48 ____	70 ____	92 ✓	116 ✓
9 ____	28 ____	49 ✓	71 ✓	93 ____	117 ✓
10 ✓	29 ✓	50 ✓	73 ____	96 ____	118 ✓
11 ____	30 ✓	51 ✓	74 ✓	97 ____	119 ✓
12 ✓	31 ____	52 ____	75 ____	98 ✓	120 ✓
13 ____	32 ✓	53 ✓	76 ✓	99 ✓	
14 ✓	33 ✓	55 ✓	79 ✓	100 ✓	
15 ✓	35 ✓	57 ✓	80 ✓	101 ✓	
16 ____	36 ✓	60 ____	81 ✓	102 ____	

TOTAL 62

Biological/Physical Sciences

34 ✓	44 ✓	46 ✓	58 ____	110 ✓	111 ✓
43 ✓	45 ✓	54 ✓	59 ____		

TOTAL 8

Fundamentals of Nursing

21 ____	25 ✓	77 ✓	78 ✓	89 ✓

TOTAL 4

Diet Therapy/Nutrition

94 ___✓___   95 ___✓___

TOTAL ___2___

Pharmacology

24 ___✓___   72 ___✓___   105 ___✓___   106 ___✓___

TOTAL ___4___

Psychosocial Sciences

56 ___✓___   64 ___✓___   87 _____   88 ___✓___   104 ___✓___   113 ___✓___
63 ___✓___

TOTAL ___6___

UNIT III

Review Tests 4 and 5

The Nursing Care of Children

Review Test 4

The Nursing Care of Infants

The Nursing Care of Toddlers

The Nursing Care of Preschool Children

Correct Answers and Rationales
Classification of Test Items

Directions: *With a pencil, blacken the circle in front of the option you have chosen for your correct answer.*

The Nursing Care of Infants

Baby Boy Adler, who is born prematurely, is hospitalized for care which includes oxygen therapy.

---

1   The nurse should understand that if oxygen is administered to Baby Boy Adler in excess of ordered amounts and the concentration of oxygen becomes too high, there is risk of damage to the infant's
- ○   1.   eyes.
- ○   2.   heart.
- ○   3.   liver.
- ○   4.   kidneys.

2   The nurse monitors Baby Boy Adler especially carefully because he is likely to lack a sufficient amount of pulmonary surfactant which predisposes him to
- ○   1.   cystic fibrosis.
- ○   2.   tracheobronchitis.
- ○   3.   hyaline membrane disease.
- ○   4.   sudden infant death syndrome.

Ms. Baroni, who has an Rh-negative blood type, is in the 38th week of pregnancy when she delivers. Ms. Baroni tells her caretakers that this is her first pregnancy. The infant is Rh-positive and is suffering with hemolytic disease.

3   Ms. Baroni starts to cry when the nurse cares for her because she says she is at fault for her infant's illness. She says she has been too embarrassed to tell anyone about certain things in her past. It is very probable that Ms. Baroni became a sensitized Rh-negative woman when some time ago, she had
- ○   1.   an abortion.
- ○   2.   used cocaine.
- ○   3.   trichomoniasis.
- ○   4.   an affair with an Rh-positive male.

4   The congenital hemolytic disease caused by Rh incompatibility with which Baby Baroni suffers is called
- ○   1.   thalassemia.
- ○   2.   sickle cell disease.
- ○   3.   megaloblastic anemia.
- ○   4.   erythroblastosis fetalis.

5   Which of the following signs of hemolytic disease is Baby Baroni most likely to develop shortly after birth?
- ○   1.   Dyspnea
- ○   2.   Jaundice
- ○   3.   Hematuria
- ○   4.   Convulsions

6   A direct Coombs' test is ordered to confirm the diagnosis of hemolytic disease. The nurse should be prepared to assist with the collection of a blood specimen taken from Baby Baroni's

    ○ 1. fingertip.
    ○ 2. jugular vein.
    ○ 3. femoral vein.
    ○ 4. umbilical cord.

7 After Baby Baroni receives an exchange transfusion, the nurse observes him for signs of neurological damage. *All* of the following signs suggest neurological damage *except* having
    ○ 1. poor muscle tonus.
    ○ 2. poor sucking ability.
    ○ 3. decreased urine production.
    ○ 4. decreased responsiveness to stimuli.

8 If Ms. Baroni had *not* been sensitized by an Rh-positive fetus previous to the time of her delivery, Rho immune globulin (RhoGAM) would have been administered. If this had been the case, the nurse should have been prepared to administer the globulin to the
    ○ 1. mother only.
    ○ 2. newborn only.
    ○ 3. mother and father only.
    ○ 4. newborn, mother and father.

Andy Jones is a 1-day-old infant who is born with spinal bifida with myelomeningocele. Andy will have a surgical repair of the myelomeningocele.

9 Before caring for Andy, the nurse should understand that spina bifida is best described as a
    ○ 1. failure in the spinal cord to develop properly during fetal life.
    ○ 2. tear in the meninges that results in chronic inflammation of the spinal cord.
    ○ 3. tear in ligaments that normally link the vertebrae together in a firm column.
    ○ 4. failure of the posterior laminae in vertebrae to close properly during fetal life.

10 Which of the following nursing measures is most important for the nurse to include in Andy's preoperative care?
    ○ 1. Preventing skin breakdown by placing a sheepskin under his head
    ○ 2. Positioning him so that there is no pressure on the myelomeningocele
    ○ 3. Keeping his myelomeningocele clean by washing it with antiseptic soap
    ○ 4. Supporting his bottle of formula on a rolled towel for ease in feeding him

Andy's surgery is completed and postoperative care begins.

11   What is the position of choice for Andy postoperatively until the operative site heals?
   ○ 1. The supine position (back-lying position)
   ○ 2. The prone position (face-lying position)
   ○ 3. Either the right or left side-lying position
   ○ 4. The position in which the infant appears most comfortable

12   Andy's caretakers discuss the infant's prognosis in a conference in which his home care is considered. What is Andy's prognosis most probably likely to be in terms of being able to walk alone?
   ○ 1. Poor. It is unlikely that the child will be able to walk without crutches or braces.
   ○ 2. Fair. The child has about a 50% chance of eventually walking alone if he has good health care.
   ○ 3. Excellent. The child has about a 95% chance of eventually walking alone if he has good health care.
   ○ 4. Indeterminate. The child's ability to walk alone depends on whether surgical procedures are successful.

13   When visiting Andy postoperatively, Andy's parents tell the nurse that they feel guilty and wonder what they did to cause Andy's spina bifida. On which of the following statements should the nurse base a response to Mr. and Ms. Jones concerning their feelings of guilt?
   ○ 1. Spina bifida is a deviation from normal without a known cause.
   ○ 2. Spina bifida is a deviation from normal believed due to trauma to the fetus.
   ○ 3. Spina bifida is a deviation from normal believed due to a chromosome abnormality.
   ○ 4. Spina bifida is a deviation from normal believed due to an inadequate prenatal diet.

14   The nurse teaches Andy's parents about Andy's needs for love and attention. According to Erikson's theory of personality development, if an infant's needs for love and attention are *not* met, the infant is most likely to develop feelings of
   ○ 1. guilt.
   ○ 2. shame.
   ○ 3. mistrust.
   ○ 4. inferiority.

One-week-old Janice Drum, who has hydrocephalus, is admitted to a children's hospital. She is being readied for surgery.

15   Janice's hydrocephalus is most probably due to
   ○ 1. an excessive growth in the cerebrospinal meninges.
   ○ 2. a blockage that prevents proper circulation of cerebrospinal fluid.
   ○ 3. an imbalance in the distribution of ions in the fluid in the brain's ventricles.

○ 4. a deviation from normal in the development of the posterior and anterior fontanels.

16 Which of the following nursing measures is especially important to include in Janice's daily preoperative care?
○ 1. Weighing the infant
○ 2. Feeding the infant a fortified formula
○ 3. Obtaining a urine specimen from the infant
○ 4. Measuring the circumference of the infant's head

17 The position of choice for Janice after feeding her is the
○ 1. sitting position.
○ 2. back-lying position.
○ 3. face-lying position.
○ 4. side-lying position.

18 The nurse places a sheepskin under Janice's head and shoulders, the primary purpose being to
○ 1. keep the infant's head higher than her trunk.
○ 2. prevent strain on the infant's neck and shoulders.
○ 3. relieve areas of pressure on the infant's head and ears.
○ 4. allow the infant to remain undisturbed for longer periods of time.

A shunting device is placed through an incision on the right side of Janice's head during the surgical procedure.

19 The postoperative position of choice is to place Janice on her
○ 1. back.
○ 2. abdomen.
○ 3. left side.
○ 4. right side.

20 Postoperatively, the nurse should observe Janice closely for signs of increased intracranial pressure, one sign being
○ 1. bulging fontanels.
○ 2. constricted pupils.
○ 3. an elevated temperature.
○ 4. a sudden gain in weight.

21 Of the following courses of action, which one plays the most important part in Janice's daily postoperative care?
○ 1. Holding and cuddling the infant
○ 2. Singing and talking to the infant
○ 3. Placing toys and mobiles within easy reach of the infant
○ 4. Doing as little as possible so that stimulation of the central nervous system is kept at a minimum

Billy Keeler, 3 weeks old, is admitted to a children's hospital. He is being readied for a surgical repair of a unilateral cleft lip.

22   The nurse should expect that, until repaired, Billy's anomaly will most
       likely make him unable to
       O 1. suck.
       O 2. salivate.
       O 3. breathe.
       O 4. swallow.

23   The position of choice when feeding Billy his formula preoperatively is the
       O 1. sitting position.
       O 2. back-lying position.
       O 3. left side-lying position.
       O 4. right side-lying position.

24   Equipment that is readily available in Billy's room to add to the safety
       of his preoperative, as well as his postoperative, care should include
       O 1. gavage equipment.
       O 2. suction equipment.
       O 3. a tracheostomy set.
       O 4. a tongue blade and flashlight.

Billy's cleft lip is surgically repaired.

25   Which of the following positions in bed is *contraindicated* for Billy
       during the immediate postoperative period?
       O 1. The side-lying position
       O 2. The face-lying position
       O 3. The back-lying position
       O 4. The semi-sitting position

26   To prevent Billy from injuring his suture line with his fingers and hands,
       the restraining method of choice is to use
       O 1. elbow restraints.
       O 2. a mummy restraint.
       O 3. a jacket restraint.
       O 4. clove-hitch restraints.

27   Which of the following utensils is best for the nurse to use
       postoperatively when feeding Billy his formula?
       O 1. A gavage tube
       O 2. A plastic spoon
       O 3. An Asepto syringe
       O 4. A firm rubber nipple

28   Which of the following preparations is the one of choice to cleanse
       Billy's suture line?
       O 1. An antiseptic solution
       O 2. A white vinegar solution
       O 3. A hydrogen peroxide solution
       O 4. A sodium bicarbonate solution

29 Which of the following techniques is best when cleansing Billy's suture line with an applicator moistened with the cleansing solution?
- ○ 1. Rolling the applicator the length of the suture line
- ○ 2. Stroking the applicator the length of the suture line
- ○ 3. Stroking the applicator back and forth across the suture line
- ○ 4. Dabbing (patting) the applicator the length of the suture line

Six-week-old Joseph Morgan, who has pyloric stenosis, is admitted to a hospital for surgery to correct the defect.

30 Joseph is suffering from a defect that prevents his food from moving normally in the gastrointestinal tract from his
- ○ 1. jejunum into his ileum.
- ○ 2. esophagus into his stomach.
- ○ 3. duodenum into his jejunum.
- ○ 4. stomach into his duodenum.

31 Intravenous therapy to correct fluid and electrolyte imbalances is started preoperatively on Joseph. The vein most frequently used for an infant receiving intravenous therapy is a vein located in the
- ○ 1. neck.
- ○ 2. scalp.
- ○ 3. upper extremity.
- ○ 4. lower extremity.

32 When atropine sulfate is prescribed for Joseph before feedings to reduce pylorospasms preoperatively, the nurse should observe him for atropine toxicity, two common signs being
- ○ 1. drowsiness and lethargy.
- ○ 2. scaling and dryness of the skin.
- ○ 3. a rapid pulse rate and flushed skin.
- ○ 4. constricted pupils and pink conjunctiva.

Joseph has surgery to correct his defect.

33 What is the position of choice for Joseph postoperatively after the nurse gives him glucose water?
- ○ 1. A back-lying position
- ○ 2. A semi-sitting position
- ○ 3. A normal left side-lying position
- ○ 4. An exaggerated right side-lying position

A nurse assists when six-month-old Cindy Connors has a cast applied to correct a congenital hip dislocation.

34 To help eliminate skin irritation from the edges of Cindy's cast, it is recommended that the cast edges be

○ 1. trimmed with a file.
○ 2. covered with squares of plastic.
○ 3. petaled with strips of adhesive.
○ 4. protected with disposable-diaper material.

35 *All* of the following behaviors can be normally expected of Cindy *except*
○ 1. showing fear of the nurse.
○ 2. holding onto her bottle of juice.
○ 3. waving "bye-bye" when mother leaves.
○ 4. cooing when her mother speaks to her.

Nicky Harris is born after 36 weeks of gestation by breech presentation. He has talipes equinovarus form of bilateral clubfoot.

36 One theory supported by some authorities is that Nicky's foot deformities are caused by
○ 1. being born before term.
○ 2. being born by breech presentation.
○ 3. having acquired an equine viral infection during embryonic life.
○ 4. having abnormal development of certain germ plasm during embryonic life.

Nicky's feet are placed in plaster casts.

37 After his feet are casted, Nicky is placed in bed with his legs and feet elevated on pillows. The most probable reason for elevating Nicky's legs and feet is to
○ 1. hasten drying of the casts.
○ 2. maintain the hips in flexion.
○ 3. help avoid postoperative shock.
○ 4. prevent the feet from swelling.

38 Of the following techniques, the best one for the nurse to use when moving Nicky's wet casts is to handle them with
○ 1. the fingers.
○ 2. gloved hands.
○ 3. slings made of gauze.
○ 4. the palms of the hands.

When Nicky is 8 weeks old, his casts are to be changed.

39 Which of the following types of amusement is most appropriate for Nicky while waiting for the procedure to begin?
○ 1. Encouraging the infant to crawl about in his crib
○ 2. Playing peek-a-boo with his favorite blanket
○ 3. Permitting the infant to reach for cuddly toys
○ 4. Placing a brightly colored mobile over his crib

40 Nicky is sent home after the casts are applied. The nurse should teach Nicky's parents to watch Nicky carefully for signs that his casts are too tight. Which of the following signs is *atypical* when leg and foot casts are too tight?
- O 1. The toes feel damp.
- O 2. The toes are swollen.
- O 3. The toes feel cool to touch.
- O 4. The toes are bluish in color.

41 If Nicky's feet had been cared for with an orthopedic device, instead of with casts, the nurse should have been prepared to assist with the application of
- O 1. Buck's extention.
- O 2. Bryant's traction.
- O 3. a Thomas leg splint.
- O 4. a Denis Browne splint.

42 During discharge teaching, Nicky's mother says to the nurse, "I can barely feel the soft spot in the back part of Nicky's head. My daughter's soft spot did not close until about 3 months of age. Is there anything wrong?" The nurse should base her response on knowledge that the amount of closure of the posterior fontanel for 8-week-old Nicky is judged to be
- O 1. normal. The posterior fontanel usually closes at 2 to 3 months of age.
- O 2. abnormal. The posterior fontanel usually closes in male children later than in female children.
- O 3. abnormal. The posterior fontanel usually does not close until about 6 to 8 months of age.
- O 4. normal. The posterior fontanel usually closes early in children with any type of congenital skeletal defects.

Acutely ill, 1-year-old Hank Phillips is admitted to the hospital with sickle cell crisis.

43 Upon Hank's admission, the nurse should be prepared to use nursing measures appropriate for the relief of Hank's
- O 1. pain.
- O 2. diarrhea.
- O 3. hemorrhaging.
- O 4. acute dyspnea.

44 The nurse should also anticipate that nursing care Hank will also most certainly need is
- O 1. receiving joint exercises.
- O 2. moving about freely in bed.
- O 3. continuing to take nutrients.
- O 4. having a generous fluid intake.

Hank's parents receive discharge preparation.

45 Mr. and Ms. Phillips speak of a vacation they wish to take when Hank's condition warrants it. Which of the following types of vacation plans is *contraindicated* for Hank?
  ○ 1. Visiting a zoo
  ○ 2. Going on an ocean cruise
  ○ 3. Staying at a seaside resort
  ○ 4. Touring a Rocky Mountain state

46 When the parents inquire, the nurse should explain that the components in Hank's blood that are profoundly affected by his disease are his
  ○ 1. blood proteins.
  ○ 2. blood platelets.
  ○ 3. red blood cells.
  ○ 4. white blood cells.

47 Hank's sickle cell disease is an inherited disorder that occurs predominantly among American
  ○ 1. blacks.
  ○ 2. Indians.
  ○ 3. Orientals.
  ○ 4. Caucasians.

48 Hank has sickle cell disease because both of his parents possess the mutant sickle cell gene. If Hank is one of four children, how many of his siblings can *statistically* be expected to have the disease?
  ○ 1. One
  ○ 2. Two
  ○ 3. Three
  ○ 4. None

There is a history of cystic fibrosis in the family of Stephanie Reed, who is in a hospital's newborn nursery.

49 Because of Stephanie's family health history, it is very important for the nurse to make physical assessments of Stephanie that include noting whether the infant
  ○ 1. can cry.
  ○ 2. has dyspnea.
  ○ 3. is able to suck.
  ○ 4. passes meconium.

Stephanie is discharged but, at 18 months of age, she is readmitted to the hospital because of her disease.

50 The nurse should judge that Stephanie has a typical sign of cystic fibrosis when her assessment includes noting that Stephanie has

○ 1. a poor appetite.
○ 2. excessive perspiration.
○ 3. scanty urine production.
○ 4. sticky foul-smelling stools.

51 If Stephanie's mother makes the following comments, which one should the nurse recognize as describing a very typical finding in a child with cystic fibrosis?
○ 1. "Stephanie cries very seldom."
○ 2. "Stephanie breathes very fast."
○ 3. "Stephanie tastes salty when I kiss her."
○ 4. "Stephanie does not care for her formula."

Stephanie is discharged and will be cared for at home. The following items concern the supervision of Stephanie's care by a visiting home-care nurse.

52 The nurse should teach the parents to give Stephanie prescribed pancreatic granules by
○ 1. sprinkling granules on the child's food.
○ 2. placing granules under the child's tongue.
○ 3. mixing granules in the child's drinking water.
○ 4. giving the granules to the child in capsule form.

53 The nutrient in Stephanie's die that should be offered only in *limited* to *moderate* amounts is
○ 1. fats.
○ 2. salt.
○ 3. proteins.
○ 4. carbohydrates.

54 The parents ask about including exercise in Stephanie's activities of daily living. In addition to improving Stephanie's well-being, exercise is particularly important for Stephanie to help
○ 1. stimulate excretory functioning.
○ 2. rid the pulmonary system of secretions.
○ 3. promote heart muscle and vascular tonus.
○ 4. enhance digestion and absorption of nutrients.

55 Stephanie will use a mist tent at home as necessary. The parents should be taught that the primary purpose for using the tent is to help
○ 1. dilate the alveoli.
○ 2. prevent dehydration.
○ 3. relieve difficult respirations.
○ 4. decrease respiratory secretions.

56 The nurse concludes that the mother is carrying out postural drainage on Stephanie correctly for draining the lower lobes of Stephanie's lungs when the mother positions the child in the
○ 1. sitting position.

○ 2. back-lying position flat in bed.
○ 3. back-lying position with the head raised.
○ 4. side-lying position with the head lowered.

57 Because of Stephanie's increased risk for complications, the parents
    should be taught to guard against exposing Stephanie to
    ○ 1. pollens.
    ○ 2. infections.
    ○ 3. pet dander.
    ○ 4. bright sunlight.

58 The serious respiratory tract problems that Stephanie is most likely to
    develop are caused primarily by
    ○ 1. constricted bronchioles.
    ○ 2. poorly developed alveoli.
    ○ 3. thick, sticky mucus secretions.
    ○ 4. insufficient surfactant production.

The Nursing Care of Toddlers.

*Johnny Bush, a 2½-year-old child, is brought to a hospital by his mother
who says that Johnny just swallowed at least 10 children's aspirin.*

59 When Johnny is admitted, the nurse's responsibilities include assessing
    for signs of salicylate poisoning, one of which is
    ○ 1. a skin rash.
    ○ 2. a slow pulse rate.
    ○ 3. an inflamed throat.
    ○ 4. a rapid respiratory rate.

60 With which of the following procedures should the nurse be prepared
    to assist upon Johnny's admission?
    ○ 1. A gastroscopy.
    ○ 2. A throat culture.
    ○ 3. A gastric lavage.
    ○ 4. An intracardial injection.

Johnny is admitted for observation following emergency care.

61 Which of the following safety measures is most appropriate for the
    nurse to take when Johnny is well enough to go to the hospital's
    playroom?
    ○ 1. Tell him not to put anything in his mouth.
    ○ 2. Show him which substances he should not eat.
    ○ 3. Remove harmful substances from areas within his reach.
    ○ 4. Post warnings in the playroom about poisonous hazards.

62 The nurse plans a teaching program for Ms. Bush concerning the ingestion of toxic substances by small children. Which of the following medications should Ms. Bush be taught to keep in a locked cupboard at home to use if Johnny eats or drinks a toxic substance?
- ○ 1. Metamucil
- ○ 2. Kaopectate
- ○ 3. Syrup of ipecac
- ○ 4. Milk of magnesia

Ms. York brings 2½-year-old Amy to a physician's office because, Ms. York says, "Amy had croup last night and was very sick."

63 Which of the following nursing measures is most appropriate to deal with the fear Amy demonstrates in the office?
- ○ 1. Encouraging her to play with a soft toy
- ○ 2. Arranging for her mother to stay with her
- ○ 3. Allowing her to watch a children's television program
- ○ 4. Explaining to her how she will be feeling better soon

64 When Amy had the attack of croup (spasmodic laryngitis), her mother will have described the toddler's cough as sounding
- ○ 1. moist.
- ○ 2. hoarse.
- ○ 3. muffled.
- ○ 4. high-pitched.

The nurse explains home care of Amy to Ms. York.

65 The type of medication Ms. York should have available in case Amy develops laryngeal spasms again is one that will help Amy by
- ○ 1. reducing pain.
- ○ 2. promoting sleep.
- ○ 3. inducing vomiting.
- ○ 4. inhibiting reflex responses.

66 The nurse should teach Ms. York that laryngeal spasms can often be relieved if Amy is in a room with air that is
- ○ 1. dry.
- ○ 2. cool.
- ○ 3. humid.
- ○ 4. dust-free.

67 During the teaching, Ms. York makes the following comments to describe Amy's typical behavior. Which behavior best illustrates the child's efforts to develop self-esteem?
- ○ 1. "Amy's favorite word is 'no.'"
- ○ 2. "Amy's favorite toy is a wagon."
- ○ 3. "Amy's favorite parent is her father."

○ 4. "Amy's favorite baby-sitter is her grandmother."

Chuck Pater, 3 years old, is admitted to a hospital for treatment of lead poisoning.

68 A measure the nurse should plan to carry out that will help determine the amount of lead in Chuck's system is to
○ 1. record the patient's food intake.
○ 2. measure the patient's urinary output.
○ 3. monitor the patient's vital signs hourly.
○ 4. collect a 24-hour urine specimen from the patient.

69 Ethylenediamine tetra-acetate acid (EDTA) is prescribed for Chuck primarily because this drug helps to
○ 1. render the lead nontoxic.
○ 2. excrete the lead in the stool.
○ 3. reverse the mental retardation.
○ 4. reduce the symptoms of lead poisoning.

70 The nurse should instruct Chuck's parents concerning possible sources of lead in Chuck's environment. If Chuck has been exposed to the following substances, he most likely ingested lead from
○ 1. paint.
○ 2. plastic.
○ 3. rubber.
○ 4. insulation.

Manuel Garcia, a 3-year-old child, is admitted to a hospital with pneumonia. He is acutely ill with an elevated temperature when the nurse admits him.

71 The nurse can expect that Manuel's respirations upon admission are most likely to be
○ 1. slow.
○ 2. rapid.
○ 3. intermittently rapid and slow.
○ 4. intermittently shallow and deep.

72 The best measure for the nurse to use to assist in determining Manuel's need for fluid is to
○ 1. test his urine *p*H.
○ 2. monitor his pulse rate.
○ 3. weigh his liquid feedings.
○ 4. record his urinary output.

73 Ms. Garcia asks the nurse, "Why does Manuel not cough if he has pneumonia?" The nurse should base her response on knowledge that
○ 1. young children rarely cough.
○ 2. lack of coughing usually indicates the child is recovering.

○ 3. coughing is likely being suppressed by a high body temperature.

○ 4. absence of coughing usually results from congestion in the lower respiratory tract.

74 Ms. Garcia tells the nurse that Manuel does not like and will not drink milk. Which of the following foods, like milk, supplies the body with all of the essential amino acids?

○ 1. Beans

○ 2. Gelatin

○ 3. Fresh fruit

○ 4. Fresh eggs ·

Manuel is to have a tepid-water sponge bath to help reduce his fever.

75 Some nurses recommend rubbing Manuel's skin with a dry wash cloth before beginning the sponge bath to reduce body temperature, because this technique helps to

○ 1. open the skin's pores.

○ 2. remove excess oil from the skin.

○ 3. stimulate nerve endings in the skin.

○ 4. bring blood to the surface of the skin.

76 An important nursing measure that should be carried out about 30 minutes *after* completing Manuel's sponge bath is to

○ 1. give the child aspirin.

○ 2. obtain the child's vital signs.

○ 3. start the child on oxygen therapy.

○ 4. offer the child fluids high in vitamin C content.

77 The Garcias' primary language is Spanish. On the day of Manuel's discharge, Ms. Garcia receives written instructions about Manuel's diet, activity, and medications, and instructions to schedule an appointment for Manuel in 2 weeks. The best action for the nurse to take to ascertain whether or not Ms. Garcia understands the instructions is to

○ 1. read the written instructions to the mother.

○ 2. have the instructions written in Spanish for the mother.

○ 3. repeat the instructions in words that the mother can understand.

○ 4. ask the mother to repeat the instructions the way she understands them.

The Nursing Care of Preschool Children

Buffy Cater, 4½ years old, has recent episodes of seizure activity. She is admitted to the hospital for observations and treatment.

78 In anticipation of Buffy's admission, the nurse prepares a crib for Buffy

that includes padding the crib sides. Placing padding in the crib is done primarily to help prevent
- ○ 1. injury to the child during seizure activity.
- ○ 2. attempts by the child to crawl over the crib sides.
- ○ 3. unnecessary drafts reaching the child that may bring on seizure activity.
- ○ 4. undue environmental stimuli to the child that may bring on seizure activity.

79 Certain equipment should be kept at Buffy's bedside for convenience when seizure activity occurs. Which of the following equipment is *unnecessary*?
- ○ 1. Suction equipment
- ○ 2. A tracheostomy set
- ○ 3. Padded tongue blades
- ○ 4. A good source of light

80 Which of the following actions should the nurse be prepared to take if Buffy stops breathing during a seizure?
- ○ 1. Stimulate her to breathe on her own.
- ○ 2. Provide her with supplemental oxygen.
- ○ 3. Administer mouth-to-mouth resuscitation.
- ○ 4. Time the period during which she fails to breathe.

81 Each day when the parents visit, Buffy cries when they arrive and when they leave. In this situation, it would be best for the nurse to suggest that the parents
- ○ 1. visit the child less frequently.
- ○ 2. visit the child more frequently.
- ○ 3. shorten the time they visit with the child.
- ○ 4. continue to visit the child as they are doing presently.

Phenytoin (Dilantin) is prescribed for Buffy to control seizure activity.

82 To help prevent side-effects, what precautions should the nurse take when administering the phenytoin to Buffy?
- ○ 1. Give the medication when the child's stomach is empty.
- ○ 2. Administer the medication while assisting the child to eat.
- ○ 3. Avoid giving the child the medication with carbonated beverages.
- ○ 4. Withhold dairy products for 1 hour after giving the child the medication.

83 Because Buffy will take the medication after discharge, her parents should be taught the side-effects of long-term use of phenytoin. One such common side-effect is
- ○ 1. a poor appetite.
- ○ 2. urinary incontinence.
- ○ 3. painful joints following exercise.
- ○ 4. an excessive growth of gum tissues.

Four-year-old Beth Norris, who is suspected of having leukemia, is admitted to a hospital for diagnosis and treatment.

84 The nurse should anticipate that the test most likely to be used to determine whether Beth has leukemia is
  ○ 1. a gastric analysis.
  ○ 2. a cardiac angiogram.
  ○ 3. a bone marrow aspiration.
  ○ 4. an arterial blood gas analysis.

85 When it is established that Beth has leukemia, the nurse should recognize that the most probable reason for an order for bed rest for Beth is to relieve a common symptom of the disease, which is
  ○ 1. dizziness.
  ○ 2. palpitations.
  ○ 3. painful joints.
  ○ 4. blurred vision.

Prednisone (Meticorten) and vincristine sulfate (Oncovin) are prescribed for Beth.

86 Prednisone and vincristine in combination act in the body to help
  ○ 1. reduce symptoms of nausea.
  ○ 2. induce prolonged remissions.
  ○ 3. prevent secondary infections.
  ○ 4. promote white blood cell production.

87 A common side-effect that Beth is very likely to experience as a result of her chemotherapy is having
  ○ 1. constipation.
  ○ 2. loss of hair.
  ○ 3. pathological fractures.
  ○ 4. gastrointestinal ulcerations.

Beth receives a blood transfusion.

88 If Beth makes the following comments after about half of the blood is transfused, which one should cause the nurse to suspect that Beth may be having a transfusion reaction?
  ○ 1. "I'm thirsty."
  ○ 2. "I feel cold."
  ○ 3. "I feel so tired."
  ○ 4. "I need to go to the toilet."

89 Beth appears to be having a reaction to the blood. The nurse's first course of action should be to
  ○ 1. administer several whiffs of oxygen.
  ○ 2. discontinue the transfusion and remove the needle.

○ 3. clamp the tubing to stop the blood flow and open the clamp to the normal saline.

○ 4. see to it that the nurse-in-charge and the blood bank are notified immediately.

Beth fails to respond to therapy and is taken home where a nurse will visit to help with Beth's care.

90 Beth asks the nurse one day, "Am I going to die?" Which of the following responses is best for the nurse to make to Beth's question?

○ 1. "Are you feeling especially bad today?"

○ 2. "You shouldn't worry about things like that."

○ 3. "We are all going to die someday. Tell me more about how you feel."

○ 4. "Let's talk about something else. What is your favorite television program?"

91 Which one of the following personal hygiene measures should the nurse recognize as being of particular importance in Beth's care?

○ 1. Swabbing the eyes

○ 2. Massaging the skin

○ 3. Giving oral hygiene

○ 4. Cleansing the nostrils

92 Which of the following signs should indicate to the nurse that Beth's illness most probably is progressing?

○ 1. Developing clubbed fingers

○ 2. Bleeding from body orifices

○ 3. Developing generalized edema

○ 4. Having scanty urine production

93 The nurse notices that Beth's father has been making excuses to cut short his visits with Beth. When asked if he is not feeling well, Mr. Norris replies, "I just can't bear seeing my little girl suffer like this. I've always been able to fix things for her. I only wish I could make her well again." The nurse is correct in recognizing that Mr. Norris is most likely in the stage of mourning known as

○ 1. denial.

○ 2. depression.

○ 3. bargaining.

○ 4. acceptance.

94 The nurse should recognize, and teach the parents as indicated, that a child of Beth's age (4 years) usually views death as

○ 1. a painful experience.

○ 2. a reversible happening.

○ 3. something that happens only to pets.

○ 4. something that happens only to the elderly.

95 The age at which children *first* recognize the phenomenon of death in a manner similar to adults is when children are between about ages
   O 1. 5 and 7 years.
   O 2. 7 and 9 years.
   O 3. 9 and 12 years.
   O 4. 12 and 14 years.

96 As Beth's condition worsens, she becomes irritable and too tired to eat. Of the following nursing measures, the one that would be best to help meet Beth's nutritional needs is
   O 1. restricting the child's diet to liquids.
   O 2. reminding the child that she needs food to gain strength.
   O 3. giving the child between-meal snacks of things she likes.
   O 4. asking the physician if the child could have vitamin supplements.

Ms. Kory telephones a nurse working in a physician's office because she believes her 5-year-old son Jack has scarlet fever.

97 The nurse should suspect that Jack has scarlet fever when the mother reports that Jack has
   O 1. a skin rash.
   O 2. a stuffy nose.
   O 3. hyperactivity.
   O 4. a hacking cough.

A diagnosis of scarlet fever is established.

98 The nurse should caution Ms. Kory that Jack's disease is contagious and that he should be kept away from other children until his
   O 1. symptoms have subsided.
   O 2. room has been disinfected.
   O 3. treatment has been started.
   O 4. medications have been completed.

Three weeks after having scarlet fever, Jack is admitted to a hospital with glomerulonephritis. He has facial edema.

99 Jack's facial edema is most likely to appear in the area around his
   O 1. nose.
   O 2. chin.
   O 3. eyes.
   O 4. mouth.

100 When Jack's edema worsens, the nurse should be prepared to restrict the child's dietary intake of foods high in
   O 1. fats.

○ 2. sodium.

○ 3. calcium.

○ 4. carbohydrates.

101 Jack objects when the nurse wishes to change his position in bed. The nurse is correct in suspecting increased intracranial pressure when Jacks says, "It hurts," and points to his

○ 1. ear.

○ 2. neck.

○ 3. back.

○ 4. head.

102 Which of the following actions should the nurse take after reporting that Jack may have increased intracranial pressure?

○ 1. Give the child warm fluids to drink.

○ 2. Position the child flat in bed on his back.

○ 3. Apply cool compresses to the child's forehead.

○ 4. Place the siderails of the child's bed in the up position.

The remaining items in this situation are individual items related to Jack's care.

103 Which of the following playtime activities is an appropriate diversion for Jack during the initial stages of his illness?

○ 1. Listening to cassettes

○ 2. Playing hide-and-seek

○ 3. Bouncing a beach ball

○ 4. Pounding on a peg board

104 Jack has been trained to use the toilet but, when he is hospitalized, he begins to wet the bed again. The nurse should judge the child's behavior to be a defense mechanism called

○ 1. regression.

○ 2. repression.

○ 3. projection.

○ 4. displacement.

Five-year-old Sally Cromwell is to be admitted to an ambulatory surgical center for the correction of strabismus (crossed eyes), a condition she has had since infancy.

105 In preparation for surgery, Sally's parents were taught that Sally was to have nothing by mouth after midnight the evening before surgery. The primary reason for this order is to

○ 1. prevent aspiration of vomitus during surgery.

○ 2. enhance the effectiveness of preoperative sedation.

○ 3. dry the respiratory mucous membranes before surgery.

○ 4. reduce the need for the child to urinate prior to surgery.

106 Sally's parents were also taught that Sally may need restraints postoperatively to prevent her from disturbing eye dressings. It was explained to them that it is best to prepare Sally for this experience by
○ 1. letting the child feel what it is like to be in restraints.
○ 2. reading stories to the child about children having surgery.
○ 3. asking a parent to stay with the child until she goes to the operating room.
○ 4. avoiding discussions with the child concerning how she is likely to feel after surgery to prevent fear.

107 Which of the following statements best explains why surgery is delayed until Sally has reached the preschool age?
○ 1. Surgical correction of strabismus during infancy is difficult because the infant's eyes are small.
○ 2. The preschool child undergoing surgical correction of strabismus is less fearful of the procedure than an infant.
○ 3. The degree of strabismus can be measured more accurately when the child has reached the preschool age than when an infant.
○ 4. In contrast to an infant, the preschool child with strabismus can better appreciate that surgical correction of her disorder will allow her to look like other children.

The corrective surgery is performed on Sally.

108 Which of the following activities is the most appropriate form of diversion for Sally during her immediate postoperative period?
○ 1. Coloring pictures
○ 2. Playing with a doll
○ 3. Listening to records
○ 4. Assembling a simple puzzle

109 Which of the following general care measures is *inappropriate* to teach the Cromwells in relation to Sally's postoperative home care?
○ 1. Allowing the child to be up and about
○ 2. Offering the child a liquid diet until dressings are removed
○ 3. Speaking to the child before touching her while both eyes are covered
○ 4. Having dark glasses available for the child to wear after dressing are removed

Bob Donelly, who is 5 years old, is admitted to a hospital for a tonsillectomy and adenoidectomy.

110 On the morning of the surgery, the nurse obtains Bob's vital signs. Which of the following signs should the nurse report immediately?
○ 1. Blood pressure, 90/60 mm Hg
○ 2. Temperature, 101°F (38.3°C)

○ 3. Respiratory rate, 20 per minute
○ 4. Pulse rate, 110 beats per minute

Bob's surgery is completed.

111 Bob is to have a clear liquid diet postoperatively. Which of the following items is included in a clear liquid diet?
○ 1. Sherbet
○ 2. Ice cream
○ 3. Popsicles
○ 4. Natural juices

112 The nurse should report her postoperative observation to the nurse-in-charge immediately when she notes that Bob is
○ 1. vomiting dark blood.
○ 2. swallowing frequently.
○ 3. refusing fluids upon awakening.
○ 4. breathing at a rate of 30 respirations per minute.

Ms. Donelly tells the nurse that she has discipline problems with Bob and adds, "I guess he just has no sense at all."

113 While teaching Ms. Donelly, the nurse should explain that of the following methods of disciplining a child of Bob's age, the one that is *inappropriate* is
○ 1. telling the child he is a bad boy.
○ 2. isolating the child for a period of time.
○ 3. withholding a desired treat from the child.
○ 4. explaining disapproval of the child's behavior.

Ms. Donelly calls 3 days after Bob's surgery because, she says, "Bob is complaining of an earache. What should I do?"

114 The nurse should base her response to Ms. Donelly on knowledge that Bob most probably
○ 1. has a collapsed eustachian tube.
○ 2. needs fluids because of dehydration.
○ 3. has developed a middle ear infection.
○ 4. is suffering with discomfort referred from the throat.

Matt Hawkins, age 5, is admitted to a hospital with a fever and severe pain in his right knee due to acute osteomyelitis. A cast is applied to Matt's right knee.

115 Reports of blood findings appear on Matt's record. The nurse should expect that the blood studies will most certainly reveal

O 1. a decreased hematocrit.
O 2. a decreased red blood cell count.
O 3. an elevated blood platelet count.
O 4. an elevated white blood cell count.

116 The primary purpose for casting Matt's knee is to help
O 1. prevent atrophy of knee tendons.
O 2. promote lymphatic drainage from the knee.
O 3. hold the knee joint in its proper alignment.
O 4. keep the knee at a state of complete rest.

Correct Answers and Rationales

Two numbers appear in parentheses following each rationale. The first number identifies the textbook listed in the references, page 649, and the second number identifies the page(s) in the textbook in which the correct answer can be verified. Occasionally, two textbooks are given.

The Nursing Care of Infants

Caring for an infant who is born prematurely

1   1.   If oxygen is given to a prematurely born infant in high concentrations, he is especially vulnerable to developing blindness due to retrolental fibroplasia. Therefore, a nurse should check the oxygen administration at frequent intervals to be sure excessive amounts are not being given.   (3:44)

2   3.   Hyaline membrane disease, also known as respiratory distress syndrome (RDS), occurs in infants who do not have enough surfactant in their lungs. In the absence of surfactant, a membrane forms around the alveoli and interferes with the exchange of oxygen across the alveolar membrane. About half of the infants born preterm are affected by hyaline membrane disease.   (3:43)

Caring for an infant with hemolytic disease

3   1.   An Rh negative woman usually becomes sensitized at the time of her first delivery. The Rh positive fetal cells enter the mother's blood system when the placenta separates from the uterine wall. The woman described in this situation was sensitized but she stated she was pregnant for the first time. However, sensitization can occur following an abortion, an ectopic pregnancy, or a stillbirth. The mother described here most probably became sensitized when she had the abortion. Using cocaine, having had trichomoniasis, and having had an affair with an Rh positive male do not sensitize an Rh negative woman.   (2:175; 3:77)

4   4.   Erythroblastosis fetalis is a congenital disease in which there is destruction of the infant's Rh-positive red blood cells by his mother's Rh-positive antibodies. This disease is much less prevalent today than it once was because of the use of Rho immune globulin (RhoGAM). The manner in which a woman is sensitized to the Rh factor rarely results in problems for her first infant. Thalassemia is a congenital blood disorder characterized by the body's inability to manufacture sufficient hemoglobin. Sickle cell

disease is characterized by improperly formed red blood cells. Megaloblastic anemia is due to an inadequate intake of vitamin C and folic acid,
resulting in abnormal blood cell formation.   (3:77)

5   2.   Bilirubin is released from hemolyzed red blood cells. The bilirubin
causes the jaundice associated with Rh incompatability. The liver of the
infant is immature and cannot handle large quantities of bilirubin, and
therefore, jaundice occurs. The infant ordinarily is pale at birth due to
anemia. When anemia is sufficiently severe, it can produce heart failure in
the fetus as well as its death.   (3:78)

6   4.   When an infant is born with hemolytic disease, the usual procedure is
to collect blood from the infant's umbilical cord for the Coombs' test. A
negative direct Coombs' test result indicates that there are no antibodies
on the infant's red blood cells. A positive test result indicates the presence
of antibodies.   (3:79)

7   3.   Signs of neurological damage in infants with hemolytic disease include
lethargy, poor sucking ability, and poor muscle tonus which is often
followed by spasticity and convulsions. Scanty urine production is not a
sign of neurological damage.   (2:175; 3:78)

8   1.   Rh immune globulin (RhoGAM) is administered to an unsensitized
mother. It is never given to the infant or to the father of the infant.   (2:174;
3:78)

Caring for an infant with spina bifida

9   4.   Spina bifida is defined as a defect in the posterior laminae in selected
vertebrae, usually vertebrae in the lumbosacral area. The defect, if large
enough, allows spinal meninges and even the spinal cord to protrude. The
defect may be so minor that the person remains asymptomatic (spina
bifida occulta). A meningocele is present when the defect allows meninges to protrude. A myelomeningocele, the most severe type of spina
bifida, is present when the defect allows meninges as well as the spinal
cord to protrude.   (3:65)

10   2.   Important nursing measures to use while caring for a child with a
meningocele or a myelomeningocele include avoiding pressure on the sac
and preventing injury to it. Some agencies use a Bradford frame to make
handling of the infant safe and convenient. The frame should be well
protected to prevent irritation on the infant's skin. Positioning the infant on
his abdomen on a Bradford frame also helps to protect the defect.   (3:66)

11   2.   The prone position (lying on the abdomen) or in some instances, the
knee–chest position, are positions of choice after the surgical repair of a
meningocele or myelomeningocele. These positions are maintained until
the operative site is healed. It is important to keep the operative area free
of pressure and as clean as possible to prevent infection.   (3:66)

12   1.   A child born with spina bifida with a myelomeningocele has a poor
prognosis in terms of being able to walk alone. The child *may* be able to

use a wheelchair or, possibly, braces and crutches. Many infants born with the condition do not survive childhood; most succumb to infections.   (3:65–66)

13 1.   Spina bifida is classified as a congenital anomaly, that is, a condition existing at, as well as before, the birth of an infant. The cause of the anomaly in fetal development is not known. A congenital condition should be distinguished from a hereditary anomaly, which is an anomaly transmitted from parents to offspring. Spina bifida has not been found to be associated with injury to the fetus or to an inadequate prenatal diet, nor is it a chromosome abnormality; an example of a chromosome abnormality is Down's syndrome.   (3:65)

14 3.   According to Erikson's theory, an infant must experience adequate love and attention to develop a sense of trust. If he does not, he develops feelings of mistrust. Feelings of doubt or shame result if autonomy needs are not met between about ages 2 and 4. Guilt results from unmet needs between ages 4 and 6. Inferiority is likely to occur when normal psychosocial needs are not met between about ages 6 and 12.   (1:29)

Caring for an infant with hydrocephalus

15 2.   The cause of hydrocephalus in most infants is a blockage (obstruction) that prevents proper circulation of cerebrospinal fluid. This is known as the noncommunicating type of congenital hydrocephalus, and is the most common type. Another type, less frequently observed, is the communicating type of hydrocephalus in which no obstruction exists but cerebrospinal fluid is inadequately absorbed for excretion.   (3:67)

16 4.   Daily measuring of the head of an infant with hydrocephalus is an especially important nursing responsibility. These daily measurements are important to evaluate the infant's defect and its progress.   (3:68)

17 4.   The side-lying position is the position of choice after feeding an infant with hydrocephalus. The infant tends to vomit easily and by placing her on her side, vomitus can escape easily from the mouth and aspiration of vomitus is less likely.   (3:70)

18 3.   The head and ears of an infant with hydrocephalus are especially prone to pressure and the development of decubitus ulcers. The primary reason for using a sheepskin in this situation is to help relieve pressure on the head and ears. The patient's position should be changed frequently to help prevent complications due to inactivity.   (3:69)

19 3.   The position of choice after installing a shunting device in an infant with hydrocephalus is on the side opposite the site for the surgical entry. The infant described in this item should be placed on her left side postoperatively because the surgical site of entry was on the right side of the head. This positioning prevents damage to the shunt valve.   (3:69; 12:532)

20 1.   Signs of increased intracranial pressure in an infant include bulging fontanels, dilated pupils, irritability, spasticity, and poor eating often associated with vomiting. (12:532)

21 1. Every infant needs cuddling and holding, including one that has hydrocephalus. These infants need nursing care that acts to comfort the infant, and such acts should be taught to parents of infants as well. Other activities, such as placing mobiles and talking and singing to the infant, are not contraindicated but do not replace holding an infant and using the sensation of touch to give the infant emotional warmth and support. (3:69)

Caring for an infant with a cleft lip

22 1. An infant with a cleft lip is unable to form a vacuum in this mouth that enables him to suck. He will need to be fed by means that do not require normal sucking. Infants with severe cleft lips tend to be mouth-breathers. (12:533)

23 1. The position of choice when feeding an infant who has a cleft lip is a sitting position to help prevent possible regurgitation and aspiration of formula. (12:533)

24 2. Infants with cleft lips usually produce considerable saliva and mucus, which they often do not handle well. It is wise, both preoperatively and postoperatively, to have suction equipment readily available to help prevent the infant's aspirating mucus and saliva. (2:410; 3:58)

25 2. The face-lying position with the infant on his abdomen is contraindicated during the immediate postoperative period following repair of a cleft lip. This position may cause injury to the operative site. The side-lying position and the back-lying position are preferred. The head should be slightly elevated when the infant is on his back. (3:60)

26 1. The method of choice for restraining an infant after repair of a cleft lip is to use elbow restraints. These restraints accomplish the intended purpose, that is, to keep the infant from injuring the suture line with his hands and fingers, while still affording the infant freedom of movement. Other types of restraints described in this item restrict the infant's movements and are more likely to cause the infant to "fight" the restraints. (3:59)

27 3. An Asepto syringe has been found very effective for feeding an infant after cleft lip repair. The end of the syringe should be protected with rubber tubing and the formula should be allowed to enter the infant's mouth slowly. Gavaging an infant and using a gavage tube are not recommended. A spoon may injure the repair. (2:410; 3:60)

28 3. Preparations that help to keep the suture line of the repaired cleft lip clean include a hydrogen peroxide solution, sterile water, and physiological saline solution. The suture line is left uncovered. It should be cleaned frequently and after each feeding to prevent infection and scarring. (3:59)

29 1. It is recommended when cleansing a suture line following repair of a cleft lip that the applicator be rolled along the length of the suture line. Stroking and dabbing the suture line are more likely to injure the suture line than rolling the applicator.   (3:59)

Caring for an infant with pyloric stenosis

30 4.   Pyloric stenosis is a congenital disorder in which there is a narrowing of the pyloric sphincter, thus preventing the normal passage of food from the stomach into the duodenum. The decrease in the size of the lumen is caused by hypertrophy of the circular muscles at the pyloric valve.   (12:544)

31 2.   Any number of veins can be used but, most often, veins in the scalp are used for infants receiving intravenous therapy. In some agencies, use of the subclavian veins is becoming increasingly popular. If the physician wishes to have a venous cannulation, he will order a surgical cutdown and will insert a catheter or needle, usually into a vein near the child's ankle.   (9:535)

32 3.   Common signs of atropine toxicity include a rapid pulse rate and flushed skin. The temperature may be elevated and the pupils will dilate. Urinary retention and vomiting may eventually occur.   (14:57)

33 2.   After the surgical repair of a pyloric stenosis, an infant is placed in a semi-sitting position after giving him fluids or formula. In this position, gravity helps carry feedings to the lower end of the stomach and makes regurgitation less likely. It is important not to overfeed because overfeeding predisposes to vomiting and places strain on the suture line.   (12:545)

Caring for an infant with congenital hip dislocation

34 3.   The edges of casts should be petaled with adhesive to prevent the edges from irritating the infant's skin. The edges may be trimmed before petaling but they should then be covered with adhesive. Plastic squares are often used for hip casts when the patient is an infant to protect the area of the cast left open around the perineal and rectal area, after petaling the edges.   (3:82; 9:599)

35 3.   It is typical for a 6-month-old infant to coo, hold onto a bottle, and show fear of strangers. Typically, an infant cannot mimic waving "bye-bye" until about 9 months of age.   (3:102–103)

Caring for an infant with bilateral clubfoot

36 4.   The cause of clubfoot is unknown, although a hereditary factor is sometimes noted. Some believe, however, that it is caused by the abnormal development or growth of certain germ plasm during early embryonic life. A less commonly accepted theory is that it may be caused by unusual pressure on the foot during pregnancy. The talipes equinovarus form of clubfoot accounts for most cases. The condition is more common in males than in females.   (3:79–80)

37 4.   After a cast is applied to the lower extremities, the extremities are elevated on pillows to improve circulation and prevent swelling of the feet. The cast is changed from time to time until correction is reached.   (3:80; 9:595)

38 4.   Wet casts should be handled by the palms of the hands. Gloves are unnecessary. A wet cast should never be lifted with fingers because this will cause indentations on the casts. Slings are inappropriate and may cut into a cast. Sturdy commercial slings made of heavy canvas-type material are sometimes used, especially for adults.   (9:595)

39 4.   An infant develops the ability to look at his surroundings during the first month of life. By 2 months, he is able to follow an object with both eyes. The mobile is an appropriate amusement for a 2-month-old infant. By 4 months, the infant can normally reach for objects, and by 7 to 9 months, he is able to crawl and play peek-a-boo.   (3:102–103)

40 1.   Typical signs when leg and foot casts are too tight include having swollen toes, having toes that are bluish in color, and having toes that feel cool to touch. Having toes that feel damp is not typical when a leg and foot cast is too tight.   (2:414; 9:596)

41 4.   A Denis Browne splint has often been used very successfully in treating clubfoot when use of the splint is started very soon after birth. The feet are taped to foot plates attached to a horizontal bar. The plates are adjusted from time to time to bring on correct alignment of the feet. After about 6 months and when the feet are overcorrected, the infant wears special shoes that are attached to the footplates. Corrective shoes ordinarily are worn after removing a Denis Browne splint.   (3:80)

42 1.   The posterior fontanel normally closes at 2 to 3 months of age in male as well as in female infants. The posterior fontanel has not been noted to close early in children with congenital skeletal defects.   (3:98)

Caring for an infant with sickle cell crisis

43 1.   The sickle-shaped cells tend to clump together in vessels and obstruct the normal blood flow. A thrombosis may form and cause death of tissues because of poor blood circulation. The characteristic symptom when tissue is denied normal blood circulation is severe pain in the affected parts of the body. Diarrhea, dyspnea, and hemorrhage are not associated with sickle cell crisis.   (3:127; 12:664)

44 4.   Nursing care of an infant with sickle cell crisis is primarily supportive and includes providing for a generous fluid intake. The above-average fluid intake prevents dehydration and also helps dilute the blood so that clumping of blood cells is less likely. Promoting rest and relieving pain are important. Some oxygen therapy may be used also, especially if the child has cardiac failure.   (3:127; 12:664–665)

45 4. When oxygen supply is low, sickling of cells increases. Therefore, the child with sickle cell disease should avoid high altitudes and traveling in unpressurized planes. (3:127)

46 3. The abnormal hemoglobin formed in sickle cell disease, called hemoglobin-S, is found in sickle-shaped red blood cells. These cells are incapable of carrying oxygen adequately as normal red blood cells do. Blood proteins, platelets, and white blood cells are not involved in the pathology of sickle cell disease. (3:127; 12:664)

47 1. Sickle cell disease occurs chiefly among black Americans with from 7% to 10% having·the disease. The condition affects whites very infrequently. It has been reported that the disease affects as many as 45% of native blacks in East Africa. (3:127; 12:664)

48 4. Sickle cell disease occurs by homozygous inheritance. This means that, when both patents carry mutant sickle cell genes, the possibilities for inheritance are as follows:

> One child in 4 will inherit sickle cell disease (In the situation described in this item, Hank has the illness.)
> Two children in 4 will inherit the sickle cell trait but be symptom free
> One child will be normal

(3:8)

Caring for an infant with cystic fibrosis

49 4. Because cystic fibrosis is an inherited disease, a child born in a family where there is a history of the disorder should be observed for signs of it. If the newborn fails to have meconium stools within the first 24 hours after birth, the situation should be reported promptly. The infant may be suffering with meconium ileus, which occurs as a complication of cystic fibrosis in the newborn when the meconium becomes too sticky and thick to be excreted. (3:158)

50 4. Typically, the stools of a child with cystic fibrosis are large, sticky, and very foul-smelling. The condition is due to a diminished or a lack of the flow of pancreatic enzymes that leads to faulty absorption of nutrients, especially fat-soluble vitamins. Other signs include malnutrition despite a hearty appetite, chronic coughing, distended abdomen, and flabby muscles. (3:158)

51 3. Many times, caretakers of children with cystic fibrosis become aware of a typical sign of the illness when they report that a child tastes salty when they kiss the child. The perspiration, tears, and saliva contain abnormally high concentrations of salt. Sweat analysis is an important diagnostic tool when children are examined for cystic fibrosis. (3:160; 12:549)

52 1. Pancreatic enzymes are prescribed for children with cystic fibrosis to help the digestive process. They are most often administered to a child by sprinkling the granules on the child's food. The granules may be given in capsule form, but the child in this item is 18 months old. It would be difficult to administer capsules to a child of that age. (3:160; 12:549)

53 1. The diet of a child with cystic fibrosis should be high in calories, protein, and carbohydrates. It should be low in fat. Because of sodium loss from the body, the child may be given extra salt in her diet. (3:160)

54 2. Exercise is important for well-being and general good health. However, for a person with cystic fibrosis, exercise is particularly important to help the body rid itself of respiratory secretions. (3:162; 12:549)

55 3. The use of a mist tent helps to relieve dyspnea in the child with cystic fibrosis. The humidity helps to liquify respiratory secretions and makes it easier to expectorate them. The humidity does not dilate alveoli, prevent dehydration, or decrease respiratory secretions. (3:160)

56 4. There are numerous positions in which patients may be placed to help drain various segments of the lungs. Because drainage occurs by gravity, the part being drained is placed higher than the large respiratory passageways into which secretions can gravitate. The left side-lying position with the head lowered is used to help drain the lower right segments of the lungs; the right side-lying position with the head lowered is used to drain the lower left segments of the lungs. The sitting position promotes drainage from the upper lobes, especially the posterior segments. Percussion and vibration are often used prior to postural drainage. These procedures help loosen thick secretions so that they are more easily moved by gravity when postural drainage is used. (3:261)

57 2. Children with cystic fibrosis are very susceptible to infections, especially infections in the respiratory tract. The children's parents should be taught to guard against exposure to infections to the greatest extent possible. Immunity to childhood diseases is highly recommended, especially those which may place the respiratory tract at risk. (3:162)

58 3. Emphysema and atelectasis are likely to develop in a child with cystic fibrosis because the thick, sticky mucous secretions in the respiratory passageways obstruct the bronchioles. Mucus plugs offer organisms an ideal environment, resulting in frequent respiratory infections. The plugs also predispose to atelectasis (collapse of lung tissues) and lung abscesses. (3:160)

The Nursing Care of Toddlers

Caring for a toddler who has swallowed a poisonous substance

59 4. A common early sign of salicylate poisoning is rapid and deep breathing, because aspirin stimulates the respiratory center. The pulse rate would increase when acidosis accompanies salicylate poisoning. Other signs of salicylate poisoning include electrolyte imbalance, restlessness, fever, profuse perspiration, bleeding, and finally convulsions and coma. (3:163)

60   3.   A goal in the emergency treatment for salicylate poisoning is to empty the stomach of the drug either by performing a gastric lavage or by inducing vomiting. This is done to prevent additional absorption of the ingested drug. Gastroscopy is more likely to be used to retrieve nonsoluble objects from the stomach, but would be useless in retrieving the dissolved aspirin. Intracardial injections may be performed to correct ventricular arrythmias, but they are not used for salicylate poisoning. (3:163)

61   3.   As can be expected of a toddler, the child in this item is sure to be naturally curious about his environment. Children between ages 1 and 4 like to taste substances and cannot determine for themselves whether a substance is poisonous. Therefore, it is most appropriate to remove harmful substances from areas where children play. A child of age 2½ years is too young to understand being told that certain substances are poisonous or to read warning signs. (3:140–143)

62   3.   Parents of small children should be taught to keep syrup of ipecac in a locked cupboard in their homes for emergency use. This drug causes vomiting. However, parents should most certainly be taught *not* to use ipecac if the child has ingested a corrosive substance, such as lye, or kerosene. Vomiting after ingestion of kerosene or corrosive substances can make the situation worse by causing dangerous inhalation of petroleum fumes or by further irritating the upper gastrointestinal tract. Whenever there is the slightest doubt, parents should be admonished to call their local poison control center for information. (3:143)

Caring for a toddler with croup

63   2.   A child who has had respiratory distress has experienced marked distress and is frightened. Separation from a parent can increase the child's fear. The nurse should focus attention on reducing the anxiety for both the mother and child. It is best to allow the mother to stay with her child while health care is being given. (3:xii)

64   2.   The child with croup has a cough that sounds hoarse, much like a loud, barking, metallic sound. A high-pitched sound is typical of the child's breathing, not a cough. Although the cause is not clearly understood, an infection or an allergy may be etiological factors for croup. (3:157)

65   3.   To relieve laryngeal spasms in children with croup, a medication is often used to induce vomiting. Vomiting usually relieves symptoms and syrup of ipecac is one such medication. Medications to induce sleep, reduce pain, and inhibit reflex activity are not indicated for the treatment of laryngeal spasms. (3:157)

66   3.   To help liquify secretions and reduce laryngeal spasms, the child with croup should breathe air that is high in humidity. A croup tent or an electric vaporizer is often used. A dust-free environment would be required for children who need a sterile environment or for patients who are allergic to dust. Dry air provides no relief for a child with croup.   (3:157)

67   1.   During the toddler age, the child is normally busy developing self-esteem and independence (autonomy) and is constantly running into restrictions. A favorite word for a toddler is "No!" He becomes impatient with routines and regulations in life. Although the toddler needs safeguards and has to learn certain restrictions, constantly thwarting the child is likely to cause him to feel shame and have doubts about himself.   (3:141)

Caring for a toddler with lead poisoning

68   4.   A 24-hour urine specimen is collected and studied to help determine the level of lead concentration in a child's system. The nurse is responsible for collecting such a specimen. Blood serum tests are also done to determine lead levels in the body. X-ray examinations may be used to note increased density of long bones.   (3:164)

69   1.   Ethylenediamine tetra-acetate acid (EDTA), a chelating agent, is used for lead poisoning to help render the lead nontoxic. EDTA causes binding of the lead with itself, that is, with the EDTA, to prevent lead from entering the bloodstream. The lead that has been chelated is then excreted through the kidneys and urine. The drug is not excreted with lead through the stool. It does not reverse mental retardation, nor is it given primarily for symptomatic relief.   (3:164)

70   1.   Lead paint, found primarily on furniture, toys, and woodwork, is a leading source of lead that is ingested by children to cause lead poisoning. Putty and gasoline also contain lead, as does water that has become contaminated with lead from lead pipes.   (3:164)

Caring for a toddler with pneumonia

71   2.   There is an increase in the respiratory rate in children with pneumonia. The rate seen in infants with pneumonia may become 40 to 80 per minute and in older children, 30 to 50 per minute. The rapid respiratory rate is the body's way of compensating for the decreased ventilation in the lungs, and to a certain extent, for helping the body rid itself of excess heat. When the temperature is elevated, the metabolism rate is increased, which also causes respirations to increase.   (3:129)

72   4.   Recording the child's urinary output will assist in determining fluid needs. Fluid loss because of high fever, vomiting, and diarrhea are common in pneumonia. As a result of fluid loss, there is a decrease in urinary output. The urine appears dark amber in color and has a high specific gravity. The nurse should measure the fluid intake as well.   (12:573)

73   4.   Lack of coughing in children with pneumonia is often mistaken for a sign of recovery. However, lack of coughing more likely indicates marked congestion in the lower respiratory tract.   (12:541)

74 4.   Foods containing complete proteins include milk, fresh eggs, meat, poultry, and cheese. Complete proteins that contain all eight of the essential amino acids required for proper growth and development are, in general, from animal sources. Proteins found in vegetables, especially legumes, fruits, and cereals, are incomplete. They do not contain all essential amino acids but are important to supplement the complete proteins in the diet.   (16:34)

75 4.   Rubbing the skin before giving a tepid-water sponge bath helps bring blood to the skin's surface. This assists with reducing the patient's temperature when cool, moist cloths are applied to the skin. The technique also helps prevent sensations of chilliness for the patient. Rubbing the skin should be done *briefly*. Prolonged rubbing causes heat by friction, which is contraindicated for a patient with an elevated temperature.   (12:514)

76 2.   During a tepid-water sponge bath to reduce body temperature, the nurse should observe the patient carefully and check his vital signs regularly. Any untoward reactions to the bath should cause the nurse to stop the procedure. About 30 minutes after the bath, the nurse should check the patient's vital signs to evaluate the effectiveness of the bath in helping to reduce the temperature. If a child is not already on oxygen therapy, its use is unlikely to depend on the result of a tepid-water sponge. Aspirin is used to help reduce body temperature but it is unlikely to be used routinely after a bath intended to lower body temperature. However, it may be prescribed if the bath has not been effective.   (9:423)

77 4.   The nurse should have the mother repeat home-going instructions so that it can be determined if she has understood them correctly. It may become necessary to write the instructions in Spanish for the mother described in this item if she does not understand. Reading the instructions again or repeating them in terms that the mother can understand does not ensure that she does comprehend.   (9:222)

The Nursing Care of Preschool Children

Caring for a child with seizure activity

78 1.   The sides of a crib should be padded to help prevent injury to a child during seizure activity. The padding serves no other therapeutic purpose.   (3:133)

79 2.   A tracheostomy set is not necessary to be kept at the bedside of a child subject to seizure activity. Suction equipment is handy to remove mucus from the child's mouth as necessary. Padded tongue blades are used to protect the child from injuring the tongue. However, a tongue blade should not be forced into the mouth during seizure because of the possibility of injuring the mouth and teeth. A good source of light is important for observations that should be made during a seizure, such as the child's color, respiratory rate, and eye movements.   (3:133)

80   4.   An appropriate action when a patient has a seizure is to time the period during which the patient fails to breathe, which is of interest for diagnostic purposes. It is normal to be breathless during a convulsion, which cannot be interrupted. Attempting to give mouth-to-mouth resuscitation could injure the patient who is thrashing about. Supplemental oxygen would not assist the patient who is unable to breathe during a convulsion. If a seizure ceases and breathlessness continues, mouth-to-mouth resuscitation may possibly become necessary.   (3:133; 12:626)

81   2.   If it is possible for parents to spend more visiting time with their child, it is best to encourage them to do so. A child is normally frightened about being left in a hospital. He usually fears his parents will not return. Extra attention and visiting decrease these fears. It is a mistake to suggest that because the child cries, the parents should not visit or should visit less often.   (3:xii)

82   2.   Phenytoin (Dilantin) should be given with food or immediately after a meal to reduce stomach irritation.   (14:207)

83   4.   Phenytoin, when used over a period of time, tends to cause an overgrowth of gum tissues. The condition is called gingival hyperplasia. Good dental care and oral hygiene can help reduce the incidence of the condition. A poor appetite, urinary incontinence, and painful joints are not associated with the use of phenytoin.   (3:242; 14:208)

Caring for a child with leukemia

84   3.   A commonly used test to help diagnose leukemia is a bone marrow aspiration. The bone marrow is characterized by being hypercellular, lacking fat globules, and having blast cells (immature white cells) in the presence of leukemia. The diagnosis also is based on the child's history, symptoms, and various tests of blood cells.   (3:206–207)

85   3.   Painful joints, a common symptom of leukemia, is often relieved by bed rest. Other signs and symptoms of leukemia include low-grade fever, pallor, listlessness, bruising, and swollen lymph glands.   (3:206)

86   2.   Prednisone (Meticorten) and vincristine sulfate (Oncovin) given in combination help to induce remissions of leukemia. Remissions may last for weeks to months, and occasionally as long as years.   (3:206)

87   2.   Hair loss (alopecia) is a common side-effect of many antineoplastic agents. Other side-effects include anuria, diarrhea, skin rashes, and bone marrow depression. Pathological fractures are associated with osteogenesis imperfecta.   (3:206)

88   2.   Signs of a transfusion reaction include feeling cold and having chills, fever, and a rapid pulse rate. The patient may also complain of itching and low back pain. If feeling chilly occurs very early in a blood transfusion, it *may* be the result of cold blood entering the body. Nevertheless, a transfusion reaction should be suspected until proven otherwise. (9:533)

89 3. If a patient is having a reaction to blood, the nurse should *first* clamp the tubing to stop the blood flow. The clamp on the second bottle (normal saline) should then be opened. The needle should not be removed because it is important to keep an intravenous line for the administration of substances other than blood, such as fluids, electrolytes, and drugs. The nurse-in-charge should be notified promptly after the flow of blood is stopped. (9:533–534)

90 3. The question, "Am I going to die?" can be answered in many different ways. However, the nurse's response should encourage the child to ventilate her feelings about dying. The nurse should avoid responses that would either make the child guilty or discourage the child from talking about her anxieties. The nurse's response also should not reinforce denials and unrealistic perceptions of the patient's prognosis. When dealing with children, it is important to answer questions honestly based on the child's level of understanding. (3:358; 9:669)

91 3. All of the nursing measures described in this item may be important when caring for a child with leukemia, but giving regular and frequent oral hygiene is particularly important. Oral mucous membranes are tender and tend to ulcerate and bleed. Good oral hygiene will promote comfort and help to prevent infection and halitosis. It also helps promote an interest in food. Oral hygiene should be carried out with the greatest gentleness to avoid injuring tender oral mucosa. (3:207)

92 2. As leukemia progresses, the patient becomes very anemic and the blood lacks the normal amount of blood platelets. These conditions tend to cause bleeding from various body orifices, including the anus. The patient also bruises easily. Vomiting, weight loss, and dyspnea are also common. Clubbing of the fingers more commonly occurs with cyanotic heart disease and with certain respiratory disorders. (12:539)

93 2. The stage of depression is one in which the parents of a dying child feel helpless and are in a state of despair. They recognize that only a miracle can cure their child. The stage of denial is one in which the parents deny that this could really be happening to them and their child. They tend not to believe the diagnosis and often then look about for additional medical opinions. During the stage of acceptance, the parents tend to become calm and are able to place the child's needs in their proper perspective. They have come to accept the inevitable. During the stage of bargaining, the parents tend to make offers of doing something in exchange for more time in the child's life. (9:653)

94 2. During preschool years, most children view death as temporary and reversible. Because their concept of time is not well developed, they do not understand the permanency of death. Some children may ask whether death is an uncomfortable experience. (2:357; 9:669)

95 3. Children usually first recognize death in a manner similar to adults between the ages of 9 or 10 and 12 years.   (9:669)

96 3. When the child with leukemia is too tired and irritable to eat, the nurse should provide small, between-meal snacks of food that the child likes. Food may be brought from home when agency policy permits for children who are hospitalized during terminal illnesses.   (9:659)

Caring for a child with scarlet fever and glomerulonephritis

97 1. Scarlet fever is characterized by a fine red rash on the body, legs, and arms. It may diffuse and cover the entire body. It is usually preceded by a sore throat caused by streptococci. Coughing, hyperactivity, and a stuffy nose ordinarily are not associated with scarlet fever.   (3:254)

98 1. Scarlet fever is contagious as long as there are discharges from the throat, nose and eyes. These symptoms usually subside in 7 to 10 days.   (3:254)

99 3. The tissues around the eyes become puffy when acute glomerulonephritis is present. This edema may accompany or precede hematuria. Edema around the eyes is often referred to as periorbital edema.   (3:212)

100 2. A low-sodium diet is ordered for a patient with acute glomerulonephritis. Eating foods high in salt content tends to increase fluid retention. In some instances, a low-protein diet may also be ordered. Eating foods high in calcium, fat, and carbohydrates does not tend to worsen edema. Potassium also is very often limited in the diet of a patient with glomerulonephritis, especially if there are any signs of renal failure present.   (16:302; 3:213)

101 4. Symptoms of increased intracranial pressure include headaches that are aggravated by moving about, blurred or double vision, drowsiness, vomiting, and seizures. An earache is associated with an inner ear infection and a backache with a kidney infection.   (12:619)

102 4. A child with increased intracranial pressure is prone to seizure activity. When increased pressure is suspected, the nurse should make certain that the child is in bed with siderails in the up position at all times. Someone should stay with the child. Restraining someone who may have seizures could result in injury and giving fluids could result in aspiration. Applying cold compresses does not relieve cerebral edema.   (12:619)

103 1. The child with acute glomerulonephritis is placed on bed rest. The nurse should provide him with quiet diversion. While all of the activities given in this item may be appropriate for the child, only listening to cassettes will help prevent fatigue and keep the youngster at rest.   (3:213)

104 1. Regression is defined as going back to an earlier stage of development in life. Many hospitalized children show signs of regression, a common behavior being wetting the bed after being toilet trained. Displacement is defined as transferring an unacceptable feeling to a more acceptable substitute. Projection is attributing unacceptable qualities to others. Repression is involuntary forgetting of unacceptable thoughts and feelings.   (1:51)

Caring for a child with strabismus

105   1.   Foods and fluids are generally withheld for 6 to 12 hours before surgery, to reduce the risk of the patient's aspirating vomitus. For hospitalized patients, it is recommended that all food and fluids should be removed from the patient's bedside. Also, a sign indicating that the child is to have nothing by mouth should be clearly posted at the bedside.   (9:381)

106   1.   It is recommended that a child be familiarized with restraints that may need to be applied postoperatively. This technique, as well as covering the child's eyes for short periods preoperatively, often lessens a child's postoperative fears. At the same time, the child should be assured that the restraints and dressings will be removed as soon as possible after surgery.   (9:391)

107   3.   Surgical intervention to correct strabismus is generally delayed until a child reaches preschool age. The physician can better measure the degree of strabismus in the preschool child than he can in an infant because an infant's control of eye muscles is poor. Surgical correction for strabismus is generally used when conservative measures, such as eye exercises and wearing corrective glasses, are ineffective.   (12:536)

108   3.   Because the patient is restrained and her eyes are covered following surgery, listening to records is an appropriate activity. The patient would be unable to work with puzzles, color, or play with a doll.   (3:155)

109   2.   The child described in this item can eat as desired. A liquid diet would not necessarily be required. When both eyes are covered, it is best to speak to a person before touching her to avoid fright. A child is allowed up and about following eye surgery for the correction of strabismus. Dark glasses are often used after dressings are removed to prevent the discomfort of photophobia, which is sometimes present after eye surgery.   (12:536)

Caring for a child who has a tonsillectomy and adenoidectomy

110   2.   It is important to report an elevated temperature of a preoperative patient promptly, along with any other signs of infection, such as a sore throat or a runny nose. Surgery will be cancelled if the child has an infection.   (12:543)

111   3.   Examples of clear liquids include Popsicles, jello, broth, synthetic juices, water, and ice chips. Natural juices are irritating to the throat. When a full liquid diet can be tolerated, sherbet, ice cream, puddings, and custard may be added.   (16:234)

112   2.   Signs of excessive bleeding following a tonsillectomy include frequent swallowing, a rapid pulse rate, restlessness, and vomiting of bright red blood. Vomiting dark old blood is to be expected unless it occurs in large amounts. Usually, children are eager for fluids upon awakening despite throat soreness. A respiratory rate of 30 per minute is within normal range for a 5-year-child.   (3:205–206)

113 1.   Correcting socially unacceptable behavior is considered best when the discipline results in helping the child to develop inner control. Constructive methods of discipline include explaining disapproval of a child's behavior, isolating the child for a period of time, using calm reasoning, withholding a desired treat, and calling attention to desirable behavior. Less effective is discipline that includes telling a child he is bad, yelling and screaming at the child, and using physical punishment.   (3:183)

114 4.   A transient earache on about the third day following a tonsillectomy and adenoidectomy is common. The discomfort is due to pain referred from the throat to the ear. A nurse should advise parents of the possibility of the occurrence of an earache around the third day postoperatively while giving discharge instructions.   (3:206)

Caring for a child with osteomyelitis

115 4.   The leukocytes (white blood cells) can be expected to be elevated in a child with acute osteomyelitis. Additional tests to study osteomyelitis include blood cultures and radiography examinations.   (3:239)

116 4.   When osteomyelitis is confirmed, the most likely reason for applying a cast to a knee is to keep the knee at complete rest. The affected area is ordinarily extremely painful. The area should be supported well, and a cast or brace is used to promote immobility. After the causative organism is identified, an aggressive antimicrobial program is ordinarily prescribed.   (12:612)

Classification of Test Items

Directions: *Each item in the previous review test is classified here according to the subject area it tests. Place a check mark after each item you answered* **correctly** *by referring to your answers. Total the number of items you answered correctly in each area and enter the numbers in the correct places on pages 553–556.*

Clinical: Nursing Care of Children

1 ✓	15 ✓	29 ____	50 ____	73 ✓	99 ✓
2 ✓	16 ✓	30 ✓	51 ✓	78 ✓	101 ✓
3 ✓	17 ____	31 ✓	54 ____	79 ✓	102 ✓
4 ✓	18 ✓	33 ____	55 ____	80 ✓	103 ✓
5 ____	19 ____	34 ✓	57 ✓	84 ✓	105 ✓
6 ____	20 ____	36 ____	58 ✓	85 ✓	106 ____
7 ✓	22 ✓	41 ____	60 ✓	88 ✓	107 ✓
8 ✓	23 ✓	43 ____	64 ____	89 ✓	109 ✓
9 ✓	24 ✓	44 ✓	66 ✓	91 ✓	110 ✓
10 ✓	25 ✓	45 ✓	68 ✓	92 ____	112 ____
11 ____	26 ✓	46 ✓	70 ✓	96 ✓	114 ____
12 ____	27 ✓	47 ✓	71 ✓	97 ✓	115 ✓
13 ✓	28 ✓	49 ____	72 ✓	98 ✓	116 ____

TOTAL _57_

Biological/Physical Sciences

42 ✓   48 ____

TOTAL _1_

Fundamentals of Nursing

37 ____   38 ✓   40 ✓   56 ✓   75 ✓   76 ✓

TOTAL _5_

Diet Therapy/Nutrition

53 _____   74 __✓__   100 __✓__   111 __✓__

TOTAL __3__

Pharmacology

| 32 _____ | 59 __✓__ | 65 _____ | 82 __✓__ | 86 _____ | 87 __✓__ |
| 52 __✓__ | 62 __✓__ | 69 _____ | 83 __✓__ | | |

TOTAL __6__

Psychosocial Sciences

14 __✓__	39 __✓__	67 __✓__	90 __✓__	95 __✓__	108 __✓__
21 __✓__	61 __✓__	77 __✓__	93 __✓__	104 __✓__	113 __✓__
35 _____	63 __✓__	81 __✓__	94 __✓__		

TOTAL __15__

Review Test 5

The Nursing Care of School-Aged Children

Caring for a Child With Appendicitis
Caring for a Child With Rheumatic Fever
Caring for a Child With Diabetes Mellitus
Caring for a Child With Second- and Third-Degree Burns
Caring for a Child With Juvenile Rheumatoid Arthritis
Caring for a Child With a Brain Tumor

The Nursing Care of Adolescents With Various Health Care Needs

Caring for an Adolescent With Dysmenorrhea
Caring for an Adolescent Who Is Abusing Amphetamines
Caring for an Adolescent With Pulmonary Tuberculosis
Caring for an Adolescent With Acne Vulgaris
Caring for an Adolescent With a Sexually-Transmitted Disease
Caring for an Adolescent With Anorexia Nervosa

The Nursing Care of Children With Various Health Care Needs

Caring for a Child With Infantile Eczema
Caring for a Child With Otitis Media
Caring for a Child Having a Checkup
Caring for a Child Who Has Been Battered
Caring for a Child Who Has Cardiopulmonary Collapse
Caring for a Child With Infantile Autism
Caring for a Child With Phenylketonuria
Caring for a Child With Hemophilia
Caring for a Child With Ulcerative Colitis
Caring for a Child With Various Health Problems

Individual Items
Correct Answers and Rationales
Classification of Items

Directions: *With a pencil, blacken the circle in front of the option you have chosen for your correct answer.*

The Nursing Care of School-Aged Children

Hillary Smith, a 5½-year-old, has an elevated temperature and complains of generalized abdominal pain. Appendicitis is suspected and she is hospitalized for observation.

1 Hillary's father tells the nurse that he fears that Hillary's appendix will rupture if it is not removed promptly. He questions the need for continued observations. Which of the following responses by the nurse would be most appropriate in this situation?

  ○ 1. "Your concern is justified. Perhaps you should tell your doctor that you want him to perform the appendectomy as soon as possible."

  ○ 2. "The appendix can be inflamed for a long period before it ruptures. Your doctor is experienced in managing cases like this."

  ○ 3. "The delay in surgery permits optimal preparation of your daughter. It is important that she knows what to expect and how she can help in her recovery."

  ○ 4. "Symptoms of appendicitis in a child are similar to those of other illnesses. It is usually considered best to observe your daughter for a while to see if she does have appendicitis."

2 The nurse would be correct in questioning an order for a medication for Hillary during the observation period that is classified as

  ○ 1. a laxative.

  ○ 2. an analgesic.

  ○ 3. an antibiotic.

  ○ 4. an antiemetic.

3 The nurse's responsibilities include observing Hillary for signs of a ruptured appendix. Two typical signs are pain and a

  ○ 1. convulsion.

  ○ 2. blood stool.

  ○ 3. rigid abdomen.

  ○ 4. sudden drop in temperature.

It is determined that Hillary has appendicitis and she is scheduled to have surgery.

4 If the following findings were noted when obtaining Hillary's health history from her parents, which one is very likely to have played a role in the child's developing appendicitis?

  ○ 1. Having had pinworms.

  ○ 2. Having had diarrhea a few days ago.

  ○ 3. Having had bronchial pneumonia a few months ago.

  ○ 4. Having allergic rhinitis (hay fever) at the present time.

5 During Hillary's hospitalization, Ms. Smith tells the nurse that she is disturbed because Hillary is showing interest in and playing with her genitals. The nurse should base her response to Ms. Smith's concern on knowledge that interest in the genitals in a 5½-year-old child is

○ 1. normal and need not be cause for concern.
○ 2. abnormal and counseling should be sought.
○ 3. believed to precede sexual promiscuity.
○ 4. due probably to a local irritation and a health examination is indicated.

Seven-year-old Melissa Martin is admitted to a hospital with rheumatic fever. She is acutely ill.

6 Melissa's health history reveals that she recently had a "sore throat." The organism that was most likely responsible for her sore throat was a

○ 1. virus.
○ 2. streptococcus.
○ 3. staphylococcus.
○ 4. pneumococcus.

7 During the acute stage of Melissa's illness, her nursing care should certainly include

○ 1. giving her a bed bath.
○ 2. helping her walk to the bathroom.
○ 3. protecting her from bright sunlight.
○ 4. seeing to it that she moves about in bed.

8 Melissa is to receive aspirin. The nurse should understand that when Melissa is to receive aspirin, the most probable reason for giving her this drug is to relieve

○ 1. headaches.
○ 2. chest pain.
○ 3. joint tenderness.
○ 4. cardiac enlargement.

A digitalis preparation is to be given to Melissa when she show signs of heart failure.

9 Two desired actions are to slow Melissa's heartbeat and to

○ 1. dilate the coronary arteries.
○ 2. strengthen the contractions of the ventricles.
○ 3. prevent damage from occurring to the mitral valve.
○ 4. reduce the pH of the blood circulating through the heart.

10 Of the following nursing measures, the one that must be carried out before administering digitalis to Melissa is

○ 1. counting the patient's pulse rate.
○ 2. obtaining the patient's blood pressure.

○ 3. determining the patient's pulse pressure.
○ 4. observing the rate of the patient's respirations.

Melissa is observed for signs of choreal activity (Chorea).

11 If Melissa develops chorea as part of having rheumatic fever, it becomes very important that nursing care includes
   ○ 1. offering a generous fluid intake to help prevent thrombi formation.
   ○ 2. using restraints to help prevent the child from getting out of bed.
   ○ 3. protecting the bed siderails to help prevent the child from injuring herself.
   ○ 4. keeping careful records of urinary output to help determine possible kidney damage.

Melissa's condition improves and preparations for discharge are begun.

12 The nurse notes that Melissa's father enjoys helping his daughter to perform simple tasks. Which of the following comments to Mr. Martin would be most helpful in explaining Melissa's needs?
   ○ 1. "Melissa enjoys having your help. However, you should avoid overdoing it because you may then become ill yourself."
   ○ 2. "It is good that you enjoy helping Melissa because it reassures us that her needs will be met when she goes home."
   ○ 3. "Melissa needs your help because her heart should be protected from any unnecessary strain for an indefinite period of time."
   ○ 4. "It is reassuring that you want to help Melissa. However, you can help her to regain her independence by allowing her to do as much for herself as she safely can."

Paul Hanlon, 8 years old, is admitted to a hospital in a coma. The tentative diagnosis is insulin dependent diabetes mellitus (IDDM).

13 The nurse should be prepared to assist with establishing a diagnosis by testing Paul's urine for the presence of
   ○ 1. blood.
   ○ 2. sucrose.
   ○ 3. ammonia.
   ○ 4. acetone.
14 Which of the following agents should the nurse be prepared to administer as part of Paul's care after it is established that he has diabetes mellitus?
   ○ 1. Glucagon
   ○ 2. Regular insulin
   ○ 3. Tolbutamide (Orinase)
   ○ 4. Vasopressin tannate (Pitressin Tannate)

Paul is to receive regular insulin and isophane insulin suspension (NPH).

15 The nurse should teach Paul and his parents that the reason for giving the two types of insulin is to
- ○ 1. allow the child to eat greater quantities of food.
- ○ 2. help prevent the occurrence of vascular complications.
- ○ 3. provide immediate as well as longer-lasting protection.
- ○ 4. provide the child with added protection during periods of exercise.

16 Mr. Hanlon asks why Paul cannot take an oral drug for his diabetes. "My mother who has had diabetes for 10 years uses Orinase and that's better than injecting insulin," he states. Before responding to Mr. Hanlon's comment, the nurse must understand that, unlike insulin, tolbutamide (Orinase) acts to
- ○ 1. stimulate the pancreas to produce insulin.
- ○ 2. retard the normal development of the pancreas.
- ○ 3. destroy cells in the liver of children with diabetes.
- ○ 4. increase the storage of glycogen in the immature liver.

17 Mr. Hanlon continues, "Why can't insulin be taken by mouth?" Which of the following responses the nurse could make is most accurate in answer to Mr. Hanlon's question?
- ○ 1. "Insulin is extremely irritating to stomach mucosa."
- ○ 2. "Giving insulin orally does not allow accurate control of the disease."
- ○ 3. "Giving insulin orally does not help prevent most complications of diabetes."
- ○ 4. "The digestive juices in the stomach destroy the effectiveness of insulin."

18 In dejection, Mr. Hanlon adds, "I guess my son will always be different from others." Which of the following responses to Mr. Hanlon's comment is best for the nurse to make?
- ○ 1. "Paul could have a much worse illness than diabetes."
- ○ 2. "Paul will adjust and everything will be fine, you will see."
- ○ 3. "With present research underway, a cure will be found soon, I feel sure."
- ○ 4. "With good health care, Paul can lead an almost normal life."

19 Mr. and Mrs. Hanlon proudly tell the nurse that Paul is a good student and enjoys learning new things. The parents' comments suggest that Paul is meeting a psychosocial need of his age for developing
- ○ 1. identity.
- ○ 2. industry.
- ○ 3. initiative.
- ○ 4. autonomy.

The nurse teaches Paul and his parents about insulin and how to inject it.

20 The nurse should explain that Paul and his parents can best help to prevent inflammation and damage to tissue at the injection site by
    ○ 1. injecting the needle at a 45-degree angle.
    ○ 2. administering the insulin in alternate sites.
    ○ 3. avoiding massage at the injection site after giving the insulin.
    ○ 4. facing the bevel of the needle toward the patient when injecting the needle.

21 Paul and his parents should be taught that two common symptoms of an insulin reaction are
    ○ 1. nausea and vomiting.
    ○ 2. hunger and dizziness.
    ○ 3. chest pain and fatigue.
    ○ 4. drowsiness and warm flashes.

22 Of the following experiences in daily living, the one that will cause Paul's body to require *less* than his usual amounts of insulin is when Paul
    ○ 1. eats too much food.
    ○ 2. increases his activity.
    ○ 3. develops an infection.
    ○ 4. undergoes emotional stress.

23 Paul is on a special diet. The nurse should teach Paul and his parents that they should report any sign that indicates Paul's diet, or possibly his insulin dosage, most probably needs adjusting if Paul observes that he has
    ○ 1. shallow respirations.
    ○ 2. glucose in the urine.
    ○ 3. an increase in appetite.
    ○ 4. a craving for sweet foods.

24 At the end of a teaching session, the nurse asks Paul and his parents to summarize what to do if Paul has an insulin reaction. They answer correctly when they say that Paul should
    ○ 1. eat a piece of hard candy.
    ○ 2. drink a large amount of water.
    ○ 3. lie down to rest for a few minutes.
    ○ 4. exercise vigorously for a few minutes.

Eight-year-old Dean Weng is hospitalized for extensive second- and third-degree burns on his chest and left arm.

25 Which of the following isolation techniques should the nurse be prepared to observe in Dean's hospital environment?
    ○ 1. Enteric isolation

    ○ 2. Protective isolation
    ○ 3. Respiratory isolation
    ○ 4. Drainage/secretion isolation

26 Equipment for an emergency that is kept in readiness in Dean's room should include
    ○ 1. a tourniquet.
    ○ 2. a tracheostomy set.
    ○ 3. a padded tongue blade.
    ○ 4. equipment to administer oxygen.

27 Of particular importance during Dean's early post-burn care is for the nurse to monitor carefully the child's
    ○ 1. unburned skin areas.
    ○ 2. intestinal elimination.
    ○ 3. intravenous fluid therapy.
    ○ 4. pupillary responses to light.

28 The nurse notes that a nursing order on Dean's care plan states that a cradle is to be used on the child's bed. The primary reason for this order is that a cradle helps to
    ○ 1. encourage movement of the child in bed.
    ○ 2. promote drainage from the child's burn sites.
    ○ 3. prevent the child from rolling onto burn sites.
    ○ 4. keep bed linens from touching the child's burn sites.

29 Of the following techniques to help prevent footdrop while Dean is bedridden, the one that is likely to be *least* effective is having the child
    ○ 1. wear antiembolism stockings.
    ○ 2. wear ankle-high tennis shoes.
    ○ 3. rest his feet against a firm pillow.
    ○ 4. rest his feet upright against a board.

30 Dean is to have a homograft. This type of skin graft is used primarily to help
    ○ 1. decrease pain in the child's burn sites.
    ○ 2. improve circulation at the child's burn sites.
    ○ 3. prevent fluid loss from the child's burn sites.
    ○ 4. stimulate growth of the child's skin at the burn site.

31 Meperidine hydrochloride (Demerol) is given to Dean when the nurse judges it to be necessary. The nurse should recognize that the primary reason for its use is to
    ○ 1. promote sleep.
    ○ 2. reduce anxiety.
    ○ 3. prevent nausea.
    ○ 4. relieve discomfort.

32 A diet high in protein is ordered for Dean. Of the following between-meal snacks that are likely to appeal to Dean, which two have the highest protein content?
    ○ 1. Cheese cubes and peanuts
    ○ 2. An apple and potato chips

○ 3. Jello with cream and jelly beans
○ 4. Popcorn with butter and pretzels

33 Dean is watched carefully for complications. When he has a black, tarry stool, the nurse reports her findings promptly because a stool of this nature is a common sign of
○ 1. a stress ulcer.
○ 2. post-burn shock.
○ 3. an electrolyte imbalance.
○ 4. an increase in blood plasma volume.

34 When Dean's condition improves, the nurse plans diversions for him. Of the following activities, the most appropriate one for an eight-year-old is
○ 1. listening to music.
○ 2. coloring simple designs.
○ 3. watching fish in an aquarium.
○ 4. playing a card game with the nurse.

Marlys Mitchell is a 10-year-old who has juvenile rheumatoid arthritis (JRA). Her knee joints are affected.

35 In what position should Marlys's knees be supported in bed?
○ 1. The knees should be hyperextended.
○ 2. The knees should be slightly flexed, no more than about 5 degrees.
○ 3. The knees should be moderately flexed, no more than about 45 degrees.
○ 4. The knees should be supported in a manner that causes the least discomfort to the child.

36 After the acute phase of the rheumatoid arthritis subsides, the nurse can best help Marlys from developing contractures by
○ 1. keeping her feet in tennis shoes.
○ 2. restraining her ankles during sleep.
○ 3. massaging her lower leg muscles with lotion.
○ 4. putting her joints through range-of-motion exercises.

37 Aspirin is to be given to Marlys. A characteristic of aspirin which makes it the drug of choice for Marlys is that it helps
○ 1. lower body temperature.
○ 2. reduce joint inflammation.
○ 3. relax spasms in long muscles.
○ 4. decrease blood clotting time.

David Foster, 11 years old, has a brain tumor.

38 If David made the following comments to the nurse, which one describes a typical symptom of increased intracranial pressure and should be reported promptly?
○ 1. "I can't see good."

○ 2. "I'm not hungry today."
○ 3. "My mouth really feels dry."
○ 4. "There is a lump in my throat."

39 If a drug is prescribed for David to relieve increased intracranial pressure, the type of drug that will most likely be used is one that acts to cause
○ 1. an increase in urinary output.
○ 2. an increase in the heart's pumping action.
○ 3. a decrease in cerebrospinal fluid production.
○ 4. a decrease in the ability of the brain to receive stimuli.

David has surgery for the removal of a malignant brain tumor that was located on the right side of his brain.

40 How should the nurse position David when he returns from the recovery room following surgery?
○ 1. Flat in bed on his left side
○ 2. Flat in bed on his right side
○ 3. On his back with his feet elevated
○ 4. On his abdomen with his feet elevated

41 David's parents express their feelings of helplessness and anxiety to the nurse after they learn of the child's poor prognosis. Which of the following statements would be best to help David's parents deal with their despair?
○ 1. "Perhaps you would feel better if you visited David for shorter periods of time."
○ 2. "This is a difficult time for you. How do you think you will feel if David dies?"
○ 3. "What are some of the things you usually do for David that make him feel good?"
○ 4. "It's sad that you feel helpless. What do you usually do to take your mind off your worries?"

A Nurse Works in a Community Health Clinic in the Unit Concerned With the Health Care of Adolescents.

Molly Mullens, 17 years old, comes to the clinic because of dysmenorrhea.

42 While waiting for her appointment, which of the following actions should the nurse take to help relieve the discomfort Molly is experiencing from menstrual cramps?
○ 1. Giving the patient a cup of tea

○ 2. Placing a warm towel on the patient's abdomen
○ 3. Having the patient lie on her abdomen on a bed
○ 4. Encouraging the patient to squeeze her hands into a tight fist

43 Molly says to the nurse, "One of my classmates says she is scared because she has amenorrhea. What does the word mean?" The nurse should explain that amenorrhea means
○ 1. absence of menstruation.
○ 2. excessive vaginal bleeding.
○ 3. discomfort prior to menstruation.
○ 4. discomfort midway between menstrual periods.

Ms. Norell calls for an appointment because she has discovered amphetamine capsules in the room of her 15-year-old son, Barry.

44 The nurse should recognize that Barry is most likely abusing amphetamines when Ms. Norell describes Barry as having
○ 1. watery eyes.
○ 2. dilated pupils.
○ 3. excoriated nostrils.
○ 4. noticeable nervousness.

45 Mr. Norell explains that Barry has been socializing with a gang of teenagers that is noted for getting into trouble with the police. Which of the following comments would provide Ms. Norrell with the most accurate information about Barry's psychosocial needs?
○ 1. "Barry is going through a stage that is commonly experienced by adolescents. He will outgrow this stage in another year or two."
○ 2. "Barry is at the age when he should be able to accept directions from you. He needs you to inform him of the dangers of being a gang member."
○ 3. "Barry should have passed the stage of needing to belong to a gang by now. it is unusual for an adolescent to willingly challenge the authority of the police."
○ 4. "Barry is at the age when it is most important for him to be accepted by his friends. He feels as though he belongs and is an important member of his group."

46 Of the following psychosocial needs, the one Barry is most likely trying to meet by his wanting to be with a group of his peers is
○ 1. identity.
○ 2. intimacy.
○ 3. integrity.
○ 4. generativity.

47 If Barry is typical of many persons using amphetamines, he is very likely also to start abusing
○ 1. heroin.
○ 2. alcohol.

O 3. cocaine.
O 4. barbiturates.

Steven Biggs is a 14-year-old student who has an intradermal (Mantoux) test for tuberculosis.

48 Two days after Steven receives the intradermal test in his left forearm, his mother telephones saying that Steven's forearm is red and swollen. The nurse should instruct Ms. Biggs to
O 1. send Steven to bed for a few days.
O 2. bring Steven to the clinic for further examination.
O 3. call again in 48 hours if Steven's arm remains swollen and red.
O 4. wrap Steven's arm in a warm, moist towel covered with plastic.

49 It is determined that Steven has pulmonary tuberculosis. Long-term therapy with isoniazid (INH) and para-aminosalicylic acid (PAS) is prescribed for him. The nurse should explain to Steven that 2 drugs in combination are used in his therapy to help prevent
O 1. tolerance to drug therapy.
O 2. allergic reactions to drug therapy.
O 3. adverse systemic reactions to drug therapy.
O 4. resistance of the causative organisms to drug therapy.

50 Which of the following suggestions would best ensure that Steven will take his medication as prescribed?
O 1. Suggest that the patient's parents administer the medications to him as prescribed.
O 2. Suggest that the patient's school nurse administer the medications to him every day.
O 3. Suggest that the patient stop at the clinic's office daily to receive the medications.
O 4. Suggest that the patient develop his own system for remembering to take his medications as prescribed.

51 The nurse reviews good oral hygiene measures with Steven when he says he dreads developing caries (cavities). In addition to brushing the teeth, daily oral hygiene should certainly include
O 1. chewing a disclosure dye.
O 2. flossing between the teeth.
O 3. using an antiseptic mouthwash.
O 4. brushing with soda bicarbonate.

Kevin Clancy is a 14-year-old student who has developed acne vulgaris on his face, back, and shoulders.

52 Tetracycline hydrochloride is prescribed for Kevin. The nurse should teach Kevin that he should wait at least an hour or two after taking the medication before he eats or drinks

    ○ 1. meat and poultry.
    ○ 2. milk and milk products.
    ○ 3. citrus fruits and vegetables.
    ○ 4. whole-grain breads and cereals.

53 The nurse should teach Kevin that the best way to help prevent the formation of blackheads is to
    ○ 1. eat nutritious meals.
    ○ 2. avoid direct sunlight.
    ○ 3. take frequent showers.
    ○ 4. maintain a high fluid intake.

54 The nurse should caution Kevin *not* to squeeze the pimples and blackheads because doing so is most likely to result in
    ○ 1. spreading the infection.
    ○ 2. injuring nerves in the skin.
    ○ 3. interfering with lymph drainage.
    ○ 4. destroying subcutaneous tissues.

55 Kevin feels that he is unattractive to girls and fears that his acne will never be better. Which of the following comments represents the most appropriate form of encouragement for Kevin?
    ○ 1. "It really does not matter what your skin looks like. After all, beauty is only skin deep."
    ○ 2. "Your acne will eventually subside as you get older. But you may have to avoid certain foods for now."
    ○ 3. "This is a most difficult time for you. You made a good choice when you decided to let us help you."
    ○ 4. "Your feelings are understandable. But if your acne does not clear up, you can consider cosmetic surgery to restore your handsome looks."

56 If Kevin's health record indicates he has *not* had a booster immunization recently to protect him from the conditions given below, he should be encouraged to receive one so that he will be further protected from
    ○ 1. tetanus.
    ○ 2. small pox.
    ○ 3. whooping cough.
    ○ 4. rubella (German measles).

Sixteen-year-old Ann Mills has learned that she has been exposed to gonorrhea. She visits the clinic for diagnosis and treatment.

57 The nurse can best assist with a common diagnostic measure when Ann learns of her exposure to gonorrhea by helping to
    ○ 1. collect a specimen of the person's blood.
    ○ 2. test the person's urine for the presence of pus.
    ○ 3. collect a specimen of the person's vaginal discharge.
    ○ 4. determine when the person had her last menstrual period.

58 Ann is diagnosed as having penicillin-resistant type of gonorrhea, and erythromycin (Erythrocin) is prescribed for her. The nurse should teach Ann to report side-effects of the medication, two common ones being
○ 1. skin rash and itching.
○ 2. vomiting and diarrhea.
○ 3. dizziness and headaches.
○ 4. deafness and an elevated temperature.

59 Before leaving the clinic, Ann asks the nurse, "When can I be certain that I am no longer infectious?" The nurse should explain that Ann will be considered noninfectious when
○ 1. her vaginal discharge has stopped.
○ 2. her next menstrual period is free of discomfort.
○ 3. she has two negative follow-up examinations after completing therapy.
○ 4. she has received drug therapy for at least 24 hours without untoward side-effects.

Larry Nelson is a 16-year-old who has come to the clinic because he thinks he may have contracted syphilis several months ago.

60 The nurse obtains a health history from Larry. She should most definitely report her findings when Larry describes the most common early symptom of syphilis, which is
○ 1. a swollen penis.
○ 2. a nocturnal emission.
○ 3. an ulcerated glans penis.
○ 4. a burning sensation when urinating.

61 A common diagnostic examination is used to establish Larry's disease. The nurse should anticipate that her most likely role while assisting in the diagnostic procedure is to help with
○ 1. positioning the person for spinal fluid collection.
○ 2. obtaining a blood specimen for serological study.
○ 3. collecting a urine specimen for microscopic analysis.
○ 4. sending a seminal fluid specimen to the laboratory for a sensitivity examination.

62 Larry is found to have syphilis, and penicillin is started. The nurse should instruct Larry to report any symptoms of an allergic reaction to penicillin promptly, one common symptom being
○ 1. a skin rash.
○ 2. a loss of hair.
○ 3. blurred vision.
○ 4. a poor appetite.

Seventeen-year-old Heather Miller has herpes genitalis (herpesvirus type II).

63 The appearance of Heather's initial lesions of genital herpes will most
nearly resemble a
- O 1. keloid.
- O 2. fissure.
- O 3. fever blister.
- O 4. ulcerated macule.

64 Heather is urged to continue with long-term, follow-up care because
research recently suggests that there may be an association between
genital herpes and the eventual development of
- O 1. cervical cancer.
- O 2. uterine fibroids.
- O 3. chronic vaginitis.
- O 4. premature menopause.

65 The nurse reviews programs designed to help prevent sexually
transmitted (venereal) diseases among teenagers. She learns that most
authorities believe that all of the following programs may be helpful.
However, the one believed to be best to help stem the rising incidence
of sexually transmitted diseases among teenagers is
- O 1. screening programs for adolescents that test for the presence of
sexually transmitted diseases.
- O 2. public clinics that treat and counsel, free of charge, adolescents
with sexually transmitted diseases.
- O 3. educational programs for adolescents that deal with the spread
and treatment of sexually transmitted diseases.
- O 4. specialty programs that prepare selected health personnel for
dealing with sexually transmitted diseases among adolescents.

Emma Watson has anorexia nervosa.

66 The nurse becomes aware of a very common manifestation of Emma's
health problem when, contrary to evidence, Emma describes herself as
being
- O 1. overweight.
- O 2. underprivileged.
- O 3. an over-achiever.
- O 4. unable to conceive.

67 Emma is admitted to a hospital for therapy. If Emma is allowed to
continue without treatment, she is likely to develop bulimia, a condition
characterized by the binge–purge syndrome. Emma says to the nurse,
"Only a fool would force herself to vomit!" What technique other than
forcing vomiting is Emma likely to use to avoid gaining weight after
overeating if she becomes bulimic?
- O 1. Using illegal drugs
- O 2. Going on a fad-type diet
- O 3. Taking laxatives frequently

    ○ 4. Exercising to the point of exhaustion

68 The nurse is aware that suicide is the third most common cause of death among teenagers and young adults. In view of this knowledge, which of the following techniques is particularly important for the nurse to use when interviewing the adolescents for whom she is caring?
    ○ 1. Listening to what the patients are saying
    ○ 2. Verifying the patients' comments with family members
    ○ 3. Using a sense of humor when interviewing the patients
    ○ 4. Keeping careful records of conversations with the patients

A Nurse Helps in the Care of Well and Ill Children Who Attend a Clinic in a County Health Center.

Ms. Scott brings 5-month-old Timmy to the clinic because the skin on the infant's face and neck is inflamed and covered with tiny vesicle-type lesions. Timmy has acute infantile eczema (atopic dermatitis).

69 When the vesicles on Timmy's skin break, they typically release a fluid containing
    ○ 1. pus.
    ○ 2. blood.
    ○ 3. lymph.
    ○ 4. serum.

70 A very probable cause of Timmy's skin condition is thought to be
    ○ 1. poor nutrition.
    ○ 2. a premature birth.
    ○ 3. an allergic reaction.
    ○ 4. a hormone imbalance.

71 The nurse should be prepared to give Timmy's mother suggestions concerning care measures that will help relieve Timmy's
    ○ 1. nausea.
    ○ 2. vomiting.
    ○ 3. severe itching.
    ○ 4. prolonged drowsiness.

72 Ms. Scott is instructed to use hydrocortisone ointment on Timmy's skin lesions. On a subsequent visit, the nurse judges that the ointment has accomplished its intended purpose for Timmy when she notes that
    ○ 1. weeping of the infant's skin has subsided.
    ○ 2. there is no spread in the infant's skin disease.
    ○ 3. inflammation of the infant's skin has decreased.
    ○ 4. there has been an increase in the infant's white blood cell count.

73 Timmy's mother is advised to use colloid baths for Timmy. A typical colloid bath consists of tepid water to which has been added

○ 1. cornstarch or baking soda.
○ 2. a little mineral, olive, or bath oil.
○ 3. unperfumed, liquid glycerine soap.
○ 4. salt to make a normal saline solution.

74 In terms of development, which of the following skills would Timmy normally be *unable* to demonstrate at his age (5 months)?
○ 1. The infant understands his name.
○ 2. The infant sits up without support.
○ 3. The infant reaches out to touch a rattle.
○ 4. The infant rolls from his abdomen to his back.

Ms. Smith brings 6-month-old Ricky, who is developing and growing normally, to the clinic because he has an elevated temperature and is restless and irritable. Ricky has otitis media.

75 The nurse weighs Ricky. This information is most probably to be used to help
○ 1. determine the nutritional needs of the infant.
○ 2. determine dosages for drugs to be prescribed for the infant.
○ 3. calculate whether the infant needs to receive parenteral fluids.
○ 4. calculate whether the infant is suffering from an electrolyte imbalance.

76 Ricky would most likely indicate he has pain in his ear by
○ 1. lying on his unaffected ear.
○ 2. pulling on his unaffected ear.
○ 3. rolling his head from side to side.
○ 4. tipping his head toward the affected ear.

77 Phenylephrine hydrochloride (Neo-Synephrine) nosedrops are prescribed for Ricky. The desired action in this situation is based primarily on the drug's ability to
○ 1. liquify sticky nasal secretions.
○ 2. constrict superficial blood vessels.
○ 3. increase blood circulation in the affected ear.
○ 4. decrease the spread of organisms from the nasal passages.

78 When instilling nosedrops, it is best for the nurse to position Ricky by
○ 1. having the child lie flat on his back.
○ 2. propping the child in the nurse's arm.
○ 3. tilting the child's head over a rolled pillow.
○ 4. placing the child in alternate side-lying positions.

79 If pressure on Ricky's eardrum is unrelieved by conservative measures, the surgical procedure usually used is
○ 1. a tonsillectomy.
○ 2. a myringotomy.
○ 3. a mastoidectomy.
○ 4. an adenoidectomy.

Ms. Zubak brings her 16-month-old son, Gary, to the clinic for a routine check-up.

80 Ms. Zubak says she is having problems with bowel training Gary and asks the nurse what to do. He uses his potty when placed on it early enough, but most often he has a bowel movement before he indicates in any way that he needs to have one. The nurse should base her response to the mother on knowledge that the child most probably

  O 1. is defying his mother's efforts to train him.

  O 2. has regressed temporarily because of feeling afraid.

  O 3. has more peristaltic activity than most children his age.

  O 4. is insufficiently mature to postpone the desire to defecate.

81 Ms. Zubak and the nurse discuss Gary's playtime activities. Which of the following toys should Ms. Zubak be taught are *unsuitable* for Gary?

  O 1. Beach balls

  O 2. Playing cards

  O 3. Colored marbles

  O 4. Plasticized books

Mr. Morris brings his daughter Liza to the clinic for her 18-month check-up. While undressing Liza, the nurse notes several bruises on Liza's back and legs. Mr. Morris explains that Liza has fallen out of her high chair and says his wife has been too ill to watch Liza closely.

82 If the nurse suspects that Liza is a battered child, it would be best for the nurse to

  O 1. report her suspicions to the local police department.

  O 2. explain her findings to the nurse-in-charge responsible for Liza's care.

  O 3. teach the father techniques to improve the safety of the child in the home.

  O 4. call a community social agency that can locate a suitable foster home for Liza.

83 Of the following characteristics in relation to Liza's bruises, the one that should lead the nurse to suspect that Liza is battered is when the bruises on her body are

  O 1. deep purple in color.

  O 2. very painful to touch.

  O 3. in various stages of healing.

  O 4. located on the lower half of the body.

84 If Liza has been battered, her behavior toward the nurse can be expected to be characterized by feelings of

  O 1. distrust.

  O 2. affection.

  O 3. confidence.

○ 4. combativeness.

85 Mr. Morris admits he and his wife have struck Liza when ". . . Liza was naughty and had it coming." He admits he needs help. The nurse should recommend an organization that offers counseling and emotional support to those who abuse children, the name of which is
○ 1. The Salvation Army.
○ 2. Parents Anonymous.
○ 3. Children's Aid Society.
○ 4. The American Red Cross.

86 Which of the following statements is most descriptive of parents like Mr. and Ms. Morris who abuse their children?
○ 1. One or both parents were abused as children.
○ 2. The parents are from a low socioeconomic group.
○ 3. The parents are from an ethnic minority culture.
○ 4. One or both parents batter the other or each other.

87 Liza is to have a booster dose of TOPV, a pharmaceutical agent that provides protection from
○ 1. tuberculosis.
○ 2. poliomyelitis.
○ 3. typhoid fever.
○ 4. infectious hepatitis.

Three-year-old Keri Nolting stops breathing in the clinic. The nurse determines that Keri requires cardiopulmonary resuscitation (CPR).

88 The nurse's first course of action when she prepares to give Keri CPR is to
○ 1. see that the child's airway is open.
○ 2. give the child a few quick whiffs of oxygen.
○ 3. deliver a precordial thump to the child's sternum.
○ 4. slap the child's back between the shoulder blades once or twice.

89 If the nurse uses the following techniques while administering CPR to Keri, which one is in *error?*
○ 1. The nurse uses 2 fingers of one hand to compress the sternum.
○ 2. The nurse applies pressure on the midsternum area.
○ 3. The nurse depresses the sternum about 1 to 1½ inches (2½ to 3¾ cm) with each compression.
○ 4. The nurse compresses the sternum at a rate of 90 compressions a minute.

90 At first, while the nurse administers CPR, Keri's chest rises and falls with each artificial respiration. But then the rising and falling of the chest stops. The most likely reason for this cessation during ventilation is that the
○ 1. child's airway is blocked.
○ 2. child is about to breathe spontaneously.

○ 3. child is beyond the point of being able to be revived.
○ 4. nurse's puffs of air into the child's mouth are not sufficiently forceful.

Six-year-old Cory Mock, who has infantile autism, visits the clinic with his parents.

91 Of the following behaviors, the one Cory is most likely to demonstrate is
○ 1. demanding attention almost constantly.
○ 2. crying loudly when his parents leave.
○ 3. resisting any efforts to touch him.
○ 4. speaking only to other children, not to adults.

92 Hospitalization is required for Cory. While he is hospitalized, it would be best to provide an environment for him that includes having
○ 1. a variety of sensory stimuli.
○ 2. his own favorite toys from home.
○ 3. a room that is well-ventilated but warm.
○ 4. a room to share with children near his age.

Mr. and Ms. Walter bring their son Barton to the clinic. Barton has phenylketonuria (PKU).

93 Barton's illness is caused by an inherited error of metabolism which, if untreated, will result in
○ 1. hepatic coma.
○ 2. renal shutdown.
○ 3. pernicious anemia.
○ 4. mental retardation.

94 Barton was found to have PKU when he was screened for the disorder a few days after his birth. The most commonly used screening test for PKU requires a specimen of
○ 1. blood.
○ 2. sputum.
○ 3. spinal fluid.
○ 4. stomach contents.

Nine-year-old Jackie Strong, who has hemophilia, visits the clinic regularly.

95 A teaching program for Jackie and his parents should include explaining that Jackie should avoid medications containing
○ 1. aspirin.
○ 2. caffeine.
○ 3. barbiturates.
○ 4. sodium bicarbonate.

96   The manner in which hemophilia is typically transmitted from parent to offspring is from
   O   1.   father to son.
   O   2.   mother to son.
   O   3.   father to daughter.
   O   4.   mother to daughter.

Betty Boylan comes to the clinic because of a flare-up of ulcerative colitis.

97   The nurse should expect that the nature of Betty's stools will typically be
   O   1.   well-formed.
   O   2.   filled with mucus.
   O   3.   chalk-white in color.
   O   4.   curd-like with balls of feces.

98   Several factors are believed to play a role in the cause of ulcerative colitis. The one that certainly should serve as a key guideline for the nurse when giving Betty care is the factor of
   O   1.   an allergy.
   O   2.   an infection.
   O   3.   emotional stress.
   O   4.   an autoimmunity disorder.

The remaining items in this situation are individual items related to the care of children attending the clinic.

99   Ms. Snead brings her 1-month-old infant to the clinic. She tells the nurse interviewing her that the baby sleeps with the Sneads because they cannot afford a crib. It would be best for the nurse to base a response to this information on knowledge that it is *not* recommended having an infant sleep with parents because the infant
   O   1.   may smother if the parents accidentally roll onto him.
   O   2.   will interfere with normal sexual activities of the parents.
   O   3.   will be unable to sleep well enough for normal physiological development.
   O   4.   may become too emotionally dependent upon the parents for normal psychological development.

100   Ms. Fred tells the nurse that her 6-month-old son, Douglas, who is well, refuses to eat strained carrots and pushes the carrots out of his mouth. She asks the nurse what to do. The nurse should explain that Ms. Fred's best course of action is to
   O   1.   avoid carrots in the infant's diet because he is probably allergic to them.
   O   2.   mix the carrots with food the infant likes and offer them no oftener than once a week.

○ 3. try to force carrots for a few days because the infant will learn to like them.

○ 4. eliminate carrots from the infant's diet and offer them again at a later date.

101 Three-year-old Sara Gandy has ingested a poisonous substance. The nurse should understand that inducing Sara to vomit is *contraindicated* if Sara has

○ 1. eaten aspirin.

○ 2. drunk alcohol.

○ 3. drunk kerosene.

○ 4. eaten poisonous mushrooms.

102 Ms. Wherry has brought Sophie, her 3-month-old infant, to the clinic. She tells the nurse that she gave the baby a piece of banana but, she says, "Sophie spit it out, just like that!" The nurse should explain to the mother that the infant's behavior demonstrates that the infant most probably

○ 1. is allergic to bananas.

○ 2. is nursing excessively.

○ 3. does not like the taste of bananas.

○ 4. does not appear ready to take solid foods.

103 Ms. Dowd says she uses an infant seat in her car for her 4-month-old infant. Before securing the car's seat belt around the infant seat, how should the seat be placed on the car seat for greatest safety to the infant?

○ 1. The infant seat should be facing forward so that the infant will be facing forward while the car is in motion.

○ 2. The infant seat should be placed backward so that the infant will be facing backward while the car is in motion.

○ 3. The infant seat should be placed sideways on the car seat with the infant facing the driver.

○ 4. The infant seat should be placed sideways on the car seat with the infant facing away from the driver.

104 Ms. Rudder calls the clinic to explain that her 4-year-old son has lodged a small stone in his ear canal. The nurse is correct when she instructs the mother to

○ 1. place oily drops in the child's ear.

○ 2. flush the stone from the child's ear with alcohol.

○ 3. remove the stone from the child's ear with tweezers.

○ 4. bring the child to the clinic for removal of the stone.

105 Ms. Letter brings Barbara, who has celiac disease, to the clinic for follow-up care. The nurse has helped teach the mother about a diet for Barbara that should be free of

○ 1. gluten.

○ 2. sodium.

○ 3. lactose.

○ 4. additives.

106 Five-year-old Ben Jordan, who has mononucleosis, is being cared for at home. The nurse should suggest appropriate diversions his mother could offer him while he is feverish. One good example is
○ 1. playing by himself in his sandbox.
○ 2. riding his tricycle for brief periods.
○ 3. swimming in a cool, well-shaded pool.
○ 4. watching his favorite television program.

107 Ms. Hector brings 6-year-old Chris to the clinic for an annual check-up. As the child undresses, the nurse and mother notice that Chris's underpants are wet. The embarrassed mother says, "These accidents seem to happen. I've tried everything I know to get him to be more careful. I just don't know what to do anymore." Which of the following actions by the nurse is best to handle this problem?
○ 1. Report the mother's concern to the nurse-in-charge.
○ 2. Reassure the mother that the child will outgrow the problem.
○ 3. Explain to the child the importance of cleanliness and proper toilet habits.
○ 4. Encourage the mother to enroll in classes on how to deal with parenting problems.

108 Lively 10-year-old Bud Strong has Legg-Calvé-Perthes' disease (coxa plana) in his right hip. He attends the clinic after recently being discharged from a hospital. The nurse should most certainly caution Bud to *avoid* activities that would result in
○ 1. moving the affected hip.
○ 2. sitting for long periods of time.
○ 3. placing weight on the affected hip.
○ 4. putting stress on the unaffected hip.

109 Joni Talor is to receive an intravenous medication through an intravenous line. A registered nurse asks you, a practical nurse, to add the medication while she attends to a child in the next room. In this situation, it is best for the practical nurse to
○ 1. check the physician's order carefully before giving the medication.
○ 2. document the registered nurse's request before giving the medication.
○ 3. give the medication but ask the registered nurse to watch you while you give it.
○ 4. explain to the registered nurse that a practical nurse is not permitted to give a medication intravenously.

110 Mr. and Ms. Peterson bring their baby, who has Down's syndrome, to the clinic. The nurse can be most helpful to parents who are distraught about what to do with their infant by saying,
○ 1. "You both seem to have a lot of love that you should share with your baby."

○ 2. "If I were you, I would seriously consider placing your baby in an institution instead of keeping him at home."

○ 3. "I know of a group of parents who meet regularly to discuss issues associated with Down's syndrome children."

○ 4. "Studies have shown that children with Down's syndrome adjust better in our society when they live with their natural parents at home."

111 Joan Drew has structural scoliosis. Which of the following orthopedic devices should the nurse anticipate using in Joan's care?

○ 1. A plaster cast

○ 2. A pelvic girdle

○ 3. An abduction bar

○ 4. A Milwaukee brace

112 Glenn George visits the clinic after having had the mumps. Which of the following types of immunity does Glenn have?

○ 1. A naturally acquired active immunity

○ 2. A naturally acquired passive immunity

○ 3. An artificially acquired active immunity

○ 4. An artificially acquired passive immunity

113 Agnes Down is brought to the clinic after a fall. X-ray examinations show a greenstick fracture of the humerus. This type of fracture means that bone fragments have

○ 1. been crushed.

○ 2. torn muscle tissues.

○ 3. penetrated the skin.

○ 4. remained partially joined.

114 Sixteen-month-old Zoe Arvekian is being observed and treated at the clinic for rickets. The vitamin that has been lacking or deficient in the child's diet is vitamin

○ 1. A.

○ 2. B_{12}.

○ 3. C.

○ 4. D.

115 The Bergers' child has Tay-Sachs disease. The nurse correctly plans that the parents will need help and emotional support because the organ damaged by this disease is the child's

○ 1. lungs.

○ 2. heart.

○ 3. brain.

○ 4. kidneys.

116 Laurie Foster comes to the clinic because of scalp ringworm (tinea capitis). Her scalp condition is an infection caused by a

○ 1. virus.

○ 2. fungus.
○ 3. rickettsia.
○ 4. staphylococcus.

117 Tony Gorski's physical condition is to be evaluated before he starts a strenuous competitive swimming program. The nurse obtains his blood pressure. The approximate time in life when a youngster's blood pressure reaches normal adult level is during
○ 1. middle childhood, at about 6 to 8 years of age.
○ 2. late childhood, at about 9 to 10 years of age.
○ 3. early adolescence, at about 11 to 13 years of age.
○ 4. late adolescence, at about 16 to 18 years of age.

118 Lawrence Baxter is a clinic patient who has pinworms. Pinworms are most often spread by children who
○ 1. share their bed with a pet.
○ 2. play in contaminated water.
○ 3. tend to eat nonfood substances.
○ 4. are careless about toilet hygiene.

The Remaining Items are Miscellaneous Items Dealing with the Nursing Care of Children.

119 A nurse is assisting with the care of a child receiving oxygen by cannula. In what way, if any, does administering oxygen by cannula to a child differ from the way it is normally administered to an adult?
○ 1. The oxygen need not be humidified before administering it to a child; it must be humidified for an adult.
○ 2. The cannula for a child has only one nasal prong; an adult's cannula has two nasal prongs.
○ 3. The amount of oxygen administered to a child by cannula should be less than the amount administered to an adult.
○ 4. The techniques used for administering oxygen by cannula to a child are essentially the same as those used for an adult.

120 A common concern of many health caretakers who are working to control communicable diseases is a tendency of the public to
○ 1. think that most communicable diseases are not preventable.
○ 2. believe that communicable diseases become less infectious with time.
○ 3. neglect having available immunization for communicable diseases.
○ 4. refuse antibiotics for communicable diseases because of possible allergic reactions.

Correct Answers and Rationales

Two numbers appear in parentheses following each rationale. The first number identifies the textbook listed in the references, page 649, and the second number identifies the page(s) in the textbook in which the correct answer can be verified. Occasionally, two textbooks are given for verification.

The Nursing Care of School-Aged Children

Caring for a child with appendicitis

1 4. Symptoms of appendicitis in the young child are similar to those of other illnesses, such as pneumonia. The child is observed carefully over a period of hours to confirm the diagnosis of appendicitis, and to prevent unnecessary surgery, which could be life-threatening when the child is ill with something other than appendicitis. (3:236)

2 1. Laxatives are *not* given to a person who is suspected of having appendicitis because their use could cause the appendix to rupture. Antiemetics, antibiotics, and analgesics sometimes may be used in the care of a patient with appendicitis. (3:236)

3 3. In addition to abdominal pain, a person with a ruptured appendix has a rigid, boardlike abdomen, due to the body's efforts to guard or protect a diseased area. Fever tends to be high in children with appendicitis. (12:717)

4 1. The lumen of the appendix tends to become obstructed when appendicitis develops. The obstruction may be due to swelling following a generalized infection, or a fecal mass may have caused the obstruction. Occasionally, pinworms may cause an obstruction. According to the health history described for the child in this item, a history of having had pinworms recently is a likely predisposing factor in the child's having appendicitis. (3:236)

5 1. Children at the age of about 5½ years or even less tend to become interested in their genitals. It is a normal curiosity for the age and should not present cause for concern. However, children should be taught that certain activities are not appropriate when carried out in public; masturbation is an example. The normal interest in genitals has not been found to lead to sexual promiscuity. (3:181)

Caring for a child with rheumatic fever

6 2. Although the pathology of rheumatic fever is not clearly understood, the disease has a tendency to follow a recent infection with Group A beta-hemolytic streptococci. A hereditary factor has also been demonstrated. Two other illnesses caused by the same type of streptococcus are scarlet fever and erysipelas; either of them may also precede rheumatic fever. These findings indicate the importance of seeking health care promptly when children are ill with infections that predispose to rheumatic fever. The illness is most frequently seen in school-aged children.   (3:243–244)

7   1.   During the acute phase of rheumatic fever, the child should have complete rest. Therefore, nursing care should include such measures as turning, feeding, and bathing the patient. Bathroom privileges are not permitted. Observing these restrictions helps provide the heart with maximum rest.   (3:246)

8   3.   Aspirin is used in the treatment of rheumatic fever primarily to reduce pain and tenderness in the joints, joint inflammation, and fever. The drug usually provides remarkable relief. If carditis is present, corticosteroids frequently are added to the patient's drug therapy, as well as digitalis if heart failure threatens. Penicillin is used to combat infection.   (3:245)

9   2.   Two desired actions of digitalis are to slow and to strengthen the heartbeat. The drug does not dilate arteries, prevent damage to heart valves, or reduce the pH of the blood.   (14:83)

10   1.   Before giving digitalis, the nurse must count the patient's pulse rate. Because normal pulse rates vary, depending on the age of the person, the nurse should consult the patient's record for previous pulse rates. If the pulse is much lower than previous recordings, the nurse should consult with the nurse-in-charge, who will then decide whether to give the medication. In adults, it is quite typical not to give digitalis when a patient's pulse rate is 60 beats per minute or less.   (14:83)

11   3.   Chorea that sometimes occurs with rheumatic fever is characterized by purposeless, jerky, uncoordinated movements, and general muscle weakness. Movements sometimes are so exaggerated in nature that the bed siderails must be protected with padding to protect the patient from harm. Chorea (Sydenham's chorea, St. Vitus' dance) is not commonly seen when the patient with rheumatic fever has polyarthritis, but carditis is likely to be present. Emotional instability is also often present when the patient has chorea.   (3:244)

12   4.   It is important to emphasize what the long-term patient can do rather than what she cannot do. This helps to prevent the patient from becoming discouraged and overdependent. The recovering patient is ordinarily not restricted for indefinite periods. Most chronic disabilities occur when repeated attacks of rheumatic fever occur.   (3:246)

Caring for a child with diabetes mellitus

13   4.   Urine specimens are studied when establishing a diagnosis of diabetes mellitus. If the patient is in a diabetic coma, glucose and acetone would be expected to be present in the urine. The body turns to fats and proteins as a source of energy in diabetes (sugar has been lost as a source of energy). These nutrients break down into ketones; when too many are present, acidosis will follow. Other diagnostic tools include fasting blood sugar tests, postprandial blood sugar tests, and the glucose tolerance test. Sucrose (table sugar) would not be found in the blood or urine. Ammonia and blood in the urine are not characteristic findings of diabetes. (3:247; 12:781)

14 2. Regular insulin is administered to a patient in diabetic coma because insulin acts quickly to reduce the blood sugar level. Tolbutamide (Orinase) would not be effective in this situation because it functions to stimulate the pancreas to secrete insulin and the pancreas is unable to produce insulin in the child with insulin dependent diabetes. Glucagon is used to treat insulin shock and vasopressin tannate (Pitressin Tannate) is used to treat diabetes insipidus. (3:247)

15 3. Regular insulin is sometimes administered in combination with long-lasting insulins, such as isophane insulin suspension (NPH insulin) and insulin zinc suspension (Lente Insulin and Lente Iletin) to provide both immediate as well as long-lasting effects. Regular insulin takes effect within ½ to 1 hour after injection, peaks in 2 to 6 hours, and lasts up to 8 hours. Insulin zinc suspension and isophane insulin suspension peak in 7 to 12 hours and their action lasts for 24 to 30 hours. (3:248)

16 1. A sulfonylurea compound, such as tolbutamide (Orinase), acts to stimulate the pancreas to produce insulin. Because the person with insulin dependent diabetes mellitus, or IDDM (once called juvenile or youth onset diabetes, brittle diabetes, or severe diabetes) is unable to produce insulin, he must receive the insulin replacement. In non-insulin dependent diabetes mellitus, or NIDDM (once called adult-onset diabetes, mild diabetes, or stable diabetes), the pancreas is still able to produce some insulin and tolbutamide than may be used successfully to stimulate the production of sufficient insulin to meet the patient's needs. (12:778–779)

17 4. Insulin is a protein. If taken orally, it will be destroyed in the stomach and lose its value to the body. (3:247; 12:778)

18 4. There is at present no cure for diabetes. It is a life-long disease that requires continuous monitoring. But with good health care and an acceptance of the disease and its ramifications, the lives of diabetics can be comfortable, rich, and fulfilling. It is no help to a dejected parent when told his son could have a worse illness than diabetes, nor is it fair to hold out hopes of a cure when none is presently in sight. (3:247)

19 2. Between the ages of about 6 and 12 years, the child tries to meet his psychosocial need for developing industry. If his need is not met, the child generally feels inadequate and inferior. Developing autonomy is a psychosocial need for the toddler, developing initiative is a need for the preschooler, and developing identity is a need for the adolescent. This theory concerning psychosocial development has been advanced by the psycho-analyst, Erik Erikson.   (17:74)

20 2.   Rotating the injection sites for insulin administration is an important measure to help prevent tissue inflammation and damage. Sites commonly used for insulin injection include the upper arms, thighs, abdomen, back, and buttocks. It is recommended that no two injections of insulin be closer than 1 inch to each other within a 2-week period. The needle for inject-ing insulin is ordinarily held at a 90-degree angle for insulin ad-ministration.   (3:250-251; 9:576-577)

21 2.   Common symptoms of an insulin reaction include hunger pangs, blurred vision, dizziness, weakness, excessive perspiration, and palpita-tions. Individual persons learn to recognize still other symptoms, such as "feeling strange," that typically for them are signs of too much insulin. Any unusual sensation should alert a diabetic to consider the possibility of hypoglycemia. Nausea and vomiting, chest pain, fatigue, drowsiness, and hot flashes are more likely to indicate that the patient needs additional, not less, insulin.   (3:247; 12:780)

22 2.   Activity requires glucose for energy. Therefore, increasing activity uses up glucose and the body then requires less-than-usual amounts of insulin. Eating too much, having an infection, and experiencing emotional stress are situations in which the patient tends to require more, not less, insulin.   (3:251)

23 2.   The goal of a special diet for a diabetic is to keep the urine free, or almost free, of glucose. The presence of glucose in the urine should be reported because it possibly will be necessary to alter the patient's diet, his insulin dosage, or both. Monitors that measure the blood glucose level are used by many patients. These instruments give a more accurate reading of glucose levels than can be determined with urine examinations. However, many persons with diabetes still rely on urine samplings.   (3:250)

24 1.   A rapidly acting source of glucose, such as hard candy, sugar, or orange juice, should be taken by the diabetic in insulin shock to counteract excessive amounts of insulin in the blood. A product on the market that also acts quickly to an insulin reaction is Glucagon. It is administered subcutaneously and acts quickly to relieve hypoglycemia. An oral prepara-tion of glucose jelly is also available.   (12:780-781; 14:130)

Caring for a child with second- and third-degree burns

25 2.   Protective, or reverse, isolation techniques are used when caring for a child with severe burns because the child is very susceptible to infection. This type of isolation is used to help prevent a highly susceptible person from acquiring an infection. A gown, mask, and cap are worn by staff and visitors when in the room of a patient on protective isolation. Other types of isolation have as their primary goal preventing a patient's organisms from being spread to others.   (3:166; 12:594; 9:298, 301)

26 2.   Respiratory distress from a blocked airway may become a problem following burns. Therefore, a tracheostomy set should be kept in readiness in the patient's room. An airway should also be readily available.   (3:166; 12:523–524)

27 3.   A burn victim requires very careful monitoring of intravenous therapy and a record of all intake and output. Burn victims are subject to shock early in their care as a result of excess fluid loss. To help prevent shock, strict monitoring is required. This monitoring is among the nurse's most important responsibilities when helping with the care of a burn victim.   (3:167)

28 4.   The primary reason for using a cradle on the bed of a burn victim is to keep linens off the burn sites. A cradle is ineffective for promoting drainage, encouraging movement in bed, or preventing rolling over onto burn sites.   (3:166)

29 1.   Wearing antiembolism stockings is an ineffective measure for helping to prevent footdrop. The stockings are used to support veins and prevent venous congestion in the legs. Using a footboard is recommended most often to prevent footdrop. Having the patient wear ankle-high tennis shoes helps prevent footdrop, but the shoes must be removed regularly to give foot care and to change stockings. Having the patient rest his feet against a firm pillow is satisfactory on a temporary basis, but this measure should not be used for long periods because support to the feet usually is not sufficiently adequate to prevent footdrop.   (9:321)

30 3.   A homograft, that is, skin taken from one person and grafted to the burn site of another person, is done primarily to help prevent fluid loss from the burn site. These grafts also help protect the burn sites from infection.   (12:596)

31 4.   There may be considerable pain associated with severe burns, and often a narcotic is used. Either meperidine hydrochloride (Demerol) or morphine sulfate may be prescribed.   (12:594; 14:58–59)

32 1.   Cheese cubes and nuts have high protein content. A diet rich in protein is essential for the body to rebuild tissue destroyed by burns. Apples, potato chips, popcorn, pretzels, jello, and jelly beans contain little or no protein.   (16:36, 331)

33 1.   Stress ulcers, often called Curling's ulcers, frequently occur in the stomach or duodenum as a complication of burns. Symptoms resemble those of a peptic ulcer, but they may be vague. If the ulcer bleeds, the patient's stools become black and tarry and have a foul odor. Post-burn shock occurs early when body fluids fill burn areas; this phenomenon leads to marked dehydration and shock. Electrolyte imbalances are more common early after a burn but will not produce changes in the patient's stools. After the initial phase when dehydration and shock are likely to occur, the patient typically experiences a phase in which fluid imbalance occurs with diuresis (excessive urinary output) or with hypervolemia (increase in normal blood volume). Hypervolemia may become sufficiently severe to cause pulmonary edema. (3:167)

34 4. Of the diversional activities described in this item, a child of 8 years is likely to enjoy most playing a competitive game, such as a card game, with the nurse. Another diversion that would be appropriate for this child is having him pretend to be the hero of his favorite television program. (3:226–227)

Caring for a child with juvenile rheumatoid arthritis

35 2. The knees should be placed in a normal anatomical position to help prevent contractures. Supporting the knees with just a slight amount of flexion prevents them from falling into a state of hyperextension, or locked knees. Overflexing the knees is likely to lead to contractures that eventually would make walking very difficult. (9:335)

36 4. After the acute phase subsides, a child with rheumatoid arthritis should resume activity gradually. Range-of-motion exercises should be performed with each joint to prevent disuse syndrome. (3:343)

37 2. Aspirin has 4 major therapeutic uses: to reduce inflammation, to lower body temperature, to decrease blood clotting time, and to relieve discomfort. It is the drug of choice for patients with rheumatoid arthritis because it relieves inflammation while reducing discomfort. Aspirin has no direct role in the relaxation of muscles. (3:343; 14:66–67)

Caring for a child with a brain tumor

38 1. Signs of increased intracranial pressure include papilledema, projectile vomiting, and headaches. Visual disturbances often occur when papilledema is present. Any signs of visual disturbance should be reported promptly. Additional signs of increased intracranial pressure include muscle weakness, convulsions, changes in vital signs, and drowsiness. Hunger, thirst, and having unusual sensations in the throat are unrelated to increased intracranial pressure. (12:619)

39 1. Diuretic drugs that are often used to relieve increased intracranial pressure cause an increase in urinary output. One such drug is mannitol (Osmitrol). The increased excretion of urine helps dehydrate tissues in the body, including those in the brain. (14:113–116)

40 1. The patient should be placed on his side to help mucus and debris escape from his oral and nasal passages after surgery. It is best to place the patient on the side opposite from the one on which he had surgery, which for the patient described in this item, would be the patient's left side.

Elevating the feet is contraindicated because of the danger of increasing intracranial pressure.   (12:624)

41   3.   The goal in helping parents through the stage of despair is to involve them in their dying child's care so that they can see their continuing importance to the child. The nurse is correct in exploring those things that the parents usually did for their child that made him feel good. The nurse can point out the importance of the child's relationship with his parents, and suggest ways they can continue to bring him comfort.   (9:660, 670)

The Nursing Care of Adolescents with Various Health Care Needs

Caring for an adolescent with dysmenorrhea

42   2.   Menstrual cramps are often relieved by applying warmth to the abdomen. Hot liquids, lying on the abdomen, and squeezing hands are unlikely to relieve cramping.   (10:309)

43   1.   Amenorrhea means the absence of menstruation. The classmate described in this item may be frightened of pregnancy because amenorrhea is a presumptive sign of pregnancy. Excessive vaginal bleeding is called menorrhagia. Discomfort between menstrual periods is called mittelschmerz. Discomfort prior to menstruation is related to premenstrual tension.   (3:281; 10:309)

Caring for an adolescent who is abusing amphetamines

44   4.   Symptoms of amphetamine abuse include marked nervousness, restlessness, excitability, talkativeness, and excessive perspiration. Dilated pupils occur with the abuse of lysergic acid diethylamide (LSD) and cocaine.

45   4.   Because the adolescent feels the need to belong and to be accepted by his peers, he will often join a gang. He will conform to gang customs in speaking, dressing, taking drugs, and even breaking laws.   (17:78)

46   1.   During adolescence, a youngster normally tries to develop self-identity. It is believed that one way in which the adolescent gains self-identity is through peer relationships. The search for intimate relationships occurs during the years between 18 and 40. Generativity is a need most often demonstrated by persons between the ages of about 40 and 65. Integrity is a need most often demonstrated by persons over 65 years of age.   (17:78)

47   4.   Many persons who abuse amphetamines, which are called "uppers" because of their effect on the body, also abuse barbiturates, or "downers." These persons fall into a vicious cycle of needing substances to elevate their mood and then needing a substance with the opposite effect to bring them down from a "high."   (3:279)

Caring for an adolescent with pulmonary tuberculosis

48   2.   Redness and swelling of the arm at the site of a tuberculin test 48 hours after the test has been done indicates a positive reaction and sensitivity to the tubercle bacillus. A positive reaction does not mean the person has an active lesion, but it is presumptive evidence of the disease. Further diagnostic procedures, such as a sputum analysis and a chest x-ray examination, are required to determine the extent of an infection when one is present.   (3:287)

49   4.   The tubercle bacillus has a tendency to develop resistance to drugs used to treat a patient with tuberculosis. Giving 2 drugs in combination helps prevent resistance to develop in the causative organism.   (14:26–27, 156)

50   4.   An adolescent needs to learn to take responsibility for taking his medication. Like most teenagers, after he understands how important the medications are to his total therapy, he most likely will take pride in being able to care for himself as evidence of his efforts to be independent. Also, self-administration is more convenient than depending on others.   (17:77–78)

51   2.   Flossing between the teeth should be part of daily hygiene measures to help prevent caries (cavities). The flossing reaches areas between the teeth to remove debris that a brush cannot reach. Also, flossing helps break up colonies of bacteria between the teeth. Chewing a disclosing dye is sometimes used to reveal areas where plaque and debris remain on teeth. Soda bicarbonate may be used instead of toothpastes but does not replace flossing. An antiseptic mouthwash is not recommended to replace either brushing or flossing.   (17:399)

Caring for an adolescent with acne vulgaris

52   2.   Tetracycline hydrochloride should be taken when the stomach is empty. It is also important to avoid taking this drug with milk or milk products because they interfere with the absorption of the tetracyclines. Other substances to avoid for the same reason are antacids.   (14:148)

53   3.   Keeping the skin clean is the best way to prevent blackheads, which form when dust and dirt collect in the pores of the skin. Exercise, adequate rest, being in sunlight, and eating nutritious foods tend to help the patient with acne, but these measures do not necessarily prevent blackhead formation. Of greatest importance for the person with acne is maintaining scrupulous cleanliness.   (3:280)

54   1.   Squeezing blackheads and pimples can cause the infection to spread and may cause scarring of the skin. A comedone extractor is often used by experienced caretakers to remove blackheads but should not be used by a lay person unless the person has been well taught and can be depended upon to use the comedone extractor properly.   (3:280; 12:555)

55 3.   It is important that the adolescent feels that there is someone who is really concerned about his problem and will offer any necessary help. It is best to avoid speaking of surgery at this time because it may be frightening to the patient and results of cosmetic surgery are not always predictable. Cliches, such as "beauty is only skin deep," and speaking of cosmetic surgery when it may not be indicated are unlikely to help the person with acne, who typically is anxious and concerned about his social relationships. Diet therapy is no longer used in the treatment of acne.   (3:280)

56 1.   Adolescents between the ages of 14 and 16 years should receive booster immunization for protection from tetanus. Smallpox vaccination is no longer advised because it is believed that the disease has been essentially eradicated. There are vaccines to protect children from rubella and whooping cough, but ordinarily they are given earlier in life. Boosters are not usually recommended during adolescence. Rubella protection is not used for adolescent girls, because if the girl is pregnant, or becomes pregnant shortly after receiving the vaccine, she may deliver a malformed infant. If rubella protection is advised for an adolescent girl, she must be instructed carefully *not* to become pregnant for at least 2 months after receiving the vaccine.   (3:264)

Caring for adolescents with sexually transmitted diseases

57 3.   A diagnosis of gonorrhea is confirmed when the organism is found in the patient's vaginal discharge. Diagnosis can be accomplished by microscopic examination of a smear of the patient's discharge. Cultures also may be made. Blood and urine examinations and determining when the patient last menstruated are not used to confirm a diagnosis of gonorrhea.   (3:284)

58 2.   Erythromycin (Erythrocin) usually is given to persons having a penicillin-resistant type of gonorrhea. Side-effects are gastrointestinal in nature, and include nausea, vomiting, diarrhea, and abdominal cramping.   (14:147)

59 3.   At least one, and better yet, two follow-up smears or cultures should be taken after completing therapy on persons who have penicillin-resistant gonorrhea. If the cultures and smears are negative, the person is considered noninfectious. Persons with gonorrhea that is not penicillin-resistant are usually considered noninfectious within a day or two of starting effective therapy. It is unsafe to assume a patient is no longer infectious when a vaginal discharge ceases, when menstrual periods are normal, or when drug therapy is free of adverse side-effects.   (3:284)

60 3.   During the primary stage of syphilis, a painless ulceration known as a chancre develops at the site on the penis where the spirochetes enter the body. This chancre, which is highly infectious, is the chief sign of early syphilis. Skin and mucosal lesions and swollen lymph nodes are signs of secondary syphilis. (3:183, 286)

61 2. Blood serology tests are performed and, if positive, they will show the presence of spirochetes and confirm a diagnosis of syphilis. Spinal fluid, urine, and seminal fluid specimens are not used to determine a diagnosis of syphilis. (3:283)

62 1. Signs of a penicillin reaction include a skin rash, hives, and itching. If anaphylactic shock occurs as a result of the person's sensitivity to penicillin, signs include hypotension, dyspnea, and unconsciousness. The medication is discontinued if the person proves to be sensitive to penicillin. Tetracyclines and erythromycin usually are used for treating patients with syphilis who are allergic to penicillin. (14:140)

63 3. The initial lesion of genital herpes (herpesvirus type II) most nearly resembles a fever blister. It may become a pustule, and then, in time, become a crusted area. Healing of the initial lesion often occurs but the condition typically recurs. Herpes genitalis has no known treatment. (12:764)

64 1. At the present time, evidence suggests that there is an association between genital herpes and the eventual development of cervical cancer. Because of these findings, it is recommended that women with the disease be urged to continue with long-term, follow-up care. (12:764)

65 3. Most authorities believe that the best way to tackle the problem of sexually transmitted diseases among adolescents is to offer educational programs to young people concerning the spread and treatment of these diseases. Screening programs, public clinics, and having only selected health personnel dealing with patients with sexually transmitted diseases have not been as effective as generalized, widespread educational programs. (3:286)

Caring for an adolescent with anorexia nervosa

66 1. Anorexia nervosa is a disease affecting primarily adolescents. Persons having this disorder have a distorted image of their body size and, even though they may be extremely thin and suffering with malnutrition, they see themselves as being overweight. The disease is sometimes described as self-inflicted starvation. Women with this condition usually are intelligent and from upper middle classes. Long-term therapy usually focuses on improving self-esteem. Immediate therapy consists of measures to correct malnutrition. (3:275; 12:726)

67 3. Persons with bulimia, when they do not force themselves to vomit, often use laxatives to "purge" themselves for weight control. Persons with bulimia overeat and use purging rather than dieting and exercising. It has not been demonstrated that bulimics go on to abuse drugs. (3:275)

68 1. It is particularly important for the nurse to *listen* to her young patients. To do otherwise may give them the impression that the nurse does not care. Also, persons who speak of suicide, either directly or indirectly, often are believed to be pleading for help and attention. Good interviewing always requires careful listening. This admonition is especially important when working with adolescents. Verifying data, keeping careful records, and having a sense of humor have important roles in nursing. But in this item, listening is of particular importance.   (3:274, 280; 12:560)

The Nursing Care of Children with Various Health Care Needs

Caring for a child with infantile eczema

69   4.   A vesicle is defined as a small sac made up of an elevation of epidermis and filled with a serous liquid. The vesicles on a child with infantile eczema (atopic dermatitis) are filled with a yellow, sticky serum. If there is blood and pus present, the child most likely has scratched the area and it has become infected.   (3:135)

70   3.   Infantile eczema is thought to be caused, at least in part, by allergic reactions to some irritant(s). Also, it appears that hereditary factors may play a role. This skin disease is most often seen during the first year of life, after about 3 months of age.   (3:134)

71   3.   An infant with eczema experiences severe itching of his skin lesions. The nurse must be prepared to teach home caretakers about nursing measures that will help to relieve itching so that the child does not scratch his skin and introduce organisms into the lesions. Itching usually is so severe that if it is not relieved, the child may require restraints, such as elbow restraints, and face masks may be necessary to protect the face.   (3:135–136)

72   3.   Hydrocortisone is an anti-inflammatory agent. It helps reduce inflammation and its symptoms, such as swelling, redness, heat, and discomfort. This drug does not influence weeping of lesions, the spread of the disease, or the white blood cell count.   (12:528)

73   1.   Colloid baths have been found effective for their soothing effects on the irritated and itching skin of a child with eczema. Baking soda and cornstarch added to tepid water is used most frequently. Cooked oatmeal or a commercial bath preparation of oatmeal is also effective for a colloid bath. The bath should last about 15 minutes, and then the child is patted dry. Soaps tend to irritate the skin. Normal saline is not particularly soothing. Oils should be avoided on the skin of a child with eczema.   (3:135)

74   2.   An infant normally cannot sit up without support until he is about 7 or 8 months old. Understanding his name, reaching out to a rattle, and rolling from his abdomen to his back are typical behaviors for a normal 5-month-old infant. Although he can reach out for a rattle, grasping ability is not well developed until about 1 year of age.   (3:135)

Caring for a child with otitis media

75   2.   Dosages for medications are determined on an individual basis after considering a child's weight and age. A common formula used to calculate a child's drug dosage is Clark's Rule:

$$\frac{\text{Weight (lbs) of child} \times \text{adult dose}}{150} = \text{Child's dose}$$

Weight is an unlikely basis for determining an infant's nutritional needs, except when the child is very much over- or under-weight.   (3:307)

76   3.   An infant usually indicates he has an earache by rolling or shaking his head from side to side or, at an older age, by tugging at the affected ear. This is usually accompanied by a piercing cry.   (3:128)

77   2.   Phenylephrine hydrochloride (Neo-Synephrine) nosedrops are used for the child with otitis media to relieve nasal congestion and improve drainage from the eustachian tube. This can be accomplished with phenylephrine hydrochloride because the drug acts to constrict superficial blood vessels and by so doing, relieve congestion. Phenylephrine hydrochloride is an adrenergic agent.   (12:544)

78   3.   To help spread nosedrops about on nasal tissues, it is best when the infant's head is tilted over a rolled pillow when introducing nose-drops.   (9:556)

79   2.   To relieve pressure on the eardrum, the drum may be pierced surgically on the child with otitis media. This procedure is called a myringotomy. A tiny tube may be placed in the artificial opening to allow for adequate drainage from the inner ear.   (3:128)

Caring for a child having a checkup

80   4.   Most children cannot be bowel trained until they are about 15 to 18 months old but some children may be even later. A child of 16 months who defecates before being able to convey the message that he must have a bowel movement is most probably not sufficiently mature to indicate having to defecate before it is too late. Bowel control comes with maturity, when control of the anal sphincter, being able to postpone defecation, and signaling before defecating are present.   (3:144)

81   3.   Small children should not be given small objects, such as marbles, which they can put in their mouth. Toys should also be free of sharp edges and small removable parts that a small child could place in his mouth. Depending on the age of a small child, beach balls, playing cards, and plasticized books are suitable.   (9:129)

Caring for a child who has been battered

82 2. When a nurse suspects a child has been battered, it is best to report her findings to the nurse-in-charge. Reporting suspected cases of battered children is required in this country. (3:391)

83 3. The typical finding in battered child syndrome is that bruises, fractures, lacerations, or burns are in various stages of healing. In addition, the parent(s) is usually vague about how the "accident" occurred. Most battered children are under 3 years of age. (3:171)

84 1. The battered child may have never experienced a trusting relationship with an adult. Typical behavior would be distrust, confusion, fear, and possibly unresponsiveness. The nurse plays a vital role in helping a battered child recognize safety in the hospital and in developing trust. (3:173)

85 2. A self-help group that offers support services to those who abuse children, or have abusive tendencies, is Parents Anonymous. Many cities have local chapters in which parents have successfully confronted their problem and overcome it. Parents Anonymous is a community agency of which nurses should be aware because of the alarming rate of child abuse. Crisis hot lines are found in many cities which offer help to abusive parents. (3:172)

86 1. Many studies have been done that examine parents who abuse their children. Some results are as follows: parents who batter come from all walks of life and from all socioeconomic and ethnic groups, many parents who batter were themselves battered as children, and many have long-term emotional problems as a result. (3:172)

87 2. TOPV, an abbreviation for trivalent oral poliovirus vaccine, provides protection from poliomyelitis. It ordinarily is given to normal children of 2, 4, and 18 months of age, and again between about 4 and 6 years of age. A booster at 6 months of age is optional but usually is given in areas where poliomyelitis is often seen. The schedule described is recommended by the Committee on Infectious Diseases of the American Academy of Pediatrics. (3:108)

Caring for a child who has cardiopulmonary collapse

88 1. The first step to take when cardiopulmonary resuscitation (CPR) is indicated is to clear the airway. While the child is flat on her back, the head should be positioned so that there is some hyperextension of the neck and the jaw is elevated so that it juts out. This "sniffing" position usually brings the tongue forward so that it does not block the airway. Any *obvious* foreign body in the mouth should be removed. Giving a precordial thump is not advised for children. Oxygen is not indicated and will be of no value if the airway is not clear. Slapping the child's back is not recommended when CPR is indicated. (3:322–323)

89 1. The heel of one hand is used for compression of the sternum for children between 1 and 8 years of age. Two fingers are used to compress the sternum of infants (1 year of age or less). The sternum for the 3-year-old child described in this item should be compressed between 1 and 1½ inches (2½ and 3¾ cm.). For an infant, compression should be ½ to ¾ inch (1¼ to about 2 cm.). The recommended number of compressions are 100 per minute for an infant and 80 to 100 for children. The sternum is compressed for infants and children. If the sternum is depressed more deeply, or lower, than recommended, there is danger of injury to internal organs.   (9:641)

90   1.   The most likely reason that the chest fails to rise and fall with each artificial ventilation is that the airway has become blocked and needs to be opened before proceeding.   (9:640)

Caring for a child with infantile autism

91   3.   Characteristics of children with autism include being unable to relate to or communicate with others, having a preoccupation with self and objects, and resisting change. They do not want to be touched or cuddled, do not seek attention, and show no concern for separation from parents. They are self-centered but do not seem to have a sense of self. The cause of autism is not clearly understood but it is thought that its origin may be genetic or organic rather than psychological.   (3:153)

92   2.   The autistic child does best in an environment that is as similar to home as possible. The child does not like change. It is best if he has his favorite toys with him. Stimulation through the various senses is best kept at a minimum. Autistic children are better off in private rooms rather than in rooms they will share with other children. Room ventilation and temperature should be comfortable but no special accommodations are required.   (3:154)

Caring for a child with phenylketonuria

93   4.   Phenylketonuria (PKU) is a disorder that occurs because of the body's inability to metabolize the amino acid phenylalanine, which is found in proteins. Phenylalanine accumulates in the blood and prevents normal brain development. Early detection of the disorder and a diet free of phenylalanine will help prevent mental retardation from occurring. PKU is a recessive hereditary defect.   (3:204)

94   1.   The most common screen test for PKU requires blood, ordinarily taken from a heel prick. The blood is placed on special filter paper. Laboratory techniques are used to determine serum phenylalanine levels. This test is called the Guthrie test.   (3:30)

Caring for a child with hemophilia

95   1.   The salicylates prolong bleeding time by interfering with blood plate-let aggregation, or collection. Aspirin is a salicylate and is contraindicated for anyone with a bleeding disorder. This is especially important knowl-edge to share with a person who has hemophilia because stopping bleed-ing is often extremely difficult, and a person can bleed to death from even a relatively small lesion.   (14:67)

96   2.   Hemophilia is inherited. A recessive trait is transmitted from a mother to her son. A male does not carry the trait, and females do not acquire hemophilia except in the very rarest of instances.   (3:208)

Caring for a child with ulcerative colitis

97   2.   When ulcerative colitis is present, the stools are usually small and contain mucus, blood, and pus. Diarrhea is usually present, and accompa-nied by severe abdominal discomfort due to cramping.   (12:714)

98   3.   The cause of ulcerative colitis is not clear but it is generally agreed that emotional stress is a very important factor and influences care the patient requires in a significant way. Many persons with ulcerative colitis require psychological counseling as part of their therapy.   (12:557)

Caring for children with various health problems

99   1.   It is unsafe for a small infant to sleep in a bed with his parents because he could easily smother if a parent accidentally rolls onto the infant during sleep. Also, when the infant is left alone on the parents' bed, which may occur during the parents' waking hours, the infant may roll off and fall onto the floor. A better practice is to prepare a separate bed for an infant. If a crib is not available, a clothes basket or a dresser drawer can be used for a bed.   (3:37)

100   4.   When an infant spits out food that he seems to dislike, it is best to eliminate the food from his diet and reintroduce it again at a later date. Forcing a child often ends up in a battle of wills and may lead to his never wanting a particular food. Most infants, after they learn how to handle food in the mouth, accept just about all foods if they are not strong or bitter in flavor, and are warm, smooth, and thin.   (3:101)

101   3.   Vomiting should not be induced when a victim has drunk any petro-leum product, such as kerosene or gasoline. There is danger of aspiration of fumes and liquids, which could cause respiratory tract irritation and pneumonia. Inducing vomiting frequently is used as a first aid measure when a victim has eaten aspirin or poisonous mushrooms, or has drunk excessive amounts of alcohol.   (3:164)

102   4.   The 3-month-old infant described in this item demonstrates the pro-trusion reflex, that is, if solid food is placed on the anterior third of the tongue, he will spit out the food. This reflex indicates that the infant is probably not ready for solid foods. Most infants are not ready until they are 4 to 6 months of age. Some authorities believe there is no advantage in giving an infant solid foods until he is at least 6 months of age.   (3:100)

103   2.   The infant seat should be placed backward on a car seat. This positioning offers the youngster the most protection in the infant seat if an accident occurs.   (3:381)

104   4.   No attempt should be made to remove a foreign object from the ear canal, because this may force the object further into the canal and injure the ear drum. The child described in this item should be brought to the clinic for removal of a stone in the ear canal.   (3:171)

105   1.   Celiac disease is characterized by an intolerance for gluten. All forms of barley, wheat, rye, and oats should be eliminated from the diet of a child with the disorder. The cause of celiac disease is unknown, but it is believed to be an inborn error of metabolism with allergies as a contributing factor. The disease also is sometimes called gluten-induced enteropathy.   (4:347)

106   4.   A person with mononucleosis who also has a fever should be placed on bed rest. After the fever subsides, activity may start gradually. Watching television is an appropriate diversion for a child on bed rest. However, care should be taken so that television watching is not done to extremes.   (3:282)

107   1.   In the situation described in this item, the nurse is correct in reporting the mother's concern with toilet training her child to the nurse-in-charge who may wish to explore possible causes for the child's behavior with an attending physician. The problem the mother describes *may* have a physiological basis. The mother already has tried unsuccessfully to teach elimination habits. Encouraging the mother to take parenting classes before the cause of the problem has been established could reinforce the mother's sense of guilt.   (3:241)

108   3.   Legg-Calvé-Perthes' disease is characterized by necrosis of the head of the femur. Trauma sometimes may have caused it, but more often the cause is unknown. The goal in the treatment of this disorder, also called coxa plana, is to keep weight off the affected hip until there is new bone formation in the acetabulum and femur. This may take as long as 2 to 3 years. Placing weight on the hip before the formation of solid new bone causes degeneration of the head of the femur. Braces and crutches are often used to protect the affected hip.   (3:238–239)

109   4.   Practical nurses are not permitted to administer medications intravenously because of the complexity of the procedure and many associated dangers. Furthermore, it is dangerous to carry out procedures for which you are not properly qualified because you are liable for your actions. If a person, such as a registered nurse or physician, asks you to do something for which you are not qualified, you should explain to that person and refuse to carry out the procedure because of the great risk you would take.   (13:43)

110 3. It is important for the nurse to be aware of her own feelings about the child with Down's syndrome. (In the past, Down's syndrome was referred to as mongolism, but the term is offensive to some ethnic groups and is rapidly disappearing from use.) Whether the child should be placed in an institution is a decision for parents to make. The nurse should be understanding of the difficulty faced by parents. Rather than reinforcing any guilt that they might feel by telling them what they should do, the nurse should make parents aware of any support groups or agencies that can help them to cope with their problem.   (3:202)

111 4. The Milwaukee brace is used to treat the lateral curvature of the spine known as scoliosis. The brace is worn continuously each day. It is removed only for daily showering or bathing. The brace helps correct the deformity by putting pressure on the chin, pelvis, and outward curvature of the spine. The pelvic girdle is used as a harness in pelvic traction. An abduction bar is used to separate the feet of the patient with a dislocated hip.   (3:238)

112 1. An immunity acquired after having a disease is called a naturally acquired active immunity. A killed or attenuated organism that promotes an immunity is called an artificially acquired active immunity.   (3:188)

113 4. A greenstick fracture, or hickory fracture, is one in which bone fragments have remained partially joined. For example, a break is seen on one side on a bone such as the humerus, but the bone is bent, not broken, on the opposite side of the fracture. A greenstick fracture is common in children because their bones still have not ossified completely.   (3:335)

114 4. Rickets is caused by a lack of sufficient vitamin D in the diet. The vitamin is essential for proper calcium and phosphorous use in the body's normal bone and teeth development. The abnormal process of development in a child lacking sufficient vitamin D is responsible for such signs of rickets as a delay in the closure of fontanels, delayed tooth growth, dental caries, and deformities of long bones.   (4:152–153)

115 3. Tay-Sachs disease is an inherited illness caused by a recessive gene that causes progressive brain damage. Because there is no treatment, and death with 3 to 5 years is usually inevitable, the parents need considerable support and help. Tay-Sachs disease occurs most frequently among eastern and central European Jews and French Canadians.   (12:564)

116 2. Tinea is caused by a fungus and an antifungal agent, such as griseofulvin (Grisactin), is commonly used to treat the condition. Ordinarily, therapy is long-term.   (3:252)

117 4. A youngster's blood pressure ordinarily reaches normal adult levels during late adolescence, when the person is between about 16 and 18 years of age.   (3:262)

118 4. The pinworm ova hatch in feces. Pinworms are spread by persons who are careless about washing their hands after a bowel movement, or who scratch the worm-infested anal area and then fail to wash hands.   (3:237)

Individual Items

119 4. Techniques for administering oxygen therapy with a cannula are essentially the same for a child as for an adult. The amount of oxygen to administer is prescribed but a child does not necessarily require lower concentrations than adults. All cannulas have two prongs. Some recent studies have indicated that oxygen administration at very low flow rates (1 to 2 liters per minute) may be sufficiently humidified by nasal passageways so that extra humidification is not necessary. However, unless agency policy states humidification in such instances is not necessary, the more common practice of humidifying oxygen is observed for persons of all ages.   (9:627–628)

120 3. There is a tendency for the public to feel secure about the control of communicable diseases. People then tend to neglect having available immunizations. In some cases, diseases that are preventable through immunization have been endemic because of this tendency. These findings denote the important work health personnel have in public educational programs to help in the prevention of communicable diseases for which immunization is available.   (9:296)

Classification of Test Items

Directions: *Each item in the previous review test is classified here according to the subject area it tests. Place a check mark after each item you answered **correctly** by referring to your answers. Total the number of items you answered correctly in each area and enter the numbers in the correct places on pages 553–556.*

Clinical: Nursing Care of Children

2 ✓	28 ✓	56 ✓	71 ✓	94 ✓	113 ✓
3 ✓	30 ___	57 ✓	73 ___	97 ✓	116 ✓
4 ___	33 ✓	60 ___	76 ___	99 ✓	118 ___
6 ✓	38 ✓	61 ✓	79 ✓	101 ✓	119 ✓
7 ✓	40 ✓	63 ✓	83 ✓	103 ✓	120 ✓
11 ✓	48 ✓	64 ✓	86 ✓	104 ✓	
13 ✓	51 ✓	66 ✓	91 ✓	107 ✓	
26 ✓	53 ✓	69 ✓	92 ✓	108 ✓	
27 ✓	54 ✓	70 ___	93 ✓	111 ✓	

TOTAL _43_

Biological/Physical Sciences

42 ✓	43 ✓	78 ✓	96 ___	112 ✓	117 ✓

TOTAL _5_

Fundamentals of Nursing

20 ___	29 ✓	36 ✓	88 ✓	89 ✓	90 ✓
25 ✓	35 ___				

TOTAL _6_

Diet Therapy/Nutrition

23 _____   32 __✓___   105 __✓___   114 _____

TOTAL _2_

Pharmacology

8 __✓__	16 __✓__	31 __✓__	49 __✓__	67 __✓__	77 _____
9 __✓__	17 __✓__	37 __✓__	52 __✓__	72 _____	87 __✓__
10 __✓__	21 _____	39 __✓__	58 _____	75 __✓__	95 __✓__
14 __✓__	22 __✓__	44 __✓__	59 __✓__		
15 __✓__	24 __✓__	47 __✓__	62 __✓__		

TOTAL _22_

Psychosocial Sciences

1 __✓__	34 __✓__	55 _____	81 __✓__	100 __✓__	109 __✓__
5 __✓__	41 _____	65 __✓__	82 __✓__	102 _____	110 __✓__
12 __✓__	45 __✓__	68 __✓__	84 __✓__	106 __✓__	115 __✓__
18 __✓__	46 __✓__	74 __✓__	85 __✓__		
19 _____	50 __✓__	80 __✓__	98 _____		

TOTAL _21_

UNIT IV

Review Tests 6 Through 14

The Nursing Care of Adults With Medical-Surgical Disorders

Review Test 6

The Nursing Care of Patients With Disorders of the Gastrointestinal System

Caring for a Patient With a Bleeding Gastric Ulcer
Caring for a Patient With an Inguinal Hernia
Caring for a Patient With Ulcerative Colitis
Caring for a Patient With Hemorrhoids
Caring for a Patient With a Malignant Tumor of the Rectum

Correct Answers and Rationales
Classification of Test Items

Directions: *With a pencil, blacken the circle in front of the option you have chosen for your correct answer.*

The Nursing Care of Patients With Disorders of the Gastrointestinal System

Mr. Knight is a 46-year-old business man who is hospitalized with a bleeding gastric ulcer.

1 When the admitting nurse obtains Mr. Knight's health history, Mr. Knight is most likely to report that he has a gnawing pain in the stomach area that is generally relieved by
○ 1. fasting.
○ 2. resting.
○ 3. eating food.
○ 4. drinking warm liquids.

Mr. Knight poses several questions to the admitting nurse.

2 Mr. Knight asks the nurse what structure in his body causes the secretion of hydrochloric acid in the stomach. The nurse should answer by saying that the cranial nerve that stimulates the secretion of hydrochloric acid is the
○ 1. fifth, or trigeminal nerve.

    ○ 2. tenth, or vagus nerve.
    ○ 3. eleventh, or accessory nerve.
    ○ 4. twelfth, or hypoglossal nerve.

3 Mr. Knight asks, "Do most people with ulcers have a gastric type of peptic ulcer as I have?" The nurse should explain that the area in the gastrointestinal tract where most peptic ulcers are located is in the
    ○ 1. ileum.
    ○ 2. jejunum.
    ○ 3. stomach.
    ○ 4. duodenum.

4 Mr. Knight asks the nurse about the cause of ulcers. The nurse should teach that, of the following factors, the one that appears most closely related to the cause of peptic ulcers is
    ○ 1. having hormonal imbalances.
    ○ 2. having chronic constipation.
    ○ 3. participating in competitive sports.
    ○ 4. experiencing frequent emotional stress.

A stool specimen is to be obtained from Mr. Knight.

5 Red meat is sometimes withheld before a stool is to be studied for the presence of blood primarily because meat may
    ○ 1. produce a bloody-appearing stool.
    ○ 2. aggravate an already bleeding ulcer.
    ○ 3. cause the test to give a false-positive result.
    ○ 4. neutralize the chemical used to test the stool for blood.

6 A very likely characteristic of Mr. Knight's stools is that they will
    ○ 1. be liquid in nature.
    ○ 2. have abnormal amounts of mucus.
    ○ 3. have a tar-like color and consistency.
    ○ 4. contain much undigested and partially digested food.

Mr. Knight receives aluminum hydroxide (amphojel).

7 Aluminum hydroxide is given to Mr. Knight primarily to
    ○ 1. reduce acid secretions.
    ○ 2. coat the gastric ulcer.
    ○ 3. neutralize stomach acids.
    ○ 4. decrease gastric motility.

8 Mr. Knight receives aluminum hydroxide q.i.d. The letter *q* in Mr. Knight's order means
    ○ 1. hour.
    ○ 2. with.
    ○ 3. take.

⚪ 4. four.

9 At home, Mr. Knight took 8 ml of aluminum hydroxide. In household measurements, 8 ml is most nearly equivalent to

⚪ 1. 1 teaspoon.

⚪ 2. 2 teaspoons.

⚪ 3. 1 tablespoon.

⚪ 4. 2 tablespoons.

Mr. Knight is constipated. He is to receive an oil retention enema and several hours later, a suppository if he does not stool following the oil enema.

10 The temperature of the oil for Mr. Knight's retention enema should be

⚪ 1. room temperature, about 72°F (21°C).

⚪ 2. body temperature, about 98°F (36°C).

⚪ 3. below body temperature. about 90°F (31°C).

⚪ 4. above body temperature, about 110°F (43°C).

11 The nurse assigned to give Mr. Knight the oil retention enema has not cared for Mr. Knight previously. To be sure that she gives the enema to the correct patient, the nurse should check the patient's identification bracelet and also

⚪ 1. ask the nurse-in-charge which patient he is.

⚪ 2. request that the patient state his full name.

⚪ 3. check the patient's nameplate on the door to his room.

⚪ 4. call the patient by his name while approaching the bed.

12 The nurse describes giving the oil retention enema to Mr. Knight and his reaction to it. Where should she record this information?

⚪ 1. In the nurses' notes

⚪ 2. On the graphic sheet

⚪ 3. In the progress notes

⚪ 4. On the nursing care plan

13 A bisacodyl (Dulcolax) suppository is used for Mr. Knight when he does not stool following the oil retention enema. Bisacodyl acts to overcome constipation by

⚪ 1. stimulating peristalsis in the intestine.

⚪ 2. softening the contents of the intestine.

⚪ 3. forming additional bulk in the intestine.

⚪ 4. increasing the water content in the intestine.

14 To help relax the anal sphincters when inserting the rectal suppository, Mr. Knight should be taught to

⚪ 1. hold his breath.

⚪ 2. cough several times.

⚪ 3. swallow several times.

⚪ 4. breathe through his mouth.

After a few weeks at home, Mr. Knight's condition worsens and he returns to the hospital for preoperative care for a subtotal gastrectomy.

15 The nurse should recognize that Mr. Knight's ulcer most probably has perforated if he suddenly complains of
○ 1. feeling very faint.
○ 2. a throbbing headache.
○ 3. sudden severe pain in the abdomen.
○ 4. extreme nausea without being able to vomit.

16 A nursing order indicates that, before his surgery, Mr. Knight is to be NPO, which means that he is *not* to
○ 1. be out of bed.
○ 2. have sedatives.
○ 3. have oxygen therapy.
○ 4. have anything by mouth.

The nurse begins postoperative care when Mr. Knight returns to his hospital room after surgery.

17 If Mr. Knight's wound separates postoperatively and a body organ is exposed, emergency measures should include covering the organ with sterile gauze and
○ 1. covering the gauze with a sterile binder.
○ 2. moistening the gauze with sterile normal saline.
○ 3. keeping the gauze dry by replacing it as necessary.
○ 4. replacing the organ *gently* with a sterile-gloved hand.

18 Mr. Knight's nursing care plan states that the patient may be ambulatory during postoperative recuperation, which means that he is able to
○ 1. walk about.
○ 2. be discharged.
○ 3. use a wheelchair.
○ 4. take care of himself.

Discharge teaching is begun for Mr. Knight.

19 After explaining about the dumping syndrome, the nurse should teach that it can often be caused by eating too fast or caused by eating food particularly high in
○ 1. fats.
○ 2. proteins.
○ 3. carbohydrates.
○ 4. water content.

20 In view of his diagnosis, which of the following beverages should Mr. Knight be taught to *avoid*?
○ 1. Tea

O 2. Postum
O 3. Eggnog
O 4. Carbonated beverages

21 After discharge, Mr. Knight is to use cimetidine (Tagamet) as necessary. Cimetidine is a drug that acts as
O 1. an analgesic to relieve pain associated with an ulcer.
O 2. an cholinergic-blocking agent to slow gastrointestinal motility.
O 3. a vasoconstrictor to constrict capillaries where bleeding may occur.
O 4. a histamine H_2 antagonist to decrease production of hydrochloric acid in the stomach.

22 Mr. Knight should be taught that he will be most likely suffering from an adverse effect of cimetidine if he develops
O 1. nausea.
O 2. headaches.
O 3. drowsiness.
O 4. fluid retention.

23 During discharge teaching, Mr. Knight tells the nurse that he used to glide for a hobby. The nurse says, "That would scare me! Weren't you afraid?" Mr. Knight hesitates momentarily as he recalls how frightened he was at times and then says, "Of course not! A piece of cake." The defense mechanism Mr. Knight is likely using in this situation is called
O 1. denial.
O 2. conversion.
O 3. compensation.
O 4. identification.

Mr. Spring has an inguinal hernia. A herniorrhaphy is planned and preoperative care starts when he is admitted to a hospital.

24 Mr. Spring says he has no pain and sees no need for surgery. The admitting nurse explains how his hernia could strangulate. If not cared for, the effect strangulation has on tissue caught in the inguinal wall defect is that the tissue
O 1. becomes malignant.
O 2. fills with blood clots.
O 3. becomes gangrenous.
O 4. fills with fibrotic scars.

25 Mr. Spring says that the small swelling in the inguinal area "comes and goes." Of the following activities, the one that Mr. Spring is most likely to describe to the nurse that causes his hernia to appear is when he
O 1. eats.
O 2. lies down.
O 3. breathes deeply.
O 4. strains to defecate.

26   Which of the following items is *least* likely to be found on Mr. Spring's preoperative checklist?
   O 1. The fact that the patient has a pacemaker
   O 2. The signature of the surgeon who is to perform surgery
   O 3. The fact that allergies have been documented in the patient's record
   O 4. The signature of the nurse receiving the patient in the operating room

Mr. Spring's postoperative care starts when he returns from surgery.

27   Spinal anesthesia was used for Mr. Spring's surgery. If the nurse notes the following postoperative orders, which one should she question before carrying it out?
   O 1. Regular diet
   O 2. Fluids as desired
   O 3. Out of bed tomorrow
   O 4. Keep in a low-Fowler's position for 8 hours

28   A suspensory, which is a sling-like support, is used postoperatively for Mr. Spring primarily to prevent
   O 1. penile impotence.
   O 2. edema of the scrotum.
   O 3. strain on the incision.
   O 4. wound contamination from the anal area.

29   An ice bag is to be placed on Mr. Spring's scrotum. It is recommended that ice chips be used in an ice bag primarily because the chips, when compared with ice cubes,
   O 1. melt less quickly.
   O 2. make is easier to fill the bag.
   O 3. are less likely to damage the bag.
   O 4. are easier to mold to a body part.

30   Of the activities given below, the one Mr. Spring should be taught to *avoid* postoperatively is
   O 1. coughing.
   O 2. deep breathing.
   O 3. moving his legs.
   O 4. lying on his operative side.

31   If the nurse gives an incorrect medication to Mr. Spring postoperatively and the patient sues the nurse because he believes the nurse's error has caused him harm, the nurse is most likely to be charged with
   O 1. fraud.
   O 2. assault.
   O 3. battery.
   O 4. negligence.

Mr. Spring is prepared for discharge.

32 Which of the following activities should Mr. Spring be advised to *avoid* for the first few weeks at home?
○ 1. Lifting heavy objects
○ 2. Wearing a trouser belt
○ 3. Eating a high-residue diet
○ 4. Drinking alcoholic beverages

33 Mr. Spring says he has trouble with constipation. If he observes the following practices of daily living, the one that is likely to contribute most to constipation is
○ 1. being a vegetarian.
○ 2. eating the large daily meal at noon.
○ 3. using cooked rather than raw fruits and vegetables.
○ 4. using low-calorie foods and beverages for weight control.

34 If the nurse uses the following types of behavior when teaching Mr. Spring about constipation, which one is most likely to stand in the way of fostering a helping nurse-patient relationship?
○ 1. The nurse sits down while the patient tells her about his favorite forms of exercise.
○ 2. The nurse teaches the patient the relationship between diet and elimination.
○ 3. The nurse tells the patient that he is failing to try to help himself overcome constipation.
○ 4. The nurse explains why the indiscriminate use of laxatives can stand in the way of natural elimination.

Ms. Manuel, a 31-year-old woman, has a long history of ulcerative colitis. She is admitted to the hospital for an ileostomy.

35 Which of the following statements concerning Ms. Manuel is most accurate when considering the incidence of ulcerative colitis?
○ 1. The patient is atypical. Ulcerative colitis is a disease of late adulthood.
○ 2. The patient is atypical. Ulcerative colitis is a disease that affects many more men than women.
○ 3. The patient is typical. Ulcerative colitis is a disease of young adulthood.
○ 4. The patient is typical. Ulcerative colitis is a disease that affects many more women than men.

36 An entry on Ms. Manuel's health record indicates that she has "idiopathic ulcerative colitis." An idiopathic disease is one in which the cause is
○ 1. not known.

○ 2. hereditary.
○ 3. congenital.
○ 4. a nonspecific infection.

37 Of the following personal grooming habits, it is recommended that when the nurse cares for Ms. Manuel during her hospitalization, the nurse should *avoid* wearing
○ 1. lipstick.
○ 2. a wristwatch.
○ 3. long braided hair.
○ 4. a diamond solitaire ring.

The nurse works to establish a helping relationship with Ms. Manuel.

38 The first step the nurse should take in the process of developing a helping relationship with Ms. Manuel is to
○ 1. place herself in the patient's situation.
○ 2. learn to understand her own behavior.
○ 3. observe the patient's behavior in a variety of settings.
○ 4. prepare a nursing care study that describes care that she gives the patient.

39 The primary purpose for building a helping nurse-patient relationship with Ms. Manuel is to
○ 1. learn to know oneself better.
○ 2. assist the patient to a state of well-being.
○ 3. develop a warm friendship between the nurse and patient.
○ 4. keep the patient as inactive as possible until recovery begins.

40 Ms. Manuel repeats her health history to the nurse several times and tells of the many treatments she has tried but to no avail. She says, "I guess I'm just not going to be cured. With my history, I am sure this surgery won't help either." In this situation, it would be best for the nurse to say,
○ 1. "You are saying that you doubt that you will recover?"
○ 2. "Do you want to talk to your doctor again before surgery?"
○ 3. "I think you are telling me that you almost hope your surgery won't be successful."
○ 4. "Oh yes, you will get well. I have seen many patients like you recover after having surgery."

41 Ms. Manuel is encouraged to take her own bath preoperatively. She states angrily, "I am clean enough now!" However, she willingly helps with her bath when the nurse stays to assist her. Which of the following statements offers the nurse the best guide to judge this situation?
○ 1. It is best to skip the bath, because an alert patient is a good judge of her own cleanliness.
○ 2. It is best to assume that the patient is illustrating a desire to dominate the nurse.

   ○ 3. It is best to teach the patient the values of self care, because apparently she is not aware of them.

   ○ 4. It is best to observe the patient further before making a judgment about what the patient has said.

42 The nurse helps Ms. Manuel with her bath without screening her from her roommate and visitors. In addition to showing lack of consideration for others, the nurse runs the possible risk of being sued by the patient for

   ○ 1. slander.

   ○ 2. assault and battery.

   ○ 3. false imprisonment.

   ○ 4. invasion of privacy.

A special diet is served to Ms. Manuel.

43 The type of diet that is most likely to be ordered for Ms. Manuel is

   ○ 1. low fat.

   ○ 2. low residue.

   ○ 3. low sodium.

   ○ 4. high carbohydrate.

44 Ms. Manuel asks the nurse how digested food is absorbed in her small intestine. The nurse answers correctly that the structures in the small intestine that are chiefly responsible for the absorption of digested food are called

   ○ 1. villi.

   ○ 2. rugae.

   ○ 3. caries.

   ○ 4. ampullae.

Ms. Manuel has diarrhea.

45 The decision that Ms. Manuel has diarrhea is based primarily on the stool's

   ○ 1. odor.

   ○ 2. color.

   ○ 3. frequency.

   ○ 4. consistency.

46 Ms. Manuel is sometimes incontinent of feces. Diapering an adult patient who has fecal incontinence is *not* ordinarily recommended primarily because the practice often causes the patient to suffer with

   ○ 1. a fecal impaction.

   ○ 2. broken skin areas.

   ○ 3. emotional discomforts.

   ○ 4. urinary tract infections.

47 When Ms. Manuel is incontinent, she cries out, "I am trying to control it but I can't." In this situation, it is best for the nurse to

○ 1. leave the patient to telephone a family member who could console her.

○ 2. remain with the patient and explain to her that she will feel better very soon.

○ 3. remain with the patient at her bedside and allow her to express her feelings.

○ 4. leave the patient so that she can have privacy to regain control of her emotions.

The nurse collects a urine specimen from Ms. Manuel.

48 If the nurse uses the following techniques when obtaining a midstream urine specimen from Ms. Manuel, which technique is in *error*?

○ 1. The nurse keeps the labia separated while collecting the specimen.

○ 2. The nurse asks the patient to void in a forceful manner.

○ 3. The nurse discards the first 30 ml that the patient voids.

○ 4. The nurse collects the specimen in a clean bedpan.

49 If Ms. Manuel's urine specimen is *not* taken directly to the laboratory after obtaining it, how should the specimen be stored temporarily?

○ 1. In a freezer

○ 2. In a refrigerator

○ 3. In a warm place

○ 4. At room temperature

Ms. Manuel's operative site is shaven preoperatively.

50 When shaving Ms. Manuel's operative site, in which direction should the nurse move the razor in relation to the patient's body hair growth?

○ 1. Straight across hair growth

○ 2. Diagonally across hair growth

○ 3. In the direction of hair growth

○ 4. Opposite the direction of hair growth

51 The primary reason for shaving Ms. Manuel's skin preoperatively is to help

○ 1. improve the surgeon's field of vision.

○ 2. assure that the operative site is clean.

○ 3. prepare the skin so that it can be made sterile.

○ 4. make it more comfortable to use adhesive to secure dressings.

Ms. Manuel returns from the recovery room postoperatively.

52 Ms. Manuel is placed in a side-lying position immediately postoperatively, primarily because this position helps to

○ 1. prevent postoperative shock.

○ 2. promote drainage from the nose and mouth.

    ○ 3. provide the greatest convenience for caretakers.

    ○ 4. place the least amount of stress on the incisional and stomal sites.

53 Of the following vital signs, the one that should suggest to the nurse that Ms. Manuel is most probably going into a state of postoperative shock is

    ○ 1. a bounding pulse rate.

    ○ 2. a slow respiratory rate.

    ○ 3. a dropping blood pressure.

    ○ 4. an increasing body temperature.

54 Ms. Manuel has hiccups. A commonly used method to overcome hiccups is to have the patient

    ○ 1. suck on ice chips.

    ○ 2. lie in the prone position.

    ○ 3. take fast, panting breaths.

    ○ 4. rebreathe into a paper bag.

55 Ms. Manuel is especially susceptible to an electrolyte imbalance during her postoperative course primarily because of

    ○ 1. loss of functioning of the large intestine.

    ○ 2. excessive losses of fluids from the ostomy.

    ○ 3. intractable vomiting commonly associated with an ileostomy.

    ○ 4. a decreased ability to absorb nutrients from the small intestine.

The nurse cares for Ms. Manuel's surgical wound.

56 The nurse uses sterile technique when dressing Ms. Manuel's surgical wound. Theoretically, an item is defined as being sterile when

    ○ 1. all viruses on it are destroyed.

    ○ 2. all organisms on it are destroyed.

    ○ 3. only encapsulated organisms on it are destroyed.

    ○ 4. only disease-causing organisms on it are destroyed.

57 The nurse assesses the amount of drainage from Ms. Manuel's ileostomy with care because slight or no discharge should cause the nurse to suspect that the patient may be suffering with

    ○ 1. a wound infection.

    ○ 2. atonic constipation.

    ○ 3. excessive gas formation.

    ○ 4. an intestinal obstruction.

58 If the hospital has windows that are allowed to be open, opening them to ventilate Ms. Manuel's room and creating a draft is *contraindicated* primarily because

    ○ 1. outdoor air pollution may enter the room.

    ○ 2. the new postoperative patient may catch a cold.

    ○ 3. organisms may be spread about the room by the air currents.

    ○ 4. the thermostat for regulating temperature may become inaccurate.

The nurse cares for Ms. Manuel's ileostomy appliance.

59 The method recommended most often for cleaning the skin around Ms. Manuel's temporary appliance at her stoma before placing the appliance on the skin is to
○ 1. pat it clean with cotton balls.
○ 2. swab it with half-strength alcohol.
○ 3. wash it with water and a mild soap.
○ 4. scrub it with sterile water and a gauze sponge.

60 After wearing a temporary appliance over her ileostomy stoma, Ms. Manuel is to be fitted for a permanent appliance. The faceplate (disc) on the permanent appliance should fit comfortably and should be sized so that
○ 1. the faceplate covers the stoma.
○ 2. at least an inch of skin is exposed around the stoma.
○ 3. the faceplate covers at least a six-inch square of skin.
○ 4. a minimum of skin is exposed immediately around the stoma.

61 After cleaning the area, preparations, such as karaya powder, may be used to protect Ms. Manuel's skin around the stoma before putting on the permanent appliance. Another commonly used agent is
○ 1. petrolatum.
○ 2. iodine tincture.
○ 3. talcum powder.
○ 4. tincture of benzoin.

62 Ms. Manuel asks how the appliance will be secured so that it does not fall off the skin. Of the following preparations, which one is most commonly used to secure the appliance?
○ 1. Karaya gum
○ 2. Cellophane tape
○ 3. Zinc oxide paste
○ 4. A and D ointment

63 One day, Ms. Manuel complains of a stinging sensation immediately after an appliance change at her stoma. The best course of action for the nurse to take in this situation is to
○ 1. call the nurse-in-charge.
○ 2. remove the appliance immediately.
○ 3. observe the patient for a few minutes.
○ 4. place cool compresses over the troublesome area.

64 The time in the day when it is best to plan to change Ms. Manuel's appliance is immediately after the patient
○ 1. awakens in the morning.
○ 2. has eaten breakfast.
○ 3. has been walking about.
○ 4. has eaten dinner.

Discharge teaching is planned for Ms. Manuel.

65 If Ms. Manuel wishes to carry out the following activities of daily living after she recovers, the one that is most *unrealistic* for her is
○ 1. playing tennis.
○ 2. being able to swim.
○ 3. having sexual relations.
○ 4. gaining control of her bowel movements.

66 During discharge teaching, the nurse should explain to Ms. Manuel that of the following types of medications, the one that is *not* recommended for her to use is
○ 1. an analgesic, such as aspirin.
○ 2. a chewable tablet, such as one used to relieve indigestion.
○ 3. a liquid medication, such as one used to control coughing.
○ 4. a time-release capsule, such as one used for the relief of nasal congestion.

67 During the time the nurse prepares Ms. Manuel for discharge, she recommends a source of help the patient may find useful. The source Ms. Manuel is likely to find most beneficial is a local
○ 1. ostomy club.
○ 2. crisis hot line.
○ 3. self-help counseling group.
○ 4. manufacturer of ostomy appliances.

About a year after having the ileostomy, Ms. Manuel investigates the possibility of having a Kock (pouch) ileostomy.

68 If Ms. Manuel has a pouch ileostomy, she will no longer experience
○ 1. having a liquid feces.
○ 2. having an external stoma.
○ 3. needing an ileostomy appliance.
○ 4. needing to avoid gas-forming food.

Forty-eight-year-old Mr. White is hospitalized for a hemorrhoidectomy.

69 Mr. White's hemorrhoids are internal and high in the anal canal. The symptoms he most likely complained of when he sought health care most nearly resemble those of
○ 1. diverticulitis.
○ 2. pilonidal cyst.
○ 3. ulcerative colitis.
○ 4. cancer of the rectum.

70 The nurse reviews Mr. White's health history. Which of the following regular incidents in Mr. White's daily living most probably contributed to his having hemorrhoids?
○ 1. Using enemas regularly
○ 2. Drinking beer every day
○ 3. Being constipated frequently
○ 4. Having a diet high in roughage

71 Mr. White asks the nurse what hemorrhoids are. The nurse describes hemorrhoids correctly as
○ 1. scar tissue.
○ 2. varicose veins.
○ 3. inflamed veins.
○ 4. blocked arteries.

Mr. White has nausea and vomiting following surgery.

72 The position in bed in which it is best to place Mr. White when he starts vomiting postoperatively is
○ 1. on his back.
○ 2. on either side.
○ 3. on his abdomen.
○ 4. in a low-Fowler's position.

73 Of the following measures, the one most likely to help Mr. White overcome nausea is to have him
○ 1. sit up in bed.
○ 2. take several deep breaths.
○ 3. place his hands over his head.
○ 4. put pressure over the stomach.

74 Of the following beverages, the one that is most likely to help Mr. White overcome nausea is
○ 1. hot coffee.
○ 2. orange juice.
○ 3. a carbonated beverage.
○ 4. sodium bicarbonate in water.

Mr. White has not voided during his first 15 hours postoperatively.

75 If the following nursing measures are not contraindicated for Mr. White, it would be best for the nurse to help Mr. White void by
○ 1. helping the patient stand at his bedside with the urinal in place.
○ 2. placing the patient in a semi-sitting position while using the bedpan rather than a urinal.
○ 3. decreasing the patient's fluid intake until voiding starts.
○ 4. suggesting that the patient use perineal exercises until the urge to void appears.

Mr. White is to have sitz baths.

76 The nurse should explain to Mr. White that the usual length of time for taking a sitz bath is from
○ 1. 5 to 10 minutes.
○ 2. 10 to 15 minutes.
○ 3. 20 to 30 minutes.
○ 4. 45 to 60 minutes.

77 After a sitz bath, Mr. White expresses concern. The most likely concern Mr. White will have following his hemorrhoidectomy is a fear of having
○ 1. impotence.
○ 2. urinary retention.
○ 3. fecal incontinence.
○ 4. a bowel movement.

Mr. White is being prepared for discharge.

78 Mr. White is to take a bulk-forming laxative, an example of one being
○ 1. epsom salts.
○ 2. mineral oil.
○ 3. psyllium (Metamucil).
○ 4. dioctyl sodium (Colace).

79 Mr. White says that he wants to start exercising regularly as soon as he recovers from surgery. Before he starts his own regular exercising program, the nurse should advise that he should first
○ 1. lose excess weight.
○ 2. have a physical examination.
○ 3. study several books on the subject.
○ 4. try the exercise of choice a few times.

80 Mr. White should be taught that after exercising, it is important that he plan to
○ 1. take a hot shower.
○ 2. taper off to cool off.
○ 3. lie down for a few minutes.
○ 4. eat a high-carbohydrate meal.

Mr. Ortez, 69 years old, is admitted to a hospital for diagnosis and treatment. It is suggested that he has a malignant tumor of the rectum.

81 Of the following symptoms, the one that most probably caused Mr. Ortez to seek health care is
○ 1. chronic indigestion.
○ 2. abdominal distention.
○ 3. a change in bowel habits.
○ 4. an inability to empty his rectum when stooling.

82   While the nurse admits Mr. Ortez, the patient makes the comments given below. Which one is the most significant in terms of the patient's state of health?

    ○   1.   "I lost 10 pounds in the last 2 weeks."
    ○   2.   "I haven't been exercising but I like to take walks."
    ○   3.   "My hair started to turn grey very suddenly recently."
    ○   4.   "I have been sleeping only about 5 hours a night but often I take daytime naps."

Mr. Ortez has several diagnostic tests.

83   Mr. Ortez's stool is examined for occult blood. The examination is done primarily to look for the presence of blood in the stool that is

    ○   1.   fresh.
    ○   2.   digested.
    ○   3.   invisible to the eye.
    ○   4.   from the arterial blood system.

84   Mr. Ortez is scheduled for a barium enema, and castor oil is given to prepare the colon. Before giving him the medication, the nurse can help to minimize the objectionable taste of the castor oil by offering the patient

    ○   1.   candy.
    ○   2.   hot tea.
    ○   3.   ice chips.
    ○   4.   dry toast.

85   The nurse should prepare Mr. Ortez for the barium enema by explaining that during the procedure, he is very likely to experience

    ○   1.   nausea and vomiting.
    ○   2.   dizziness and a headache.
    ○   3.   bowel and urinary incontinence.
    ○   4.   abdominal distention and cramping.

86   To prevent problems in the colon from barium, following the barium enema, the nurse should be prepared to give Mr. Ortez

    ○   1.   an antacid.
    ○   2.   a laxative.
    ○   3.   a liquid diet.
    ○   4.   small but frequent meals.

87   A sigmoidoscopy with a biopsy is done on Mr. Ortez to help establish a diagnosis. The position of choice for performing this procedure is the

    ○   1.   Sims's position.
    ○   2.   lithotomy position.
    ○   3.   back-lying position.
    ○   4.   knee-chest position.

It is determined that Mr. Ortez has a malignant tumor of the rectum. He is prepared for an abdominoperineal resection.

88   A characteristic of Mr. Ortez's malignant tumor, in *contrast* to a benign tumor, is that a malignant tumor
   ○ 1. grows slowly.
   ○ 2. is encapsulated.
   ○ 3. tends to spread to lymph nodes.
   ○ 4. is unlikely to recur after removal.

89   Mr. Ortez is to have chlordiazepoxide (Librium) for 2 days preoperatively, primarily to help
   ○ 1. decrease bleeding time.
   ○ 2. reduce anxiety and worry.
   ○ 3. improve urinary production.
   ○ 4. prevent nausea and vomiting.

90   Mr. Ortez is to receive 10 mg t.i.d. orally of chlordiazepoxide. The drug is dispensed in 5 mg capsules. How many capsules should Mr. Ortez receive each day?
   ○ 1. 2 capsules
   ○ 2. 4 capsules
   ○ 3. 6 capsules
   ○ 4. 9 capsules

91   A low-residue diet is prescribed for Mr. Ortez during the preoperative period. Which of the following foods is *contraindicated* for him?
   ○ 1. Fried eggs
   ○ 2. Baked fish
   ○ 3. Crisp bacon
   ○ 4. Broiled hamburger patty

92   An order for Mr. Ortez states that he is to receive 5 mg of atropine sulfate, intramuscularly, at 7:30 A.M. on the day of surgery. The nurse should question the order because
   ○ 1. the dosage is unusually large.
   ○ 2. the route of administration is in error.
   ○ 3. the drug is contraindicated for most elderly persons.
   ○ 4. the drug is contraindicated for most persons having intestinal surgery.

93   The primary purpose for giving atropine sulfate to Mr. Ortez preoperatively is to help
   ○ 1. prevent nausea.
   ○ 2. produce sleepiness.
   ○ 3. promote muscle relaxation.
   ○ 4. decrease respiratory secretions.

94   Mr. Ortez's preoperative orders include giving him 75 mg of meperidine hydrochloride (Demerol) intramuscularly. The drug is dispensed in a cartridge and the label states that there are 100 mg of the drug per milliliter. What part of a milliliter should the nurse administer to Mr. Ortez?

   ○ 1. 0.25 ml
   ○ 2. 0.50 ml
   ○ 3. 0.75 ml
   ○ 4. 0.85 ml

95 Because of one of its side effects, before meperidine hydrochloride is administered, it is recommended that the nurse check Mr. Ortez's

   ○ 1. blood pressure.
   ○ 2. urinary output.
   ○ 3. red blood count.
   ○ 4. body temperature.

Mr. Ortez returns from surgery when the abdominoperineal resection is completed. He has a colostomy.

96 Because of the nature of Mr. Ortez's surgery, the nurse caring for him during his immediate postoperative period should be especially alert for signs and be prepared to assist with the prevention and treatment of

   ○ 1. shock.
   ○ 2. wound infection.
   ○ 3. thrombophlebitis.
   ○ 4. abdominal distention.

97 Mr. Ortez's sigmoid colon is brought up to the abdominal wall to form the stoma for a colostomy. At which site in the sketch below is the sigmoid colon located?

   ○ 1. Site A
   ○ 2. Site B
   ○ 3. Site C
   ○ 4. Site D

98   During the first few postoperative days, the nurse should anticipate that
Mr. Ortez is very likely to require nursing measures and drug therapy
that act to
- ○ 1. reduce nausea.
- ○ 2. relieve discomfort.
- ○ 3. stimulate urinary production.
- ○ 4. dilate peripheral blood vessels.

*Mr. Ortez has a nasogastric tube in place after surgery to remove stom-
ach contents by suction.*

99   An irrigation of Mr. Ortez's gastric tube is ordered. The irrigating
solution of choice is
- ○ 1. sterile water.
- ○ 2. normal saline.
- ○ 3. bacteriostatic water.
- ○ 4. sodium bicarbonate.

100   When Mr. Ortez's gastric tube is being irrigated, the amount of solution
the nurse plans to use should be approximately
- ○ 1. 10 ml, but no more than 30 ml.
- ○ 2. 30 ml, but no more than 60 ml.
- ○ 3. 60 ml, but no more than 90 ml.
- ○ 4. 90 ml, but no more than 120 ml.

101   If the following nursing orders appear on Mr. Ortez's care plan, which
one should the nurse question before carrying it out?
- ○ 1. Fluids as desired
- ○ 2. Throat lozenges every 4 hours as necessary
- ○ 3. Irrigate nasogastric tube once every day
- ○ 4. Oral hygiene every 4 hours when awake

102   When Mr. Ortez's nasogastric tube is eventually removed, which of the
following nursing measures should be carried out promptly?
- ○ 1. Giving the patient oral hygiene
- ○ 2. Offering the patient a soft diet
- ○ 3. Administering a sedative to the patient
- ○ 4. Discontinuing the patient's intravenous therapy

*The nurse cares for Mr. Ortez's abdominal wound which has profuse
drainage.*

103   The gauze dressings on Mr. Ortez's wound should be fluffed and
loosely packed primarily to help to
- ○ 1. prevent pressure on the wound.
- ○ 2. approximate the edges of the wound.
- ○ 3. keep the dressing as light in weight as possible.
- ○ 4. cause discharge to be carried away from the wound.

104   A disadvantage of using waterproof material over Mr. Ortez's dressing to protect bed linens is that waterproof material
    ○ 1. cannot be sterilized.
    ○ 2. traps moisture and heat in the dressing.
    ○ 3. cannot be used when the patient is ambulatory.
    ○ 4. prevents drainage and debris from leaving the wound.

105   When the dressings on Mr. Ortez's wound are changed, it is recommended that the nurse discard soiled dressings in
    ○ 1. the toilet.
    ○ 2. a wastebasket.
    ○ 3. a waterproof bag.
    ○ 4. an old newspaper.

Mr. Ortez is to receive colostomy irrigations and is to be taught how to perform irrigations at home.

106   Of the following solutions, the one of choice for Mr. Ortez's colostomy irrigation is
    ○ 1. normal saline.
    ○ 2. sterile water.
    ○ 3. a mild soap solution.
    ○ 4. a mild antiseptic solution.

107   The nurse notes that Mr. Ortez's stoma is much lighter in color than it has been. A very likely reason for the stoma's appearance is that
    ○ 1. fecal material is obstructing the stoma.
    ○ 2. the patient's fluid intake is inadequate.
    ○ 3. the patient's diet contains too much roughage.
    ○ 4. circulation of blood to the stoma is diminished.

108   One day Mr. Ortez exclaims, "How will I ever adjust to this colostomy!" In this situation, it would be best for the nurse to
    ○ 1. allow the patient to express his concerns.
    ○ 2. suggest that he discuss his concerns with his physician.
    ○ 3. avoid further discussion about his concerns until he is being prepared to go home.
    ○ 4. explain that his concerns will be discussed when he is taught how to care for his colostomy.

109   The nurse can expect that teaching in relation to Mr. Ortez's colostomy irrigation will most probably require that the nurse plan to
    ○ 1. move along slowly as she teaches the patient.
    ○ 2. first teach a relative how to care for the patient.
    ○ 3. refer the patient to a visiting nurse agency for care.
    ○ 4. realize that the patient will be unwilling to learn how to care for himself.

110   In relation to the care of skin and a colostomy bag at home, it would be *least* appropriate to explain to Mr. Ortez the importance of
○ 1. showering rather than taking a tub bath.
○ 2. keeping the skin clean and dry around the stoma.
○ 3. cleaning a reusable colostomy bag in soap and water.
○ 4. using a karaya preparation as a skin protectant as necessary.

111   While irrigating the colostomy, Mr. Ortez opens the lower end of his colostomy bag for drainage. The recommended position for Mr. Ortez during an irrigation he performs on himself is
○ 1. sitting on a toilet.
○ 2. standing at a sink.
○ 3. lying in a bathtub.
○ 4. sitting in a mid-Fowler's position on the bed.

112   During a conversation with Mr. Ortez concerning his feelings about his colostomy, Mr. Ortez remains silent for 15 to 20 seconds before proceeding with what he was saying to the nurse. During this silence, it would be best for the nurse to judge that the patient most likely
○ 1. wants the nurse to talk more.
○ 2. is taking his time to explore his feelings.
○ 3. does not want to talk about his colostomy.
○ 4. has not yet learned how to care for his colostomy.

Mr. Ortez is prepared for discharge.

113   The type of diet recommended for Mr. Ortez is most likely to be a
○ 1. bland diet.
○ 2. regular diet.
○ 3. high-bulk diet.
○ 4. low-residue diet.

114   If Mr. Ortez says he likes the following foods, which one should he be taught to *avoid* or *limit* because of his colostomy?
○ 1. Rice
○ 2. Tortilla shells
○ 3. Refried beans
○ 4. Raw tomatoes

115   Nurses caring for Mr. Ortez discuss the importance of education to help control cancer. The acronym CAUTION is often used to help teach signs that may suggest the presence of cancer. What does the letter A stand for in this acronym?
○ 1. *A* sore that does not heal
○ 2. *A* persistent feeling of abdominal fullness
○ 3. *A* systolic blood pressure frequently above normal
○ 4. *A* body temperature that is regularly slightly above normal

Correct Answers and Rationales

Two numbers appear in parentheses following each rationale. The first number identifies the textbook listed in the references, page 649, and the second number identifies the page(s) in that textbook on which the correct answer can be verified. Occasionally, two textbooks are given for verifying the correct answer.

The Nursing Care of Patients With Disorders of the Gastrointestinal System

Caring for a patient with a bleeding gastric ulcer

1 3. Patients with peptic ulcers generally find that eating relieves stomach pain. The pain is believed due to the irritation of hydrochloric acid and pepsin on the ulcer. Food, especially high-protein food, such as milk, tends to neutralize acid content in the gastrointestinal tract. (15:414)

2 2. The tenth, or vagus, nerve stimulates the stomach to secrete hydrochloric acid. The nerve is sometimes severed in a patient with ulcers to help decrease acid in the stomach as well as to decrease gastric motility. The procedure is called a vagotomy. It is often used in conjunction with a gastroenterostomy because when a vagotomy is used as a sole procedure, recurrences of ulcers tend to be significant. The trigeminal nerve is a sensory nerve of the face and head. The accessory nerve controls muscles of the neck. The hypoglossal nerve controls muscles of the tongue. (10:124; 12:712)

3 4. A peptic ulcer is an open lesion in the gastrointestinal tract. Most peptic ulcers are in the duodenum and are called duodenal ulcers. It is called a gastric ulcer when it occurs in the stomach. Ulcers may occur in the jejunum if a patient has had a surgical joining of the stomach and jejunum to bypass the duodenum. (12:711; 15:414)

4 4. Finding the cause of peptic ulcers has remained elusive. However, persons who experience frequent emotional stress appear to be especially prone to developing ulcers and teaching should include explaining to a patient that eliminating stress in daily living as much as possible is desirable. Participating in competitive sports, having chronic constipation, and having hormonal imbalances do not appear related to the development of ulcers. (12:415; 15:710)

5 3. Red meat contains hemoglobin and enzymes that can cause the stool specimen to give a false-positive result when the specimen is being tested for occult, or hidden, blood. If a guaiac (Hemoccult) method for detecting blood is used, withholding meat is usually not necessary due to the lesser sensitivity of the test.   (5:196)

6 3.   The stools of a person who has slow, oozing blood high in the gastrointestinal tract, such as occurs when a patient has a bleeding gastric ulcer, characteristically are tar-like in color and consistency. The stools also have a very offensive odor.   (12:711)

7 3.   Aluminum hydroxide (Amphojel) is an antacid and acts to neutralize stomach acids, which are especially irritating to peptic ulcers. It is a nonsystemic antacid, that is, it is not readily absorbed into the blood-stream.   (14:233, 237)

8 4.   The letter *q* is commonly used in prescriptions and means *four*. "Take" is abbreviated *Sig*. "With" is abbreviated *c̄*. "Hour" is abbreviated with the letter *h*.   (9:541)

9 2.   In household measurements, 8 ml is equivalent to approximately 2 teaspoons. Fifteen or sixteen ml is equivalent to approximately 1 table-spoon. Because household teaspoons and tablespoons tend to differ in size, it is recommended that a patient obtain a dosing spoon at a phar-macy. The spoon is calibrated to provide accurate dosages of liquid medications.   (9:539)

10 2.   Oil for an oil retention enema should be administered at about body temperature. If the oil is warmer or cooler than body temperature, the patient may have muscular contractions and expel the oil instead of retaining it as he should.   (9:478)

11 2.   The safest way to be sure the nurse is giving the enema to the correct patient is to check the patient's name on his identification bracelet and ask the patient to state his name. Patients sometimes will appear to respond positively when the nurse uses a name as she approaches the bedside, even though the nurse has not spoken the patient's name. These precau-tions should be used by nurses who have cared for the patient previously, as well as by those who have not, whenever a nurse is about to carry out a procedure or administer a therapeutic agent.   (9:546)

12 1.   Procedures carried out by the nurse, the patient's reaction to them, and the results are recorded in the nurses' notes. Such information as the patient's vital signs, fluid intake and output, weight, and the like are entered on a graphic sheet. Progress notes ordinarily are made by a physician in a traditional record. A nursing care plan is a guide to a patient's nursing care.   (9:258)

13 1.   Bisacodyl (Dulcolax) stimulates intestinal mucosa chemically to stimu-late peristalsis and defecation by irritating intestinal mucosa. This laxative is classified as an irritant or stimulant laxative. Increasing water in the intestine is produced by saline laxatives. Epsom salts (magnesium sulfate) and magnesium hydroxide (milk of magnesia) are examples of saline laxatives. An example of a bulk-forming laxative is psyllium (Metamucil). An example of a fecal softener is dioctyl sodium (Colace). Another type of laxative is the lubricant or emollient laxative. Mineral oil is an example of a lubricant laxative.   (14:238)

14   4.   When a rectal suppository is inserted, the patient should be taught to breathe through his mouth to help relax anal sphincters. Holding his breath, coughing, and swallowing tend to contract the anal sphincters.   (9:474)

15   3.   When a peptic ulcer perforates, the patient complains of sudden severe abdominal pain. His abdomen becomes rigid, and eventually distended. He perspires profusely, becomes ashen in color, and is likely to assume a fetal position, with the knees sharply flexed, to help lessen the pain.   (12:712; 15:415)

16   4.   NPO means the patient is to have nothing by mouth. This means the patient has nothing to eat or drink. Oral medications are discontinued unless ordered to the contrary.   (9:260)

17   2.   An exposed organ should be covered with sterile gauze and the gauze should be moistened with sterile normal saline. No attempt should be made to replace the organ. Wound separation with organ exposure is called evisceration. Dehiscence refers to a wound separation without organ exposure.   (9:390)

18   1.   The term ambulate means that one is permitted to walk about. An ambulatory patient may or may not be able to take care of himself or be ready for discharge.   (9:162)

19   3.   The dumping syndrome is believed to be caused in large part by the rapid passage of food through the stomach, especially carbohydrates. A diet low in carbohydrates, high in protein, and moderate in fat is recommended. Foods high in water content are not necessarily contraindicated but liquids should be limited to times between meals or delayed until at least one hour after eating.   (15:418; 16:326)

20   1.   Tea should be avoided by a patient with a peptic ulcer, along with coffee, cola drinks, and alcoholic beverages. These beverages tend to increase the secretion of hydrochloric acid in the stomach.   (16:245)

21   4.   Cimetidine (Tagamet) is a histamine H_2 antagonist that works to decrease the production of hydrochloric acid. This action allows an ulcer a chance to heal. Because of its action, discomfort may also be relieved but the drug is not an analgesic. Nor is it a cholinergic-blocking agent or vasoconstrictor.   (14:235)

22   3.   Adverse effects of cimetidine may occur although they are relatively uncommon. A patient taking this drug should be taught that drowsiness is one likely side effect. Other symptoms that may be caused by an adverse reaction to the drug include diarrhea, muscular discomfort, dizziness, and a skin rash.   (14:237)

23   1.   A person is using denial when he indicates he had no fear in a situation when he was experiencing real fear. Denial is a very strong defense to shut out awareness of the unpleasant. Conversion means changing an emotional conflict into a physical symptom. Compensation means developing behaviors that compensate or make up for various inadequacies. Identification means attaching to oneself qualities that belong to others.   (1:50)

Caring for a patient with an inguinal hernia

24 3.   Strangulation of a hernia is an emergency condition. The loop of the intestine caught in the defect causes a bowel obstruction. The strangulated portion loses its blood supply and becomes gangrenous. A gangrenous portion of the bowel must be excised surgically and the remaining portions of intestine must then be joined (anastomosed).   (8:414)

25 4.   Straining tends to cause the swelling to appear over a herniated area. Examples include straining at stool, coughing, standing, and lifting heavy objects.   (8:415)

26 2.   The preoperative checklist serves as a guide for nurses caring for a patient preoperatively and does not contain the signature of a physician. The following types of information normally are included on a checklist: whether the patient has had a bath with special soap of the agency's choice and has had oral hygiene; whether make-up, hairpins, and hair pieces were removed; whether the patient has voided; how jewelry has been cared for; and where the family is waiting. There is ordinarily a section checked by a unit and an operating room nurse concerning prostheses, the surgical informed-consent form, and a record of examination findings. Still other sections describe patient identification and comments made by a unit nurse about the patient that are helpful for the operating and recovery room nurses to know. Signatures of responsible nurses are required.   (9:383)

27 4.   To help prevent headaches after having spinal anesthesia, it is customary that the patient be kept flat on his back for 6 to 12 hours postoperatively. Such orders as a regular diet, fluids as desired, and out of bed the next day are appropriate in the situation described in this item.   (15:121)

28 2.   A suspensory and ice bags are often used following a herniorrhaphy on a male to help prevent edema of the scrotum. A suspensory does not help to prevent penile impotence, strain on the incision, and wound contamination from the anal area.   (15:426)

29 4.   An ice bag should be filled one-half to one-third full of ice chips. Ice chips mold to the patient's body more readily than ice cubes.   (9:422)

30 1.   To avoid increased intra-abdominal pressure and strain on the operative site, a patient who has had a herniorrhaphy should not cough, sneeze, and exert strain by lifting and straining at stool.   .(15:426)

31 4.   Giving a patient the wrong medication is an act of negligence. Assault is a threat or an attempt to make bodily contact with another person without that person's consent. Battery is an assault that is carried out.

Fraud is false representation with the intention that it will be acted upon by another person. (9:50–51)

32 1. Following a hernia repair, the patient should not strain from lifting heavy objects, straining at stool, coughing, and sneezing. (15:426–427)

33 3. A person complaining of constipation should have roughage and fiber in his diet to increase bulk that promotes peristalsis and evacuation. Raw fruits and vegetables offer more bulk and fiber than cooked fruits and vegetables. Being a vegetarian, eating the large daily meal at noon, and using low-calorie foods and beverages do not necessarily contribute to constipation. (4:348–349)

34 3. Telling a patient that he is not trying while teaching him is likely to strain a nurse-patient relationship, because the nurse is making a demeaning value judgment and assuming that she knows more about the patient than he knows about himself. It is better to use positive approaches, such as teaching the relationship between diet and elimination, and explaining that the indiscriminate use of laxatives can stand in the way of natural elimination. Sitting down while teaching the patient is recommended. It gives the patient the impression that the nurse has the time to care. Listening to what the patient says is also important to help develop a helping nurse-patient relationship. (9:24)

Caring for a patient with ulcerative colitis

35 3. Ulcerative colitis is a disease most often observed in persons of early to middle adulthood, although it can occur at any age in life. The disease affects women and men about equally. (15:428)

36 1. An idiopathic disease is one whose exact cause is unknown. Some theories have been advanced, but there is no general agreement on the cause of ulcerative colitis. Some believe it may have multiple causes, including infection, allergy, autoimmunity, and emotional stress. (15:428)

37 4. Only band rings should be worn on duty. Stones may scratch the patient and tend to collect dirt and organisms. Having long hair braided is recommended. Using lipstick in good taste is appropriate. A nurse needs a watch on duty. (9:276–277)

38 2. Before a nurse can understand another person's behavior, it is best if she has studied and come to understand her own behavior. After knowing herself and examining her own attitudes and prejudices, a nurse is then better able to accept a patient as he is and to respect him as a unique person. (9:18)

39 2. The primary purpose of building a helping nurse-patient relationship is to help the patient to a state of well-being. A friendship may develop between a patient and a nurse, and one may learn to know oneself better when relating well with a patient, but these are not primary purposes for developing the relationship. In general, patients are encouraged to assume as much activity as their condition permits because activity in most instances tends to hasten recovery and well-being.   (9:17)

40   1.   In the situation described in this item, the nurse should listen to the patient and comment by repeating something that the patient has said to verify it. This technique helps a patient most to explore his real feelings. The patient needs acceptance and her need will not be met if her feelings are ignored or avoided in conversation.   (9:21–23)

41   4.   When the patient objected to taking her own bath preoperatively in this situation, it is best to observe the patient's behavior further before making a judgment. Because the patient was willing to help with her bath, possibly she was seeking extra attention; she may be fearful of surgery and want someone with whom she can talk. Having a bath or shower is an important part of preoperative care, and a patient about to have surgery is rarely ready to be taught the values of self-care.   (9:368)

42   4.   Unnecessary exposure of a person without his consent constitutes invasion of privacy. False imprisonment involves preventing the movement of a person without his consent. Assault is a threat or attempt to make bodily contact with another person without his consent. A battery is an assault that is carried out. Slander is an untruthful oral statement about a person that subjects him to ridicule or contempt.   (9:51)

43   2.   A low-residue diet is usually recommended for a person with ulcerative colitis, because this diet is least irritating to intestinal mucosa. The diet should be high in protein and high in vitamin and mineral content. In most instances, the patient is also in need of a diet high in calories.   (16:246)

44   1.   The villi are chiefly responsible for absorbing nutrients from the small intestine. Rugae are folds in the walls of the stomach. Ampullae are sac-like dilatations in a canal or duct. Caries refers to tooth decay.   (10:259)

45   4.   Diarrhea is described as the passage of watery, unformed stools. Often patients with diarrhea have stools at frequent intervals, but frequency is not sufficient in itself to judge whether a patient has diarrhea. Color and odor do not play a part. Some patients say they have diarrhea when they have frequent yet formed stools, but this is an inaccurate use of the term.   (9:471)

46   3.   Using a diaper when the patient has fecal incontinence is usually emotionally distressing and should be done only as a last resort, preferably with the patient's permission. Other measures, such as keeping a bedpan within easy reach for the patient, answering call lights promptly, and using waterproof pads to protect bed linen and clothing are preferable. Diapering is not necessarily associated with a fecal impaction, broken skin areas, and urinary tract infections.   (9:473)

47   3.   When a patient is suffering with emotional distress, it is best for the nurse to remain with the patient and listen to her while she expresses her feelings. Telling her that she will be better soon is of little help. The patient should not be left alone when she is distressed, nor should the nurse's responsibilities be turned over to family members, especially when they too may be emotionally upset about the patient's condition.   (9:23, 472)

48 4.   Clean catch or midstream urine specimens must be collected in a sterile container. If it is difficult to direct the urinary flow directly into a sterile specimen container, a sterile bedpan is used and the specimen then is poured into the specimen container. The labia should be kept well separated while obtaining the specimen to prevent contaminating the specimen. The first flow of urine may wash remaining organisms at the meatus into the specimen and therefore is discarded. Having a female patient void forcibly helps prevent urine from dribbling down over the perineal and anal areas.   (9:458)

49 2.   A urine specimen should be stored in a refrigerator. Storing it at room temperature or in a warm place causes bacteria to grow in the specimen. This will interfere with the accuracy of the findings. Freezing a specimen is unnecessary and is not recommended.   (9:457)

50 3.   When shaving a patient, the nurse should move the razor in the direction in which hair grows. This helps prevent skin irritation and adds to comfort for the patient.   (9:378)

51 2.   The primary reason for the preoperative shave is to help ensure that the skin is scrupulously clean and thus, help minimize wound infections postoperatively. The skin cannot be made sterile.   (9:381)

52 2.   A side-lying position is preferred postoperatively to allow for drainage from the patient's mouth and nose. The supine position, sometimes with the feet slightly elevated, ordinarily is used for the patient who shows signs of shock. The side-lying position does not necessarily place the least amount of stress on the operative site, nor does it necessarily provide the convenience for caretakers.   (9:384)

53 3.   A dropping blood pressure frequently suggests that the patient may be going into shock. A systolic pressure of 90 mm Hg to 100 mm Hg indicates shock is pending. Below 80 mm Hg, shock is present. Other signs of shock include a rapid thready pulse, pale, cold, and clammy skin, rapid respirations, a falling body temperature, and restlessness. A common cause of shock postoperatively is excessive blood loss.   (9:386)

54 4.   Rebreathing into a paper bag often helps relieve hiccups. Other techniques that have been found helpful to relieve hiccups include placing pressure on the patient's closed eyelids, giving the patient a slice of lemon sprinkled with a few drops of bitters, and placing pressure with a cotton swab on the top of the mouth where the hard and soft palate meet. The reason why these methods help to relieve hiccups is not understood. If none of the conservative methods just described helps, a medication, such as chlorpromazine hydrochloride (Thorazine) may be prescribed.   (9:387)

55 2.   Maintaining electrolyte balance following an ileostomy is often difficult during the postoperative period primarily because there is frequently a profuse output of fluids, which contain electrolytes, from the ostomy. The nurse should be alert to such signs as general weakness, confusion, trembling, and dehydration and should be prepared to assist with therapy to correct and prevent electrolyte imbalances. Loss of functioning of the large intestine has little if anything to do with electrolyte imbalance. Most absorption of nutrients occurs high in the small intestine rather than in the ileum, where the ostomy has been formed. Intractable vomiting can threaten electrolyte balance, but the condition is not associated with having an ileostomy. (15:450)

56 2. Theoretically, an item is considered to be sterile when all organisms on it are destroyed. (9:280)

57 4. Little or no discharge from an ileostomy should suggest to the nurse that the patient may have an intestinal obstruction, and the condition should be reported promptly. Surgical intervention may be required if the intestine is strangulated or twisted. Sometimes, irrigating the ostomy may flush out debris that may be causing the obstruction. Unlikely causes of a decreased output from an ileostomy include excessive gas formation, atonic constipation, and a wound infection. (15:454)

58 3. Open windows may bring in air pollution, may cause some persons to be uncomfortable, and may influence a thermostat. However, the primary reason for keeping windows closed because of drafts is that organisms can be spread about by air currents. (9:277, 296)

59 3. The skin should be immaculately clean before an ileostomy appliance is used. A mild soap and tepid water are most often recommended. Alcohol is likely to dry and irritate the skin. Scrubbing should be avoided because friction is likely to irritate the skin. Patting the skin with cotton balls is ineffective for a thorough cleansing. (15:451)

60 4. A faceplate (disc) surrounds the stoma; it does not cover it. Various designs are available but the faceplate should be comfortable and should be sized so that a minimum of skin is exposed around the stoma. Approximately ⅛ inch is recommended. The discharge from an ileostomy stoma is very irritating to the skin. Exposing a minimum amount of skin is recommended to avoid skin irritation and breakdown. (15:453)

61 4. Tincture of benzoin and karaya powder are two agents commonly used to protect the skin under the appliance's faceplate. Tincture of benzoin should not be used on irritated or broken skin; it contains alcohol, which could cause additional irritation and discomfort when applied. The tincture should be dry but sticky before applying the ostomy appliance. Talcum powder does not protect the skin well from irritating fecal drainage. Petrolatum tends to soften the skin and increase the danger of skin breakdown. Iodine tincture is used primarily for antiseptic purposes and does little to protect the skin from irritation. (15:453)

62 1. Karaya gum or skin cement is used most often to fasten an ostomy appliance on the skin. Some appliances may use adhesive. Pastes, ointments, and cellophane tape will not secure the appliance well to the skin. (15:452–453)

63 3. When a patient complains of stinging, tingling, or itching after an ostomy appliance change, it is best to observe the patient for a few minutes. Usually, the unpleasant sensation will subside relatively quickly. If the uncomfortable sensation continues beyond a few minutes, the appliance should be removed and the nurse-in-charge notified. A temporary appliance may be used until the problem with the permanent appliance has been identified.   (15:453)

64 1. There is less likelihood of intestinal content spilling onto the skin when the nurse changes an ostomy appliance when the patient's bowel is inactive. Therefore, most patients find it best to change the appliance immediately upon awakening in the morning or several hours after eating. Exercise and eating tend to increase bowel activity.   (15:453–454)

65 4. Because the discharge from an ileostomy is high in water content, it is difficult for most patients to gain control of bowel movements, although some persons can be without a bag over the stoma for short periods of time. It is realistic for many persons with an ileostomy to play tennis, swim, have sexual relations, and in general, pursue careers and enjoy all manner of social activities.   (8:484)

66 4. Time-release capsules and hard-coated pills are not ordinarily recommended for a patient with an ileostomy. These types of medications are likely to be expelled from the stoma before the body has a chance to absorb them. Other types of medication, such as aspirin, a chewable tablet, and a liquid cough medication, are not necessarily contraindicated for a patient with an ileostomy.   (8:483)

67 1. Many cities have clubs whose members are living successfully and happily with an ostomy. Patients new to living with an ostomy often derive great benefit from seeing and talking with club members. It is common agency policy that the patient with an ostomy be visited by a club member; in some instances, a physician's permission is required for such a visit.   (8:484)

68 3. There is a creation of a reservoir to collect the feces when a patient has a pouch, or continent, ileostomy. The reservoir is formed with a portion of the terminal ileum, and a nipple-type valve is constructed at the distal ileal segment of the reservoir. The pouch empties through a stoma on the abdomen, but unlike a traditional ileostomy, fecal material collects in the pouch, which is emptied with a catheter 3 to 4 times a day. When it functions properly, this type of ileostomy eliminates a need for an external ileostomy appliance. The biggest problem with a pouch ileostomy has usually been a poorly functioning nipple valve with leakage of fecal material. The fecal material remains liquid in nature, and the patient still needs to avoid gas-forming foods to control problems with flatus.   (15:455)

Caring for a patient with hemorrhoids

69 4. The symptoms of internal hemorrhoids and cancer of the rectum are similar and include bleeding, swelling of tissues, discomfort, and interference with normal bowel habits. Because of the danger of a malignancy, it is unwise for a person who has bleeding from the rectum to assume that it is due to hemorrhoids.   (15:718)

70   3.   Constipation favors the development of hemorrhoids. Intra-abdominal tumors, pregnancy, and hereditary factors may also predispose to hemorrhoids. Using enemas, drinking beer, and having a diet high in roughage are not likely causes of hemorrhoids.   (15:718)

71   2.   Hemorrhoids are best defined as varicose veins in the rectum.   (15:718)

72   2.   It is best to place a bedridden patient on either side, with his head over a pillow, when he is vomiting. This positioning allows for best drainage from the mouth and helps prevent aspiration of vomitus. The face-lying position would not necessarily be contraindicated but very few patients who have just had surgery find the position to be comfortable.   (9:97)

73   2.   The patient who experiences nausea should take a few deep breaths. Most patients feel best lying quietly, rather than sitting or standing. Pressure on the stomach area may bring on vomiting. If food and fluids are permitted, they should be limited temporarily until nausea subsides.   (9:96)

74   3.   Nausea often is relieved when a patient sips carbonated beverages, if these beverages are permitted. Cola drinks are especially effective. Some patients tolerate ice chips. Such liquids as coffee, fruit juices, and sodium bicarbonate in water are likely to increase nausea.   (9:96)

75   1.   Urinary elimination can be promoted when retention is present in various ways: have the male patient stand at the bedside with a urinal in place; use a commode or bathroom when permitted; warm a bedpan or urinal before having the patient try to use it; offer the patient fluids to drink; place the patient's hands in warm water; pour warm water over the perineal area; and place the patient in a tub of warm water. If conservative measures fail, it is then necessary to obtain an order for catheterization. Retention of urine is not uncommon following a hemorrhoidectomy and should be corrected because continued retention may lead to postoperative complications.   (15:719)

76   3.   To be most effective, a sitz bath should take between 20 and 30 minutes. Longer periods are likely to cause the patient undue fatigue and may cause the body to have a reverse reaction from the initial response to warmth.   (9:427)

77   4.   Typically, patients are fearful of having the first bowel movement after a hemorrhoidectomy because of anticipated discomfort. Usually, the first bowel movement is uncomfortable but often less so than most patients anticipate. A stool softener is used to keep feces soft, and an enema may be ordered if the patient does not have a bowel movement for 2 to 3 days postoperatively. Concerns related to impotence, urinary retention, and fecal incontinence are not reported in patients who have had a hemorrhoidectomy.   (15:719)

78   3.   Psyllium (Metamucil) is an example of a bulk-forming laxative. Epsom salts is a saline laxative. Mineral oil is an emollient laxative. Dioctyl sodium (Colace) is a surface-active agent and acts to soften feces by allowing water to enter the hardened stool.   (12:238)

79   2.   Before starting a regular exercise program, a person should have a complete examination so that he can be guided by a physician's advice concerning the type of exercising recommended for him. Many authorities recommend using a stress test as part of the examination.   (9:126, 128)

80   2.   Before exercising, a person should plan to do warming-up exercises. This prepares the body and will put less strain on muscles and the cardiopulmonary system. After exercising, the person should taper off for cooling down, which helps the body adjust to the change in activity. Stretching exercises are good for warming up and cooling off, or the exercise of choice can be started slowly and ended by gradually tapering off.   (9:128)

Caring for a patient with a malignant tumor of the rectum

81   3.   Bowel habits ordinarily change when a patient is suffering with a malignancy in the rectum. The patient may complain of constipation, diarrhea, or both. Also, the stool is likely to change as the tumor becomes large enough to encroach on the colon passageway to alter its normal shape. If the patient ignores early signs, the tumor may eventually completely obstruct the rectum. Bright red blood on the stool may also be a sign of rectal malignancy and should not be ignored or attributed to hemorrhoids unless confirmed by a physician.   (15:442, 426)

82   1.   A weight loss of 10 pounds in 2 weeks is significant and may have implications for both medical and nursing care. Lack of exercise except for walking, a sudden change in hair coloring, and sleeping less at night but napping during the day are not necessarily significant in terms of the health of a person with a suspected malignant tumor in the rectum.   (12:579)

83   3.   Occult means obscure, hidden, or concealed. Examining a stool specimen for occult blood means that the specimen is examined for blood not visible to the naked eye. Testing for occult blood is a common diagnostic tool when malignancies of the colon and rectum are suspected.   (12:696)

84   3.   Ice chips help to numb taste buds and therefore, minimize the objectionable taste of an oral medication, such as castor oil.   (9:549)

85   4.   There are discomforts associated with a barium enema. The patient is likely to experience abdominal cramping and distention. The barium and the air injected into the colon account for these discomforts. Dizziness, headaches, nausea, vomiting, and bowel and urinary incontinence are not associated with a barium enema.   (5:573; 17:578)

86 2.   After a barium enema, a laxative is ordinarily given to prevent the barium from causing constipation and possibly a fecal impaction. Retained barium is unrelated to gastritis and intestinal herniation. It will not predispose to colitis but may aggravate pre-existing acute colitis.   (15:400; 17:578)

87 4.   The position of choice for a sigmoidoscopy is the knee-chest position. The position provides the most comfort for the patient and convenience for the examiner.   (15:402)

88 3.   When compared with a benign tumor, a malignant tumor tends to grow rapidly. It is rarely encapsulated, infiltrates to surrounding tissues, spreads to lymph nodes, and is likely to recur after removal. In contrast, a benign tumor grows slowly, is almost always encapsulated, does not spread to surrounding tissues, and usually does not recur after removal. The differences in the characteristics of malignant and benign tumors account largely for the differences in prognosis for the host of the tumor.   (15:577)

89 2.   Chlordiazepoxide (Librium) is a psychotherapeutic agent commonly used to help relieve worry, anxiety, and tension. It is prescribed preoperatively to help alleviate worry and anxiety, especially when the patient is having surgery of a nature fearful to the patient. The drug has no effect on bleeding time, urinary production, and nausea and vomiting.   (14:218)

90 3.   A basic formula to determine the correct dosage of a solid oral medication is as follows:

$$\frac{D(\text{desired})}{H(\text{have})} = X \ (1 \ \text{dose})$$

$$\frac{10 \ \text{mg}}{5 \ \text{mg}} = 2 \ \text{tablets per dose}$$

The patient is to receive 10 mg three times daily (t.i.d.). Therefore, the patient should receive a total of 6 capsules daily ($3 \times 2 = 6$).   (14:10–11)

91 1.   Fried foods of any sort are contraindicated on a low-residue diet. Eggs are permissible when they are not fried. Crisp bacon, broiled or baked fish, and broiled hamburger are permissible. The diet aims to leave as little residue as possible in the colon.   (16:248)

92 1.   The usual dosage of atropine sulfate for an adult is 0.4 to 0.6 mg. A dosage of 5 mg is dangerously large and should be questioned. Atropine sulfate ordinarily is administered intramuscularly before surgery and it is not contraindicated for most elderly patients and for those having intestinal surgery. It is contraindicated for persons with glaucoma and for most men with prostatic hypertrophy.   (14:54–57)

93 4.   Atropine sulfate is used preoperatively to decrease respiratory secretions. In some people, it may also produce sleepiness, which is desirable in the preoperative period, but this is not the primary reason for using atropine sulfate preoperatively.   (14:54–57)

94 3.   The nurse should use 0.75 ml in order to give the patient described in this item the ordered 75 mg. A common formula to compute proper dosage is as follows:

$$\frac{\text{Dosage desired}}{\text{Dosage on hand}} \times \text{quantity} = \text{Amount to administer}$$

(14:11–12)

$$\frac{75 \text{ mg}}{100 \text{ mg}} \times 1 \text{ ml} = \frac{75}{100} = 0.75 \text{ ml to administer}$$

95   1.   Meperidine hydrochloride tends to cause a drop in blood pressure and therefore, the patient's blood pressure is often checked before administering the drug. It is not usually given without consulting a physician if the systolic blood pressure is below about 100 mm Hg.   (14:61)

96   1.   An abdominoperineal resection requires a prolonged period of anesthesia and extensive exposure and excision of body tissues with a considerable loss of fluid and blood. These factors, as well as the fact that the patient is elderly, predispose to postoperative shock, which is usually due to a reduction in the volume of intravascular fluid.   (15:443)

97   1.   Site A is the sigmoid colon in the drawing in this item. Site B is the descending colon. Site C is the transverse colon. Site D is the ascending colon.   (10:255)

98   2.   A patient who has had an abdominoperineal resection has had extensive surgical intervention and has two operative sites, one on the abdomen and the other in the perineal area. The nurse should anticipate that the patient is very likely to experience considerable discomfort following surgery. She should expect to use various nursing measures as well as prescribed analgesics to promote comfort.   (15:443)

99   2.   Normal saline is the solution of choice when irrigating a nasogastric tube and is used unless ordered otherwise. The tube should not be irrigated without an order. Normal saline is less irritating to mucous membranes than water, bacteriostatic water, and sodium bicarbonate solution because normal saline most nearly approximates the body's tissue fluids.   (9:109)

100   2.   Approximately 30 ml of solution and no more than 60 ml usually is recommended to be used to irrigate a suction tube. Less than that amount is likely to be ineffective. Using more than 60 ml is likely to cause distention. Distention can be a serious problem because it places strain on sutures, especially when surgery has been performed on the stomach.   (9:109)

101   1.   It is usual for a patient with gastrointestinal suctioning to have nothing by mouth, including fluids, because oral fluids will be suctioned out with gastric secretions and wash the gastrointestinal content of important constituents. This will contribute to electrolyte and acid-base imbalances. Sometimes, a few ice chips or very small sips of water *may* be allowed. Appropriate nursing orders for a patient having gastrointestinal suctioning include having oral hygiene regularly. The drainage tube may be ordered to be irrigated. Without an order, it should not be irrigated. Throat lozenges are used to relieve discomfort in the throat due to the mechanical irritation cause by the tube.   (15:418)

102   1.   After removing a nasogastric tube, it is important to give the patient oral hygiene promptly. The tube has been resting in the stomach and often also in duodenal contents, and the odor and taste of the contents in the tube are very offensive. Ordinarily, the patient begins taking oral nourishment by being offered clear liquids. He then gradually progresses to additional nourishment. Administering a sedative is not indicated after a suction tube is removed. Intravenous therapy is discontinued only with a specific order.   (9:105)

103   4.   A fluffed and loosely packed dressing helps to carry drainage away from a wound by capillary action. Liquid (drainage) rises on dressing fibers that act as small wicks. Fluffed dressings also allow for air circulation, thus helping to prevent skin irritation by increasing evaporation of moisture and dissipating heat.   (9:409)

104   2.   Using waterproof material to cover a dressing over a drainage wound traps moisture and heat in the dressing. This tends to cause skin irritation and eventually skin breakdown. The warmth and moisture also favor the growth of microorganisms.   (9:414)

105   3.   To prevent the spread of organisms, soiled dressings should be discarded in waterproof bags, and bags should be sealed tightly. Dressings are likely to clog a toilet. Placing them in a wastebasket contaminates the container and allows for the spread of organisms. Placing soiled dressings in a newspaper is unsafe. Drainage may soak through the paper, thereby contaminating the hands of everyone handling the package.   (9:407)

106   1.   Normal saline is the best choice for irrigating a colostomy. Some persons use plain water, but sterile water is unnecessary because the intestinal tract is not sterile. Sterile water is also expensive. Soap and antiseptic solutions are not recommended because of possible irritating effects.   (9:483)

107   4.   When the stoma becomes light and blanched in color, possibly circulation to the stoma is inadequate. The nurse-in-charge should be notified in such a situation. The stoma normally appears dark pink to red. A deep color with a purplish hue also suggests that the stoma may not be receiving adequate blood flow.   (9:481; 15:455)

108   1.   It is best for the nurse to allow the patient time in a nonjudgmental atmosphere to discuss concerns openly about his care and illness. Suggesting that he speak to his physician and avoiding further conversation at the time of the patient's comment offer the patient no support and ignore his feelings.   (9:20–21, 23)

109   1.   Elderly patients can most certainly learn, but the nurse should anticipate that the older patient is slower in his or her movements and responses than younger adults. Learning will therefore take longer. There is nothing to indicate in the situation described in this item that the nurse should plan to teach a relative to care for the patient, that he needs to be referred to a visiting nurse agency at this time for care, or that the patient is unwilling to care for himself.   (15:31)

110   1.   A person with a colostomy can safely use either a shower or a bathtub. It is also appropriate to teach a patient with a colostomy to keep the skin clean and dry around the stoma, to clean a reusable colostomy bag with soap and water, and to use a karaya preparation, tincture of benzoin, or vanishing cream as a skin protectant as necessary.   (9:490-491)

111   1.   Patients are taught to open the lower end of the colostomy bag and sit on a toilet while irrigating a colostomy. The drainage then goes directly into the toilet and the position is like the one that the patient normally used for a bowel movement. Lying down and standing while irrigating a colostomy are not as convenient for the patient.   (9:484)

112   2.   Very often, persons will stop discussing their feelings about something in order to take time to explore and study these feelings further. The nurse should learn to respect silences rather than assume that the patient wants the nurse to talk more or that the patient does not want to talk. Moments of silence are often an important part of communication.   (9:19-20)

113   2.   Following a colostomy, most patients are able to eat a regular diet when they are ready to go home. The patient may need to restrict certain foods and beverages that irritate his intestinal tract, but these usually are identified on an individual basis. In general, most patients do best by avoiding gas-forming foods, such as cabbage, beans, cheese, uncooked onions, highly spiced foods, and garlic.   (16:327)

114   3.   Beans are likely to cause gas in the gastrointestinal tract and therefore, most persons with a colostomy prefer to avoid them. Rice, tomatoes, and tortilla shells should normally present no problem to the person with a colostomy.   (15:459)

115   1.   The acronym CAUTION is frequently used to recall the 7 warning signs of cancer:

> C — Change in bowel or bladder habits
> A — A sore that does not heal
> U — Unusual bleeding or discharge
> T — Thickening or lump in the breast or elsewhere
> I — Indigestion or difficulty with swallowing
> O — Obvious change in a wart or mole
> N — Nagging cough or hoarseness

An elevated body temperature, a persistent feeling of abdominal fullness, and an elevated systolic blood pressure are not among typical early signs of a malignancy.   (12:579)

Classification of Test Items

Directions: *Each item in the previous review test is classified here according to the subject area it tests. Place a check mark after each item you answered **correctly** by referring to your answers. Total the number of items you answered correctly in each area and enter the numbers in the correct places on pages 553–556.*

Clinical: Medical/Surgical Nursing (Adults)

1 ✓	24 ✓	35 ✓	55 ✓	70 ✓	87 ✓
3 ✓	25 ✓	36 ✓	57 ✓	71 ✓	88 ✓
4 ✓	26 ✓	50 ___	65 ___	72 ✓	96 ✓
5 ✓	27 ✓	51 ✓	66 ___	77 ✓	98 ✓
6 ✓	28 ✓	52 ___	67 ✓	81 ✓	107 ✓
15 ✓	30 ✓	53 ✓	68 ___	82 ✓	115 ✓
17 ✓	32 ✓	54 ✓	69 ✓	83 ___	

TOTAL 35

Biological/Physical Sciences

2 ✓	44 ___	97 ✓	103 ___

TOTAL 2

Fundamentals of Nursing

8 ✓	18 ✓	58 ✓	73 ✓	85 ✓	105 ✓
9 ✓	29 ___	59 ✓	74 ✓	86 ___	106 ✓
10 ___	37 ✓	60 ___	75 ✓	99 ✓	110 ___
11 ✓	45 ✓	61 ___	76 ___	100 ✓	111 ✓
12 ✓	48 ✓	62 ✓	79 ✓	101 ✓	
14 ✓	49 ✓	63 ___	80 ✓	102 ___	
16 ✓	56 ✓	64 ___	84 ___	104 ✓	

TOTAL 30

Diet Therapy/Nutrition

19 ___✓___   33 ___✓___   43 ___✓___   91 ___✓___   113 _____   114 _____

20 ___✓___

TOTAL ___5___

Pharmacology

7 ___✓___   21 ___✓___   78 ___✓___   90 ___✓___   93 ___✓___   95 ___✓___

13 ___✓___   22 ___✓___   89 ___✓___   92 _____   94 ___✓___

TOTAL ___10___

Psychosocial Sciences

23 ___✓___   38 ___✓___   40 ___✓___   42 ___✓___   47 ___✓___   109 ___✓___

31 ___✓___   39 ___✓___   41 ___✓___   46 ___✓___   108 ___✓___   112 ___✓___

34 ___✓___

TOTAL ___13___

Review Test 7

Directions: *With a pencil, blacken the circle in front of the option you have chosen for your correct answer.*

The Nursing Care of Patients With Disorders of the Gastrointestinal System (Continued)

A nurse is assigned to admit and care for 22-year-old Mr. Wagner, who has appendicitis. An appendectomy is planned.

   1   Upon admission, Mr. Wagner has a complete blood count that, in view of the diagnosis, is most likely to show a rise in his blood's
      ○ 1. red cell count.
      ○ 2. platelet count.
      ○ 3. white cell count.
      ○ 4. reticulocyte count.

2 Mr. Wagner is most likely to complain of tenderness over McBurney's point. The quadrant of the abdomen in which McBurney's point is located is the
  O 1. left lower quadrant.
  O 2. left upper quadrant.
  O 3. right lower quadrant.
  O 4. right upper quadrant.

3 If Mr. Wagner had tried self-treatment before seeking health care when he had abdominal pain, it would have been most dangerous for him if he had
  O 1. taken aspirin.
  O 2. used a laxative.
  O 3. applied cold to his abdomen.
  O 4. chosen to lie on his right side in bed.

4 Mr. Wagner asks the admitting nurse where his appendix is located in his body. From which part of the intestine does the vermiform appendix arise?
  O 1. From the cecum
  O 2. From the jejunum
  O 3. From the sigmoid flexure
  O 4. From the ascending colon

5 After the nurse explains that the appendix has no known function in the body, Mr. Wagner asks, "Well, what is the function of the colon?" The nurse should answer that the colon has two primary functions: to store and eliminate wastes and to absorb
  O 1. salt.
  O 2. iron.
  O 3. water.
  O 4. carbohydrates.

Preoperatively, Mr. Wagner is given atropine sulfate.

6 The atropine sulfate is most likely to make Mr. Wagner feel
  O 1. dizzy.
  O 2. thirsty.
  O 3. listless.
  O 4. confused.

Mr. Wagner complains of abdominal distention postoperatively.

7 If Mr. Wagner can safely assume all of the following positions in bed, which one is most likely to help relieve distention?
  O 1. The side-lying position

    ○ 2. The back-lying position
    ○ 3. The knee-chest position
    ○ 4. The semi-sitting position

8 A rectal tube is used for Mr. Wagner to relieve distention. The length of time that the tube should be left in place each time it is used is
    ○ 1. 5 minutes.
    ○ 2. 20 minutes.
    ○ 3. 1 hour.
    ○ 4. 2 hours.

The nurse prepares to change Mr. Wagner's dressing.

9 When the nurse's working area is too low for her, she is most likely to put strain on her
    ○ 1. legs.
    ○ 2. arms.
    ○ 3. back.
    ○ 4. abdomen.

10 Mr. Wagner is lying on his abdomen when the nurse wishes to change his dressing. The nurse helps him turn *away* from her and onto his back. In which position should Mr. Wagner's face be placed for most comfort and convenience while he is being turned?
    ○ 1. Toward the nurse
    ○ 2. Away from the nurse
    ○ 3. Toward his chest with the neck straight
    ○ 4. Toward the head of the bed with his neck straight

Mr. Wagner and the nurse discuss oral hygiene.

11 Mr. Wagner says he has several cavities that need to be filled as soon as he recuperates. It is believed that a factor making a person prone to developing cavities is
    ○ 1. using strong antiseptic mouthwashes.
    ○ 2. having a diet high in roughage content.
    ○ 3. drinking black coffee in large amounts.
    ○ 4. eating sugar-sweetened snacks frequently.

12 Mr. Wagner should be taught that of the following substances in many toothpastes and powders, the one that has been found helpful in preventing cavities is
    ○ 1. bromine.
    ○ 2. chlorophyll.
    ○ 3. sodium chloride.
    ○ 4. stannous fluoride.

13 Mr. Wagner asks the nurse if using a jet water spray is good for oral hygiene. The nurse should explain that, if used *incorrectly*, the spray is likely to
O 1. damage tooth enamel.
O 2. force debris into tissue pockets.
O 3. injure cells on the surface of the tongue.
O 4. spread microorganisms about the mouth.

14 Mr. Wagner asks the nurse how many teeth he has. If he has had none removed, including his third molars (wisdom teeth), the number of teeth Mr. Wagner should have is
O 1. 24.
O 2. 28.
O 3. 32.
O 4. 36.

Nurses caring for Mr. Wagner discuss their interpersonal relationships with Mr. Wagner.

15 Mr. Wagner is encouraged to be up and about and to start self-care on his first postoperative day. He has a reason to justify ignoring suggestions for every health worker who speaks to him. The type of defense mechanism that Mr. Wagner is demonstrating is called
O 1. projection.
O 2. compensation.
O 3. symbolization.
O 4. rationalization.

16 The primary reason for Mr. Wagner's using a defense mechanism is to
O 1. dispel fear.
O 2. channel the id.
O 3. relieve anxiety.
O 4. change an emotionally laden situation.

17 The defense mechanism that Mr. Wagner is using is largely nonconstructive. It is generally agreed that of the following defense mechanisms, the one that is usually most constructive is
O 1. denial.
O 2. repression.
O 3. conversion.
O 4. sublimation.

18 Shortly before he is discharged, Mr. Wagner tells the nurse that he did not like her and wishes that someone else could have cared for him. Which of the following courses of action is *least* constructive in terms of coping with the tension and anger the nurse feels?
O 1. Discuss the situation with a supervisor.
O 2. Engage in an active sport, such as swimming.

○ 3. Write a description of the situation and then destroy what was written.

○ 4. Go to bed early to allow sufficient time to sleep off the tension and anger.

The Nursing Care of Patients With Disorders of the Biliary System

Ms. Bidell, a 50-year-old woman, has cholecystitis and gallstones. She is hospitalized for a cholecystectomy.

19 Because Ms. Bidell is allergic to the dye ordinarily used to visualize the gallbladder by x-ray examination, sonography is used. What preparation, if any, is necessary for a study of the gallbladder by this method of examination?

○ 1. No special preparation is necessary.

○ 2. Preparation includes eating a test meal.

○ 3. Preparation includes having a cleansing enema.

○ 4. Preparation includes fasting before the examination.

20 The word used to describe Ms. Bidell's stone formation in her body is

○ 1. lithium.

○ 2. lithemia.

○ 3. lithiasis.

○ 4. lithicosis.

Ms. Bidell is to receive a large-volume cleansing enema preoperatively.

21 The temperature of the solution used for Ms. Bidell's cleansing enema should be *no greater* than

○ 1. 95 °F (35°C).

○ 2. 100°F (38°C).

○ 3. 105°F (41°C).

○ 4. 110°F (43°C).

22 When giving Ms. Bidell the enema, the nurse should hold the solution container above the patient's anal area a distance of between

○ 1. 4 and 6 inches (10 and 15 cm).

○ 2. 8 and 10 inches (20 and 25 cm).

○ 3. 12 and 20 inches (30 and 50 cm).

○ 4. 22 and 30 inches (55 and 75 cm).

23 When giving the enema to Ms. Bidell, the nurse should insert the rectal tube a distance of about

○ 1. 1 to 2 inches (2½ to 5 cm).

○ 2. 3 to 4 inches (7½ to 10 cm).
○ 3. 6 to 8 inches (15 to 20 cm).
○ 4. 9 to 10 inches (22½ to 25 cm).

24 Toward which of the following anatomical structures should the nurse direct the rectal tube when giving Ms. Bidell the cleansing enema?
○ 1. Toward the pubis
○ 2. Toward either hip
○ 3. Toward the umbilicus
○ 4. Toward the lower back

25 If the rectal tube meets resistance when it is introduced, the nurse should stop inserting the tube and ask Ms. Bidell to
○ 1. cough several times.
○ 2. flex her knees sharply.
○ 3. take several deep breaths.
○ 4. change her position in bed.

The nurse cares for Ms. Bidell's operative wound postoperatively.

26 A Penrose drain is placed in Ms. Bidell's wound at the time of surgery, primarily to
○ 1. help drainage escape from the surgical area.
○ 2. decrease the likelihood of scar tissue formation.
○ 3. provide a means for irrigating the surgical wound.
○ 4. prevent the accumulation of gas in the intestinal tract.

27 A T tube present in Ms. Bidell's surgical wound acts primarily to help
○ 1. carry bile outside of the body.
○ 2. prevent infection in the common bile duct.
○ 3. carry any remaining sandy material to the surface of the abdomen.
○ 4. prevent bile from entering the intestine until adequate healing has occurred.

28 If bile appears on Ms. Bidell's dressing, the color of the drainage can be expected to be
○ 1. dark red.
○ 2. clay-white.
○ 3. dark brown.
○ 4. greenish-yellow.

29 When changing Ms. Bidell's dressing, which of the following preparations is recommended for the nurse to use when removing adhesive remnants from Ms. Bidell's skin?
○ 1. Normal saline
○ 2. Hydrogen peroxide
○ 3. An antiseptic, such as alcohol
○ 4. An ointment, such as A and D ointment

30 A *disadvantage* in using acetone to remove adhesive remnants from Ms. Bidell's skin is that acetone

    O 1. is flammable.
    O 2. dries the skin.
    O 3. stains the skin.
    O 4. is difficult to remove from the skin.

31   To protect Ms. Bidell's skin where adhesive will be applied when securing a fresh dressing, it is best for the nurse to cover the area with collodian or
    O 1. petrolatum.
    O 2. calamine lotion.
    O 3. paste of zinc oxide.
    O 4. tincture of benzoin.

32   After changing Ms. Bidell's dressing, the nurse uses the following techniques when washing her hands. Which one is in *error*?
    O 1. The nurse uses warm running water.
    O 2. The nurse uses bar soap.
    O 3. The nurse washes her wrists and lower forearms.
    O 4. The nurse returns the soap to its dish between latherings.

Postoperative exercises and moving about in bed are discussed with Ms. Bidell.

33   The nurse should take into account that of the following activities, it will be more *uncomfortable* for Ms. Bidell than for patients with most other types of abdominal surgery to
    O 1. turn in bed.
    O 2. sit up in bed.
    O 3. do leg exercises.
    O 4. take deep breaths.

34   The nurse teaches Ms. Bidell how to help prevent thrombophlebitis. The best exercises to prevent thrombophlebitis for the bedridden person are
    O 1. sit-ups.
    O 2. active leg exercises.
    O 3. isometric thigh exercises.
    O 4. body rollings from side to side.

35   When Ms. Bidell develops thrombophlebitis postoperatively, the nurse should understand that massaging her affected leg is dangerous primarily because massage may cause
    O 1. injury to affected tissues.
    O 2. collapse of affected veins.
    O 3. inflammation to spread in the leg.
    O 4. a clot to dislodge, resulting in an embolism.

36   To help promote venous return in Ms. Bidell's leg where thrombophlebitis is present, the nurse should expect that one nursing order will most likely indicate that Ms. Bidell's leg should be

    ○   1.   elevated.
    ○   2.   exercised passively.
    ○   3.   wrapped with cold compresses.
    ○   4.   wrapped with pressure dressings.

Ms. Bidell is to be out of bed.

37   Before helping Ms. Bidell out of bed, the nurse should prepare the patient by having her
    ○   1.   nap for about a half hour.
    ○   2.   take several deep breaths.
    ○   3.   use leg exercises for a few minutes.
    ○   4.   sit in a high-Fowler's position for a few minutes.

38   When Ms. Bidell stands at the side of her bed, her base of support is in her
    ○   1.   feet.
    ○   2.   knees.
    ○   3.   ankles.
    ○   4.   thighs.

39   When she is in a standing position, where is Ms. Bidell's center of gravity?
    ○   1.   In the feet
    ○   2.   Near the end of the spine
    ○   3.   Centered and about halfway between the pubis and umbilicus
    ○   4.   Centered and about halfway between the umbilicus and shoulders

40   When Ms. Bidell is sitting in a chair, in relation to her posture, the nurse should teach her to *avoid*
    ○   1.   crossing her legs at her knees.
    ○   2.   keeping her feet flat on the floor.
    ○   3.   placing her hands crossed on her lap.
    ○   4.   holding her head up with the chin tucked in slightly.

During a shift-change report, Ms. Bidell is described as having abdominal distention and constipation.

41   Abdominal distention means Ms. Bidell's problem is that the intestines have accumulated larger-than-average amounts of
    ○   1.   gas.
    ○   2.   mucus.
    ○   3.   bacteria.
    ○   4.   enzymes.

42   Ms. Bidell is to have a rectal suppository. If the nurse inserts the suppository while using the following techniques, which one is in *error*?
    ○   1.   The nurse dons a waterproof glove.
    ○   2.   The nurse lubricates the suppository.
    ○   3.   The nurse inserts the suppository just beyond the external sphincter into the anal canal.

○ 4. The nurse encourages the patient to walk about while waiting for the suppository to take effect.

Ms. Bidell queries the nurse concerning her gallbladder and liver.

43 Ms. Bidell asks the nurse, "I no longer have a gallbladder but of what use was it anyway?" The nurse should explain that one function of the gallbladder is to
○ 1. store bile.
○ 2. manufacture bilirubin.
○ 3. produce blood platelets.
○ 4. secrete a digestive juice.

44 "And bile?" Ms. Bidell asks. The nurse should explain that bile contains salts that are particularly important for the digestion of
○ 1. fats.
○ 2. proteins.
○ 3. fibrous foods.
○ 4. carbohydrates.

45 Ms. Bidell goes on to ask, "And what does the liver do?" The nurse should answer that one function of the liver is to manufacture
○ 1. pepsin.
○ 2. trypsin.
○ 3. heparin.
○ 4. peptidases.

46 Ms. Bidell asks, "Is liver cirrhosis associated with my gallbladder problem?" The nurse explains that cirrhosis of the liver is a disease most commonly associated with
○ 1. alcoholism.
○ 2. hypoglycemia.
○ 3. drug addiction.
○ 4. diabetes mellitus.

The remaining items in this situation are individual items related to Ms. Bidell's care.

47 Ms. Bidell's electrolyte balance is monitored postoperatively. The term describing the chemical activity of an electrolyte in the body is
○ 1. ion.
○ 2. anion.
○ 3. cation.
○ 4. milliequivalent.

48 When entering the room while Ms. Bidell has thrombophlebitis, assume the nurse observes that Ms. Bidell is experiencing chest pain and dyspnea and that she has a rapid pulse rate. The nurse's first course of action should be to

○ 1. report the observations.
○ 2. document the observations.
○ 3. place the patient in a side-lying position.
○ 4. discontinue the patient's intravenous line.

49 If the nurse notes the following information on Ms. Bidell's record, which entry is subjective in nature?
○ 1. The patient's skin is moist.
○ 2. The patient's feet are swollen.
○ 3. The patient has an elevated temperature.
○ 4. The patient states that she feels nauseous.

Ms. Colbert, a 23-year-old college student, is hospitalized with type A (infectious) hepatitis. She is acutely ill and is placed on isolation precautions.

50 If Ms. Colbert had type B (serum) hepatitis, she most probably would have acquired the disease after being infected with contaminated
○ 1. urine.
○ 2. stool.
○ 3. blood.
○ 4. sputum.

51 Before clear evidence of infectious hepatitis developed, Ms. Colbert states that she felt achey, out of sorts, and anorexic. Such symptoms, noted before an illness develops, are called
○ 1. cardinal symptoms.
○ 2. negative symptoms.
○ 3. equivocal symptoms.
○ 4. prodromal symptoms.

52 It is of primary importance when caring for Ms. Colbert that nursing measures include seeing to it that she
○ 1. obtains total bed rest.
○ 2. has care to prevent decubitus ulcers.
○ 3. deep breathes and coughs at regular intervals.
○ 4. receives antibiotics and supplementary feedings on a strict time schedule.

53 The type of isolation that the nurse can expect to be used for Ms. Colbert is
○ 1. wound precautions.
○ 2. enteric precautions.
○ 3. secretion precautions.
○ 4. contact precautions.

54 Of the following pieces of equipment, it is recommended that the one that should *not* be used when the nurse gives Ms. Colbert care while isolation precautions are used is
○ 1. a stethoscope.

    O 2. a reusable blanket.
    O 3. a sphygmomanometer.
    O 4. an electronic thermometer.
55 Of the following practices of medical asepsis, the one that is particularly important to observe by health personnel caring for Ms. Colbert is
    O 1. discarding the patient's bath water in a toilet.
    O 2. wearing a gown and mask while in the patient's room.
    O 3. ventilating the patient's room frequently with fresh air.
    O 4. washing the hands thoroughly before and after giving the patient care.

When documenting the medications she has given, the nurse discovers that she has administered a wrong medication to Ms. Colbert.

56 The nurse's first course of action in the situation described above should be to
    O 1. notify the physician.
    O 2. call the nurse-in-charge.
    O 3. prepare an accident report.
    O 4. check the patient's condition.

Ms. Colbert has jaundice.

57 The place in Ms. Colbert's body where the nurse can expect jaundice to be observed first is in the
    O 1. lips.
    O 2. nailbeds.
    O 3. whites of eyes.
    O 4. mucous membranes.
58 Ms. Colbert's jaundiced skin color is most likely to appear
    O 1. pinkish.
    O 2. brownish.
    O 3. yellowish.
    O 4. bluish purple.
59 Ms. Colbert's jaundice is due to an abnormally high blood level of
    O 1. bile.
    O 2. ures.
    O 3. bilirubin.
    O 4. albumin.

Ms. Colbert's diet and fluid intake requirements are considered.

60 The nurse can anticipate that Ms. Colbert will have a diet that is moderate in its content of
    O 1. fats.

○ 2. proteins.
○ 3. roughage.
○ 4. carbohydrates.

61 To encourage fluid intake, in addition to beverages, the nurse should explain to Ms. Colbert that *all* of the following foods are considered fluid or are very high in water content *except*
○ 1. fish.
○ 2. jello.
○ 3. melons.
○ 4. ice cream.

Ms. Colbert is to have liver function tests and then be prepared for discharge.

62 When preparing Ms. Colbert for the liver function tests, the nurse should anticipate that most liver function tests require specimens of
○ 1. urine.
○ 2. stool.
○ 3. blood.
○ 4. gastric contents.

63 Ms. Colbert will be cared for at home by her mother. The mother should be taught that before reusable equipment used in Ms. Colbert's care is sterilized or disinfected, it should first be
○ 1. soaked in a germicide.
○ 2. wiped off with a cloth.
○ 3. boiled in distilled water.
○ 4. rinsed under cool running water.

64 The nurse should teach Ms. Colbert that it is recommended that a practice or procedure she must *avoid* during her lifetime because of having had hepatitis is
○ 1. taking aspirin.
○ 2. donating blood.
○ 3. receiving blood extracts.
○ 4. receiving immunological agents.

65 When Ms. Colbert returns to normal eating after her illness, the nurse is correct in teaching her to have a diet that is rich in the mineral
○ 1. iron.
○ 2. iodine.
○ 3. copper.
○ 4. phosphorus.

66 Ms. Colbert asks how her friends may be protected from acquiring infectious hepatitis. The nurse should base her response on knowledge that a pharmaceutical preparation having some success in protecting a person from type A hepatitis, or at least in decreasing its severity, is
○ 1. a toxoid.

    ◯ 2. a vaccine.
    ◯ 3. an antitoxin.
    ◯ 4. an immune serum globulin.

The Nursing Care of Patients With Disorders of the Integumentary System

An employed graduate practical nurse attends a conference on the care of patients with dermatological disorders.

67 By attending the conference, the nurse is involved in an activity frequently called
    ◯ 1. a refresher course.
    ◯ 2. continuing education.
    ◯ 3. preservice education.
    ◯ 4. a postgraduate course.

The management of patients with itching skin is a conference subject.

68 Included in the conference discussions is that itching of the skin tends to be aggravated when fabric in the patient's clothing consists of
    ◯ 1. wool.
    ◯ 2. nylon.
    ◯ 3. rayon.
    ◯ 4. cotton.

69 An oil may be added to bath water when the skin is itching and dry. A danger in this measure is that the person using an oil bath is predisposed to
    ◯ 1. acne due to clogging of skin pores with the oil.
    ◯ 2. poor hygiene due to the ineffective cleansing by the oil.
    ◯ 3. contact dermatitis due to prolonged contact with the oil.
    ◯ 4. falling due to the slipperiness of the oil residue on the tub.

70 When added to water for a tub bath, which of the following ingredients tends to relieve itching?
    ◯ 1. Salt
    ◯ 2. Milk
    ◯ 3. Starch
    ◯ 4. A mild antiseptic

71 Of the following patients, the nurses should know that the one who is most likely to complain of itching is the patient who has
    ◯ 1. cyanotic skin.
    ◯ 2. jaundiced skin.
    ◯ 3. a high temperature.

○ 4. scleroderma (progressive systemic sclerosis).

Psoriasis is discussed at the conference.

72 The leader of the conference teaches that the cause of psoriasis is
○ 1. an allergy.
○ 2. undetermined.
○ 3. overexposure to the sun.
○ 4. an endocrine disturbance.

73 A person with psoriasis often uses warm medicated baths to relieve symptoms. If the bath water becomes cool, which of the following precautions should the nurse use while re-warming the water?
○ 1. Ask the patient to step out of the tub temporarily while hot water is added.
○ 2. Lift the patient's feet out of the tub temporarily while hot water is added.
○ 3. While the patient remains in the tub, allow warm water to enter the tub continuously until the desired water temperature is reached.
○ 4. While the patient remains in the tub, agitate the bath water continuously while adding hot water until the desired water temperature is reached.

Shingles (herpes zoster) is discussed at the conference.

74 The moderator of the conference correctly points out that shingles (herpes zoster) is caused by the same virus that causes
○ 1. mumps.
○ 2. smallpox.
○ 3. chicken pox.
○ 4. German measles.

75 A nurse caring for a patient with shingles should be prepared to administer nursing care that includes measures to help
○ 1. relieve itching.
○ 2. prevent bedsores.
○ 3. relieve discomfort.
○ 4. prevent dehydration.

Several of the nurses ask questions about athlete's foot.

76 Athlete's foot is best prevented by keeping the feet dry and by
○ 1. wearing only white stockings.
○ 2. cleaning the feet and toes regularly with alcohol.
○ 3. using slippers in public bathrooms and locker rooms.

    ○ 4. wearing one comfortable pair of shoes for the duration of the infection.

77 Various agents used in the treatment of athlete's foot are discussed. One common agent is griseofulvin (Fulvicin), which is ordinarily given by
    ○ 1. the oral route.
    ○ 2. the intramuscular route.
    ○ 3. rubbing it into the skin.
    ○ 4. soaking the skin with it.

78 Athlete's foot is caused by an organism called a
    ○ 1. virus.
    ○ 2. fungus.
    ○ 3. bacterium.
    ○ 4. protozoa.

Burn injuries are discussed at the conference.

79 Unless burns are extensive, the recommended emergency care at the accident site is to care for the burns by
    ○ 1. placing the part in cold water.
    ○ 2. applying an ointment to the part.
    ○ 3. swabbing the part with an antiseptic.
    ○ 4. wrapping the part in absorbent cotton.

80 The moderator explains that a common reason for leaving certain burn wounds undressed is that the wound
    ○ 1. will not develop a scar.
    ○ 2. will not be irritated by dressings.
    ○ 3. can be cleansed better when not covered.
    ○ 4. can be irrigated more easily when not covered.

81 When a person's clothing is on fire and if the equipment described below are available, first aid treatment should begin with
    ○ 1. cutting off the victim's clothing as quickly as possible.
    ○ 2. placing the victim on the floor and rolling him in a blanket.
    ○ 3. having the victim sit down and dousing him with cool water.
    ○ 4. directing a fire extinguisher on the victim while spraying him with solution.

82 When caring for a victim of extensive burns that are infected with staphylococcal or streptococcal organisms, the victim is ordinarily placed on strict isolation precautions. If caretakers use the following practices, which one is in *error*?
    ○ 1. A mask is worn by caretakers whenever they are in the patient's room.
    ○ 2. A gown is worn by caretakers whenever they are in the patient's room.

    ○ 3. The patient's soiled linens are double-bagged before being sent to the laundry.

    ○ 4. The door to the patient's room is open for the convenience of frequent observations.

83 Changing dressings on a patient with burns is ordinarily a painful procedure. In general, the best time for a nurse to give the patient a medication for discomfort is

    ○ 1. shortly before the procedure starts.

    ○ 2. when the procedure starts.

    ○ 3. as soon as the patient complains of pain during the procedure.

    ○ 4. immediately after the procedure is completed.

84 While caring for a patient with extensive burns, it is most certainly important that efforts be made by caretakers to decrease the likelihood of the patient's developing

    ○ 1. a bedsore.

    ○ 2. contractures.

    ○ 3. fecal impactions.

    ○ 4. a wound infection.

The remaining items in this situation are individual items related to the care of patients with skin disorders.

85 A nurse attending the conference asks about pediculosis. A characteristic of lice causing pediculosis is that they

    ○ 1. cannot be destroyed.

    ○ 2. have a poisonous bite.

    ○ 3. spread easily to others.

    ○ 4. produce an allergic reaction.

86 The moderator correctly teaches that, before rubbing a medicated ointment into a patient's skin, the nurse should first prepare the area by

    ○ 1. shaving the area.

    ○ 2. swabbing the area with an antiseptic.

    ○ 3. cleaning the area with soap and water.

    ○ 4. applying cool water or alcohol to the area.

87 Various bandages and binders used to hold dressings on the skin are discussed. A straight binder is used most often to bandage a patient's

    ○ 1. hand.

    ○ 2. chest.

    ○ 3. thigh.

    ○ 4. shoulder.

88 Skin cancer is discussed. Nurses should help in teaching the public that the leading cause of skin cancer is

    ○ 1. prolonged exposure to the sun.

    ○ 2. excessive irritation of skin moles.

    ○ 3. excessive irritation of scars (keloids).

○ 4. prolonged exposure to swimming pool chemicals.

89 The nurses attending the conference are taught that patients often feel chilly when bed linens are supported so that they will not touch the patient's skin. If a heat lamp is used to overcome chilliness, it is generally recommended that the wattage of an incandescent light bulb be *no greater* than
○ 1. 25 watts.
○ 2. 60 watts.
○ 3. 75 watts.
○ 4. 100 watts.

90 Various body sensations are discussed. The body is *least* likely to adapt to the sensation of
○ 1. heat.
○ 2. pain.
○ 3. cold.
○ 4. odor.

91 Various types of skin lesions are described. A synonym for a blister is
○ 1. wheal.
○ 2. vesicle.
○ 3. papule.
○ 4. macule.

92 Antipruritics are described. These are agents used on the skin primarily to relieve
○ 1. flaking.
○ 2. itching.
○ 3. dryness.
○ 4. blistering.

93 If a nurse uses her position as a hospital employee to promote certain personal skin care products, the nurse is in violation of the
○ 1. patient's bill of rights.
○ 2. state's nurse practice act.
○ 3. practical nurses' code of ethics.
○ 4. federal government's rules on fairness in advertising.

The Nursing Care of Patients With Disorders of the Musculoskeletal System

Ms. Washington, a 49-year-old woman, is admitted to a hospital for a laminectomy because of a herniated intervertebral disc.

94 Ms. Washington practices a religion very different from the one practiced by a nurse assigned to admit the patient. If the nurse refuses to care for Ms. Washington because of her religious beliefs and does

not see to it that someone else cares for Ms. Washington, the nurse's behavior would be most accurately described as being
○ 1. illegal.
○ 2. immoral.
○ 3. insincere.
○ 4. unethical.

95 Ms. Washington tells the nurse while being admitted that she is angry about having surgery on her back and says she is afraid of it. A recommended guideline to follow when Ms. Washington expresses fear and anger is for the nurse to
○ 1. reassure the patient that her feelings are typical of most patients having surgery.
○ 2. listen to the patient while giving opportunities to express her feelings.
○ 3. attempt to direct the patient's thoughts into more constructive channels.
○ 4. help the patient understand that her feelings are standing in the way of her recovery.

96 Local heat is applied to Ms. Washington's back to help reduce
○ 1. disc edema.
○ 2. muscle spasms.
○ 3. nerve sensitivity.
○ 4. bone deterioration.

Ms. Washington is prepared for a laminectomy.

97 The nurse teaches Ms. Washington how to deep-breathe in preparation for her postoperative period. In which of the following ways should the patient be taught to exhale?
○ 1. Against pursed lips
○ 2. Through both nostrils
○ 3. Through an open mouth
○ 4. While holding one nostril shut

98 While practicing deep-breathing, Ms. Washington says that she feels dizzy and light-headed. She most probably is breathing too
○ 1. slowly.
○ 2. deeply.
○ 3. rapidly.
○ 4. shallowly.

99 Of the following immediate preoperative orders for Ms. Washington, the one that will help most to prevent nausea and vomiting is having
○ 1. nothing by mouth.
○ 2. a cleansing enema.
○ 3. intravenous therapy.
○ 4. a medication to dry secretions.

Ms. Washington returns from surgery when postoperative care, including special considerations because of her laminectomy, begins.

100 Unless Ms. Washington's condition is in question, it is usual to check her blood pressure and pulse and respiratory rates for several hours postoperatively every
  ○ 1. 5 minutes.
  ○ 2. 10 minutes.
  ○ 3. 15 minutes.
  ○ 4. 20 minutes.

101 Which of the following activities should Ms. Washington be taught is *contraindicated* for her?
  ○ 1. Coughing
  ○ 2. Using a bedpan
  ○ 3. Drinking carbonated beverages
  ○ 4. Having her upper back massaged

102 When turning Ms. Washington, it is particularly important to keep her spinal column in a position of
  ○ 1. flexion.
  ○ 2. extension.
  ○ 3. slight rotation.
  ○ 4. slight hyperextension.

103 Which of the following activities is *contraindicated* for Ms. Washington when she is out of bed?
  ○ 1. Using a wheelchair
  ○ 2. Walking to the bathroom
  ○ 3. Sitting in a straight-back chair
  ○ 4. Bending over to pick up her shoes

104 Assume Ms. Washington has had a laminectomy with a spinal fusion and had been placed in a body cast. In which of the following positions in bed, while lying on her back, would usually be most comfortable for Ms. Washington?
  ○ 1. In a position so that the patient's head is slightly lower than the rest of her body
  ○ 2. In a position so that the patient's head is slightly higher than the rest of her body
  ○ 3. In a position so that the patient's feet are slightly lower than the rest of her body
  ○ 4. In a position so that the patient's feet are slightly higher than the rest of her body

Ms. Washington is to receive morphine sulfate for the relief of pain.

105 The vital sign that the nurse should check before administering morphine sulfate to Ms. Washington is her

○ 1. pulse rate.
○ 2. blood pressure.
○ 3. respiratory rate.
○ 4. body temperature.

106 With which of the following drugs, any one of which may have been prescribed for Ms. Washington, is there a *minimal* risk of its causing physical dependency?
○ 1. Codeine
○ 2. Paraldehyde
○ 3. Oxycodone (Percodan)
○ 4. Hydromorphone (Dilaudid)

Ms. Washington and the nurse discuss diet and health.

107 When Ms. Washington tells the nurse that she wishes to lose weight, it is best for the nurse to teach Ms. Washington to limit her intake of
○ 1. fats.
○ 2. calories.
○ 3. proteins.
○ 4. carbohydrates.

108 The nurse teaches Ms. Washington about the proper number of servings from each food group in a well-balanced diet. According to nutritionists, the daily *minimum* number of servings of food substances from the bread and cereal group in a well-balanced diet should be
○ 1. 1 serving.
○ 2. 2 servings.
○ 3. 3 servings.
○ 4. 4 servings.

109 Ms. Washington says that she does not care for many meats, and asks what to eat instead. Which of the following foods is classified by nutritionists as being in the meat group?
○ 1. Eggs
○ 2. Yogurt
○ 3. Potatoes
○ 4. Macaroni

110 Ms. Washington says that food is so expensive that she finds it difficult to plan nutritious meals within her budget. With few exceptions, the most expensive food substances in the diet are
○ 1. fats.
○ 2. proteins.
○ 3. carbohydrates.
○ 4. minerals and vitamins.

111 Ms. Washington asks about several common beliefs in relation to food. Which of the following statements about food preparation and substances is a fact, rather than a false claim?

○ 1. Natural organic fertilizers are safer than chemical fertilizers.
○ 2. Aluminum and Teflon-coated utensils often cause intestinal illnesses.
○ 3. A well-balanced diet usually cannot supply the body with sufficient minerals and vitamins.
○ 4. The healthy body ordinarily uses man-made synthetic vitamins and natural vitamins equally well.

Ms. Washington is black and has thick, curly hair.

112 Which of the following hair care aids is recommended for grooming Ms. Washington's hair?
○ 1. A brush
○ 2. A ratting comb
○ 3. A fine-toothed comb
○ 4. A large-toothed comb

Ms. Washington says that her menstrual periods are irregular and her physician says she is in menopause.

113 Ms. Washington tells the nurse that some people believe that menopausal and postmenopausal women generally no longer respond to sexual activity with the interest and vigor they did before menopause. Which of the following statements is most accurate concerning the belief Ms. Washington describes?
○ 1. The belief is false. Studies have shown that sexual response need not necessarily fade with menopause.
○ 2. The belief is false. Studies have shown that sexual response tends to fade about a decade before menopause begins.
○ 3. The belief is true. With shrinking of reproductive organs at menopause, interest in sex fades.
○ 4. The belief is true. With a gradual decrease in the body's production of hormones at menopause, interest in sex fades.

Correct Answers and Rationales

Two numbers appear in parentheses following each rationale. The first number identifies the textbook listed in the references, page 649, and the second number identifies the page(s) in that textbook on which the correct answer can be verified. Occasionally, two textbooks are given for verifying the correct answer.

The Nursing Care of Patients With Disorders of the Gastrointestinal System (Continued)

Caring for a patient with appendicitis

1 3. Typically, a person with appendicitis has a moderately elevated white blood cell count. Red cell, platelet, and reticulocyte counts tend to be within normal ranges in the presence of appendicitis.   (12:716; 15:423)

2 3. McBurney's point is located in the right lower quadrant of the abdomen, about halfway between a person's umbilicus and the right iliac crest. A person with appendicitis usually first has generalized abdominal pain, which later localizes over McBurney's point.   (15:423)

3 2. When persistent abdominal pain is present, using laxatives and enemas should most certainly be avoided. They stimulate peristalsis, which could cause the appendix to rupture and empty intestinal content into the peritoneum. Eating also should be avoided because it too stimulates peristalsis. Applying cold, taking aspirin, and lying on the right side are much less likely to cause perforation of an inflamed appendix. Applying heat is contraindicated when appendicitis is believed present, especially if the appendix may have ruptured, for heat may cause a spread of infection.   (12:716; 15:423)

4 1. The vermiform appendix arises from the cecum.   (10:259)

5 3. Water is absorbed in large amounts in the large intestine, or colon. Iron, sodium, and carbohydrates are absorbed chiefly in the small intestine.   (10:259)

6 2. Atropine sulfate is a cholinergic-blocking agent that dries secretions in the respiratory tract, including the mouth. This action makes the person feel thirsty and causes difficulty with swallowing because of dry mucous membranes.   (14:119)

7 3. Gas rises in a liquid, and therefore, the knee-chest position helps gas to rise in the intestine toward the anus, where it can be expelled.   (9:471)

8 2. A rectal tube should remain in place only about 20 minutes at one time when it is being used to help the patient with abdominal distention. Over a longer period, the body adjusts to the presence of the tube, and peristalsis is not likely to be stimulated. If the patient has no relief after about 20 minutes, the tube should be removed and inserted again in an hour or two.   (9:477)

9   3.   When the working area is too low for the nurse, she will strain her back. When the working area is too high, the nurse has to stretch her arms and she will also throw her back out of alignment.   (9:122)

10   1.   The patient's face should be turned toward the nurse when she turns him away from her, from his abdomen to his back. This positioning prevents the patient from rolling onto his face.   (9:328)

11   4.   A major factor in the development of tooth cavities is eating sugar-sweetened snacks frequently. Other factors include a hereditary predisposition, mechanical factors, and hormonal imbalances. Using strong antiseptic mouthwashes, having a diet high in roughage content, and drinking black coffee do not predispose to cavity formation.   (10:256)

12   4.   Stannous fluoride in toothpastes and powders has been found to help reduce cavity formation.   (9:72)

13   2.   A danger in using a water jet spray is that it may force debris into tissue pockets, where an infection can then easily develop. Jet sprays have not been found to damage tooth enamel, injure cells on the tongue, and spread microorganisms about the mouth. Persons wearing braces on their teeth or having dental implants often find water jet sprays helpful in removing debris from about the teeth.   (9:75)

14   3.   An adult normally has 32 teeth, including the 4 wisdom (third molar) teeth. The 20 baby (deciduous) teeth are lost during childhood and replaced by permanent teeth.   (10:265)

15   4.   Rationalization is finding a logical reason or an excuse for not doing what one should do. According to one authority, rationalization is ". . . said to be the joy and delight of the average human being and is self-deception at its subtle best." Rationalization is also sometimes called intellectualization. Projection is attributing one's own unacceptable behavior onto others. Compensation means putting forth extra efforts to make up for an area of deficiency in oneself. Symbolization means using one object or idea as a substitute for another.   (1:292; 13:57)

16   3.   Defense mechanisms are used primarily to relieve anxiety, that is, reduce what an individual perceives as a threat. They do not dispel fear, channel the id, or change a situation.   (9:22, 24; 13:57)

17   4.   The defense mechanism that appears to be constructive in most situations is sublimation, which is defined as channeling unacceptable behavior into acceptable areas.   (1:52; 13:57)

18   4.   It is generally recommended that coping with tension when something bothers one requires talking about it and "getting it off" one's chest. Writing about it and then destroying what was written, talking about it with someone in whom one can confide, and using an active sport are usually most often recommended ways to handle tension and anger. Least effective would be to do nothing to explore and express feelings and try to "sleep off" the tension and anger.   (13:60-61)

The Nursing Care of Patients With Disorders of the Biliary System

Caring for a patient with gallbladder disease

19   1.   A sonogram, which uses ultrasound waves, requires no special preparation. Sonography produces images because of the various densities of body tissue that reflect sound in various ways. There is no discomfort associated with sonography.   (15:401)

20   3.   Lithiasis means stone formation. When stones are located in the ducts of the biliary system, they are called choledocholithiasis. Lithicosis is a pulmonary disease caused by inhaling silica. Lithemia is an excess of uric acid in the blood. Lithium is a metallic element.   (15:473, 740)

21   4.   The solution for a cleansing enema should be no warmer than 110°F (43°C). Solutions hotter than that may injure the mucous membranes of the lower intestinal tract. A cool or cold solution may cause intestinal cramps.   (9:474)

22   3.   The container of solution should be held between 12 inches and 20 inches (30 cm and 50 cm) above the patient's anal area when giving a cleansing enema. If the container is held higher than that, the rapidity with which the solution enters the intestine may cause cramping and a desire to evacuate too soon, with poor results. Holding the container lower than about 12 inches (30 cm) prolongs giving the solution and is unnecessary.   (9:475)

23   2.   The rectal tube should be inserted about 3 to 4 inches (7.5 to 10 cm) when one is giving a cleansing enema. This allows the tube to enter the anal canal and pass the internal sphincter, where the solution should be introduced into the rectum. Introducing the tube farther may injure mucous membranes. Introducing it a shorter distance places the solution in the rectum and causes the patient to expel the enema before it has had a chance to be effective.   (9:476)

24   3.   In order for the rectal tube to follow the normal contour of the anal canal and rectum, the nurse should insert the rectal tube for an enema while directing it toward the patient's umbilicus.   (9:476)

25   3.   Sometimes, the rectal tube meets resistance when it is inserted for an enema because the patient is tense. Asking the patient to take several deep breaths helps her to relax, and often allows the tube to be introduced without further resistance. Do *not* force a rectal tube when introducing it. Coughing, changing position, and flexing the knees do not promote relaxation of the anal sphincter.   (9:477)

26   1.   A Penrose drain is placed in an operative site to help drainage escape from a surgical wound. Drains in a wound do not decrease scar formation, nor do they prevent the accumulation of gas in the intestinal tract. A drain provides no means for a wound irrigation.   (15:474)

27   1.   The primary purpose of placing a T tube in the wound of a patient who has had a cholecystectomy is to carry bile to the outside of the body. This helps prevent bile from accumulating in the ductal tree with spasms of the duct. However, most of the bile continues to enter the intestinal tract unless a total obstruction is present.   (15:475)

28   4.   The dressing will be stained with greenish-yellow drainage if bile seeps from the operative site following the removal of the gallbladder. The patient should be taught that the greenish-yellow color is normal for bile because many patients become upset by its appearance when they are unprepared for it.   (8:428)

29   4.   An ointment, such as A and D ointment, is recommended for removing adhesive remnants from the skin. It is soothing and will not irritate the skin. The ointment is applied to the skin and allowed to "soak" for a while before it is removed with a cotton ball or gauze dressing. Normal saline, hydrogen peroxide, and antiseptics are ineffective for removing adhesive remnants from the skin.   (9:413)

30   2.   Acetone is very drying and therefore, tends to irritate the skin. It is not ordinarily recommended to remove adhesive remnants from the skin.   (9:413)

31   4.   Tincture of benzoin and collodion are preparations that protect the skin before adhesive is applied. Adhesive will not adhere well to skin on which petrolatum, calamine lotion, or zinc oxide has been applied. Tincture of benzoin should not be applied to irritated skin because it contains alcohol that will further irritate the skin and cause discomfort.   (9:414)

32   4.   If a nurse using bar soap returns the soap to its dish between latherings while washing her hands, she must start the hand-washing procedure from the beginning because a soap dish is considered contaminated, and the soap can harbor organisms. Warm water is preferred to hot or cold water to prevent excessive drying and better cleansing of the skin. It is recommended that after changing a dressing, the hands, wrists, and lower forearms be washed well to minimize dangers of carrying organisms about on contaminated skin.   (9:278-279)

33   4.   The operative site for removing a gallbladder is high on the abdomen, making deep breathing more uncomfortable than it is for patients with surgical sites lower on the abdomen. Splinting the surgical area before performing deep breathing and coughing exercises helps to prevent discomfort.   (15:474)

34   2.   The best exercises to help prevent thrombophlebitis for the bedridden patient are active leg exercises. Bending the knees followed by extending the legs, rotating the feet, wiggling the toes, and adducting and abducting the legs are examples. If the patient is unable to perform these exercises on her own, the nurse should use passive exercises with the patient. Sit-ups are likely to be too strenuous for a postoperative patient, but furthermore, sit-ups do not exercise the legs. Rolling from side to side and doing isometric thigh exercises do not help to improve circulation to any extent in the legs. (15:127)

35 4. It is dangerous to massage a leg when thrombophlebitis is present, primarily because massage may dislodge a clot that will travel in the bloodstream as an embolism. The affected leg should be kept at rest, and activity should be limited. An embolism can be life-threatening. (15:387)

36 1. In most instances when thrombophlebitis is present, a nursing order will indicate that the leg should be elevated. However, an order should be followed because not all authorities favor elevating the leg. Applications of heat are very often ordered, but not applications of cold. The leg should not be exercised, actively or passively. When the patient is able to ambulate, it is usual to use pressure on the leg by applying elastic bandages or stockings. (15:387–388)

37 4. Before ambulating a patient who has been bedridden, it is best to have the patient become accustomed to the upright position by having him sit in a high-Fowler's position for a few minutes. This technique helps to avoid feelings of weakness and faintness when the patient next is helped to dangle and then is helped out of bed to ambulate. (9:356)

38 1. The base of support is the area on which a person or object rests its weight. A person's base of support when in the standing position is in the feet. (9:118)

39 3. The center of gravity is the point at which the mass of a person or object is centered. A person's center of gravity in the standing position is centered and about halfway between the pubis and umbilicus. An understanding of the center of gravity and of the base of support helps to place the body in a position of good posture. Having good posture means the body is in good alignment and good balance. In this position, the musculoskeletal system can be used in the best way possible. Good posture also helps other systems in the body, such as the cardiopulmonary system, to function efficiently. (9:116, 118)

40 1. It is best not to cross the legs at the knees when sitting, because this position tends to interfere with circulation in the legs. Keeping the feet flat on the floor, placing the hands on the lap, and holding the head up with the chin tucked in slightly describe a good sitting position. (9:117)

41 1. Abdominal distention is most often due to an accumulation of gas (flatus) trapped in the intestines. (9:227)

42 3. A suppository should be inserted well beyond the internal sphincter, for a total of 3 inches to 4 inches (7.5 cm to 10 cm) beyond the anus. If the suppository rests in the anal canal, it is unable to serve its intended purpose and is likely to be expelled prematurely. A suppository may be lubricated before insertion, and the nurse wears a glove while inserting it. Peristalsis is often stimulated when the patient walks about while the suppository is in place, if the patient is permitted to be ambulatory.   (9:474)

43   1.   The chief functions of the gallbladder are storing and concentrating bile before emptying it into the cystic duct, the common bile duct, and into the duodenum.   (10:263)

44   1.   The salts contained in bile act like a detergent to break up fats. The production of bile is one of the main functions of the liver.   (10:261)

45   3.   The liver manufactures heparin which is a powerful anticoagulant, that is, it helps in the prevention of blood clotting. The liver has many other functions also: it stores glycogen, helps in the formation of blood plasma proteins and clotting factors, synthesizes urea, manufactures bile, destroys old red blood cells, detoxifies certain harmful substances in the body, and stores some vitamins and iron. Pepsin is a component of gastric juice that is important in the digestion of protein. Peptidase is secreted in the small intestine and helps in the digestion of protein. Trypsin is secreted by the pancreas; it is a protein-digesting enzyme.   (10:261; 12:148)

46   1.   Cirrhosis of the liver is most commonly associated with chronic alcoholism. It is believed that liver damage is due to malnutrition, a common condition among alcoholics. However, it is unsafe to assume that a patient with liver cirrhosis is also an alcoholic. There are other etiological factors, such as hepatitis, obstruction in the biliary system, and inadequate circulation to the liver because of cardiac disease, but these factors are involved less frequently than alcoholism in the presence of cirrhosis.   (15:465)

47   4.   The unit of measure that describes chemical activity of an electrolyte is milliequivalent. It is abbreviated mEq. An ion is an atom or molecule that carries an electrical charge. A cation carries a negative charge and an anion, a positive charge.   (9:493)

48   1.   A patient with thrombophlebitis is at risk for developing a pulmonary embolism, which usually develops quickly and can be life-threatening. When the nurse observes signs of pulmonary embolism, including pain, dyspnea, a rapid pulse rate, cyanosis, and shock, she should report her findings immediately. Documenting can wait until the patient receives immediate necessary care. The patient should be kept at rest in bed, and an intravenous line should be in place for the administration of emergency intravenous therapy.   (9:387; 15:390)

49   4.   A subjective finding, often called a symptom, is felt and described by a patient. It cannot be observed directly by another person. Feeling nauseous is an example of a subjective symptom. An elevated temperature, moist skin, and swollen feet describe objective findings because they can be observed directly and verified by another person. Objective findings are often referred to as signs.   (9:35)

Caring for a patient with hepatitis

50   3.   Serum hepatitis most often is spread by infected blood through the use of contaminated needles, syringes, and other surgical and dental equipment. It also may be spread by transfusion of blood or plasma, when the donor harbors the organism in his blood. (15:470)

51 4.   Signs and symptoms that are present before an illness clearly develops are called prodromal. Cardinal symptoms pertain to the body temperature, pulse and respiratory rates, and blood pressure. The absence of a symptom that normally occurs when a specific illness is present is called a negative symptom, and it rules out that specific disease. An equivocal symptom may occur in several illnesses and is therefore of doubtful value in diagnosing a specific illness. (9:215)

52 1.   A patient with infectious hepatitis must have strict bed rest, which includes measures to promote comfort and freedom from disturbances and annoyances. A patient with infectious hepatitis is rarely at risk for decubitus ulcers, does not ordinarily require deep breathing and coughing exercises, and does not receive antibiotics because antibiotics are ineffective for treating illnesses caused by viruses. (8:422)

53 2.   The virus causing type A, or infectious, hepatitis is spread from person to person primarily by organisms in the stool. The fecal-oral route is the major mode of transmission and enteric precautions are used. In many agencies, blood as well as enteric precautions are used, especially if there is question of whether the patient has type A (infectious) or type B (serum) hepatitis. When an epidemic of type A hepatitis occurs, ill persons usually have received the virus from contaminated food, milk, polluted water, or shellfish. The respiratory route may possibly be a route of transmission, although some question this theory. Rarely, if ever, is a blood transfusion responsible for type A hepatitis. (8:422)

54 4.   Either disposable or glass clinical thermometers should be used when caring for patients with a communicable disease. The mechanism of the electronic thermometer is difficult to clean thoroughly. A stethoscope, a sphygmomanometer, and a reusable blanket can be cleaned with relative ease after being used for a patient with a communicable disease. (9:299)

55 4.   It is important to observe practices of medical asepsis that are appropriate to the care of a patient who has hepatitis. However, it cannot be emphasized too strongly that washing the hands *thoroughly* before and after care is of particular importance. The virus causing hepatitis can be easily spread about when caretakers are careless about washing hands before and after giving care. (9:299; 12:722)

56 4.   When a medication error has been made and a patient receives a wrong medication, the nurse should first check the patient's condition so that she can describe the patient's reaction to the medication given in error. The nurse should then notify the nurse-in-charge immediately. When an error occurs, an accident (incident) report can wait until the patient is cared for properly and proper persons are notified. (9:547)

57 3.   Jaundice usually is observed first in the white part of the person's eyes, that is, in the sclera. (15:720)

58 3. The skin color of a patient with jaundice appears yellowish. (15:720)

59 3. Jaundice is staining of the skin due to abnormally high blood levels of the pigment bilirubin. Normally, total bilirubin concentration is 1.0 mg or less per 100 ml of blood. Jaundice becomes visible when the level reaches 3.0 mg or more per 100 ml of blood. (8:421)

60 1. A person with infectious hepatitis is ordinarily on a moderate fat, high protein, high carbohydrate, and moderate to high caloric diet. The person with hepatitis can be expected to have a poor appetite. As a result, the nurse may need to use patience and ingenuity to promote good nutrition, which is important for a recovery without complications and delay. (16:250)

61 1. Such items as sherbet, ice cream, and jello are considered fluids and should be offered to persons for whom fluids are to be encouraged. Certain fruits, melons being a typical example, are also very high in water content and should be included in the diet of a person whose fluid intake should be encouraged. Fish do not have a high water content. (9:502)

62 3. Most liver function tests require blood samples taken from the patient after he has been fasting. Occasionally, blood findings may be confirmed by using urine bilirubin, urine urobilinogen and fecal urobilinogen pigment tests. (15:463)

63 4. Equipment to be sterilized or disinfected first should be rinsed under cool running water. This technique helps to remove heavy contamination before the equipment is washed in soap or detergent and water. Wiping contaminated equipment is not satisfactory. Hot and boiling water are not recommended for this preliminary cleaning because heat tends to coagulate particles in which organisms can harbor and grow. (9:280)

64 2. Donating blood is not recommended by persons who have had hepatitis because the virus in the blood, even years after the person has had hepatitis, can be passed on to others. Personnel in blood banks are taught to question persons concerning having hepatitis and also blood tests are used to determine the presence of the virus that causes hepatitis. (12:722)

65 1. A balanced diet containing sufficient quantities of all necessary minerals is important for everyone. However, women during the years that they menstruate are advised to have a diet rich in iron because considerable iron is normally lost during menstruation. Ten mg of iron each day is recommended for men and for women who are post-menopausal; 18 mg per day is recommended for women during the years they menstruate. (4:143)

66 4. An immune serum globulin (gamma globulin) is the only pharmaceutical preparation to ensure at least some protection from type A hepatitis, but it does not offer 100% protection. However, it is of no help if the exposed person has already contracted the disease, nor is it of value to protect against type B (serum) hepatitis. A vaccine exists for type B hepatitis. (14:262–263; 15:471)

The Nursing Care of Patients With Disorders of the Integumentary System

Attending a conference on dermatological disorders

67 2.   Education offered to nurses who have completed basic programs in nursing is called continuing education. The primary purpose of continuing education is to keep one's skills and knowledge up to date. A refresher course is offered to nurses who have not worked for a period of time. Preservice education is on-the-job orientation. A postgraduate course, often given for college credit, consists of planned courses in nursing that usually take weeks or months to complete.   (9:3, 10)

68 1.   Itching tends to be aggravated when the patient wears clothing made of woolen and other rough fabrics. Other types of fabrics do not have the same effect. Excessive warmth, being idle, and emotional stress tend to increase itching.   (15:604)

69 4.   The danger associated with oil baths is that the person can easily fall because a residue of oil on the tub causes it to become very slippery. Oil baths are not associated with acne, poor personal hygiene, and contact dermatitis.   (15:604)

70 3.   Starch added to water for a tub bath helps to relieve itching. So does sodium bicarbonate and also oils when itching is caused by excessively dry skin.   (15:604)

71 2.   A patient whose skin is jaundiced often complains of itching. Itching also is associated with very dry skin, drug allergies, and diabetes mellitus. Itching is not associated with high fever and cyanosis, nor is it associated with scleroderma, which is a disease that involves blood vessels and connective tissues, causing the skin to become thick and taut.   (15:604)

72 2.   The cause of psoriasis is undetermined, although it is believed that it may be related to metabolic disorders, heredity, or emotional conflicts. It is neither infectious nor contagious.   (12:590)

73 4.   To prevent burning the patient, hot water should be added to a tub when medicated water has cooled, until the desired temperature is reached. However, the bath water should be agitated constantly while adding hot water. Adding warm water while the patient remains in the tub will require so much water that the effectiveness of the medicated bath will be lost. Asking the patient to step out of the tub tends to make the patient feel chilly and is not necessary if the nurse is careful to agitate the water. Simply lifting the patient's feet out of the water while adding hot water is of no value in terms of preventing burning the patient.   (9:427)

74 3.   Shingles and chicken pox are caused by the same virus. The skin lesions of shingles usually follow the course of a sensory nerve while the lesions are widespread on the patient with chicken pox.   (15:608–609)

75 3.   A patient with shingles is very uncomfortable and will require nursing measures to relieve pain. Analgesics ordinarily are prescribed for a patient with shingles. Itching is not associated with shingles, nor does the illness predispose to bedsores and dehydration.   (15:609)

76 3.   Athlete's foot is often spread by going barefooted in public bathrooms and locker rooms. Slippers should be worn in those areas. Cleaning the feet with alcohol, wearing white stockings, and using one pair of shoes for the duration of the infection are not indicated. Changing shoes and airing them frequently are recommended.   (12:555; 15:609)

77 1.   Griseofulvin (Fulvicin) is given orally and is used for the treatment of athlete's foot. Athlete's foot is also called tinea pedis.   (15:609)

78 2.   Athlete's foot is caused by a fungus.   (15:609)

79 1.   Unless an extensive part of the body is involved, a burned area should be immersed in cold water or wrapped in cool compresses. This care reduces pain and edema and lowers tissue temperature to help stop cell damage. Ointments and salves are contraindicated. They are extremely painful to remove and do not lower the temperature of the skin to stop cell damage.   (15:593)

80 2.   A common reason for leaving a wound undressed is to prevent a dressing from irritating the patient's wound. An undressed wound also eliminates the need to change painful dressings, allows for good observation of the wound, and requires less equipment and supplies for wound care.   (9:404)

81 2.   First aid treatment when a person's clothing is on fire is to place the victim on the ground or floor and roll him in a blanket to smother the fire. Placing the victim flat on the ground or floor prevents him from inhaling fumes and smoke. Fire extinguishers are not recommended because of the damage the solution may cause to burned skin areas.   (15:685)

82 4.   The door to the room of a patient with infected burn wounds should be closed for as long as strict isolation practices are followed. This practice helps prevent the spread of organisms borne on air currents. A mask, gown, and gloves are worn by caretakers. Articles, including all linens, should be double-bagged before being sent to another department for disinfection and sterilization.   (9:299)

83 1.   It is best to give medication to a patient a short time before a painful procedure is to start. It is easier to control pain before the pain becomes noticeable or excruciating.   (9:137; 15:689)

84 4.   It is important to use measures to prevent wound infections, bedsores, contractures, and fecal impactions when caring for burn patients. Of primary importance, however, is to take every precaution to prevent wound infection and septicemia. These are common causes of death following severe burns.   (15:691)

85 3.   Lice can spread easily to others by either direct or indirect contact. The bite of the lice is not poisonous, nor do lice produce allergic reactions. Many preparations that help destroy lice and their nits (eggs) are available on the market. (15:610)

86 3. To remove debris and oil that interfere with absorption of medications placed on the skin, the nurse should first wash the skin with soap and water. Shaving the area is rarely indicated. After the inunction, absorption is further promoted when warm applications are applied to the area. (9:550)

87 2. A straight binder is used most often to bandage a patient's chest or abdomen. It is not effective for bandaging extremities or a shoulder. (9:420)

88 1. Excessive exposure to the sun is the leading cause of skin cancer. The prevention of skin cancer should include teaching the public the importance of avoiding prolonged sun bathing, avoiding using tanning equipment, protecting the skin with sunscreen lotions when in the sun, and wearing protective clothing and hats when exposed to the sun. Prolonged irritation of a benign mole may cause the mole to become cancerous but this is not among the leading causes of skin cancer. Swimming pool chemicals and irritation of scars (keloids) are not associated with skin cancer. (12:591)

89 1. It is generally recommended that the incandescent light bulb used in a heat lamp be no greater than 25 watts, to help prevent burning patients. The bulb in a heat lamp should be placed between 18 and 24 inches (45 and 60 cm) from the skin. (9:427)

90 2. The body adapts to sensations of heat, cold, and odor. It does not appear to adapt to the sensation of pain in a similar manner. (9:133)

91 2. A synonym for a blister is vesicle, which is a skin lesion containing serous fluid. A wheal is an area of local swelling, an extreme being a hive. A papule is a small, solid red elevation on the skin. A macule is a patch on the skin, usually neither depressed nor elevated. (15:602)

92 2. An antipruretic is an agent used to relieve itching of the skin. (15:404)

93 3. The practical nurses' code of ethics states that a nurse not use her position or her uniform in an advertising program. A similar admonishment exists in the code of ethics for registered nurses. (13:160)

The Nursing Care of Patients With Disorders of the Musculoskeletal System

Caring for a patient with a herniated intervertebral disc

94 4. It would be considered unethical for a nurse to refuse to care for a patient without making provisions for someone else to care for him because he holds to a religious belief different from her own. Codes for nurses describe or imply giving or providing care for all patients needing it without regard to such factors as the patient's age, race, creed, or political or economic status.   (9:6)

95   2.   It is recommended that patients showing emotional responses to illness and prescribed care be given opportunities to express their feelings while the nurse listens to what is being said. Techniques that are used to reassure the patient that his feelings are typical, to direct his thoughts elsewhere, and to tell the patient his feelings stand in the way of recovery tend to block communications.   (9:20–23)

96   2.   Heat applied to the back relieves the discomfort of a ruptured intervertebral disc by helping reduce muscle spasms. Heat does not function in this situation to relieve edema, nerve sensitivity, or bone destruction.   (8:271)

97   1.   When deep-breathing, the patient should be taught to exhale against pursed lips. This technique helps improve air distribution in the lungs, helps keep the respiratory passages from narrowing, and helps maximize the exhalation of carbon dioxide.   (9:371)

98   3.   Feeling dizzy and light-headed when practicing deep-breathing exercises most probably is due to breathing too rapidly. An excess in the elimination of carbon dioxide and the intake of oxygen produces these symptoms.   (9:370)

99   1.   An important reason for having a patient in a fasting state preoperatively is to help prevent vomiting during surgery, and nausea and vomiting during the postoperative period. Nausea and vomiting are uncomfortable for the patient, but there is also a danger of aspirating vomitus during surgery or immediately after surgery, which can lead to serious respiratory complications.   (9:381)

100   3.   Usual policy is to check a patient's blood pressure and pulse and respiratory rates every 15 minutes for several hours postoperatively. If the patient's condition is stable, these vital signs are then obtained less frequently.   (9:384)

101   1.   Coughing during the postoperative period following a laminectomy is contraindicated and should be used only when really necessary. Coughing tends to increase pressure within the spinal canal. A bedpan is used but the patient's back should be well supported at the upper edge of the pan. It is better to use a so-called "fracture" pan which is very small and does not cause hyperextension of the back. Massaging the back and using carbonated beverages are not containdicated for the patient who has had a laminectomy.   (15:248)

102   2.   When turning a patient who has had surgery for a ruptured intervertebral disc, the nurse should keep the spinal canal in its normal anatomical position, that is, in a position of extension, to prevent injury to the column and spinal nerves. This method of turning the patient is similar to rolling a log.   (8:273)

103   4.   Bending over is contraindicated for a patient who has had a laminectomy. Instead, the patient should lower the body while bending the knees. Using a wheelchair, walking to the bathroom, and sitting in a straight-back chair are appropriate activities. (15:249)

104 2. A patient in a body cast usually is most comfortable when the head is slightly elevated. This is usually best accomplished by placing bed blocks under the head of the bed. Having the head slightly higher than the rest of the body helps prevent heartburn caused by stomach contents entering the esophagus. (9:597)

105 3. Morphine sulfate has a depressing effect on the respiratory system. Therefore, it is important to obtain a patient's respiratory rate prior to administering the drug. If the respiratory rate is 10 or less per minute, morphine should not be given until the nurse-in-charge has been notified and approves of the nurse's giving it. (14:59)

106 2. Paraldehyde, a nonbarbiturate used as a hypnotic, is not associated with physical dependency. Codeine, oxycodone (Percodan), and hydromorphone (Dilaudid) are associated with dependency when used improperly. (14:80)

107 2. The best way to control weight is to eat a well-balanced diet while reducing the total number of calories and increasing exercise. Excess weight almost always is caused by taking in more calories than the body needs. (9:95-96)

108 4. Nutritionists recommend that a well-balanced diet include at least 4 servings of food classified in the bread and cereal group, 4 or more servings of vegetables, 2 or more servings of meat or high-protein alternates, and 2 or more cups of milk for adults. (9:94; 4:174)

109 1. Eggs are classified in the meat group. If the person's cholesterol level is high, eggs may be contraindicated, in which case, vegetable proteins are used, such as legumes, seeds, and nuts. Potatoes are classified in the fruit and vegetable group. Yogurt is milk that is thickened and soured by the action of cultured bacteria. Macaroni is in the bread and cereal group. (4:185)

110 2. Proteins are generally the most expensive food substance in the diet. Beans and peas are relatively inexpensive sources of protein. However, unlike meat and eggs, they are incomplete proteins. (9:89)

111 4. The healthy body uses synthetic and natural vitamins equally well. Natural fertilizers are no safer than chemical fertilizers, aluminum and Teflon-coated utensils are safe, and a well-balanced diet supplies the body with sufficient minerals and vitamins for health. (17:512-513)

112 4. A large-toothed comb is best when grooming hair that is curly and kinky. Brushes and other types of combs are very difficult to get through very curly hair. (9:82)

113 1. It is a myth that women generally can no longer respond to sexual activity with interest and vigor after menopause. Studies have shown that sexual response need not fade, and often increases, during and after menopause. (15:25-26)

Classification of Test Items

Directions: *Each item in the previous review test is classified here according to the subject area it tests. Place a check mark after each item you answered **correctly** by referring to your answers. Total the number of items you answered correctly in each area and enter the numbers in the correct places on pages 553–556.*

Clinical: Medical/Surgical Nursing (Adults)

1 ✓	34 ✓	58 ✓	72 ✓	85 ✓	100 ✓
3 ✓	35 ✓	59 ✓	74 ✓	86 ✓	101 ✓
19 ✓	36 ✓	62	75 ✓	88 ✓	102
20 ✓	46 ✓	64 ✓	76	91 ✓	103 ✓
26 ✓	48 ✓	68 ✓	79 ✓	96 ✓	104 ✓
27 ✓	50 ✓	69 ✓	80 ✓	97 ✓	
28 ✓	52	70	81 ✓	98 ✓	
33 ✓	57 ✓	71	84 ✓	99 ✓	

TOTAL *39*

Biological/Physical Sciences

2 ✓	14 ✓	39 ✓	44 ✓	47	90 ✓
4 ✓	38	43 ✓	45 ✓	78 ✓	113 ✓
5 ✓					

TOTAL *12*

Fundamentals of Nursing

7	13 ✓	29	41 ✓	55 ✓	87 ✓
8 ✓	21	30 ✓	42 ✓	56 ✓	89 ✓
9 ✓	22 ✓	31	49 ✓	63 ✓	112 ✓
10 ✓	23 ✓	32 ✓	51	73	
11 ✓	24	37 ✓	53	82 ✓	
12 ✓	25 ✓	40 ✓	54 ✓	83 ✓	

TOTAL *25*

Diet Therapy/Nutrition

60 ✓   65 ✓   108 ✓   109 ✓   110 ✓   111 _____

61 ✓   107 _____

TOTAL __6__

Pharmacology

6 ✓   66 ✓   77 _____   92 ✓   105 _____   106 _____

TOTAL __3__

Psychosocial Sciences

15 ✓   17 ✓   67 ✓   93 _____   94 ✓   95 ✓

16 ✓   18 ✓

TOTAL __7__

Review Test 8

Correct Answers and Rationales
Classification of Test Items

Directions: *With a pencil, blacken the circle in front of the option you have chosen for your correct answer.*

The Nursing Care of Patients With Disorders of the Musculoskeletal System (Continued)

Ms. Hundford receives emergency care at the site of an automobile accident. She has a back and a head injury and is bleeding from a wound on her leg.

1 Ms. Hundford is lying on the pavement when a rescuer arrives. Of the following emergency measures, which one should the rescuer take first?
    ○ 1. Take steps to open the victim's airway.
    ○ 2. Place a blanket for warmth over the victim.
    ○ 3. Help move the victim to the nearest hospital.
    ○ 4. Search for wounds covered by the victim's clothing.

2 Ms. Hundford is bleeding profusely from a mangled and crushing wound on her leg above the ankle. The artery on which the rescuer should apply pressure to help control the bleeding is on the
    ○ 1. femoral artery in the groin.
    ○ 2. dorsalis pedis artery at the ankle.
    ○ 3. popliteal artery at the back of the knee.

    ○ 4. anterior tibial artery on the front of the leg.

3 Pressure on the artery and on the wound does not stop bleeding near Ms. Hundford's ankle. If the following articles are available and using a tourniquet becomes necessary, which article should the rescuer use?

    ○ 1. A plastic cord
    ○ 2. A nylon stocking
    ○ 3. A blood pressure cuff
    ○ 4. A roller gauze bandage

4 Ms. Hundford is suspected of having a broken back. The preferred position in which to transport her to a health care agency is the

    ○ 1. side-lying position.
    ○ 2. face-lying position.
    ○ 3. back-lying position.
    ○ 4. semi-sitting position.

An ambulance transports Ms. Hundford to a hospital for care.

5 To judge Ms. Hundford's condition in relation to the head injury, it is particularly important for the nurse to observe Ms. Hundford's

    ○ 1. pupils and how they react to light.
    ○ 2. oral mucosa and note the amount of cyanosis.
    ○ 3. eyes and note whether the corneas are injured.
    ○ 4. ears and determine whether the eardrums are intact.

6 Ms. Hundford is difficult to arouse, but after awakening one time, she speaks a partial sentence ("Yes, I want . . .") and falls into an unconscious state again. The victim's state of consciousness is best described as

    ○ 1. stupor.
    ○ 2. confusion.
    ○ 3. disorientation.
    ○ 4. traumatic delirium.

7 The answer to which one of the following questions will help *least* to guide the nurse when she assesses Ms. Hundford for level of consciousness?

    ○ 1. Is the patient oriented when awake?
    ○ 2. How easily does the patient awaken?
    ○ 3. How does the patient respond to painful stimuli?
    ○ 4. Is the patient maintaining a normal blood pressure?

8 Ms. Hundford's pulse rate is noted to be fast and barely perceptible. This type of pulse is best described as being

    ○ 1. thready.
    ○ 2. bounding.
    ○ 3. bigeminal.
    ○ 4. intermittent.

9 Ms. Hundford's axillary temperature is obtained. The *minimum* length of time a thermometer should be left in place to obtain an accurate axillary temperature is

- ○ 1. 3 minutes.
- ○ 2. 5 minutes.
- ○ 3. 10 minutes.
- ○ 4. 20 minutes.

10 Ms. Hundford's axillary temperature, when compared with an oral temperature, will be approximately

- ○ 1. the same.
- ○ 2. 1°F (0.6°C) lower.
- ○ 3. 1°F (0.6°C) higher.
- ○ 4. 3°F (1.8°C) lower.

11 It is determined that Ms. Hundford has a fracture in the lumbar area of the spine with cord damage at the fracture site. She is expected to recover from the accident but the cord damage appears permanent. In terms of eventual ability to take care of herself, Ms. Hundford's prognosis is

- ○ 1. poor.
- ○ 2. good.
- ○ 3. questionable.
- ○ 4. unpredictable.

Seventeen-year-old Sharon Wendy is transported to a hospital following a motorcycle accident. Her lower left leg and left foot are crushed. No other serious injuries are noted.

12 Upon admission to the hospital, Sharon has symptoms of shock. In this situation, the position of choice for Sharon is

- ○ 1. in a very low-Fowler's position.
- ○ 2. on either side with her head elevated on a pillow.
- ○ 3. flat on her back with her right knee flexed about 90 degrees.
- ○ 4. flat on her back with both legs and feet elevated about 8 inches to 12 inches (20 cm to 30 cm) higher than her head.

13 Of the following signs, the most typical finding if Sharon goes into a state of shock is a decreasing

- ○ 1. pulse rate.
- ○ 2. blood pressure.
- ○ 3. respiratory rate.
- ○ 4. body temperature.

Because of injuries, Sharon's left leg is amputated below the knee. The nurse begins postoperative care.

14 Sharon cries and shouts when she realizes that her lower left leg is gone. In this situation, it would be best for the nurse to

   ○ 1. ask if she would like to see her parents.
   ○ 2. hold her hand while she expresses her feelings.
   ○ 3. explain that a prosthesis will soon be fitted for her.
   ○ 4. describe other young patients who have done well after an amputation.

15 Sharon's stump is observed for bleeding. The body's defense to prevent hemorrhage is blood clotting, which is accomplished primarily by a blood constituent known as
   ○ 1. platelets.
   ○ 2. hemoglobin.
   ○ 3. erythrocytes.
   ○ 4. reticulocytes.

16 Sharon is placed on a firm mattress on a bed that is elevated at the foot, rather than having the stump placed on a pillow. This positioning is used primarily to help
   ○ 1. prevent contracture of the hip joint.
   ○ 2. limit shock from blood lost during surgery.
   ○ 3. prepare the leg for fitting with a prosthesis.
   ○ 4. promote lymphatic drainage away from the stump.

17 A nursing assistant asks the nurse why Sharon is *not* on a Stryker or Foster frame. The nurse bases her reply on knowledge that these frames are most appropriately used for a patient whose health problem is caused by a
   ○ 1. stroke.
   ○ 2. heart attack.
   ○ 3. fractured spine.
   ○ 4. blood clot in a leg.

18 Sharon has a closed amputation with a drain in the wound. The wound is without a rigid dressing. Sharon is helped to turn from side to side, to lie on her abdomen and adduct the stump, and while on her back, to flex the left knee. These exercises are carried out primarily to help
   ○ 1. promote circulation in the stump.
   ○ 2. promote drainage from the stump.
   ○ 3. prevent a contracture of the left knee.
   ○ 4. prevent a decubitus ulcer on the left hip or knee.

19 Because Sharon does not have a rigid dressing on her stump, which of the following pieces of equipment should be kept in readiness for use in Sharon's room in case of an emergency?
   ○ 1. A tourniquet
   ○ 2. A surgical clamp
   ○ 3. A tracheostomy set
   ○ 4. A blood transfusion set

20 One day when Sharon is to have her dressing on the stump changed, she states, "I can't stand to look at it!" Of the following comments the nurse could make, which one is best in this situation?

O 1. "You may watch when you feel ready to do so."
O 2. "Maybe you should discuss this with your doctor."
O 3. "It is healing well now. Don't you want to see it?"
O 4. "You will become used to your wound if you look at it."

21 Sharon's wound is infected. If arrangements are made for a wound débridement for Sharon's wound, the nurse should be prepared to assist with

O 1. closing the wound.
O 2. packing the wound.
O 3. opening the wound.
O 4. cleaning the wound.

22 It is generally believed that the most effective way to help prevent the spread of organisms found in Sharon's wounds is to

O 1. use disposable equipment.
O 2. observe good handwashing techniques.
O 3. isolate persons with infections from others.
O 4. sterilize personal care items after each use.

Sharon complains of phantom-limb pain.

23 Phantom-limb pain means that Sharon feels pain in the

O 1. stump.
O 2. amputated leg.
O 3. leg on which no surgery has been done.
O 4. arm on the same side from which the leg was amputated.

The nurse prepares to bathe Sharon, give her a backrub, and change bed linens.

24 The nurse carries a bath basin of water to Sharon's bedside stand. She is using the best technique when she carries the basin so that her

O 1. neck is flexed about 60 degrees and the basin rests on her hip.
O 2. elbows are flexed about 90 degrees and the basin is held near her body.
O 3. arms encircle the basin and the basin rests against her waist.
O 4. shoulders are somewhat rounded and the basin is well away from her body.

25 During a bed bath, the nurse should clean Sharon's eyes by moving the washcloth from the area of the eyes near the nose toward the patient's temples. This technique is recommended because it helps to

O 1. reduce irritation to the eyes.

○ 2. prevent water from entering the eyes.
○ 3. prevent material from entering the lacrimal ducts.
○ 4. reduce unpleasant sensations when the eyes are closed.

26 Which of the following body systems is *least* likely to be affected by the process of the nurse's giving Sharon a bed bath?
○ 1. The digestive system
○ 2. The circulatory system
○ 3. The respiratory system
○ 4. The musculoskeletal system

27 A characteristic of alcohol that acts as a primary *disadvantage* when giving a backrub to Sharon is that alcohol
○ 1. is flammable.
○ 2. dries the skin.
○ 3. softens the skin.
○ 4. evaporates too quickly.

28 Of the following techniques used to give Sharon a backrub, which one is most often recommended?
○ 1. The nurse uses the entire surfaces of her fingers for massaging with long strokes.
○ 2. The nurse gently lifts her hands from the patient's back after each long stroke.
○ 3. The nurse allows her strokes to become lighter as she completes the backrub.
○ 4. The nurse ends the backrub using circular motions down the length of the patient's spine.

29 If the nurse uses the following techniques while removing bottom soiled linens from Sharon's bed and replacing them with clean linens, which one is in *error*?
○ 1. The nurse has the bed siderail up on the side opposite the one where she works.
○ 2. The nurse rolls soiled bottom linens toward the patients' back while the patient lies on her side.
○ 3. The nurse drops each piece of soiled linen in a hamper as she removes it.
○ 4. The nurse unfolds clean linens in place on the bed.

30 When positioning Sharon following the bath, the nurse observes that Sharon's right leg tends to roll outward when she is in a back-lying position. The nurse uses a commonly recommended device to prevent outward rotation of the leg, which is a
○ 1. cradle.
○ 2. trapeze.
○ 3. sandbag.
○ 4. footboard.

31 The nurse prepares to turn Sharon from her back onto her abdomen. When Sharon is turned *toward* the nurse, where should Sharon's arm

(the one nearer the nurse) be positioned for most comfort and convenience?

  ○ 1. Across the patient's chest
  ○ 2. Under the patient's buttocks
  ○ 3. Over the patient's abdomen
  ○ 4. Alongside the patient's body

32 When Sharon is in the face-lying position, the part of her body to which the nurse should give special care to prevent discomfort and possible complications is Sharon's

  ○ 1. left hip.
  ○ 2. right hip.
  ○ 3. right foot.
  ○ 4. right knee.

33 While the nurse cares for Sharon, Sharon often says "my room," "my bathroom," and "my windows," when speaking of her hospital room. By so doing, she is most accurately illustrating a basic human need for

  ○ 1. privacy.
  ○ 2. personal space.
  ○ 3. feelings of intimacy.
  ○ 4. feelings of belonging.

While bathing Sharon, she and the nurse discuss various measures related to skin care, oral hygiene, and contact lens care.

34 Sharon complains to the nurse about her acne. The nurse should explain that the best home care found to date to control acne is to

  ○ 1. avoid cola drinks.
  ○ 2. stay out of direct sunlight.
  ○ 3. wash the skin with soap and water frequently.
  ○ 4. use a cream cleanser and an astringent on the skin frequently.

35 The nurse explains correctly when she tells Sharon that her acne is related to an increase in the body's

  ○ 1. excretory activity.
  ○ 2. metabolic activity.
  ○ 3. hormonal activity.
  ○ 4. autoimmune activity.

36 Sharon asks, "Which is better—a hand or an electric toothbrush?" When compared with a hand toothbrush, in terms of effectiveness, an electric toothbrush is considered

  ○ 1. less effective.
  ○ 2. more effective.
  ○ 3. equally effective.
  ○ 4. unproven in terms of effectiveness.

37 The nurse should teach Sharon that the best way to dislodge bacteria from between the teeth is to

    ◯ 1. chew sugarless gum.
    ◯ 2. floss between the teeth.
    ◯ 3. use a toothbrush with widely spaced tufts.
    ◯ 4. rinse the teeth with an antiseptic mouthwash.

38 When Sharon asks, the nurse explains to her that a term used for cavities is
    ◯ 1. caries.
    ◯ 2. halitosis.
    ◯ 3. pyorrhea.
    ◯ 4. gingivitis.

39 Sharon wears contact lenses which she removes each night and replaces each morning. She says, "Removing the lenses is a big nuisance." The nurse should explain that if the lenses are left in place too long, the structures in Sharon's eyes that could easily be injured are the
    ◯ 1. lenses.
    ◯ 2. retinas.
    ◯ 3. scleras.
    ◯ 4. corneas.

Sharon is to be out of bed and is to be taught crutch-walking.

40 In preparation for being out of bed, Sharon is taught to contract and relax muscles alternately on the front of her thigh. Exercises that produce muscle tension but do not significantly change the length of the muscles are called
    ◯ 1. active exercises.
    ◯ 2. passive exercises.
    ◯ 3. aerobic exercises.
    ◯ 4. isometric exercises.

41 The nurse prepares Sharon for standing by the side of her bed. She first places Sharon in a high-Fowler's position in bed. The nurse's next course of action should be to
    ◯ 1. place a walking belt on the patient.
    ◯ 2. dangle the patient on the side of the bed.
    ◯ 3. perform passive exercises on the patient's right leg.
    ◯ 4. teach the patient how to support herself with a walker.

42 If Sharon can safely perform the following exercises in bed, which one will help her most to be ready for crutch-walking?
    ◯ 1. Alternately sitting up and lying down in bed (sit-ups)
    ◯ 2. Rolling back and forth from one side to the other
    ◯ 3. While on her back, alternately contracting and relaxing the muscles on the front of the thigh
    ◯ 4. While on her abdomen, alternately flexing and extending her elbows while her palms are flat on the bed near the shoulders (push-ups)

43 While teaching Sharon to use crutches, if the nurse makes the following comments, which one is in *error?*
   ○ 1. "Keep your elbows slightly flexed."
   ○ 2. "Keep crutch tips on the ends of your crutches."
   ○ 3. "Put most of your weight in your armpits as you walk."
   ○ 4. "Use your regular walking shoe while on your crutches."

Sharon has a cassette player in her room and ignores suggestions to keep the volume low.

44 Sharon's type of behavior best illustrates an adolescent's efforts to
   ○ 1. express a sense of security.
   ○ 2. prove she is almost an adult.
   ○ 3. be different from her friends.
   ○ 4. develop a feeling of independence.

Ms. Cortland, who is 82 years old, is hospitalized with a fracture in the neck of the right femur. She has surgery when an internal fixation device (a nail) is placed through an anterior incision.

45 Ms. Cortland has a typical sign of a broken hip when admitted, which is
   ○ 1. a shuffling gait.
   ○ 2. paralysis of the affected leg.
   ○ 3. lengthening of the affected leg.
   ○ 4. external rotation of the affected leg.

46 Ms. Cortland is placed in bed on her back when she returns from surgery. Where should the nurse be especially careful to inspect when she checks the patient for signs of bleeding from the surgical wound?
   ○ 1. On the top layers of the patient's dressing
   ○ 2. On the bottom bed linens near the patient's wound
   ○ 3. On the side of the dressing nearest the patient's groin
   ○ 4. On the lower edge of the dressing that crosses the patient's thigh

47 If Ms. Cortland's feet are not supported in the normal walking position while she is in bed, Ms. Cortland is most likely to develop
   ○ 1. flat feet.
   ○ 2. footdrop.
   ○ 3. calluses on the feet.
   ○ 4. contractures of the knee joints.

The dangers of inactivity are taken into account when Ms. Cortland's nursing care plan is prepared.

48 The greatest danger to the urinary system if Ms. Cortland remains inactive is the development of
   ○ 1. hematuria.

    ○ 2. kidney tumors.

    ○ 3. ureteral spasms.

    ○ 4. urinary tract infection.

49 A common complication of inactivity that is likely to affect Ms. Cortland's gastrointestinal tract is

    ○ 1. heartburn.

    ○ 2. constipation.

    ○ 3. hyperacidity.

    ○ 4. reverse peristalsis.

50 A complication affecting the circulatory system if Ms. Cortland remains inactive is the development of

    ○ 1. air emboli.

    ○ 2. blood clots.

    ○ 3. varicose veins.

    ○ 4. arteriosclerosis.

51 If calcium leaves Ms. Cortland's body in abnormally large amounts because of inactivity, the patient is most likely to develop

    ○ 1. anemia.

    ○ 2. muscle spasms.

    ○ 3. mental confusion.

    ○ 4. brittleness of the bones.

Ms. Cortland is to have an x-ray examination and will be taken to the x-ray department on a stretcher.

52 Three carriers will carry Ms. Cortland from her bed to the stretcher. For greatest convenience and safety, where, in relation to the bed, should the stretcher be placed before the carriers lift Ms. Cortland from the bed and place her on the stretcher?

    ○ 1. Parallel with the side of the bed

    ○ 2. Diagonally to the head of the bed

    ○ 3. At a right angle to the head of the bed

    ○ 4. At a right angle to the foot of the bed

53 For greatest convenience and safety, when the three carriers are lifting Ms. Cortland from her bed to the stretcher, the parts of her body that the *tallest* carrier should plan to carry are the patient's

    ○ 1. legs and feet.

    ○ 2. hips and waist.

    ○ 3. chest and waist.

    ○ 4. head and shoulders.

54 Immediately after the carriers have lifted Ms. Cortland off the bed, they should next

    ○ 1. pivot toward the stretcher.

    ○ 2. step back from the patient's bed.

    ○ 3. roll the patient onto their chests.

    ◯ 4. slide their arms farther under the patient.

55 One of the carriers transports Ms. Cortland to the x-ray department. To reduce muscle strain, it is best for the carrier to move the stretcher by using her body in a manner so that she is

    ◯ 1. leaning toward the stretcher while pushing it.

    ◯ 2. moving her feet in a shuffling manner while pushing it.

    ◯ 3. grasping the stretcher with her hands behind her back while pulling it.

    ◯ 4. keeping her elbows straight, with her trunk upright, while pushing it.

Ms. Cortland is to have passive and active range-of-motion exercises.

56 Which of the following exercises planned for Ms. Cortland is an example of passive exercise?

    ◯ 1. Having the patient comb her hair

    ◯ 2. Having a nurse rotate the patient's thumb

    ◯ 3. Having the patient reach for her telephone and water glass

    ◯ 4. Having a nurse observe the patient flex and extend her knees.

57 When putting one of Ms. Cortland's joints through range-of-motion, the nurse should *stop* the exercising when the patient

    ◯ 1. says she feels no benefit from the exercising.

    ◯ 2. moves the joint without the nurse's assistance.

    ◯ 3. offers some resistance when the joint is moved.

    ◯ 4. complains of discomfort when the joint is moved.

58 In which of the following ways can the nurse expect Ms. Cortland's vital signs to change, if at all, after the nurse has just completed active and passive range-of-motion exercises with the patient?

    ◯ 1. The pulse rate will increase.

    ◯ 2. The respiratory rate will decrease.

    ◯ 3. The temperature will become slightly elevated.

    ◯ 4. The vital signs will remain essentially as they were before exercising.

59 After giving Ms. Cortland active and passive exercises, the nurse wishes to position Ms. Cortland in bed by turning her from her back onto her left side. Before turning Ms. Cortland, the nurse should first

    ◯ 1. place pillows between the patient's legs.

    ◯ 2. have the patient point her toes outward.

    ◯ 3. flex the patient's knee on the affected side.

    ◯ 4. place a bedboard onto which the patient can roll.

Ms. Cortland is to be out of bed and is to walk while using a walker.

60 Because Ms. Cortland has had an open reduction of a fractured hip, which of the following precautions should the nurse use when helping Ms. Cortland out of bed?

    ○ 1. Splinting the leg on the affected side
    ○ 2. Avoiding weight-bearing on the affected leg
    ○ 3. Keeping the leg on the affected side well elevated
    ○ 4. Bandaging the affected hip with a pressure bandage

61 The nurse is helping Ms. Cortland to learn how to use a walker while she ambulates. When she is using her walker, it is *inappropriate* for Ms. Cortland to
    ○ 1. keep her elbows flexed a bit.
    ○ 2. hold her neck in a position of extension.
    ○ 3. walk with her feet as close together as possible.
    ○ 4. grasp the hand supports on her walker with a firm hand grip.

Ms. Cortland develops aseptic (avascular) necrosis of the femur.

62 Symptoms Ms. Cortland is most likely to experience when aseptic necrosis of the femur develops include pain and
    ○ 1. edema in the leg.
    ○ 2. paralysis of the leg.
    ○ 3. walking with a limp.
    ○ 4. inability to move the leg.

Twenty-three-year-old Mr. Korski injures his legs in an accident at work. An industrial nurse gives Mr. Korski first-aid care.

63 To expose Mr. Korski's injured legs, the nurse should remove the patient's trousers by
    ○ 1. cutting the trouser legs for their full length.
    ○ 2. sliding both trouser legs above the injuries.
    ○ 3. slipping the trouser leg off his left leg first, then off the right leg.
    ○ 4. slipping the trouser leg off the right leg first, then off the left leg.

64 After exposing Mr. Korski's legs, the nurse notes that Mr. Korski has broken a bone in his left lower leg and the bone has pierced the skin. The type of fracture Mr. Korski has is called a
    ○ 1. complete fracture.
    ○ 2. greenstick fracture.
    ○ 3. compound fracture.
    ○ 4. comminuted fracture.

65 Mr. Korski tells the nurse that the area around his sprained right knee hurts, ". . . especially on my kneecap." Which of the following terms do health-care personnel use when referring to the kneecap?
    ○ 1. The tarsal
    ○ 2. The patella
    ○ 3. The phalange
    ○ 4. The calcaneus

66 The term health care personnel often use to describe the type of wound Mr. Korski has at his right knee is
○ 1. a contusion.
○ 2. an impaction.
○ 3. an incomplete fracture.
○ 4. an inflammatory process.

67 Of the following measures the industrial nurse could use at the time of Mr. Korski's accident after the extremities are exposed, it would be best first to
○ 1. assess the right knee for fractures.
○ 2. place the patient on a firm bed or stretcher.
○ 3. splint the broken leg while the patient is on the floor.
○ 4. irrigate the patient's wound where the bone has pierced the skin.

68 Which of the following conditions, if present, would *contraindicate* the nurse's applying an ice bag to the area on Mr. Korski's right knee?
○ 1. The knee is swollen.
○ 2. The ligaments are torn.
○ 3. The skin has a deep scratch.
○ 4. The kneecap is believed to be fractured.

Mr. Korski is transported to a hospital where an elastic (ace) bandage is applied to his right leg from the foot to above the knee.

69 The position in which the nurse should place Mr. Korski's knee before bandaging it is in a position of
○ 1. extension.
○ 2. slight flexion.
○ 3. slight rotation.
○ 4. slight hyperextension.

70 Where should the nurse begin bandaging Mr. Korski's right leg?
○ 1. Above the patient's knee
○ 2. At the patient's knee
○ 3. At the patient's ankle
○ 4. At the arch of the patient's foot

71 Which turn should the nurse use to anchor Mr. Korski's elastic bandage before the leg is bandaged?
○ 1. A spica turn
○ 2. A spiral turn
○ 3. A circular turn
○ 4. A spiral-reverse turn

72 If Mr. Korski's toes become swollen after applying the elastic bandage, the nurse should judge that the bandage is very likely to be too
○ 1. tight.
○ 2. loose.

    ○ 3. near the toes.
    ○ 4. high on the ankle.

An open reduction of the fracture of the left tibia will be done on Mr. Korski.

73 The nurse anticipates that the skin on Mr. Korski's left leg should be washed, shaven, and
    ○ 1. scrubbed with an antiseptic.
    ○ 2. sprayed with a skin anesthetic.
    ○ 3. flushed with an antibiotic solution.
    ○ 4. irrigated with sterile normal saline.

74 Skin preparation for surgery on Mr. Korski's left leg is done with great care to help prevent postoperative
    ○ 1. embolism formation.
    ○ 2. infection in the operative site.
    ○ 3. hemorrhaging at the operative site.
    ○ 4. thrombophlebitis in the leg on which surgery is to be performed.

75 The nurse compares Mr. Korski's preoperative blood pressure with what is considered normal for a person of his age and sex. The most commonly used term to describe the process the nurse has used in this situation is
    ○ 1. planning.
    ○ 2. synthesis.
    ○ 3. evaluation.
    ○ 4. assessment.

The nurse prepares a bed to receive Mr. Korski from the recovery room after surgery.

76 The mattress is too soft on the bed to support Mr. Korski's back adequately. A device often used by nurses when a bed's mattress is too soft for a patient is a
    ○ 1. cradle.
    ○ 2. footboard.
    ○ 3. bedboard.
    ○ 4. foot block.

Mr. Korski returns from the recovery room with a plaster cast on his left leg and foot.

77 Mr. Korski's casted leg should be positioned in bed by
    ○ 1. elevating it on several pillows.
    ○ 2. extending it flat on the mattress.
    ○ 3. resting it over the edge of a footboard.

○ 4. placing it over the edge of the bed on a chair.

78   The nurse is in *error* when one of the techniques she uses while caring for Mr. Korski's cast is
○ 1. using a cradle over the cast to support bed linens.
○ 2. placing an ice bag next to the cast to help prevent edema in the leg.
○ 3. moving the wet cast by handling it carefully with her fingers to prevent indentations on the cast.
○ 4. making an inked line around a drainage stain on the cast to help make comparisons in the amount of drainage.

79   During the first 24 hours, Mr. Korski's cast should be checked at least every
○ 1. 15 to 20 minutes.
○ 2. 1 to 2 hours.
○ 3. 3 to 4 hours.
○ 4. 5 to 6 hours.

80   If the nurse pinches Mr. Korski's toenails, then releases them, and notes a slow return of color to the nailbeds, a very probable cause of her observation is that the
○ 1. cast is still wet.
○ 2. cast is too tight.
○ 3. patient has an infection.
○ 4. patient has been moving too much.

81   When Mr. Korski's cast is dry, the usual procedure is to pull the stockinet under the cast over the edges of the cast and then
○ 1. roll the stockinet to the cast's edges.
○ 2. cut off the stockinet at the cast's edges.
○ 3. hold the stockinet in place with a bandage.
○ 4. cover the edges of the cast with adhesive petals.

82   About 3 days after Mr. Korski's cast has been applied, the nurse uses a recommended technique to determine whether an infection may be developing in the patient's wound under the cast by
○ 1. feeling the cast for hot spots.
○ 2. checking to see if the cast has wet areas.
○ 3. observing whether the patient's toes are swollen.
○ 4. noting whether the patient complains of itching under the cast.

83   If a foul odor develops about Mr. Korski's cast, the nurse should report it promptly because the odor is a common sign when
○ 1. the cast has dried improperly.
○ 2. bleeding is occurring under the cast.
○ 3. the bone edges have become dislodged.
○ 4. an infection has developed under the cast.

84   When crumbs and small debris accumulate between Mr. Korski's cast and skin, it is best for the nurse to remove them with a
○ 1. tongue blade.
○ 2. plastic spoon.

   ○ 3. surgical clamp.
   ○ 4. vacuum cleaner.

85 In time, Mr. Korski's cast is bivalved, which means that the cast is
   ○ 1. cut open on both sides.
   ○ 2. split partially up the front and back.
   ○ 3. removed from above the knee and below the ankle.
   ○ 4. windowed with an opening over the surgical wound.

Mr. Korski, who is lying on his back in bed, is moved up in bed by two nurses.

86 Before moving Mr. Korski up in bed, one nurse should first
   ○ 1. turn the patient onto his side.
   ○ 2. remove the top linens on the bed.
   ○ 3. lower the position on the adjustable bed.
   ○ 4. place a pillow against the bed's headboard.

87 The two nurses plan to slide Mr. Korski up in bed on a drawsheet. They are standing on opposite sides of the bed and are facing the foot of the bed. The nurses have positioned themselves in this manner so that they can better
   ○ 1. observe how far they are moving the patient.
   ○ 2. use a backward rock while moving the patient.
   ○ 3. grasp the drawsheet securely under the patient.
   ○ 4. prevent the patient from bumping the headboard.

88 A nursing order for Mr. Korski states that the patient should be placed in the prone position 3 times a day. The prone position is the same as the
   ○ 1. side-lying position.
   ○ 2. face-lying position.
   ○ 3. back-lying position.
   ○ 4. semi-sitting position.

The remaining items in this situation are individual items related to Mr. Korski's care.

89 Mr. Korski is observed closely for signs and symptoms of a fatty embolism. If fat emboli reach the brain, a common sign or symptom the patient is most likely to present is
   ○ 1. feeling dizzy.
   ○ 2. seeing double.
   ○ 3. being confused.
   ○ 4. being unable to talk.

90 Mr. Korski complains of excessive perspiration. A synonym caretakers use to describe excessive perspiration is
   ○ 1. diurnal.
   ○ 2. dipsesis.

    ○ 3. diplopia.

    ○ 4. diaphoresis.

91 If the nurse gathers information about Mr. Korski by using auscultation, she is using her sense of

    ○ 1. smell.

    ○ 2. touch.

    ○ 3. vision.

    ○ 4. hearing.

92 The nurse teaches Mr. Korski about granulation tissue, which is best defined as

    ○ 1. infected tissue that is slow to heal.

    ○ 2. excess tissue that causes large scars.

    ○ 3. new tissue that forms over a wound.

    ○ 4. necrotic tissue that has to be removed.

93 In terms of developmental tasks, most young adults of Mr. Korski's age are concerned primarily with

    ○ 1. searching for a sexual identity.

    ○ 2. testing the abilities of the body.

    ○ 3. developing independence from parents.

    ○ 4. learning control over emotional behavior.

94 Mr. Korski tells the nurse, "My father will be furious about this accident. He says I should be in school instead of working." Of the following responses the nurse could make, it would be best for her to say,

    ○ 1. "Father knows best, you know."

    ○ 2. "All mothers and fathers tend to feel that way."

    ○ 3. "It is difficult when a father and son disagree, isn't it?"

    ○ 4. "You are adult enough to make decisions, don't you agree?"

Mr. Marble has a fractured femur. Russell traction is used to maintain alignment and immobilization of his fracture.

95 Mr. Marble is scheduled to go to the x-ray department while remaining in his bed. Which of the following techniques should the nurse use in relation to his traction, while transporting him in his bed?

    ○ 1. Leave the traction as it is.

    ○ 2. Disconnect the traction pulleys.

    ○ 3. Decrease the weights by about half.

    ○ 4. Rest the weights on the foot of the bed.

96 It is important that traction and countertraction be maintained in Mr. Marble's Russell traction. If the weights on the Russell traction represent the force of traction, how is countertraction maintained?

    ○ 1. By the weight of the patient's body

    ○ 2. By the pulleys on the Russell traction

    ○ 3. By the sling supporting the patient's leg

    ○ 4. By the traction tapes attached to the patient's skin

97   What measure, if any, is ordinarily recommended in relation to daily fluid intake for Mr. Marble while using Russell traction?

    ○ 1.   Fluid intake should be above normal daily amounts.
    ○ 2.   Fluid intake should be below normal daily amounts.
    ○ 3.   Fluid intake should be at about normal daily amounts.
    ○ 4.   Fluid intake is of no particular significance in this situation.

98   If Mr. Marble remains inactive for a period of time, a common effect on his muscles is that they will become

    ○ 1.   longer than normal.
    ○ 2.   weaker than normal.
    ○ 3.   more subject to spasms than usual.
    ○ 4.   more sensitive to ordinary stimuli than usual.

99   The nurse assigned to care for Mr. Marble has several other patients to care for also. When the nurse must decide how to allocate her time and services among patients for whom she is caring, the primary criterion on which her decision-making should be based is on the patients'

    ○ 1.   ages.
    ○ 2.   needs.
    ○ 3.   cultures.
    ○ 4.   personalities.

Ms. Dugan, 79 years old, is hospitalized for a total right hip replacement. Postoperative nursing care is underway.

100   The following nursing order appears on Ms. Dugan's postoperative care plan: Do not allow the patient to bring her right leg toward or over her left leg. The word used to describe this *contraindicated* move is

    ○ 1.   flexion.
    ○ 2.   abduction.
    ○ 3. · adduction.
    ○ 4.   extension.

101   The primary reason for not allowing Ms. Dugan to bring her right leg toward or across her left leg is to help prevent

    ○ 1.   opening the surgical wound.
    ○ 2.   dislodging the replacement device in the hip.
    ○ 3.   disturbing blood circulation in the operative area.
    ○ 4.   obstructing lymphatic drainage in the lower extremities.

102   Ms. Dugan complains of pain whenever she is moved in bed. Which of the following courses of action should the nurse take when preparing to move Ms. Dugan?

    ○ 1.   Allow the patient to assist when moving her.
    ○ 2.   Plan moving the patient after she has had a nap.
    ○ 3.   Prepare to move the patient about 30 minutes after a meal.
    ○ 4.   Give the patient a prescribed analgesic about 15 minutes before moving her.

103 Ms. Dugan's body temperature has been normal postoperatively for 3 days. However, her temperature continues to be monitored every 4 hours primarily because Ms. Dugan is at risk for developing
○ 1. hypothermia.
○ 2. an infection.
○ 3. aseptic necrosis.
○ 4. bleeding in the operative site.

104 If Ms. Dugan is receiving the following medications and she develops diarrhea, which agent is most likely to be a possible cause?
○ 1. Vitamin C
○ 2. Ferrous sulfate
○ 3. Aluminum hydroxide
○ 4. Propranolol hydrochloride (Inderal)

105 The nurse can expect that certain of Ms. Dugan's abilities are decreasing with age. Of the following abilities, the one that is most likely to remain highly acute among elderly persons in normal health is the ability to
○ 1. recall past experiences.
○ 2. remember recent events.
○ 3. adjust to temperature changes.
○ 4. respond to stresses of daily living.

Hygienic care is given to Ms. Dugan.

106 If the nurse uses the following techniques when giving Ms. Dugan perineal care as part of a bed bath, which one is in *error?*
○ 1. The nurse uses techniques of medical asepsis during the procedure.
○ 2. The nurse places the patient on a bedpan.
○ 3. The nurse holds cotton balls for cleaning with a pair of forceps.
○ 4. The nurse moves cotton balls from the patient's anal area toward the pubic area.

107 While giving Ms. Dugan hygienic care, the nurse can expect that the patient's skin is most likely to be
○ 1. dry.
○ 2. red.
○ 3. thick.
○ 4. damp.

108 Of the following personal hygienic measures that the nurse wishes to use for Ms. Dugan, which one most often requires a specific order to do so?
○ 1. Cleaning dentures.
○ 2. Cutting toenails.
○ 3. Giving perineal care.
○ 4. Shampooing the hair.

Mr. Mack suffers with gout.

109 Which system in Mr. Mack's body is considered to be at fault in relation to his having gout?
○ 1. The metabolic system
○ 2. The hormonal system
○ 3. The neurological system
○ 4. The connective system

110 In addition to swelling of the involved joint, Mr. Mack is most likely to complain of
○ 1. tingling in the joint.
○ 2. numbness in the joint.
○ 3. dislocation of the joint.
○ 4. severe pain in the joint.

Mr. Mack is to have generous (larger than normal) amounts of fluid daily.

111 The time in the day when it is best to offer proportionately greater amounts of fluid to Mr. Mack is
○ 1. in the morning.
○ 2. soon after lunch.
○ 3. immediately before dinner.
○ 4. during early evening hours.

Mr. Mack receives allopurinal (Zyloprim).

112 Allopurinal is used for Mr. Mack primarily because of the drug's ability to
○ 1. control discomfort in the affected joint.
○ 2. interfere with the formation of uric acid.
○ 3. stimulate the proper metabolism of purines.
○ 4. reduce the inflammation in the affected joint.

The nurse obtains Mr. Mack's oral temperature.

113 Where should the nurse place the thermometer in Mr. Mack's mouth to obtain an accurate oral temperature?
○ 1. Well back in the mouth on top of the tongue
○ 2. Between the lower back teeth and cheek on either side of the mouth
○ 3. At the base of the tongue on either side under the patient's tongue
○ 4. At the base of the tongue on either side on top of the patient's tongue

114 The number of minutes that a glass clinical thermometer should be left in place in Mr. Mack's mouth to obtain an accurate oral temperature should be no less than
○ 1. 3 minutes.
○ 2. 5 minutes.
○ 3. 7 minutes.
○ 4. 10 minutes.

Correct Answers and Rationales

Two numbers appear in parentheses following each rationale. The first number identifies the textbook listed in the references, page 649, and the second number identifies the page(s) in that textbook where the correct answer can be verified. Occasionally, two textbooks are given for verifying the correct answer.

The Nursing Care of Patients With Disorders of the Musculoskeletal System

Caring for a patient with back and head injuries

1 1. All of the measures described in this item may become necessary in an emergency, but the first step a rescuer should take is to see that the victim's airway is open. The patient must receive air in his respiratory tract in order to sustain life. (15:105)

2 1. To control bleeding in the lower leg and foot, pressure should be placed on the femoral artery in the groin. The dorsalis pedis artery is too low on the leg to control bleeding near the ankle. The popliteal and anterior tibial artery are also low on the leg and, therefore, compressing them is less effective for controlling profuse bleeding in the lower leg. (15:106–107)

3 3. A blood pressure cuff of an inflatable (pneumatic) type is preferred when a tourniquet becomes necessary and when a regular tourniquet is unavailable. It is less likely to cause tissue injury and more effectively controls bleeding than a plastic cord, a nylon stocking, or a roller gauze bandage. (15:107)

4 3. An accident victim with a suspected back injury should be flat on his back on a hard surface when being transported. The side-lying, face-lying, and semi-sitting positions are likely to cause more injury to the back and spinal cord if the victim has a broken back with cord injury. (15:173–174)

5 1. It is particularly important to check a victim's pupils for size and equality and note how they react to light when checking a victim's condition following a head injury. Significant and serious signs include pupils that remain dilated or are irregular in size. (15:699)

6 1. Stupor means that it takes effort to arouse the patient to a state of consciousness. Often, the patient will say a few words and then fall back into unconsciousness. Confusion is a disturbance in which the patient lacks the ability to recognize and interpret things in his environment. Disorientation means the patient is unaware of who he is, where he is, and what he is doing, but he is awake and responds to stimuli. Delirium is characterized by a clouding of consciousness. (15:210)

7 4. Questions that relate to how easily a patient awakens, whether he is oriented as to place, time, and person, how well he responds to stimuli, whether he understands commands, and whether he is combative or restless help to guide a nurse who is assessing a patient's level of consciousness. Observations related to blood pressure are least helpful for determining level of consciousness. (8:245)

8 1. A fast and barely perceptible pulse is called a thready pulse. An intermittent pulse is one that occasionally skips a beat. A bounding pulse feels full and strong. A bigeminal pulse has two regular beats followed by a longer-than-normal pause without a beat. (9:196)

9 3. A thermometer should be left in the axillary area for a minimum of 10 minutes, but preferably 15 minutes, to obtain an accurate reading of body temperature. (9:194)

10 2. An axillary temperature is about 1°F (0.6°C) lower than an oral temperature. (9:188)

11 2. An injury low in the spine with cord damage at the site of the injury offers a good prognosis in terms of the patient's being able to take care of herself. The higher in the spinal cord that injury occurs, the poorer the prognosis in terms of self-care and being able to work. (8:267)

Caring for a patient with an amputation

12 4. The position of choice when a patient shows signs of shock is flat on his back with legs and feet elevated about 8 inches to 12 inches (20 cm to 30 cm). This positioning promotes blood flow from the extremities to the body's vital organs. Lowering the head and elevating the feet when shock is present generally is no longer recommended because of possible congestion of blood in the head. Having the patient supine in bed with the knees flexed does little to promote blood flow to the body's vital organs and decreases blood circulation to the lower legs because of pressure behind the knees. Elevating the head does not bring blood from extremities to vital organs. (9:386)

13 2. The blood pressure falls and the pulse rate increases when a patient suffers with shock. Other signs of shock due to blood loss include cold and clammy skin, pallor, air hunger, and eventually loss of consciousness. If shock is not treated, death ultimately will occur. (9:386)

14 2. Crying and anger are forms of grief many patients demonstrate when a part of the body has been removed. It is best to allow the patient to express feelings and use touch, as indicated, to show support and caring. It is also important for the nurse to listen while the patient expresses her feelings. In a moment of intense emotional outburst, it is unlikely that this patient is ready to be comforted by knowing she will have a prosthesis and that others have done well after an amputation. It would also be of little or no comfort to suggest that the patient's parents be called in this situation. (9:20–21)

15 1.   Blood platelets are essential for the clotting of blood. They also are sometimes called thrombocytes. Platelets disintegrate to release a chemical that, with a protein called fibrinogen, changes to fibrin to form the clot. Erythrocytes are red blood cells. Their main ingredient is hemoglobin, which functions to carry oxygen and carbon dioxide in the body. Reticulocytes are young red blood cells. (10:170)

16 1.   Elevating the foot of the bed, rather than elevating just a stump when a lower extremity has been amputated, helps prevent flexion and contracture of the hip joint on the affected side. The positioning also helps to prevent swelling in the stump. (15:196–197)

17 3.   A patient with a fractured spine often is placed on a Stryker or Foster frame or on a circular bed. These devices allow the patient to be turned while the spine is held in proper alignment. (9:320–321)

18 3.   When a stump does not have a rigid dressing that would help prevent a flexion contracture in its remaining joint, exercises are used primarily to prevent a contracture. These exercises should include rolling from side to side and to the abdomen to promote extension of the knee in the patient described in this situation. Adducting the stump while the patient is on the abdomen is recommended. While on the unaffected side or back, the patient with a below-the-knee amputation should be encouraged to flex and extend the knee. Bed exercises help to promote circulation and drainage and help prevent decubitus ulcers. However, for a patient who has an amputation, the exercises just described have a very important function to prevent a flexion contracture in the remaining joint in the stump, so that fitting a prosthesis can be done with success. (15:197)

19 1.   A tourniquet should be kept in the room of a patient who has had an amputation. In case of hemorrhaging, the tourniquet is readily available to help stop bleeding. A patient can bleed to death quickly when hemorrhaging starts in an amputated extremity. (15:196–197)

20 1.   A patient who does not care to look at his wound should not be cajoled into doing so. It is best to wait until the patient is ready and to offer what support is necessary in the meantime. (9:405)

21 4.   Débridement means cleaning a wound of debris. (9:398)

22 2.   All the techniques described in this item may help to prevent the spread of organisms, but most authorities agree that the single most effective weapon to help prevent the spread of organisms is for health workers to observe good hand-washing techniques. (9:275)

23 2.   Phantom-limb pain is discomfort (stinging, itching, burning, or throbbing sensations) in the amputated limb. This type of pain is experienced by many patients after having an amputation and should be explained to the patient so that he understands its nature. Phantom-limb sensation is painless; the patient feels the presence of the amputated limb. (15:194)

24 2.   To place the least amount of strain on muscles and also to protect her uniform from contamination, it is best when the nurse carries a basin, or other object, while her elbows are flexed about 90 degrees and while she holds the object near, but not resting on her body. Resting an object against the waist or on the hip and holding an object well away from the body place extra strain on muscles.   (9:121)

25   3.   Moving a cloth during a bath from the area of the eyes near the nose outward toward the temples helps prevent material from entering the lacrimal ducts. These ducts carry tears that "wash" the surface of the eyes to the nasal corner of the eyes where they drain into the nose by way of the lacrimal ducts.   (9:64)

26   1.   The process of bathing a patient tends to promote the patient's circulatory, respiratory, and urinary system. It acts as a muscle toner and conditioner as well. A bath is least likely to influence digestion.   (9:59–60)

27   2.   In general, most health agencies prefer using lotions and creams for backrubs because alcohol tends to dry the skin. However, alcohol may be used for a patient with an oily skin.   (9:68)

28   3.   Recommended techniques for giving a patient a backrub include the following: the surface of the entire hand, not just the fingers, should be used for massaging with long strokes; the hands should be kept on the skin surface during the entire backrub for greatest comfort to the patient; strokes should become lighter to promote relaxation as a backrub is completed; and the backrub should be ended with long strokes over the length of the back and buttocks.   (9:68–69)

29   3.   The nurse should roll soiled linens together in the bottom sheet. If she handles each piece of linen separately, she is more likely to spread organisms about the room. Appropriate techniques when making an occupied bed include having the bed siderail up on the side opposite from the one where the nurse is working, rolling soiled linens toward the patient's back while he lies on his side, and unfolding clean linens in place on the bed.   (9:71)

30   3.   A sandbag frequently is used to support a patient's leg when he is lying on his back in bed, so that the leg will not turn outward. A cradle is used to support top bed linens. A trapeze is used to help the patient move himself about in bed. A footboard is used to help prevent footdrop.   (9:322)

31   2.   When the nurse turns a patient toward her from his back onto his abdomen, the patient's arm nearer the nurse should be under the patient's buttocks. This positioning prevents the patient from rolling onto his arm. Having the arm nearer the nurse placed across the patient's chest, over the abdomen, or alongside the body will not accomplish this goal.   (9:326)

32   3.   In the face-lying, or prone, position, special attention should be given to the patient's feet. They should be resting over the edge of the foot of the mattress or over a small pillow so that the feet are not forced into the footdrop position. In Wendy's case, this applies to her right foot.   (9:337)

33   2.   People have a basic need for personal space, and this is illustrated by claims of ownership to whatever space a person occupies. The nurse is well advised to respect the patient's personal space in a hospital as a sign of respect for the patient's needs and feelings. (9:163)

34 3. Acne is best controlled by washing the skin frequently with soap and water. Creams should be avoided. Exposure to the sun helps control acne in some persons, but exposure should be limited to prevent predisposing to skin cancer and burning of the skin. Some people find that certain beverages and foods aggravate acne, and they should avoid them. For most people, however, dietary measures have no noticeable effect in controlling acne. (9:84–85)

35 3. It is believed that acne is related to an increase in the body's hormonal activity. Hormones probably affect the skin pores in a way so that secretions are blocked and blackheads and pustules eventually develop. (8:610)

36 3. Hand toothbrushes and electrically operated toothbrushes have been found equally effective for oral hygiene. (9:75)

37 2. Flossing between the teeth helps to break up colonies of bacteria that cannot be reached with a brush. Other methods, such as chewing gum, using toothbrushes only, and rinsing the teeth with an antiseptic, have not been found to accomplish the goal of dislodging bacteria from between the teeth. (9:75)

38 1. Caries and cavities are synonymous terms. Halitosis is offensive breath. Pyorrhea is a severe form of gingivitis that eventually destroys bone and teeth structures. Gingivitis is an inflammation of oral mucous membranes. (9:58)

39 4. If contact lenses are left in place too long, there is danger of injury to the person's corneas. Because the corneas depend on atmospheric air and tears for their oxygen supply, the lenses should be removed regularly in order to permit time for replenishing the corneas with oxygen. There are extended-wear contact lenses on the market, but some authorities continue to be skeptical concerning their safety, except for patients under very specific conditions. (9:78)

40 4. Isometric exercises produce muscle tension but do not change the length of the muscles significantly. Active exercises are those performed by a person without assistance from others. Passive exercises are those in which one person moves body parts of another person. Aerobic exercises are exercises during which energy needs are supplied adequately by inspired air. (9:115, 346)

41 2. Bed exercises, passive and active, are used before helping a patient who has been bedridden for considerable time to stand at the bedside. The patient should be prepared to get out of bed by first placing the patient in a high-Fowler's position to accustom the patient to a sitting position. This helps prevent feelings of faintness. The patient is then dangled at the side of the bed to further prepare the patient for a standing position. If the

42 patient has had no adverse effects, the patient can then be assisted to a standing position at the side of the bed. A walking belt and a walker are used to assist a patient with walking.   (9:356–357)

42 4.   Push-ups help to strengthen the arms and shoulders in preparation for crutch-walking. They are performed by having the patient lie on his abdomen and alternately flexing and extending his elbows while the palms rest flat on the bed near the shoulders. Push-ups may also be performed by sitting in an armchair and raising the body while lifting oneself with the hands placed on the chair's armrest.   (9:346, 356)

43 3.   A patient using crutches should be taught to place his body weight on his arms and hands, not in his axillary areas. The pressure of weight-bearing in the axillary areas may damage nerves and cut off effective circulation to the arms. When the patient is crutch-walking, the elbows should be slightly flexed, the crutches should have rubber protective tips, and regular walking shoes should be worn.   (9:360)

44 4.   Defying adult authority is believed to illustrate an adolescent's attempts to develop independence and self-reliance. The teen years are years when the youngster still sometimes depends on and needs authority figures, but at other times wants to test his own independence.   (12:63–64)

Caring for a patient with a fractured hip

45 4.   A typical sign of a fractured hip is external rotation of the leg on the affected side. The patient ordinarily complains of pain, cannot walk, and has a shortening of the leg on the affected side. An x-ray examination is used to confirm the diagnosis.   (15:171)

46 2.   Gravity will cause blood to flow toward the bottom bed linens. Therefore, when checking for signs of bleeding from a surgical wound on the hip, the nurse should be especially careful to check the bottom bed linens for signs of bleeding when the patient is on her back.   (9:386)

47 2.   Supporting the feet in bed in the normal walking position helps to prevent footdrop. The patient will have difficulty with walking if footdrop occurs. Contractures of the knees may occur if the knees are kept in a state of flexion.   (9:321)

48 4.   Inactivity causes stagnation of urine, which often leads to infections in the urinary tract. Inactivity also leads to stone formation in the urinary tract because of increased excretion of certain body minerals.   (9:318)

49 2.   A common complication of inactivity that affects the gastrointestinal tract is constipation.   (9:318)

50 2.   Inactivity predisposes to blood clot formation. The clots may obstruct a blood vessel or move about in the circulatory system, thus becoming a threat to the patient's life. An inflammation in a vessel, called phlebitis, may also occur.   (9:317–318)

51 4.   Calcium leaving the body in abnormally large amounts tends to leave the bones, and the patient is likely to suffer with osteoporosis, which is characterized by fragile and brittle bones.   (9:317)

52 4.   It is best to place a stretcher at a right angle to the foot of a bed when the patient will be carried from the bed to a stretcher. This positioning of the stretcher is convenient and also minimizes the distance the patient must be carried.   (9:339)

53 4.   The tallest carrier should carry the patient's head and shoulders when using the three-carrier lift. The tallest person's longer arms help to support the patient's head and shoulders well.   (9:336)

54 3.   After lifting a patient off the bed, the carriers next should roll the patient onto their chests. This causes the center of gravity to be more directly over the carriers' bases of support and decreases strain on the backs of the carriers. The carriers then pivot toward the stretcher. The carriers should place their arms well under the patient before lifting the patient off the bed.   (9:339)

55 1.   The weight of the body can be used to help push a stretcher when the nurse leans toward it as she pushes it. Such techniques as moving feet in a shuffling gait, keeping the elbows straight with the trunk upright, and grasping the stretcher with hands behind the back while pulling the stretcher are maneuvers that are likely to cause the carrier to strain and twist muscles.   (9:122)

56 2.   Passive exercises are those in which one person moves body parts for another person. An example of passive exercise is having the nurse rotate the patient's thumb. Having the patient comb her hair, reach for a telephone and water glass, and flex and extend her knees are active exercises because the patient is performing them without the help of another person.   (9:115)

57 4.   Range-of-motion exercises should not be uncomfortable and should be stopped if they are. Each joint should be moved until there is some resistance to movement. The patient should be encouraged to exercise his joints if he is able to do so. Unless there are other reasons to stop, the nurse should teach the patient to continue with the exercises, because sometimes benefits are not easy for the patient to detect.   (9:343)

58 1.   Under normal conditions, the nurse can expect the patient's pulse and respiratory rates to increase after range-of-motion exercises for both passive and active exercises. These rates should return to normal relatively quickly, within a few minutes, when the exercises have not been too strenuous for the patient.   (9:119)

59 1.   When a nail is placed through a hip fracture, a pillow should be placed between the patient's legs before turning her onto her side. The patient should be turned all at one time (log-rolled), with the affected leg kept in a straight line with the trunk of the body. These techniques are used to prevent strain and displacement of the affected hip.   (15:172)

60 2.   Until tissues heal following an open reduction of a fractured hip, weight-bearing on the affected leg should be avoided. Weight-bearing is started gradually beginning when x-ray examinations indicate healing is occurring. (15:172)

61 3. When one is using a walker, it is inappropriate to keep the feet as close together as possible. The feet should be kept apart about 6 inches to 8 inches (15 cm to 20 cm) in order to provide the patient with a wide base of support. The elbows should be flexed about 30 degrees, the neck should be held in a position of extension so that the patient looks straight ahead while walking, and a firm hand grip is used on the hand supports to help provide stability when using a walker. (9:358)

62 3. Symptoms of necrosis of the femur include pain and walking with a limp. These symptoms should be noted and reported promptly because if the patient continues to walk on the affected leg, the bone will crumble. (15:172)

Caring for a patient with a fractured tibia

63 1. In emergencies, clothing should be cut off as necessary to expose injuries. Greater injury may occur if attempts are made to remove clothing by sliding it up or down on an extremity. Care should be taken that bits of cloth and thread do not fall into an open wound when cutting off clothing. (15:159)

64 3. A compound fracture describes a fracture in which the bone sticks out through broken skin. A greenstick fracture is bent and partially broken bone. A comminuted fracture has shattered ends. A fracture is not described as complete or incomplete. (8:508)

65 2. The kneecap is the patella. The calcaneous is the heel bone. A tarsal is a bone in the foot. The phalanges are bones in the toes and fingers. (10:81)

66 1. A closed wound, such as the patient described in this item has on his right leg at the knee, often is called a contusion. Impaction refers to a condition in which something is firmly wedged or lodged. An inflammation is a localized response caused by an injury or destruction of body tissues. An inflammatory process ordinarily occurs at the sight of a wound but the term is not used to describe the type of wound itself. (9:396)

67 3. The broken leg described in this situation is the first concern when the accident occurred. The leg should be splinted while the patient remains on the floor to prevent further injury to soft tissues and to the fractured bone. A good word of advice to prevent further damage at the site of a fractured bone is to "splint the victim where he lies" before carrying out any further action. (15:158)

68 1. Cold applications slow circulation to a body part and hence help prevent edema. Therefore, cold is contraindicated after a sprain if swelling is already present because circulation will be decreased to the area. This will prevent fluid causing edema to be reabsorbed. (9:421)

69   2.   A knee should be positioned with slight flexion when the leg is bandaged. This is most nearly the normal anatomical position of the knee and will contribute to the patient's comfort. If the knee is placed so that it is forced into an abnormal position, a deformity could result.   (9:419)

70   4.   Bandaging a leg should begin at the arch of a patient's foot. Bandaging should be directed toward the trunk of the body to avoid congestion and interference with circulation in the extremity. Only the toes should be left exposed so that circulation to the patient's bandaged leg can be checked with ease.   (9:419)

71   3.   A circular turn is used to anchor a roller, elastic bandage, such as the one used for the patient described in this item. A spica turn is used to bandage a hip. A spiral turn is one that overlaps each turn only partially so that bandaging moves up an extremity. A spiral-reverse turn often is used to cover a cone-shaped body part, such as the leg. This turn is used after the bandage is anchored with a few circular turns.   (9:417)

72   1.   A bandage likely is too tight if the toes become swollen when the lower extremity is bandaged. The pressure of the bandage is interfering with proper circulation in the extremity. The toes also are likely to be cold, and when the nailbeds are pinched, normal pink coloring is slow to return if a bandage is too tight.   (9:419)

73   1.   Prior to bone surgery, the skin ordinarily is washed, shaven, and scrubbed with an antiseptic. The area then is bandaged with sterile materials which are not removed until the time of surgery. These precautions ordinarily are used when orthopedic surgery is to be performed.   (9:380; 15:160)

74   2.   It is especially important to prepare the site where orthopedic surgery is to be performed to help prevent infection in the operative site. This is especially true when surgery is being done to reduce a compound fracture. Skin preparation is not related to the prevention of hemorrhage, thrombophlebitis or emboli formation.   (15:117, 158)

75   4.   The process of comparing a finding made on a patient with what is considered to be normal is called assessment, and it is an important part of the nursing process. A nursing assessment is used to judge a patient's health-illness status. The entire process of assessment consists of these parts: collecting data about the patient, such as obtaining the patient's blood pressure; comparing the data with standards, such as when the nurse compares the patient's blood pressure with what is considered normal for a person of the patient's age and sex; analyzing the findings when data are compared with standards, such as when the nurse studies the relationship between the patient's blood pressure and normal blood pressure; stating a nursing diagnosis, such as that the patient's blood pressure is within normal range for his age and sex; and ranking nursing diagnoses in order of priority when the patient has more than one nursing diagnosis.   (9:36)

76   3.   A bedboard is used to offer support when a mattress is not sufficiently firm. A cradle is used to support bed linens so that they do not rest on the patient. A footboard or foot block is used to help hold the feet in proper alignment to prevent footdrop.   (9:319)

77   1.   A cast on a leg and foot should be well elevated on pillows to prevent swelling and promote circulation in the extremity. It is also better to place a wet cast on a surface with some "give" so that the cast does not bend or become distorted on a hard surface.   (9:593)

78   3.   A wet cast should be handled with the palms of the hands. Using the fingers is likely to cause indentations in the cast, which can cause pressure areas under the cast. It is appropriate to use a cradle over the cast to support bed linens, to place an ice bag next to the cast to prevent edema in the leg, and to make an inked line around a drainage stain on the cast to help make comparisons with subsequent drainage stains.   (9:593)

79   2.   A new cast should be checked at least every 2 hours, during the first 24 hours after it has been applied. This precaution is taken so that any sign of the cast's being too tight can be noted and corrected promptly. Checking every 15 to 30 minutes has been found to be unnecessarily frequent and disturbs the patient's rest.   (9:594)

80   2.   A cast may be too tight when nailbeds are slow to regain normal color after the nails have been pinched. This is known as the blanching sign and occurs when blood circulation is poor in the extremity. The color in pinched nails should return almost immediately if the cast is not too tight.   (9:596)

81   4.   Usual procedure is to bring the stockinet over the edges of the cast and then to cover the edges of the cast with adhesive petals. This technique, often called petalling, helps hold the stockinet in place and protects the skin from rough edges on the cast.   (9:599)

82   1.   Hot spots on a cast often indicate that an infection may be developing in the patient's wound. Wet spots on the cast, swollen toes, and complaints that the cast is too tight are not associated with an infection in a wound under the cast. However, they are pertinent observations that require further assessment, action, and evaluation.   (9:597)

83   4.   A common sign of an infection under a cast is a foul odor. The patient may or may not complain of pain. Bleeding will stain a cast.   (9:597)

84   4.   A vacuum cleaner is best to remove crumbs and small debris that accumulate between a cast and the skin. Instruments, such as clamps, dinnerware, tongue blades, or clothes hangers, should not be used because there is danger of injuring the skin or having these instruments become lodged under the cast.   (9:598)

85   1.   Bivalving a cast means cutting it open on both sides. A cast may be bivalved for various reasons: to allow for tissue expansion, to wean a patient from a cast, to obtain sharp x-ray examinations, and to splint a part intermittently. A bivalved cast is held together with bandaging material or straps.   (15:165, 180)

86   4.   A pillow should be placed against the headboard before moving a patient up in bed. This technique will prevent the patient from bumping against the headboard and hurting his head. Removing top linens is unnecessary. The bed should be in a high position to decrease strain on the nurses' back. A patient should be asked to flex his knees and push with his feet to assist the nurses, if this is permitted activity for the patient. It is easier to move a patient up in bed when he is lying on his back. (9:331)

87 2. When two nurses are sliding a patient up in bed on a draw sheet, they should use a rocking motion when they face either the head or the foot of the bed. The forward or backward rocking motion causes the least strain on the nurse's backs as they slide the patient on the draw sheet. (9:333)

88 2. The prone position is the face-lying position, that is, the patient lies on his abdomen. Lying on one's back is called the supine position. The side-lying position is also called the Sims's position. A mid-Fowler's position is a semi-sitting position. (9:316)

89 3. The development of emboli after a long bone, such as the tibia, has been fractured is not uncommon, and the patient should be observed carefully for signs of emboli. These emboli are usually composed of fat globules being released into the bloodstream. The fat globules occlude small blood vessels that supply the brain, lungs, kidneys, and other body organs. Common signs and symptoms when blood supply to the brain is occluded because of fatty emboli include confusion, agitation, delirium, and coma, all of which result from the body's response to hypoxemia in areas of the brain. (12:601, 609)

90 4. Diaphoresis is excessive perspiration. Diurnal means an event that occurs during the daytime. Dipsesis is abnormal thirst. Polydipsia is a synonym of dipsesis. Diplopia is double vision. (12:924)

91 4. Auscultation means listening to sounds within the body. A stethoscope usually is used to auscultate. The term *observation* is used when the nurse gathers information about a patient through the senses of smell, touch, and vision. (9:214)

92 3. Granulation tissue is best defined as new tissue that forms over a wound. The tissue is normally pinkish-red in color. (9:395–396)

93 3. Most young adults are seeking independence, especially from parents. Developmental tasks concerned with self-identity, testing the body's ability, and learning control over emotional behavior are handled more commonly before adulthood. (15:24)

94 3. When a patient expresses a concern or fear, it is best for the nurse to listen and to offer what support she can. A response that shows understanding of the patient and a willingness to listen is one in which the nurse indicates an understanding of the problem and asks the patient to confirm it. This type of response also encourages the patient to explore his feelings further. Employing cliches and grouping all patients together in one class are of little help to a patient struggling to find answers to a personal problem. (9:21)

Caring for a patient with a fractured femur

95 1.   Traction using weights, pulleys, and slings, should be carefully maintained, and no changes should be made without special orders, even while transporting a patient in his bed.   (15:165–166)

96 1.   Russell traction is a form of skin traction. It is very important that traction and countertraction, which are two forces pulling away from a center, are maintained. If the weights on the traction represent traction and exert force away from the fracture, the weight of the patient's body represents countertraction to exert force in the opposite direction.   (15:165)

97 1.   Unless contraindicated, fluids should be above normal daily average amounts for the patient in Russell traction. Increased fluid intake helps to prevent constipation and complications involving the urinary system, such as kidney stones and urinary tract infections.   (16:168)

98 2.   Inactivity causes muscles to lose their normal tone and the patient experiences muscle weakness as a result. Muscle weakness develops quickly, and if steps are not taken to prevent it, the results may be more damaging than the original injury or illness.   (9:317)

99 2.   The patient's needs are of primary consideration when allocating health care services. Nurses have codes of ethics that act as guidelines concerning the allocation of their time and services. The need for health care is universal and is offered without regard to the patient's racial, religious, sexual, ethnic, economic, age, and personality differences.   (6:199)

Caring for a patient with a hip replacement

100 3.   Adduct means to move a body part toward the center of the body. Abduct means to move a body part away from the center of the body. Extension increases or straightens an angle between two adjoining parts. Flexion reduces an angle between two adjoining parts.   (9:315)

101 2.   A patient with a total hip replacement should not bring the leg on the affected side toward or across the leg on the unaffected side, to help prevent dislodging the prosthetic femoral head from the acetabulum.   (15:189)

102 4.   It is recommended that when a patient faces a painful procedure, it is best to give the patient a prescribed analgesic about 15 minutes before the procedure. It is much more difficult to handle pain after it has become intense.   (9:137)

103 2.   An infection and thrombophlebitis are complications for which health caretakers should be especially alert in patients who have had orthopedic surgery. Therefore, in most instances, body temperature is monitored regularly postoperatively so that at the first sign of complications, such as an infection, therapy is started. Usual treatment is aggressive antibiotic therapy in the presence of infection.   (15:189)

104 2.   Ferrous sulfate tends to irritate the gastrointestinal tract and to cause diarrhea. Aluminum hydroxide is an antacid and its use often leads to constipation. Propranolol hydrochloride (Inderal), an antihypertensive agent, and vitamin C rarely cause undesirable side effects.   (14:257)

105 1.   Most elderly persons in normal health recall past experiences well and usually with joy. Other functions, such as remembering recent events, adjusting to temperature changes, and responding to stresses of daily living, tend to decrease as age increases.   (17:89)

106 4.   While cleaning a patient's perineal area, the nurse should move cotton balls from the patient's pubis toward the anal region. This technique helps prevent the spread of organisms from the anal area to the urinary meatus and vaginal opening. Appropriate techniques when cleansing the perineal area include using medical asepsis, placing the patient on a bedpan, and holding the cotton balls with which a nurse is cleansing the area with a pair of forceps or with a gloved hand.   (9:67)

107 1.   The skin of elderly patients normally is dry, wrinkled, and thin. It is more likely to be pale or pink rather than red. Because of the nature of their skin, a nurse should use extra precautions to avoid injuring the skin of elderly patients.   (9:85)

108 2.   An order is required in many health agencies before nurses may cut a patient's toenails because of the serious complications that may result if tissues are injured in the process. This is especially true of persons with diabetes mellitus and vascular disorders. Such measures as giving perineal care, cleaning dentures, and shampooing hair do not ordinarily require a physician's order.   (9:81)

Caring for a patient with gout

109 1.   Gout is a metabolic disorder. It is classified in that manner because the body is unable to metabolize purines properly. Purines are the end product in the digestion of certain proteins. Urate crystals deposit mostly around joints to cause arthritis-like symptoms. Because gout interferes with mobilization, the illness is ordinarily discussed with musculoskeletal disorders.   (15:183)

110 4.   Gout causes swelling and severe pain in the involved joints. Deposits of urate crystals, which are salts of uric acid, tend to accumulate in and around joints to cause pain and swelling.   (15:183)

111 1.   Because the patient usually has not had fluids during sleeping hours, it is best to serve proportionately larger amounts of fluid in the morning. Serving large amounts of fluids immediately before or after meals tends to interfere with proper eating. Consuming large amounts of fluid during evening hours usually interferes with sleep because the patient is then likely to use the bathroom frequently during the night. (9:502)

112 2. Allopurinal (Zyloprim) interferes with the formation of uric acid from which urate crystals develop. It also helps in the prevention of uric acid stones that develop in the urinary system. The medication is of no use in the treatment of gout in its acute stage. Acute attacks of gout are often treated with phenylbutazone (Butazolidin). Allopurinal is ineffective in controlling discomfort, stimulating the proper metabolism of purines, or reducing joint inflammation. (14:276)

113 3. An oral thermometer should be placed at the base of and underneath the tongue on either side. Body temperature can be obtained by placing the thermometer under the tongue because there are many surface blood vessels in the area. Using other areas in the mouth does not result in accurate readings. (9:192)

114 1. It is recommended that a glass clinical thermometer be left in place for no less than 3 minutes to obtain an accurate oral temperature. This period of time has been found to result in accurate readings. Electronic thermometers register accurately in less time. (9:193)

Classification of Test Items

Directions: *Each item in the previous review test is classified here according to the subject area it tests. Place a check mark after each item you answered **correctly** by referring to your answers. Total the number of items you answered correctly in each area and enter the numbers in the correct places on pages 553–556.*

Clinical: Medical/Surgical Nursing (Adults)

1 ✓	12 ✓	35 ✓	66 ✓	81 ✓	95 ✓
2 ✓	13 ✓	45 ✓	67 ✓	82 ✓	97 ✓
3 ✓	16 ✓	46 ✓	73 ✓	83 ✓	101 ✓
4 ✓	17 ✓	59 ✓	74 ✓	84 ✓	103 ✓
5 ✓	18	60 ✓	77 ✓	85 ✓	109 ✓
6 ✓	19 ✓	62	78	89 ✓	110 ✓
7 ✓	21	63 ✓	79 ✓	92	
11	23 ✓	64 ✓	80 ✓	93	

TOTAL 40

Biological/Physical Sciences

15 ✓	65 ✓	96 ✓	105 ✓

TOTAL 4

Fundamentals of Nursing

8	30 ✓	42 ✓	55 ✓	75 ✓	106 ✓
9	31	43 ✓	56 ✓	76 ✓	107 ✓
10 ✓	32	47 ✓	57 ✓	86 ✓	108 ✓
22 ✓	34	48 ✓	58 ✓	87 ✓	111 ✓
24 ✓	36 ✓	49 ✓	61 ✓	88 ✓	113
25 ✓	37 ✓	50 ✓	68	90 ✓	114
26 ✓	38 ✓	51 ✓	69 ✓	91 ✓	
27 ✓	39	52	70	98 ✓	
28 ✓	40 ✓	53	71	100 ✓	
29	41 ✓	54	72 ✓	102 ✓	

TOTAL 44

Pharmacology

104 _____   112 __✓__

TOTAL __1__

Psychosocial Sciences

14 __✓__   20 __✓__   33 _____   44 __✓__   94 __✓__   99 __✓__

TOTAL __5__

Review Test 9

Directions: *With a pencil, blacken the circle in front of
the option you have chosen for your correct answer.*

The Nursing Care of Patients With Disorders
of the Musculoskeletal System (Continued)

*Ms. Rizak has acute rheumatoid arthritis. Her wrists, fingers, knees,
ankles, and toes are involved. A nurse admits Ms. Rizak to a hospital.*

1 Ms. Rizak is most likely to tell the nurse that the first symptom that
caused her to seek health care was
○ 1. swollen and sore joints.
○ 2. insensitivity to heat and cold.
○ 3. distortion of joints with contractures.
○ 4. lack of pulse at the wrists and ankles.

2 Ms. Rizak asks the admitting nurse what causes rheumatoid arthritis.
The nurse should base her response on knowledge that it is generally
agreed that the cause of rheumatoid arthritis is

○ 1. a virus.
○ 2. chronic anxiety.
○ 3. a childhood injury.
○ 4. unknown.

3 While helping to plan Ms. Rizak's short- and long-term care, the nurses' selection of appropriate care should take into account that the only other disease in this country causing more permanent disability than rheumatoid arthritis is
○ 1. heart disease.
○ 2. diabetes mellitus.
○ 3. chronic emphysema.
○ 4. chronic brain syndrome.

Ms. Rizak is to receive aspirin therapy.

4 Ms. Rizak is to receive a total of 5 g of aspirin in each 24-hour period. If each tablet contains 5 grains, how many tablets will Ms. Rizak need in each 24-hour period?
○ 1. 5 tablets
○ 2. 10 tablets
○ 3. 15 tablets
○ 4. 20 tablets

5 When the nurse reads that Ms. Rizak is to receive 5 g of aspirin in each 24-hour period, she should judge that because the patient has rheumatoid arthritis, the dose, in terms of dosage range, is.
○ 1. excessively high.
○ 2. much lower than usual.
○ 3. lower than usual but not excessively low.
○ 4. within normal range.

6 While caring for Ms. Rizak, the nurse should understand that another name for aspirin is
○ 1. acetaminophen.
○ 2. phenylbutazone.
○ 3. acetylsalicylic acid.
○ 4. propoxyphene hydrochloride.

7 If Ms. Rizak has an adverse reaction to the aspirin she receives, she is likely to complain of tinnitus, which is best described as
○ 1. blurred vision.
○ 2. itching of the skin.
○ 3. ringing in the ears.
○ 4. tingling in the fingers.

8 Of the following techniques, the one most likely to help reduce gastric irritation when Ms. Rizak takes aspirin is to give it to her with
○ 1. tea.
○ 2. food.

    ○ 3. orange juice.

    ○ 4. a carbonated beverage.

9 Ms. Rizak says she is surprised she is taking a drug as common as aspirin when she feels so sick. The nurse should respond to Ms. Rizak's comment by teaching that aspirin is used for rheumatoid arthritis primarily because of the drug's ability to relieve discomfort and to

    ○ 1. stimulate the body's immune system.

    ○ 2. relax muscles surrounding the affected joints.

    ○ 3. reduce the inflammatory process in the affected joints.

    ○ 4. decrease nerve impulses traveling along sympathetic nerve fibers.

10 The nurse goes on to teach Ms. Rizak that aspirin also functions to

    ○ 1. decrease respirations.

    ○ 2. combat some drug overdoses.

    ○ 3. improve a sense of well-being.

    ○ 4. lower an elevated body temperature.

11 Ms. Rizak says she finds it best to watch television when, despite aspirin, her discomfort increases. Which of the following interpretations of Ms. Rizak's behavior is most probably the appropriate one?

    ○ 1. The patient is probably being hypnotized by television.

    ○ 2. The patient is probably having less pain than she thinks.

    ○ 3. The patient probably has very little joint damage from her arthritis.

    ○ 4. The patient is probably using television as a distraction from her pain.

12 Ms. Rizak should be taught that if aspirin causes bleeding in her stomach, the color of her stools is most likely to be

    ○ 1. light grey.

    ○ 2. dark red.

    ○ 3. tarry black.

    ○ 4. deep yellow.

13 When Ms. Rizak shows signs and symptoms of aspirin toxicity, the nurse's first course of action should be to

    ○ 1. give buffered aspirin. It is less toxic than plain aspirin.

    ○ 2. continue giving aspirin. The patient requires the drug.

    ○ 3. omit a dose of the drug. This usually relieves symptoms.

    ○ 4. notify the nurse-in-charge. The dosage of aspirin may need to be changed.

14 Ms. Rizak is given prednisone (Meticorten). This drug is used primarily to help

    ○ 1. relieve inflammatory activity.

    ○ 2. limit the spread of the disease.

    ○ 3. stimulate leukocyte production.

    ○ 4. prevent calcium deposits in the joints.

Mrs. Rizak is transferred to an extended care facility. A nurse at the facility is responsible for helping to serve meals to patients.

15   If the nurse is serving a meal to the patients described below, to which patient should she serve the meal *last*?
   ○ 1.   Ms. Rizak, who must be fed
   ○ 2.   Mr. Crow, who is a self-help patient
   ○ 3.   Mr. Loring, who is an ambulatory diabetic
   ○ 4.   Ms. Laughlin, who has one hand in a cast

16   The nurse helps Ms. Rizak eat. If the nurse uses the following techniques while helping Ms. Rizak, the one that is *least* appropriate is to
   ○ 1.   use a drinking tube to serve liquids.
   ○ 2.   sit conveniently at the patient's bedside.
   ○ 3.   use some of the time to teach the patient about her disease.
   ○ 4.   encourage the patient to serve herself bread when she tries to do so.

The nurse gives care to Ms. Rizak that is appropriate for an inactive patient.

17   Ms. Rizak has slipped down in her bed. To prevent friction on her skin, when the nurse prepares to move her up in bed, it would be best to
   ○ 1.   sprinkle powder on the patient's skin.
   ○ 2.   plan to slide the patient rather than lift her.
   ○ 3.   remove upper linens from the patient's bed.
   ○ 4.   ask the patient to push with her heels while the nurse moves her.

18   Which of the following pieces of equipment is *least* effective when the nurse arranges top bed linens so that they do not rest on Ms. Rizak's painful feet and ankles?
   ○ 1.   A cradle
   ○ 2.   Sand bags
   ○ 3.   A high footboard
   ○ 4.   The bed siderails.

19   Ms. Rizak should be helped with exercising after acute inflammation has subsided, and taught its importance. Exercise for Ms. Rizak will help her by
   ○ 1.   limiting the spread of the disease.
   ○ 2.   minimizing inflammation in the joints.
   ○ 3.   decreasing stagnation of blood in the joints.
   ○ 4.   preventing the joints from becoming immobile.

20   Ms. Rizak is taught to avoid fatigue when exercising and to take regular rest periods. The nurse should see to it that when Ms. Rizak is resting, her joints are supported in a position of
   ○ 1.   flexion.
   ○ 2.   extension.
   ○ 3.   slight rotation.
   ○ 4.   slight hyperextension.

21   Ms. Rizak is 38 years old. The nurse should understand that at her age,

prolonged illness and inactivity may upset Ms. Rizak psychologically because they threaten a normal developmental need of adults in middle life, which is to

○ 1. be free of depending on people.
○ 2. prepare for her children leaving home.
○ 3. establish a firm relationship with her husband.
○ 4. find new interests as reproductive ability wanes.

Ms. Rizak is concerned about being overweight because her excess weight adds to the difficulty in moving about with ease.

22 If Ms. Rizak decides to limit her intake without having health care supervision, and if her diet is balanced, what is the maximum number of pounds she can safely lose each week?

○ 1. 1 pound
○ 2. 2 pounds
○ 3. 3 pounds
○ 4. 4 pounds

23 Ms. Rizak should be taught that when amounts are comparable, of the following nutrients, those containing the most calories are

○ 1. fats.
○ 2. proteins.
○ 3. carbohydrates.
○ 4. vitamins and minerals.

24. Ms. Rizak says she is tired of diet soft drinks. If she likes the following beverages, the nurse should explain that the one *lowest* in calories is

○ 1. buttermilk.
○ 2. cranberry juice.
○ 3. pineapple juice.
○ 4. clear beef broth.

In time, Ms. Rizak has knee arthroplasty.

25 Arthroplasty means that Ms. Rizak's knee joint is

○ 1. fused.
○ 2. removed.
○ 3. reconstructed.
○ 4. cleansed of calcium deposits.

Ms. Rizak's mother-in-law, who has had rheumatoid arthritis for many years, receives corticosteroid therapy.

26 If Ms. Rizak describes her mother-in-law in the following ways, the condition most likely to be caused by corticosteroid therapy is that her mother-in-law has

○ 1. cataracts.
○ 2. dry, flaking skin.
○ 3. a moon-shaped face.
○ 4. prematurely grey hair.

Mr. Posti has iron-deficiency anemia. He is to have a liquid iron preparation, administered orally, and a diet high in iron content.

27 The nurse instructs Mr. Posti to take the iron preparation after meals. The abbreviation most commonly used to indicate that a medication should be taken after meals is
○ 1. a.c.
○ 2. a.a.
○ 3. p.c.
○ 4. q.s.

28 Mr. Posti should be taught to take the iron medication while using a
○ 1. drinking tube.
○ 2. china tea cup.
○ 3. plastic tablespoon.
○ 4. paper medicine cup.

29 Mr. Posti should be taught that the iron medication will most likely cause the color of his stools to become
○ 1. grey.
○ 2. black.
○ 3. dark green.
○ 4. very light brown.

30 If Mr. Posti enjoys the following foods, which one should he be taught has little or no iron content?
○ 1. Eggs
○ 2. Meats
○ 3. Citrus fruits
○ 4. Green leafy vegetables

When Mr. Posti does not respond to the oral intake of iron and to diet therapy, he is to receive iron dextran (imferon) intramuscularly. The nurse will teach Mr. Posti to give himself the medication in his thigh muscle while using the Z-track technique.

31 Why is Mr. Posti taught to use the Z-track technique when injecting iron dextran into his thigh muscle?
○ 1. The medication should be absorbed slowly.
○ 2. The medication is large in amount, more than 3 ml.
○ 3. The medication is irritating to subcutaneous tissue.
○ 4. The medication is fatal if accidentally injected into a vein.

32 Approximately where between the knee and the greater trochanter of the femur should the needle enter when Mr. Posti injects his medication?
- O 1. The lower third of the thigh
- O 2. The middle third of the thigh
- O 3. The upper third of the thigh
- O 4. Any area on the thigh that is convenient

33 The direction in which Mr. Posti should move his leg muscle with his hand when using the Z-track technique is
- O 1. laterally.
- O 2. upwardly.
- O 3. diagonally.
- O 4. downwardly.

34 When should Mr. Posti be taught to release the pressure he is using to move the muscle that he will inject?
- O 1. Immediately after the needle is positioned in his tissue
- O 2. Immediately after testing to see whether the needle is in a blood vessel
- O 3. Immediately before removing the needle from his tissue.
- O 4. Immediately after removing the needle from his tissue

Ms. Orr, a 50-year-old woman, is suspected of having pernicious anemia. She is hospitalized for diagnostic purposes and care.

35 If the nurse makes the following notes in Ms. Orr's record after admitting the patient, which entry is *inappropriate*?
- O 1. States, "I get nauseated when I eat."
- O 2. ID bracelet indicates she is Roman Catholic.
- O 3. Skin over back and buttocks is pink and feels damp.
- O 4. Requests that her son-in-law *not* be allowed to visit.

A gastric analysis is ordered for Ms. Orr.

36 If the plastic tube to be used to obtain a specimen of stomach content from Ms. Orr is resistant and difficult to handle, it is best to prepare it for easier manipulation by
- O 1. cooling it in ice chips.
- O 2. immersing it in alcohol.
- O 3. placing it in warm water.
- O 4. lubricating it with petrolatum.

37 The approximate distance for inserting the tube for obtaining a specimen of gastric content is most nearly equivalent to the distance on Ms. Orr's body from her
- O 1. forehead to the umbilicus.
- O 2. lips to the middle of the lower abdomen.

○ 3. ear lobe to the bridge of the nose plus the distance from the lips to the umbilicus.

○ 4. ear lobe to the bridge of the nose to the end of the sternum

38 Most authorities recommend that the position of choice when inserting a tube into a nostril for obtaining a specimen of gastric content is to have the patient (in this situation, Ms. Orr) hold her head so that her neck is

○ 1. flexed.

○ 2. rotated.

○ 3. extended.

○ 4. hyperextended.

39 The sign that should indicate to the nurse that the nasogastric tube has most probably entered Ms. Orr's lower respiratory passageway is when the

○ 1. patient is unable to hum.

○ 2. patient is unable to swallow.

○ 3. tube causes the patient to gag.

○ 4. tube cannot be seen at the back of the throat.

40 If Ms. Orr has pernicious anemia, the laboratory report will indicate that her gastric juice lacks sufficient amounts of

○ 1. lipase.

○ 2. pepsinogen.

○ 3. prosecretin.

○ 4. intrinsic factor.

An examination is ordered for Ms. Orr that will help to study the formation of her erythrocytes (red blood cells).

41 The nurse should anticipate that a specimen for the examination described above will be taken of Ms. Orr's

○ 1. spleen.

○ 2. arterial blood.

○ 3. venous blood.

○ 4. bone marrow.

A sample of blood is obtained from Ms. Orr for laboratory analysis.

42 When studying the results of blood tests, the nurse should take into account that of the following factors, the one *least* likely to influence Ms. Orr's hemoglobin and red blood cell count is the

○ 1. patient's age.

○ 2. patient's sex.

○ 3. altitude at which the patient lives.

○ 4. the climate in which the patient lives.

43 Laboratory findings indicate that Ms. Orr has leukopenia, which means that her blood has a

○ 1. low white blood cell count.
○ 2. high white blood cell count.
○ 3. small number of blood platelets.
○ 4. large number of immature white blood cells.

44 Ms. Orr's hematocrit will be considered to be normal if it falls within a range of
○ 1. 16% and 26% per 100 ml of blood.
○ 2. 26% and 36% per 100 ml of blood.
○ 3. 36% and 46% per 100 ml of blood.
○ 4. 46% and 56% per 100 ml of blood.

45 Hematocrit describes the percentage of space (volume) in a given quantity of Ms. Orr's blood that is occupied by
○ 1. plasma.
○ 2. platelets.
○ 3. red blood cells.
○ 4. white blood cells.

46 Laboratory analysis indicates that Ms. Orr's hemoglobin is below normal. The average number of grams of hemoglobin per 100 ml of blood in healthy adult females is between approximately
○ 1. 6 g and 8 g.
○ 2. 10 g and 12 g.
○ 3. 12 g and 14 g.
○ 4. 18 g and 20 g.

It is confirmed that Ms. Orr has pernicious anemia.

47 Because Ms. Orr is acutely ill with pernicious anemia, she especially needs personal hygiene that will protect her
○ 1. skin.
○ 2. eyes.
○ 3. oral mucosa.
○ 4. nasal mucosa.

48 If Ms. Orr was found to have iron-deficiency anemia due to poor eating habits, rather than pernicious anemia, the mineral she would most likely require to correct the deficiency is
○ 1. iron.
○ 2. zinc.
○ 3. copper
○ 4. calcium.

Ms. Orr has had personality and behavioral changes due to pernicious anemia.

49 Ms. Orr's family and friends are most likely to report that since she became ill, Ms. Orr has become unusually

    ○ 1. irritable.
    ○ 2. egotistical.
    ○ 3. hyperactive.
    ○ 4. distrusting of others.

50 Ms. Orr sometimes seems confused and not sure of where she is. A person who is unaware of surroundings and of time and place is commonly described as being
    ○ 1. neurotic.
    ○ 2. paranoic.
    ○ 3. incoherent.
    ○ 4. disoriented.

51 Ms. Orr's habits of personal hygiene have become poor and her hair is noted to be very dirty. However, she *cannot* have a soap-and-water shampoo. In this situation, it is recommended that the nurse cleanse the patient's hair with
    ○ 1. hair spray.
    ○ 2. fine powder.
    ○ 3. a blow drier.
    ○ 4. setting lotion.

Ms. Orr is to receive injections of Vitamin B_{12} after discharge at home. Her daughter will administer the vitamin to Ms. Orr.

52 Before administering vitamin B_{12} to Ms. Orr, the nurse explains the procedure to the patient. By so doing, the nurse is recognizing Ms. Orr's psychological need for
    ○ 1. safety.
    ○ 2. security.
    ○ 3. belonging.
    ○ 4. understanding.

53 Concerning unfavorable reactions to vitamin B_{12}, the daughter and Ms. Orr should be taught that
    ○ 1. there are no known toxic side-effects.
    ○ 2. skin rashes are the most common toxic side-effect.
    ○ 3. nausea and vomiting are the most common toxic side-effects.
    ○ 4. gastrointestinal distress is the most common toxic side-effect.

54 Ms. Orr's daughter is taught to remove 1 ml of vitamin B_{12} for administration from a multiple-dose vial. How much air should she inject into the vial before removing solution?
    ○ 1. 0.5 ml of air
    ○ 2. 1.0 ml of air
    ○ 3. 1.5 ml of air
    ○ 4. 2.0 ml of air

55 Ms. Orr's dorsogluteal area will be used to inject the vitamin B_{12}. The daughter should be taught that after exposing the area of her mother's body where she will inject the medication, the first step to take to locate the proper site is to draw an imaginary line, as follows:

- O 1. A straight line that divides the buttock into a right and left side.
- O 2. A straight line that divides the buttock into a lower and upper half.
- O 3. A diagonal line from the base of the spine to the greater trochanter.
- O 4. A diagonal line from the greater trochanter to the posterior superior iliac spine.

56 The daughter should be taught that the chief danger when the site for an intramuscular injection is located improperly on Ms. Orr's buttock is that the

- O 1. pelvic bone may be struck and damaged.
- O 2. sciatic nerve may be struck and damaged.
- O 3. medication is likely to be poorly absorbed.
- O 4. muscle tissues are likely to become infected.

57 The daughter is observed using the following techniques while giving Ms. Orr vitamin B_{12}. Which one of her techniques is in *error*

- O 1. The daughter cleans the area of injection with a pledget moistened with an antiseptic.
- O 2. The daughter presses down on the tissue with her thumb and forefinger while injecting the needle.
- O 3. The daughter aspirates for blood as soon as the medication is injected.
- O 4. The daughter massages the area of injection after removing the needle.

58 The daughter asks why the arm muscle is not used to inject Ms. Orr's vitamin B_{12}. She should be taught that a disadvantage of using the deltoid muscle for injecting intramuscular medications is that it

- O 1. is small in size.
- O 2. is difficult to locate.
- O 3. has a poor blood supply.
- O 4. has numerous pain receptors.

59 Ms. Orr's daughter will use reusable equipment to give her mother injections at home. It is most often recommended that this equipment be sterilized between uses by

- O 1. boiling it in water.
- O 2. using a pressure cooker.
- O 3. placing it in a hot baking oven.
- O 4. soaking it in an antiseptic solution.

60 Ms. Orr's daughter asks the nurse how long her mother will require injections of vitamin B_{12}. The nurse's response should be based on knowledge that the length of time Ms. Orr will require the vitamin is for

- O 1. the rest of the patient's life.
- O 2. approximately 2 to 3 years.
- O 3. approximately 2 to 3 months.

O 4. the time it takes for her red blood count to reach and maintain
       normal levels.

*Mr. Irvine, who is believed to have Hodgkin's disease, is hospitalized for
diagnosis and therapy.*

61 The admitting nurse makes Mr. Irvine comfortable in bed in a mid-
       Fowler's position. If the nurse uses the following techniques for
       positioning Mr. Irvine, which one is appropriate?
       O 1. The patient's forearms are supported on pillows.
       O 2. The patient's knees are well flexed over a rolled pillow.
       O 3. The patient's head rests on a pillow so that his head is tilted
              forward slightly.
       O 4. The patient's body is flexed so that the angle of elevation
              begins in the middle of the back.

62 Mr. Irvine's white blood count is found to be above the average normal
       level at the time of admission. The average normal adult white blood
       cell count per cubic milliliter of blood is between approximately
       O 1. 1,000 and 2,000.
       O 2. 3,000 and 5,000.
       O 3. 5,000 and 7,000.
       O 4. 10,000 and 12,000.

63 The evening of admission, Mr. Irvine insists on smoking a cigarette,
       although the nurse believes he appears very sleepy. In this situation, it
       would be best for the nurse to
       O 1. refuse to allow the patient to smoke.
       O 2. remain with the patient while he smokes.
       O 3. allow the patient to smoke but be sure he has a large ashtray.
       O 4. allow the patient to smoke but return to his room every few
              minutes to check on his safety.

*Mr. Irvine's diagnosis of Hodgkin's disease is confirmed when a speci-
men reveals the presence of Reed-Sternberg cells.*

64 The specimen obtained from Mr. Irvine that was used when observing
       for Reed-Sternberg cells is obtained from
       O 1. the spleen.
       O 2. bone marrow.
       O 3. a lymph node.
       O 4. a carotid artery.

65 Mechlorethamine hydrochloride (Mustargen) is used for Mr. Irvine.
       Drugs that are used to treat malignant diseases are classified as
       O 1. antiemetic agents.
       O 2. antipyretic agents.
       O 3. antineoplastic agents.

    ○ 4. anticholinergic agents.

66 The nurse caring for Mr. Irvine should know that the most common route for administering mechlorethamine hydrochloride is the
    ○ 1. oral route.
    ○ 2. intravenous route.
    ○ 3. subcutaneous route.
    ○ 4. intramuscular route.

67 The system of Mr. Irvine's body that is most likely to be involved if he suffers adverse side effects during drug therapy for his malignant disease is the
    ○ 1. urinary system.
    ○ 2. respiratory system
    ○ 3. reproductive system.
    ○ 4. gastrointestinal system.

68 If Mr. Irvine is typical of people who develop Hodgkin's disease, his age is most probably
    ○ 1. under 20 years.
    ○ 2. between 20 and 35 years.
    ○ 3. between 50 and 65 years.
    ○ 4. over 65 years.

Mr. Irvine is placed on reverse (protective) isolation.

69 The primary purpose for placing Mr. Irvine on reverse (protective) isolation is to help prevent microorganisms from reaching
    ○ 1. visitors.
    ○ 2. the patient.
    ○ 3. health workers.
    ○ 4. housekeeping personnel.

70 While reverse isolation is in effect, the air pressure inside Mr. Irvine's room, when compared with atmospheric air pressure in hospital corridors, ideally should be
    ○ 1. much lower.
    ○ 2. slightly lower.
    ○ 3. higher.
    ○ 4. about the same.

71 Gowns are used by health workers when caring for Mr. Irvine and by visitors. Where is it recommended that clean gowns for health workers and visitors be stored?
    ○ 1. In the patient's private bathroom
    ○ 2. On top of the dresser in the patient's room
    ○ 3. In the corridor near the door to the patient's room
    ○ 4. At the nurses' station of the unit where the patient is housed

72 A psychological reaction that Mr. Irvine is *unlikely* to experience while he is on isolation is feeling

○ 1. lonely.
○ 2. rejected.
○ 3. depressed.
○ 4. aggressive.

73 The nurse uses measures to help prevent Mr. Irvine from experiencing sensory alteration while he is on isolation. *All* of the following measures have been found helpful to prevent sensory alteration *except*
○ 1. using touch as a means of communication.
○ 2. keeping the light in the patient's room at a low level.
○ 3. giving explanations to the patient when administering care.
○ 4. changing furniture arrangements occasionally in the patient's room.

74 Which one of the following signs or symptoms is *unlikely* to occur if Mr. Irvine suffers from sensory alteration?
○ 1. The patient appears to be lonesome.
○ 2. The patient appears to be "down on the world."
○ 3. The patient complains of heartburn and constipation.
○ 4. The patient says he is afraid and cannot recall what he hears.

Mr. Irvine is to receive a blood transfusion.

75 In order to make comparisons during and after Mr. Irvine's blood transfusion, it is recommended that before one is started, the nurse should first
○ 1. weigh the patient.
○ 2. obtain the patient's vital signs.
○ 3. collect a urine specimen from the patient.
○ 4. call the laboratory to obtain a blood count for the patient.

76 Mr. Irvine states that he feels chilly and nauseated during the blood transfusion. When this occurs, the nurse's first course of action should be to
○ 1. stop the flow of blood.
○ 2. notify the nurse-in-charge.
○ 3. place a blanket over the patient.
○ 4. check to see if the blood is outdated.

77 If Mr. Irvine had refused the blood transfusion because of his religious beliefs, the religious denomination of which he is most probably a member is
○ 1. Mennonites.
○ 2. Society of Friends.
○ 3. Jehovah's Witnesses.
○ 4. Church of Jesus Christ of Latter-Day Saints.

Penicillin is ordered for Mr. Irvine when he develops an infection.

78 Before giving the penicillin to Mr. Irvine, the nurse should be sure to check whether the patient has
  ○ 1. nausea.
  ○ 2. an allergy to penicillin.
  ○ 3. an abnormally fast pulse rate.
  ○ 4. an abnormally low blood pressure.

79 Which of the following areas of Mr. Irvine's body is a *poor* place for most microorganisms to enter?
  ○ 1. The nose
  ○ 2. The intact skin
  ○ 3. The genital tract
  ○ 4. The urinary tract

80 If Mr. Irvine acquires his infection in the health agency where he is a patient, the infection is called
  ○ 1. a local infection.
  ○ 2. an enteric infection.
  ○ 3. a primary infection.
  ○ 4. a nosocomial infection.

Radiotherapy is used for Mr. Irvine.

81 The primary purpose for giving Mr. Irvine radiotherapy is to
  ○ 1. destroy malignant cells.
  ○ 2. protect normal body cells.
  ○ 3. prevent malignant cells from dividing.
  ○ 4. promote the development of antibodies.

82 After discharge, Mr. Irvine will continue radiotherapy on an outpatient basis. In relation to his daily fluid intake while having radiotherapy, the nurse should teach Mr. Irvine that
  ○ 1. it is best to take average daily amounts.
  ○ 2. it is best to take more than average daily amounts, up to 3,000 ml daily.
  ○ 3. it is best to take less than average amounts, as little as 800 ml daily.
  ○ 4. amounts of fluid intake are irrelevant when a patient is receiving radiotherapy.

83 In relation to the care of his radiated skin, Mr. Irvine should be taught to *avoid*
  ○ 1. taking a tub bath.
  ○ 2. exposing the skin to sun.
  ○ 3. wearing clothes over the skin.
  ○ 4. using cornstarch where skin surfaces contact each other.

Mr. Irvine is soon readmitted to the hospital and then receives hyperalimentation.

84 Nutrients will ordinarily be introduced into Mr. Irvine's body during hyperalimentation through peripheral veins or through
○ 1. a gastrostomy.
○ 2. a nasogastric tube.
○ 3. the peritoneal cavity.
○ 4. the superior vena cava.

85 The nurse judges correctly that Mr. Irvine is most probably receiving the nourishment by hyperalimentation too rapidly when she notes that the patient has
○ 1. nausea.
○ 2. dyspnea.
○ 3. diarrhea.
○ 4. pain at the site of entry.

Mr. Irvine's condition worsens and he is now judged to be terminally ill.

86 The question is posed by Mr. Irvine's caretakers concerning what to tell him when it is judged that his prognosis is very poor. Before making a decision, to which of the following persons is it recommended that the health care personnel turn first for guidance?
○ 1. To the patient's clergyman
○ 2. To the patient's family members
○ 3. To the hospital's psychiatric-oncologist consultant
○ 4. To a psychologist who has been counseling the patient.

87 Mr. Irvine is told of his poor prognosis but says he wonders if there is some mistake. According to Dr. Elisabeth Kübler-Ross, a person who is told he is terminally ill but states that a mistake must have been made is most probably in a stage of
○ 1. anger.
○ 2. denial.
○ 3. bargaining.
○ 4. depression.

88 It is generally agreed that, of the following methods, the one that would tend to help Mr. Irvine most to come to grips with his death is to
○ 1. read the literature on death and dying.
○ 2. contemplate his death and dying in private.
○ 3. discuss his feelings on death and dying with others.
○ 4. have had a personal experience with the death and dying of a loved one.

89 Mr. Irvine prepares a will and asks the nurse to witness his signature on the document. By so doing, the nurse indicates that to the best of her knowledge, Mr. Irvine
○ 1. is not leaving property to a minor.
○ 2. has prepared his will without coercion.
○ 3. is dividing his estate equally among legal heirs.

○ 4. has had the help of an attorney to prepare the will properly.

90 Mr. Irvine's condition continues to worsen and death appears imminent. Which of the following signs is typical when death is near?

○ 1. Intense pain
○ 2. A slow pulse rate
○ 3. Noisy respirations
○ 4. A subnormal temperature

The Nursing Care of Patients Receiving Emergency Care

A nurse helps in the care of patients who come to an emergency care facility.

91 Mr. Torreck is a victim of an automobile accident. If Mr. Torreck appears to have a head injury, the position that is *contraindicated* for him is the

○ 1. Sims' position.
○ 2. supine position.
○ 3. low-Fowler's position.
○ 4. Trendelenburg position.

92 Mr. Carson exhibits signs of heatstroke upon admission. If Mr. Carson's emergency care does not cause body temperature to drop, the body organ that is very likely to be damaged is the

○ 1. brain.
○ 2. liver.
○ 3. heart.
○ 4. kidneys.

93 Eighteen-year-old Jim Roach comes to the emergency room with friends after being bitten by a skunk. Because of the circumstances surrounding the accident, Jim is to be started on Pasteur treatment. The type of immunity Jim develops as a result of receiving rabies vaccine is

○ 1. species immunity.
○ 2. naturally acquired immunity.
○ 3. artificial, active immunity.
○ 4. artificial, passive immunity.

94 Mr. Shore reports that he has been vomiting with force on his way to the emergency care facility and adds, "But I don't feel any nausea." Vomiting forcefully without nausea, as Mr. Shore reports, is typical when a person suffers with

○ 1. peritonitis.
○ 2. infectious hepatitis.
○ 3. an acute myocardial infarction.
○ 4. increased intracranial pressure.

95 An examiner asks the nurse for equipment to remove cerumen from
Ms. Trace. The organ is Ms. Trace's body from which the examiner will
remove cerumen is the
- O 1. ear.
- O 2. eye.
- O 3. nose.
- O 4. throat.

96 Mr. Edmond is admitted following a diving accident. He is paralyzed
from the shoulders down (quadriplegia) and is to be hospitalized for
continued care after emergency measures are completed. Of the
following nursing measures, which one should be given highest priority
in Mr. Edmond's long-term care?
- O 1. Preventing decubitus ulcers
- O 2. Helping to overcome incontinence
- O 3. Improving circulation in the lower extremities
- O 4. Ensuring that the patient receives a high fluid intake

97 Mr. Schmidt comes to the emergency care facility because, he says, "It
is very difficult for me to pass urine." The term used by describe Mr.
Schmidt's urinary problem is
- O 1. dysuria.
- O 2. diuresis.
- O 3. dystocia.
- O 4. dysplasia.

98 After receiving emergency eye care, Mr. Keesler states, "While I am
here, will you check my prostate, please? That organ seems to have no
value but it sure can cause trouble!" The nurse should explain that an
important function of the prostate gland is to produce secretions that
help sperm to
- O 1. reach maturity
- O 2. multiply rapidly.
- O 3. absorb antibodies.
- O 4. sustain motility.

*An evening nurse goes off duty and finds an adult woman in the parking
lot on the pavement. The woman is not breathing and has no pulse.*

99 The nurse's first efforts in the situation described should be directed
toward
- O 1. running for help
- O 2. opening the victim's airway.
- O 3. starting cardiac compressions.
- O 4. administering several precordial thumps.

100 When in relation to cardiac compressions is it recommended that the
nurse give rescue breaths to the victim during cardiopulmonary
resuscitation (CPR) when she is the only rescuer?

      ○ 1. After every 5 cardiac compressions
      ○ 2. After every 10 cardiac compressions
      ○ 3. After every 15 cardiac compressions
      ○ 4. After every 20 cardiac compressions

101 A man arrives and gives cardiac compressions while the nurse gives rescue breathing. The recommended number of cardiac compressions that the second rescuer should administer to the victim every minute is a *minimum* of
      ○ 1. 40 to 50.
      ○ 2. 50 to 60.
      ○ 3. 60 to 80.
      ○ 4. 100 to 110.

102 The nurse explains to the second rescuer that the danger when pressure between cardiac compressions is *not* released completely is that the
      ○ 1. lungs cannot expand fully.
      ○ 2. heart cannot fill with blood properly.
      ○ 3. liver may be accidently punctured.
      ○ 4. stomach may become distended with air.

103 The nurse also explains that pressure for cardiac compressions should be exerted at a point about $1\frac{1}{2}$ inches (3.75 cm) from the xiphoid process at the end of the sternum. If pressure is exerted on the xiphoid process, the victim may suffer as a result of
      ○ 1. fractures to the ribs.
      ○ 2. pressure on the diaphragm.
      ○ 3. injury to internal soft organs.
      ○ 4. compressions that are too shallow.

104 Of the following arteries, the one that is most often recommended for checking the victim's pulse rate during CPR is the
      ○ 1. radial artery.
      ○ 2. carotid artery.
      ○ 3. femoral artery.
      ○ 4. temporal artery.

105 Several persons from the hospital arrive, and a self-inflating breathing mask and bag are used on the victim. When using this device, the victim's head should be positioned so that the neck is
      ○ 1. flexed.
      ○ 2. rotated.
      ○ 3. extended.
      ○ 4. hyperextended.

106 When using a self-inflating breathing mask and bag, the rescuer should be positioned near the victim's
      ○ 1. head.
      ○ 2. chest.
      ○ 3. waist.
      ○ 4. shoulder.

107 Of the following persons, CPR is *not* ordinarily recommended for one who is a
   O 1. newborn.
   O 2. terminally ill person.
   O 3. person who is drowning.
   O 4. person over 80 years of age.

A nurse is eating in a restaurant. A man at the next table appears to be choking. The nurse goes to the man to help him.

108 After quickly assessing the man, the nurse decides that his airway is most probably blocked when the victim
   O 1. is unable to speak.
   O 2. turns red in the face.
   O 3. waves his arms frantically.
   O 4. bolts to a standing position.

109 The nurse performs abdominal thrusts. The nurse should have her arms around the victim while standing behind him when performing thrusts, and she should place her fisted hand within her other hand on the victim's
   O 1. lower sternum.
   O 2. lower rib cage.
   O 3. abdomen between the naval and pubic area.
   O 4. abdomen between the naval and the lower sternum.

110 When the first series of abdominal thrusts were unsuccessful, the nurse places the victim on the floor and sweeps his mouth. She sweeps the mouth correctly while using
   O 1. a fork.
   O 2. a spoon.
   O 3. her thumb.
   O 4. her index finger.

111 The nurse dislodges the foreign object on her next attempt with abdominal thrusts. These thrusts create force to pop out the foreign object when sufficient pressure is developed over the victim's
   O 1. diaphragm.
   O 2. phrenic nerve.
   O 3. abdominal soft organs.
   O 4. residual air spaces in the lungs.

Correct Answers and Rationales

Two numbers appear in parentheses following each rationale. The first number identifies the textbook listed in the references, page 649, and the second number identifies the page(s) in that textbook where the correct answer can be verified. Occasionally, two textbooks are given for verifying the correct answer.

The Nursing Care of Patients With Disorders of the Musculoskeletal System (Continued)

Caring for a patient with arthritis

1 1. Early symptoms of acute rheumatoid arthritis include swollen and sore joints. These symptoms most commonly cause the patient to seek health care. Other common symptoms include redness of the skin over the affected joints, weakness or fatigue, malaise, fever, and less tolerance for stress. Because of the effect of this disease on blood-forming organs in the body, the patient is often found to be anemic. (15:178)

2 4. Rheumatoid arthritis is a systemic disease. The cause (etiology) is unknown although various factors, such as infection, injury, tissue degeneration, metabolic disorders, and immune system problems, appear to play some part in its occurrence. (12:613; 15:177)

3 1. Only heart disease causes more permanent disability in this country than arthritis. Arthritis is a crippling and painful disease and takes a great toll from persons suffering with it, as well as from society as a whole. These factors should be kept in mind when planning the patient's care. (8:517)

4 3. A person who is to have 5 g of aspirin in each 24-hour period requires 15 tablets when each tablet contains 5 grains.

> 1 g (gram) contains 15 grains
> 5 g contains 75 grains (15 × 5 = 75)
> 75 grains ÷ 5 grains = 15 tablets

(14:9)

5 4. The salicylates are used in large doses for the patient with acute rheumatoid arthritis. For adults, the daily dosages can be even more than 5 g per day, but 5 g is not unusual and falls within normal range. (14:70)

6 3. Aspirin is acetylsalicylic acid. Darvon is propoxyphene hydrochloride. Tylenol is acetaminophen. Butazolidin is phenylbutazone. (14:66)

7 3. Tinnitus is best described as a ringing or a roaring sound in the ears. It is a common adverse reaction to large doses or overuse of aspirin. (14:69–70)

8 2. Taking irritating drugs with food or milk helps decrease gastric distress. Aspirin, especially in large doses, tends to irritate stomach mucosa. (14:69)

9 3. Aspirin is classified as an analgesic and as an anti-inflammatory agent. The next item describes still another of aspirin's actions. (14:66–67)

10 4. Aspirin is an antipyretic, that is, it lowers an elevated body temperature. It does not lower body temperature in the absence of fever. (14:66–67)

11 4. In the situation described in this item, the patient probably unknowingly is using television as a distraction from her discomfort. Distraction is a very legitimate and often very effective method for the relief of discomfort, and watching television is one method of distraction. (9:136)

12 3. When there is bleeding high in the gastrointestinal tract, the stool becomes tarry black and has a very offensive odor. (15:415)

13 4. It is best to notify the nurse-in-charge promptly when signs or symptoms of aspirin toxicity appear. A change in dosage or a change in medication may be required. It is not advised to give the aspirin or to omit a dosage. A change in medication is not a nurse's responsibility; an order would be required to do so. (14:69)

14 1. Prednisone (Meticorten) is an anti-inflammatory agent that helps relieve pain, heat, swelling, and redness in the affected joints. The drug is not used to stimulate leukocyte formation, limit the disease, or prevent calcium deposits in joints. (14:171–172)

15 1. The person requiring the most help should be served last so that other meals can be served without delay and without food becoming cold. In the situation described in this item, Ms. Rizak should be served last because she needs the most help with eating. (9:101)

16 3. It is best to converse about pleasant and light subjects rather than using mealtimes for discussing or teaching about a patient's illness. It is appropriate to sit while helping a patient to eat, to use a drinking tube for serving liquids, and to encourage patients to help themselves as much as possible in order to promote regaining and maintaining independence. (9:101)

17 1. When moving a person up in bed, friction can best be prevented by sprinkling powder or starch on the patient's skin and on the bottom bed linens. When help is available, a patient can be lifted, or a drawsheet under the patient can be used as a lift. Removing upper bed linens, sliding the patient, or asking the patient to push with her heels will not relieve friction when moving a patient up in bed. (9:334)

18 2. Sandbags cannot be used as effectively as a cradle, a high footboard, or the bed siderails when top linens are to be supported to keep them off the patient's feet. (9:322–323)

19 4. For a patient with rheumatoid arthritis, exercise helps maintain muscle tone and helps keep joints mobile. Exercise also helps to improve muscle coordination and strength. Exercise is not used to limit the spread of the disease and to minimize inflammation. Exercise promotes circulation but it is not used primarily for that reason for a patient with arthritis whose joints are likely to become immobile. Excessive exercise to the point of pain or fatigue, exercising an inflamed part, or carrying out movements that increase joint stability and abnormal deviation, however, could cause even further damage to involved joints. Therefore, exercising should be carried out carefully and as prescribed.   (15:180)

20 2.   To maintain joints in the best anatomical position, they should be supported in extension during periods of rest.   (15:180)

21 1.   The adult in middle life is normally concerned with maintaining independence and finds dependence on others especially difficult to accept. Middle life is characterized by a desire to be productive and responsible. Establishing a firm relationship with a person of the opposite sex normally occurs during early adulthood. Preparing for children leaving home and finding new interests as the time when reproductive ability ends normally occur during later adulthood for women.   (15:25)

22 2.   It is generally agreed that no one should lose more than 2 pounds a week unless the person is under health-care supervision. It is also recommended that persons on diets of less than 1,000 calories per day should be hospitalized to prevent problems with malnutrition.   (4:270)

23 1.   Fats contain the largest number of calories when compared with proteins and carbohydrates. There are 4 calories in a gram of carbohydrate, 4 calories in a gram of protein, and 9 calories in a gram of fat. Vitamins and minerals contain no calories.   (16:42)

24 4.   Clear beef broth has practically no calories. Buttermilk has about 100 calories per cup. Cranberry juice has about 80 calories per half cup. Pineapple juice has about 80 calories per half cup.   (4:404, 414, 417; 16:388)

25 3.   Arthroplasty refers to reconstructive surgery. Total knee (or hip) replacements are done by using a prosthesis. An arthrodesis refers to a fusion of joint surfaces and usually is used when a joint cannot be salvaged.   (15:187)

26 3.   Signs of prolonged corticosteroid therapy include having a moon-shaped face, a "buffalo" hump on the back, osteoporosis, oily skin and acne, and various types of skin pigmentation.   (12:615)

The Nursing Care of Patients With Disorders of the Blood and Lymphatic System

Caring for a patient with iron-deficiency anemia

27 3.   The abbreviation for after meals is p.c. The abbreviation for before means is a.c. The letters a.a. means "of each," and q.s. means "a sufficient amount."   (9:541)

28 1. Iron preparations stain the teeth. The patient should be taught to take a liquid iron preparation through a drinking tube. This technique minimizes contact of the drug with the teeth. Using a china or paper cup or a plastic spoon will not protect the teeth from unsightly staining.   (12:403)

29 2. Oral iron preparations cause the stool to become black in color. The patient should be told of this so that he does not become fearful of bleeding in the upper gastrointestinal tract, a condition that also causes the stool to become black. Iron may also cause constipation or diarrhea in some patients.   (12:403)

30 3. Citrus fruits are a poor source of iron. Foods rich in iron include eggs (the yolks), meats, and green leafy vegetables.   (16:87)

31 3. The most common reason for using the Z-track technique to inject a medication intramuscularly is that the medication is irritating to subcutaneous tissues. The technique is also often used when the medication stains heavily. The Z-track technique locks medication in muscle tissue to prevent it from leaking into subcutaneous tissue through the needle track or from the injection site. The Z-track technique is not used because the medication will absorb slowly, the amount of medication is more than 3 ml, or the medication is fatal if injected accidentally into a vein.   (9:574)

32 2. An area in the middle third of the thigh should be entered when injecting into the rectus femoris muscle. The muscle is largest in this area of the thigh.   (9:568)

33 1. The person's muscle should be moved laterally when using the Z-track technique. This movement is best to seal the medication in muscle tissues.   (9:575)

34 4. The muscle should be held laterally when one is using the Z-track technique until *after* the needle is removed from the person's tissue. The purpose of using the technique will be defeated if the muscle is allowed to return to its normal position sooner.   (9:575)

Caring for a patient with pernicious anemia

35 2. It is unnecessary and wasteful to repeat information in the nurses' notes of a patient's record that can be found elsewhere easily. The patient's religious preference is appropriate information but because it is found on the ID bracelet, there is no need to enter it in the nurses' notes when admitting the patient. Entries on a patient's record should be brief, concise, and useful to caretakers. Entries such as complaints concerning nausea, the appearance of the skin over an area of the body, and requests concerning visitors meet these criteria.   (9:261–262)

36 3. A plastic tube becomes more pliable and easier to manipulate if it is placed in warm water. If it is soft and too pliable to handle, a tube becomes firm and easier to handle when placed in ice chips.   (9:102)

37 4. The recommended distance for inserting a nasogastric tube is from the patient's earlobe to the bridge of the nose, plus the distance from the bridge of the nose to the end of the sternum   (9:102)

38 4.   When introducing a nasogastric tube into a nostril, it is easiest to pass it when the patient places his head with his neck hyperextended. The neck is hyperextended when a patient, who is in a sitting position, looks at the ceiling directly overhead. Flexing the neck is recommended after the tube is through the nostril. This position collapses the trachea partially and opens the esophagus widely so that the nasogastric tube can pass.   (9:102–103)

39 1.   A patient is unable to hum, is dyspneic, and becomes cyanotic when a nasogastric tube enters respiratory passageways. Most patients gag when the tube is introduced as it passes the nasopharyngeal area.   (9:104)

40 4.   Gastric juices of persons with pernicious anemia lack sufficient amounts of the intrinsic factor, which is responsible for the proper absorption of vitamin B_{12}.   (15:332)

41 4.   Erythrocytes are formed in red bone marrow. In pernicious anemia, immature red cells accumulate in bone marrow in abnormally large quantities. Therefore, a specimen of bone marrow is often used to help diagnose pernicious anemia.   (15:331)

42 4.   Of the factors described in this item, the climate in which a person lives is least likely to influence hemoglobin and red blood cell levels. The age and the sex of the person do influence these levels. Also, persons living at a high altitude have more red blood cells than those living at a lower altitude and at sea level.   (10:166–169)

43 1.   Leukopenia means a low white blood cell count, usually below 5,000 per ml of blood. A white blood count over 9,000 or 10,000 is called leukocytosis.   (10:175)

44 3.   Normal hematocrit in adult females is between approximately 36% and 46% per 100 ml of blood. Some persons may give a slightly wider range. Women tend to have a somewhat lower hematocrit than men do. For a male, normal range is about 42% to 54% per 100 ml of blood.   (10:176)

45 3.   Hematocrit describes the percentage of space in a given quantity of blood that is occupied by red blood cells. This blood finding is often used to help diagnose various types of anemia, instead of or to supplement a standard red blood cell count.   (10:176)

46 3.   The average normal hemoglobin content of blood in healthy adult females is between 12 and 14 g per 100 ml of blood and in healthy adult males, between 14 and 16 g per 100 ml of blood.   (12:664)

47 3.   Patients acutely ill with pernicious anemia usually complain of sore oral mucosa, and their tissues tend to bleed readily. Therefore, special oral hygiene measures are particularly important.   (12:664; 15:333)

48 1.   Iron is most necessary for hemoglobin production, although zinc may be a minor contributor. Persons with iron-deficiency anemia are ordinarily treated with diet and drug therapy.   (12:664)

49 1. A person with pernicious anemia may show personality changes, especially if the disorder is severe. Being irritable, depressed, and confused are common signs. These signs usually disappear when treatment starts. (15:333)

50 4. A person who is unaware of his surroundings and of time and place is commonly described as being disoriented. Neurotic means that there is a disorder of thought processes, but contact with reality is ordinarily present. A paranoic person has a persecution complex, is suspicious, and is often resentful and bitter. Incoherent means displaying disconnected thought and speech. (12:123)

51 2. Sprinkling hair with a fine powder (dry shampoo) and then brushing the hair helps keep it clean when a patient cannot have a soap-and-water shampoo. Powder hair cleaners tend to dry the hair and therefore, should be used only when a wet shampoo is contraindicated. Hair driers, setting lotions, and hair sprays are not recommended for cleaning the hair. (12:303)

52 4. Teaching and explaining to patients help them meet normal needs for understanding. Patients also have a right to be informed about their care and about risks and benefits of the care. Needs, such as safety, security, and a sense of belonging, are better met by other means. (9:14, 22)

53 1. There are no known toxic side effects to the use of vitamin B_{12}. (15:332)

54 2. A multiple-dose vial should be injected with the same amount of air as the amount of medication to be withdrawn. To remove 1 ml of solution from a multiple-dose vial, 1 ml of air should be injected into the vial before removing any medication. If less is injected, the vial will develop a partial vacuum. If more is injected, solution in the vial will be under pressure. In either case, removing accurate doses from the vial becomes difficult. (9:561)

55 4. An imaginary diagonal line should be drawn from the trochanter of the femur to the posterior superior iliac spine. The needle is injected superior and lateral to the midpoint of this line. Dividing the buttock into fourths, a technique used in the past, often caused the injection to be given too low in the buttock, and nerve damage resulted in many instances. (9:568)

56 2. The sciatic nerve may be struck and injured if the site for injecting an intramuscular medication in the patient's buttock is improperly located. (9:567)

57 3. The daughter should aspirate to see whether she is in a blood vessel when the needle is in place but *before* she injects the medication. If she aspirates blood, she should change the injection site because injecting a drug into the blood vessel *may* harm the patient. Proper techniques for an intramuscular injection include cleaning the entry site with an antiseptic, pressing tissue down at the entry site, and massaging the area after giving vitamin B_{12}. (9:570-574)

58 1. A disadvantage of using the deltoid muscle for injecting intramuscular medications is that the muscle is small and discomfort from the pressure of the drug is common. The deltoid muscle is easy to locate, has a good blood supply, and does not have numerous pain receptors. (9:564)

59 1. For home purposes, it most often is recommended that patients be taught to sterilize reusable equipment by boiling in water. A pressure cooker can be used, but it has been found that boiling water is more convenient for the patient and is safe. Also, the technique does not require having a special cooker. For safety and convenience, most patients today use disposable equipment. (9:293)

60 1. A patient with pernicious anemia needs to take vitamin B_{12} for the rest of his life. The disease does not respond to diet therapy. The patient should be taught the importance of continuing to obtain the vitamin, even when he begins to feel good, because signs and symptoms of the disease will recur if the patient stops taking vitamin B_{12}. (12:664)

Caring for a patient with Hodgkin's disease

61 1. The patient's arms should be supported on pillows when in the Fowler's position to help prevent pull on his shoulders. To prevent flexion of the neck, his head should be resting on the mattress or a very small pillow. The angle of elevation should begin at the patient's hips to help keep the spine in proper alignment. The knees should not be flexed sharply over a pillow because this may cause pressure on nerves and blood vessels behind the knees. (9:338)

62 3. Normal leukocyte count in adults is between 5,000 and 7,000 per ml of blood. Some persons may consider a slightly wider range normal, but rarely will the range be more than between 4,500 and 10,000. (10:168; 15:733)

63 2. When conditions indicate that it may be unsafe for the patient to smoke, but he insists on doing so, it is best for the nurse to remain with the patient. It usually presents more difficulties if the patient is not allowed to smoke. It is unsafe to leave any lethargic or sleepy patient alone if he insists on smoking because of the great danger of fire. (9:177)

64 3. A diagnosis of Hodgkin's disease is established by obtaining a biopsy of an affected lymph node. A typical finding is the presence of abnormal cells, called Reed-Sternberg cells, in the node. Bone marrow specimens sometimes are obtained when Hodgkin's disease is suspected, but the Reed-Sternberg cells are not found in bone marrow. (15:341)

65 3. Drugs used to treat malignant diseases are called antineoplastic agents. Anticholinergic agents interfere with certain normal nerve impulse transmission. Antipyretics are used to reduce an elevated body temperature. Antiemetics are used to help control vomiting. (14:197)

66 2. Mechlorethamine hydrochloride (Mustargen) is administered intravenously while a rapidly flowing solution is being introduced simultaneously. Practical nurses do not administer intravenous medications, but they may be asked to assist caretakers qualified to do so. (14:202)

67 4. The gastrointestinal tract is most commonly involved when a patient receiving chemotherapy for a malignant disease suffers with adverse effects to the drug. Common symptoms include nausea and vomiting, anorexia, diarrhea, and constipation. There is a great variety of other side effects to chemotherapy for malignancies but they occur less often than side effects involving the gastrointestinal tract. (14:202)

68 2. Hodgkin's disease most often strikes during young adulthood between the ages of about 20 and 35. The illness tends to occur more frequently in men than in women. (15:341)

69 2. Using reverse (protective) isolation primarily helps to prevent organisms from reaching the patient. In other types of isolation, the purpose is to help to prevent organisms from the patient from spreading to others. (9:302)

70 3. Ideally, the air pressure in the room of a patient on reverse isolation should be higher than air pressure outside his room. This technique helps to carry organisms distributed by air currents *away* from the patient when a door or window is opened. If the room's air pressure is lower, organisms distributed by air currents would move *toward* the patient. (9:303)

71 3. Gowns for caretakers and visitors should be stored just outside the door to the patient's room. They may become contaminated if stored in the patient's room or bathroom. Gowns are less likely to be worn when they are inconveniently stored away from the patient's unit, such as at the nurses' station. (12:343)

72 4. Patients who are placed on isolation very often experience feelings of loneliness, rejection, and depression and frequently say they feel "unclean," or "dirty." These patients are unlikely to become aggressive or destructive. To prevent feelings of rejection, depression, and loneliness, it is important to provide for a variety of sensory experiences, including human contacts, to the extent they are possible and safe. The patient should be helped to understand that it is organisms that are unwanted, not the patient. (9:313)

73 2. Patients suffering with sensory alteration need varied stimuli in their environments. This is not well accomplished when the degree of light in the room is kept low. Such activities as using touch, giving explanations to the patient, and changing furniture arrangements occasionally as possible help to prevent sensory alteration. (9:172)

74 3. The patient suffering with sensory alteration often shows signs or symptoms of depression, anxiety, fear, loneliness, and the like. He is less likely to complain of heartburn and constipation, although eventually patients may also complain of various physical symptoms when sensory alteration is present. (9:170)

75 2. The patient's vital signs, especially temperature, should be obtained before starting a blood transfusion. Changes in vital signs may indicate that the patient is having an unfavorable reaction to the blood. Except possibly in certain emergency situations, the patient's blood count has already been determined to help make a decision concerning whether a blood transfusion is necessary.   (9:532)

76 1.   Chilliness and nausea are symptoms of an unfavorable reaction to a blood transfusion. The nurse should stop the flow of blood first and then notify the nurse-in-charge promptly. If a tandem set is being used, the solution in the second bottle, usually normal saline, should be allowed to enter the vein. Placing a blanket on the patient can be done after the blood is no longer entering the vein and the proper people have been notified. The date on the blood should be carefully checked before starting a blood transfusion.   (9:533)

77 3.   Jehovah's Witnesses do not accept blood transfusions. Most other religious denominations accept this type of therapy. Jehovah's Witnesses have no objections to the use of artificial blood.   (9:16)

78 2.   Before administering the drug, the nurse should check to see whether a patient has had allergic reactions to penicillin. This is particularly important because a reaction can be serious! It is satisfactory to note whether the patient feels nausea or has an abnormally fast pulse rate or low blood pressure. However, before giving any drug, the nurse should be *sure* the patient is not allergic to the drug before administering it.   (14:141)

79 2.   The intact skin is a good defense against the entry of organisms into the body. This is important to know when giving care that will help to protect the skin. Organisms enter the nose, the genital tract, and the urinary tract with greater ease than intact skin.   (9:273, 398)

80 4.   An infection acquired in a health agency is called a nosocomial infection. An enteric infection is spread by feces containing the causative organism. A local infection, such as an abscess, is limited to the body's tissues and remains there. A primary infection is one that occurs before a subsequent infection develops.   (9:272)

81 1.   The primary purpose of radiotherapy is to destroy malignant cells. Radiotherapy is not used to protect normal body cells, prevent malignant cells from dividing, or promote the development of antibodies.   (15:147)

82 2.   To help prevent kidney complications when having radiotherapy, a patient should have generous amounts of fluid daily, up to at least 3,000 ml.   (15:149)

83 2.   Radiated skin should not be exposed to the sun, nor should ointments and creams be used unless they are prescribed. Heating pads, diathermy, saunas, and steam baths should also be avoided. Careful bathing and loose clothing are satisfactory. Cornstarch is recommended where two radiated areas of skin touch each other.   (15:149)

84 4.   Nutrients are introduced into the body by placing a catheter into a peripheral vein or into the superior vena cava when a patient receives hyperalimentation. Occasionally, the jugular vein is used. The procedure most often is used for very ill patients who are debilitated and cannot be nourished satisfactorily in other ways.   (8:404; 12:702)

85   2. A typical sign when nourishment is introduced by hyperalimentation too rapidly is dyspnea. Noisy breathing and coughing may also result from circulatory overload. These same symptoms are likely to occur when any fluid is introduced into a vein too rapidly. Nausea, diarrhea, and pain at the site of entry are not associated with administering nourishment too rapidly when using hyperalimentation.   (9:525)

86   2. In very few instances is an alert adult denied information concerning a poor prognosis. However, a problem may exist concerning exactly what to say and when. It is generally agreed that family members of the patient are in the best position to help health caretakers concerning such problems. They know the patient well, including his values. Other persons, such as psychological counselors, clergymen, and psychiatric-oncologists, may also offer valuable help but it is generally agreed that family feelings and opinion should be sought first.   (6:58)

87   2. When a terminally ill person states that there must be a mistake or that he is being confused with someone else, he is most probably denying his impending death. Anger often is expressed with a comment such as "Why me?" A typical comment when bargaining is done is "Yes, me, but . . . ", and then the patient makes a promise in exchange for more time. Depression is characterized by feelings of sadness, and the patient is likely to say, "Yes, me." Acceptance, the final stage, expresses a readiness for an acceptance of death. These stages are described by Dr. Elisabeth Kübler-Ross.   (9:653)

88   3. It generally is agreed that it is most helpful when persons discuss their feelings about life, death, and dying with others to help them come to grips with their own death. Reading the literature on the subject, contemplating death and dying, and having experienced the death of a loved one may help, but are not believed to help as much as talking about feelings with others.   (9:649)

89   2. Any person who witnesses a will indicates that to the best of the witness's knowledge, the person making the will is of sound mind, has prepared his will without coercion, and is free of the influence of medications that could alter his thinking processes. The witnesses should sign in the presence of each other. Two or three witnesses are required, depending on the state's law. Witnesses need not read the will but they should be sure that the document they are signing is a will. In most states, a person who is a beneficiary is not eligible to act as a witness to the signing of a will. A legal will may leave property to a minor, does not need to indicate that the estate is divided equally among heirs, and need not be prepared by a lawyer.   (9:51)

90   3. When death is near, signs include noisy respirations due to an accumulation of mucus in the respiratory tract. The noise is often called the "death rattle." A rapid, thready pulse and an elevated temperature are usually also present. Pain tends to diminish as death approaches.   (9:662)

The Nursing Care of Patients Receiving Emergency Care

Caring for patients in an emergency care facility

91   4.   The Trendelenburg position most often is contraindicated after a patient has a head injury or has had brain surgery. The position tends to increase blood circulation to the head, where edema usually is already present when there has been a head injury or head surgery.   (9:386; 15:702)

92   1.   Prolonged high body temperature is likely to cause permanent brain damage. The patient's chances of recovery are very poor if the temperature reaches 109°F or 110°F (43°C to 43.5°C).   (15:110)

93   3.   Rabies vaccine stimulates the body to manufacture its own defenses against rabies, and therefore, it is called an active immunity. The immunity is artificially acquired because it develops as the result of giving the patient a vaccine containing an antigen. A species immunity means that a disease is not transmitted between species. For example, humans do not acquire distemper from dogs, and therefore, this type of immunity in humans is called species immunity. An immunity that is naturally acquired does not rely on stimulating the body artificially to produce an immunity. An example of a naturally acquired immunity is the immunity developed after having measles; the body's immune system protects one from acquiring the disease again. An artificial passive immunity means that immunity is acquired by injecting antibodies from an outside source. It is a type of artificial immunity because the body did not develop its own antibodies.   (10:231)

94   4.   Nausea *may* be present but usually is not when a person has increased intracranial pressure. Also, the vomiting may be forceful, or projectile, and occur without warning.   (15:210, 696)

95   1.   Cerumen is the waxy material found in the outer ear canal. The examiner needs a syringe, an irrigating solution, and a waste basin to catch the returning irrigating solution when removing cerumen by irrigation from an ear.   (10:142)

96   1.   Although many nursing measures are important for a patient with quadriplegia, helping to prevent decubitus ulcers usually has highest priority. Measures include frequent turning, proper positioning, and careful skin care. Decubitus ulcers are serious complications for the quadriplegic patient because the ulcers are difficult to treat and slow to heal. They also can cause additional problems for the patient when they become infected.   (15:251)

97 1. Difficulty in urinating is called dysuria. The production of above average amounts of urine is called diuresis. Dystocia is difficult labor. Dysplasia is an abnormal development in body tissues. (9:431)

98 4. Prostatic secretions are believed to serve as a lubricant and to help enhance motility of the sperm. Also, prostatic secretions are alkaline and thereby help to neutralize acidity in the vaginal tract. An acidic vaginal environment is an unfriendly environment in terms of promoting the survival of sperm. (10:302)

Caring for a victim of cardiopulmonary collapse

99 2. When a victim is found suffering with cardiopulmonary failure, the rescuer's first efforts should be directed toward opening the victim's airway. Rescue breathing should be started if opening the airway does not start spontaneous breathing. Cardiac compressions then should start if no pulse can be felt at the carotid artery. If a victim has fainted and does not need cardiopulmonary resuscitation (CPR), the victim will be breathing, the pulse rate most likely will be rapid and weak, and he will recover shortly. (9:623)

100 3. When there is one rescuer, two rescue breaths should be given after every 15 cardiac compressions. When there are two rescuers, one rescue breath is interspersed between every five compressions. (15:639)

101 3. The minimum number of cardiac compressions that should be administered each minute to an adult receiving cardiopulmonary resuscitation is 60 to 80. However, authorities differ somewhat concerning the total number of compressions each minute when administering CPR. Some indicate 60 to 80, some indicate 80 to 100, and some indicate about 60 per minute. It is important that pulses be present during cardiac compression and that the victim's color improves as a sign of a favorable response to CPR. (9:641; 12:892)

102 2. The heart cannot fill with blood properly if pressure is not released completely between cardiac compressions when administering cardiopulmonary resuscitation. (9:639)

103 3. If pressure is placed less than about $1\frac{1}{2}$ inches (3.75 cm) from the end of the sternum, the patient may suffer injuries to internal organs, especially the liver. Fractures of ribs are likely to occur if the fingers are not interlocked or are displaced to one or the other side of the sternum. This positioning of the fingers (interlocked) helps to keep them off the ribs. Compressions that are too shallow result when insufficient pressure is being exerted on the sternum. (9:638)

104 2. The carotid artery is recommended when one is checking the pulse during CPR. It is easily accessible and large. Often, a pulse can be felt at the carotid artery when it may be imperceptible in the smaller arteries of extremities. The femoral artery is satisfactory but very often, is not easily accessible. (9:639)

105 4. The head should be positioned so that the neck is hyperextended when using a self-inflating mask and bag on a patient. This positioning helps to keep the victim's airway open and provides for the best exchange of air. (9:639)

106 1. It is best when the rescuer stands near the victim's head, or kneels if the victim is on the floor or ground, when using a self-inflating breathing bag and mask. This positioning makes it easy to keep the neck hyperextended and the airway open. It also places the rescuer out of the way of persons who may be performing other rescue techniques simultaneously. (9:639)

107 2. It is ordinarily not recommended that CPR be used on a person who is terminally ill, when death is expected. However, an ethical dilemma *may* be involved when the victim's or the victim's family's wishes are unknown, especially if the victim has not prepared a Living Will. Other persons are given CPR as necessary. For example, the procedure is used for drowning victims. Age in itself is not a criterion concerning when and when not to administer CPR. (9:633, 635)

Caring for a victim of choking

108 1. A victim most likely is choking because his airway is obstructed when he is unable to speak, grasps for his throat (the universal sign of choking), turns pale and then becomes blue. The victim is unlikely to move, but he will collapse and become unconscious unless the foreign body is removed to allow for air exchange in the lungs. (9:614)

109 4. When administering abdominal thrusts, the rescuer's fisted hands should be placed on the victim's abdomen between the navel and lower sternum. Placing the fisted hands on the sternum or rib cage is likely to cause injury to the victim and will not remove the foreign object effectively, nor will the thrusts remove the object if the hands are placed low on the abdomen. (9:616)

110 4. The index finger should be used when performing an oral sweep. The finger should be positioned like a hook while moving the finger through the mouth and upper throat. Care should be used so that the finger does not force a foreign object farther into the respiratory passages. The thumb is not convenient for making a sweeping motion through the mouth. Such objects as forks and spoons are likely to injure oral tissues. (9:617)

111 4. Abdominal thrusts create pressure on residual air spaces in the lungs. Residual air being forced from the lungs with thrusts causes the foreign object to pop out of the respiratory tract. The diaphragm, phrenic nerve, and abdominal soft organs are not involved in forcing a foreign object out of the respiratory tract when abdominal thrusts are used. (9:616)

Classification of Test Items

Directions: *Each item in the previous review test is classified here according to the subject area it tests. Place a check mark after each item you answered **correctly** by referring to your answers. Total the number of items you answered correctly in each area and enter the numbers in the correct places on pages 553–556.*

Clinical: Medical/Surgical Nursing (Adults)

1 ✓	20 ____	47 ____	64 ✓	83 ✓	92 ✓
2 ✓	25 ____	49 ✓	68 ____	84 ✓	94 ✓
3 ____	40 ✓	50 ✓	81 ✓	85 ____	96 ✓
19 ✓	41 ✓	60 ✓	82 ✓	91 ____	

TOTAL _16_

Biological/Physical Sciences

| 42 ✓ | 44 ____ | 46 ✓ | 79 ____ | 95 ____ | 98 ✓ |
| 43 ✓ | 45 ✓ | 62 ____ | 93 ____ | | |

TOTAL _7_

Fundamentals of Nursing

11 ✓	32 ✓	51 ✓	63 ✓	90 ____	105 ✓
15 ____	33 ✓	54 ✓	69 ✓	97 ✓	106 ✓
16 ✓	34 ____	55 ____	70 ✓	99 ✓	107 ✓
17 ____	35 ✓	56 ✓	71 ✓	100 ____	108 ✓
18 ____	36 ✓	57 ____	75 ____	101 ✓	109 ✓
27 ✓	37 ✓	58 ✓	76 ✓	102 ____	110 ✓
28 ✓	38 ✓	59 ✓	80 ✓	103 ✓	111 ____
31 ✓	39 ____	61 ____	87 ✓	104 ✓	

TOTAL _34_

Diet Therapy/Nutrition

22 _____   23 ✓_____   24 _____   30 _____   48 ✓_____

TOTAL 2

Pharmacology

4 ✓_____   7 ✓_____   10 ✓_____   14 ✓_____   53 _____   67 ✓_____

5 _____   8 ✓_____   12 ✓_____   26 ✓_____   65 ✓_____   68 _____

6 ✓_____   9 ✓_____   13 ✓_____   29 ✓_____   66 ✓_____

TOTAL 14

Psychosocial Sciences

21 _____   72 ✓_____   74 ✓_____   86 _____   88 ✓_____   89 ✓_____

52 ✓_____   73 ✓_____   77 ✓_____

TOTAL 7

Review Test 10

The Nursing Care of Patients With Disorders of the Respiratory System

Caring for a Patient With Lobar Pneumonia
Caring for a Patient With Emphysema and Asthma
Caring for Patients With Various Respiratory Disorders

Correct Answers and Rationales
Classification of Test Items

Directions: *With a pencil, blacken the circle in front of the option you have chosen for your correct answer.*

The Nursing Care of Patients With Disorders of the Respiratory System

Mr. Zitani, who is 29 years old, is hospitalized. His admission temperature is 105.8° F. The admitting nurse's observations include noting frequent coughing. She judges that Mr. Zitani is "acutely ill." He has lobar pneumonia.

1 When Mr. Zitani's oral temperature is noted to be 105.8°F, on the Celsius scale, Mr. Zitani's temperature is
○ 1. 39°C.
○ 2. 39.8°C.
○ 3. 40.5°C
○ 4. 41°C.

2 When Mr. Zitani is described as being "acutely ill," it means that his illness is characterized by having a
○ 1. rapid onset.
○ 2. long convalescence.
○ 3. serious complications.
○ 4. questionable prognosis.

3 The admitting nurse reports that Mr. Zitani has tachypnea. This means that Mr. Zitani has respirations that are
○ 1. noisy.

    ○ 2. shallow.

    ○ 3. rapid.

    ○ 4. labored.

4 If the nurse makes the following observations while admitting Mr. Zitani, which one is a constitutional sign?

    ○ 1. Edema of the ankles

    ○ 2. Pain when coughing

    ○ 3. Abdominal distention

    ○ 4. An elevated temperature

5 The nurse should plan that an acutely ill patient with a respiratory infection, such as Mr. Zitani, has a critical need for

    ○ 1. fluids.

    ○ 2. oxygen.

    ○ 3. vitamins.

    ○ 4. electrolytes.

6 One of the admitting orders appearing on Mr. Zitani's record reads as follows:

12/12/89 3 P.M. Codeine sulfate, 30 mg stat (The order is signed by the admitting physician)

Which one of the following courses of action should the nurse take after reading this order?

    ○ 1. Administer the medication

    ○ 2. Consult the nurse-in-charge

    ○ 3. Obtain the patient's blood pressure

    ○ 4. Prepare the medication under a registered nurse's supervision

7 Mr. Zitani complains to the admitting nurse of having chest pain. Which of the following statements should the nurse recognize as being the most accurate description of the word, pain?

    ○ 1. Pain is subjective in nature.

    ○ 2. Pain is without cultural influences.

    ○ 3. Pain is only as great as proportionate body injury.

    ○ 4. Pain occurs only after body tissues have been damaged.

8 After assessment, the nurse describes Mr. Zitani's pain as being diffuse, which means that his pain

    ○ 1. comes and goes.

    ○ 2. covers a large part of the body.

    ○ 3. moves from one part of the body to another.

    ○ 4. is felt in a part of the body removed from the diseased area.

The nurse positions Mr. Zitani comfortably in bed on his back after completing admission assessments and care.

9 Where should a *small* pillow or rolled towel be placed when support under Mr. Zitani's knees is indicated?

    ○ 1. Directly under the knees

    ○ 2. Slightly below the knees

    ○ 3. Slightly above the knees

    ○ 4. Wherever the patient experiences the most comfort

10 When placing top linens on Mr. Zitani's bed, which of the following techniques is recommended to help provide adequate room for the patient's feet?

    ○ 1. Making a toe pleat in the top linens

    ○ 2. Using square corners to secure the top linens

    ○ 3. Placing top linens even with the bottom of the mattress

    ○ 4. Allowing the bedspread to fall free at the foot of the bed.

11 When Mr. Zitani is described as being in good alignment in bed, it means that he is positioned so that

    ○ 1. he is lying on his back.

    ○ 2. his center of gravity is near his head.

    ○ 3. his joints are in an extended position.

    ○ 4. his body parts are in proper relationship to each other.

12 The nurse uses the strongest muscles in her body to avoid injury to herself while positioning and caring for Mr. Zitani. Of the following muscles, the ones that are the strongest are the muscles in the

    ○ 1. arms.

    ○ 2. back.

    ○ 3. legs.

    ○ 4. abdomen.

The nurse helps prepare a nursing care plan for Mr. Zitani.

13 The primary purpose of preparing a nursing care plan for Mr. Zitani is to help

    ○ 1. plan nursing care assignments

    ○ 2. describe the patient's responses to therapy.

    ○ 3. ensure that the patient receives needed nursing care.

    ○ 4. keep a record of nursing care that the patient receives.

A sputum specimen is to be obtained from Mr. Zitani.

14 Mr. Zitani's respiratory secretions are sticky and difficult to raise. If measures given below are allowed for the patient, the one that often helps make sputum less tenacious is to

    ○ 1. offer the patient a generous fluid intake.

    ○ 2. encourage the patient to lie on either side.

    ○ 3. include more roughage in the patient's diet.

    ○ 4. see to it that the patient has frequent rest periods.

15 At what time in the day would it usually be easiest to obtain a sputum specimen from Mr. Zitani?

    ○ 1. Before the patient's bedtime

○ 2. Promptly after the patient has eaten
○ 3. Midway between the patient's meals
○ 4. When the patient awakens in the morning

16 The nurse can expect that the color of Mr. Zitani's sputum most probably will be
○ 1. grey.
○ 2. rusty.
○ 3. green.
○ 4. yellow.

A cool-water sponge bath, with alcohol added to the water, is to be given to Mr. Zitani to help reduce his temperature.

17 Alcohol is added to water to be used for Mr. Zitani's sponge bath primarily because alcohol
○ 1. toughens the skin.
○ 2. reduces feelings of chilliness.
○ 3. acts as an antiseptic on the skin.
○ 4. evaporates more rapidly than water.

18 During the cool-water/alcohol sponge bath, a warm-water bag (or its equivalent) should be placed at Mr. Zitani's
○ 1. back.
○ 2. head.
○ 3. feet.
○ 4. abdomen.

19 The part of Mr. Zitani's body that the nurse should *omit* bathing when she gives him the cool-water/alcohol sponge bath is the patient's
○ 1. neck.
○ 2. face.
○ 3. back.
○ 4. abdomen.

Penicillin is to be given intramuscularly to Mr. Zitani.

20 The penicillin will act in Mr. Zitani's body by
○ 1. destroying the causative organisms.
○ 2. promoting the production of antitoxins.
○ 3. increasing the production of white blood cells.
○ 4. stimulating an immunity to the causative organisms.

21 The nurse chooses to inject the ventrogluteal site while Mr. Zitani lies on his abdomen. The recommended technique to help reduce discomfort when the needle is injected is to have Mr. Zitani
○ 1. point his toes inward.
○ 2. spread his legs widely.
○ 3. cross his legs at the ankles.

○ 4. place his hands under the abdomen.

22 When locating the ventrogluteal site for injecting the penicillin, the palm of the nurse's hand should be placed on Mr. Zitani's

○ 1. sacral spine.
○ 2. crest of the ilium.
○ 3. anterior superior iliac spine.
○ 4. greater trochanter of the femur.

23 Where in relation to the point of entry should the nurse begin cleansing Mr. Zitani's skin before injecting the needle?

○ 1. At the point of entry
○ 2. Slightly below the point of entry
○ 3. Slightly above the point of entry
○ 4. On either side near the point of entry

24 While removing the needle from Mr. Zitani after injecting the penicillin, the nurse uses a gauze pledget to place pressure against the injection site primarily because this technique helps to

○ 1. prevent bleeding from the injection site.
○ 2. prevent organisms from entering the injection site.
○ 3. decrease the discomfort of pulling skin with the needle.
○ 4. decrease the escape of solution through the needle track.

25 The nurse massages the injection site with the pledget after giving Mr. Zitani penicillin, primarily to help

○ 1. spread the medication in tissues to promote its absorption.
○ 2. minimize bruising of tissues that are entered by the needle.
○ 3. reduce the possibility of organisms entering the injection site.
○ 4. place pressure on blood vessels to prevent unnecessary bleeding.

26 The nurse uses a disposable needle and syringe to administer Mr. Zitani's penicillin. It is recommended that the needle and syringe used for Mr. Zitani's injection be discarded in a special locked waste container, primarily to

○ 1. avoid injuries to persons handling the garbage.
○ 2. avoid reuse of equipment that cannot be resterilized.
○ 3. minimize space required for solid waste disposal.
○ 4. prevent reuse of the equipment by persons abusing drugs.

27 If Mr. Zitani has an allergic reaction to penicillin, a very likely symptom that he will demonstrate is

○ 1. nausea.
○ 2. a skin rash.
○ 3. a feeling of dizziness.
○ 4. a sudden elevation in temperature.

28 If Mr. Zitani develops systemic shock after having penicillin, he is most likely to experience

○ 1. double vision.
○ 2. marked dyspnea.
○ 3. urinary retention.

○ 4. projectile vomiting.

Mr. Zitani is to have oxygen therapy by nasal catheter.

29 The distance that a nasal catheter should be inserted into one of Mr. Zitani's nostrils is most nearly equivalent to the distance from his
○ 1. lips to an earlobe.
○ 2. chin to a nostril.
○ 3. forehead to the lips.
○ 4. nostril to an earlobe.

30 To help prevent irritation of mucous membranes when oxygen therapy is administered to Mr. Zitani, the oxygen is given *after* it has been
○ 1. cooled.
○ 2. warmed.
○ 3. nebulized.
○ 4. humidified.

31 It is generally recommended that the *minimum* number of times in every 24 hours that Mr. Zitani's catheter should be changed is
○ 1. one time.
○ 2. two times.
○ 3. three times.
○ 4. four times.

32 While Mr. Zitani receives oxygen therapy, a nursing measure of particular importance is to see to it that he has regular
○ 1. back rubs.
○ 2. rest periods.
○ 3. oral hygiene.
○ 4. range-of-motion exercises.

33 When caring for equipment being used to administer Mr. Zitani's oxygen, the nurse should *avoid* using
○ 1. oils.
○ 2. antiseptics.
○ 3. paper towels.
○ 4. cotton cleaning cloths.

34 The characteristic of oxygen that makes special precautions in Mr. Zitani's room necessary is that oxygen
○ 1. is very irritating.
○ 2. is soluble in water.
○ 3. supports combustion.
○ 4. weighs more than air.

Mr. Zitani is to have Robitussin A-C, i̅3̅ q.i.d.

35 The household equivalent of Mr. Zitani's dosage of Robitussin A-C, i̅3̅, is
○ 1. ½ teaspoon.

    ○ 2. 1 teaspoon.
    ○ 3. 2 teaspoons.
    ○ 4. 1 tablespoon.

36 The label on Mr. Zitani's bottle of Robitussin A-C has come off and is found lying near the bottle. The recommended procedure for the nurse to follow in this situation is to
    ○ 1. glue the label back onto the bottle properly.
    ○ 2. return the bottle to the pharmacy for relabeling.
    ○ 3. use a rubber hand to secure the label to the bottle.
    ○ 4. ask the nurse-in-charge to assist you to replace the label.

37 Mr. Zitani's Robitussin A-C contains codeine. The desired action of the codeine for Mr. Zitani is to
    ○ 1. liquify thick mucus.
    ○ 2. dilate the bronchioles.
    ○ 3. depress the cough center.
    ○ 4. soothe respiratory passages.

38 The nurse should judge that Mr. Zitani is likely to be having an adverse effect to codeine when he complains of
    ○ 1. nausea.
    ○ 2. dyspnea.
    ○ 3. dizziness.
    ○ 4. headaches.

Mr. Zitani awakens one morning about 3 A.M. and complains that he cannot get back to sleep.

39 If the following nursing measures are permissible for Mr. Zitani, which one should the nurse consider using *last* to promote rest and sleep for the patient?
    ○ 1. Giving the patient a back rub
    ○ 2. Offering the patient a bedpan
    ○ 3. Offering the patient a beverage
    ○ 4. Giving the patient a medication to promote sleep

40 One exercise the nurse should teach Mr. Zitani to use to promote sleep consists of alternately
    ○ 1. taking short and deep breaths.
    ○ 2. flexing and extending joints in the body.
    ○ 3. rolling from one side to the other in bed.
    ○ 4. contracting and relaxing muscles in the body.

41 During sleep, Mr. Zitani's sense that normally would be most difficult to arouse is his sense of
    ○ 1. pain.
    ○ 2. touch.
    ○ 3. hearing.
    ○ 4. smell.

42   Mr. Zitani's health record indicates that he suffers with the sleeping disorder, somnabulism. This term is used to describe
  ○ 1. bed-wetting.
  ○ 2. sleep talking.
  ○ 3. sleepwalking.
  ○ 4. early awakening from sleep.

While recuperating from pneumonia, Mr. Zitani becomes interested in and studies several booklets distributed by the hospital and prepared for lay persons that describe the respiratory system.

43   Mr. Zitani learns correctly that external respiration takes place within his body's
  ○ 1. nose.
  ○ 2. lungs.
  ○ 3. bronchi.
  ○ 4. body cells.

44   Mr. Zitani explains correctly when he tells the nurse that the mechanism in his respiratory tract chiefly responsible for helping remove debris from the tract is the
  ○ 1. movement of cilia.
  ○ 2. movement of the rib cage.
  ○ 3. opening and closing of the epiglottis.
  ○ 4. opening and closing of the bronchioles.

45   According to one booklet, the chief nerve supplying Mr. Zitani's diaphragm is the
  ○ 1. vagus nerve.
  ○ 2. sciatic nerve.
  ○ 3. phrenic nerve.
  ○ 4. accessory nerve.

46   Mr. Zitani learns that the structure in his body that separates the thoracic from the abdominal cavity is his
  ○ 1. sternum.
  ○ 2. pleurae.
  ○ 3. diaphragm.
  ○ 4. mediastinum.

The remaining items in this situation are individual items related to Mr. Zitani's care.

47   Laboratory reports indicate that the causative organism of Mr. Zitani's pneumonia is *Diplococcus pneumoniae*. The prefix *diplo* describes the coccus causing the patient's illness and means
  ○ 1. one.
  ○ 2. two.

○ 3. three.
○ 4. four.

48 Which of the following items is considered *unsafe* to use in Mr. Zitani's bathroom?
○ 1. An electric radio
○ 2. A shower curtain
○ 3. A ceiling heat lamp
○ 4. A plastic drinking glass

49 Mr. Zitani is proud of his physical condition and comments about an exercise program he follows when well. Between approximately what ages in life is it believed that a slow, almost imperceptible *normal* decline in many physical abilities begins?
○ 1. Between 18 and 20 years
○ 2. Between 25 and 30 years
○ 3. Between 38 and 40 years
○ 4. Between 40 and 45 years

50 Mr. Zitani wears glasses with plastic lenses. When cleaning them for him, the nurse should use precautions because the lenses are very easily
○ 1. pitted.
○ 2. broken.
○ 3. warped.
○ 4. scratched.

51 Mr. Zitani becomes angry and shouts at the nurse when a meal she serves him is not to his liking. In this situation, it would be best for the nurse to
○ 1. humor the patient and excuse herself to call the dietician.
○ 2. say nothing while allowing the patient to talk out his anger.
○ 3. leave the room to allow the patient privacy to express his anger.
○ 4. be firm and explain how important eating is to promote his well-being.

52 When the nurse fails to answer Mr. Zitani's call light with reasonable promptness, she risks being legally accused of
○ 1. libel.
○ 2. battery.
○ 3. negligence.
○ 4. false imprisonment.

Mr. Yee, who is 72 years old, has emphysema and asthma. He is hospitalized while having an asthma attack.

53 Which of the following drugs should the nurse plan to have ready to help counter Mr. Yee's asthma attack?
○ 1. Atropine
○ 2. Morphine
○ 3. Epinephrine

○ 4. Scopolamine

54 A common abbreviation for Mr. Yee's lung condition is
○ 1. CRD.
○ 2. ASEM.
○ 3. COPD.
○ 4. A & E.

55 A blood sample taken upon admission to examine Mr. Yee's blood gases indicates that his carbon dioxide level ($PaCO_2$ or PCO_2) is elevated. Mr. Yee is in an altered physiological state, in terms of his acid-base balance, that is called
○ 1. metabolic acidosis.
○ 2. metabolic alkalosis.
○ 3. respiratory acidosis.
○ 4. respiratory alkalosis.

56 Mr. Yee's blood is tested for its *p*H level. The blood's normal *p*H level is between
○ 1. 7.00 and 7.10.
○ 2. 7.25 and 7.35.
○ 3. 7.35 and 7.45.
○ 4. 7.45 and 7.50.

57 The nurse prepares to auscultate Mr. Yee's chest wall with her stethoscope. The position of choice is to have Mr. Yee
○ 1. sit up.
○ 2. stand up.
○ 3. lie flat on his back.
○ 4. lie flat on his abdomen.

58 A symptom that Mr. Yee most likely experienced early in the course of his emphysema is
○ 1. bloody sputum.
○ 2. exertional dyspnea.
○ 3. repeated headaches.
○ 4. a nonproductive cough.

59 A characteristic sign of Mr. Yee's disease and often noted on a patient's fingers when he has a chronic respiratory disease is
○ 1. stiff finger joints.
○ 2. enlarged finger joints.
○ 3. clubbing of the fingers.
○ 4. pitting of the fingernails.

Oxygen therapy administered by cannula is to be started on Mr. Yee.

60 When in need of oxygen, Mr. Yee is most likely to show emotional signs of
○ 1. fear and worry.
○ 2. anger and depression.

○ 3. hysteria and illusions.
○ 4. euphoria and excitement.

61 Before placing the cannula prongs in Mr. Yee's nostrils, the nurse should first start the oxygen supply and then
○ 1. lubricate the prongs.
○ 2. place the prongs in a glass of water.
○ 3. position the prongs in the patient's nostrils.
○ 4. direct the flow of oxygen from the prongs near the patient's nostrils.

62 The nurse should question the amount of oxygen Mr. Yee is to receive each minute unless the amount is ordered to be between approximately
○ 1. ¼ liter and ¾ liter.
○ 2. 2 liters and 3 liters.
○ 3. 6 liters and 8 liters.
○ 4. 10 liters and 12 liters.

An intravenous infusion is to be started for Mr. Yee.

63 It is generally recommended that if Mr. Yee has veins available in the following areas, the one that should be chosen *last* to enter for an infusion is a vein on the
○ 1. back of the hand.
○ 2. back of the forearm.
○ 3. inner side of the elbow.
○ 4. inner side of the forearm.

64 The needle for Mr. Yee's intravenous infusion is a 22-gauge. The gauge of a needle describes the needle's
○ 1. length.
○ 2. diameter.
○ 3. bevel length.
○ 4. bevel diameter.

65 The hospital in which Mr. Yee is a patient uses intravenous equipment with a drop factor of 15. If Mr. Yee is to receive 1,200 ml of intravenous solution over a period of 8 hours, at what rate per minute should the solution enter Mr. Yee's vein?
○ 1. About 25 or 26 drops
○ 2. About 30 or 31 drops
○ 3. About 37 or 38 drops
○ 4. About 54 or 55 drops

66 The nurse raises Mr. Yee's bed while he is receiving the intravenous infusion, but does not change the height of the infusion bag, which hangs on a stand. What effect, if any, will this have on the rate at which the solution enters Mr. Yee's vein?
○ 1. Insufficient information is given to make a judgment.
○ 2. The rate will remain essentially unchanged.

○ 3. The rate will increase.

○ 4. The rate will decrease.

67 During the time Mr. Yee receives the intravenous infusion, the nurse observes him for signs of an inflammation of the vein, a condition which is called

○ 1. phlebitis.

○ 2. inunction.

○ 3. infiltration.

○ 4. thrombosis.

68 Aminophylline (theophylline) is given to Mr. Yee through his infusion line. The nurse judges that the primary purpose for using this drug for Mr. Yee is being met when she observes that the patient now is having less

○ 1. coughing.

○ 2. sputum production.

○ 3. respiratory distress.

○ 4. viscosity of respiratory secretions.

69 Mr. Yee's intravenous therapy, which he has been receiving through a needle placed in a vein, is to be continued. If the nurse uses the following techniques while discontinuing the therapy, which one is in *error*?

○ 1. The nurse presses a pledget over the needle before removing it.

○ 2. The nurse raises and turns the needle as she removes it.

○ 3. The nurse puts a small piece of gauze over the entry site of the needle.

○ 4. The nurse fastens the gauze tightly with adhesive over the entry site.

Mr. Yee is in need of oral hygiene.

70 Which of the following preparations is most helpful to break up dried and sticky secretions that accumulate in Mr. Yee's mouth?

○ 1. A salt solution

○ 2. Full strength mouthwash

○ 3. A sodium bicarbonate solution

○ 4. Half-strength hydrogen peroxide solution

71 If a mixture of lemon and glycerine is used to moisten Mr. Yee's mouth and lips, in time, the mixture tends to

○ 1. destroy enamel on the teeth.

○ 2. dry oral mucous membranes.

○ 3. cause blisters on the tongue.

○ 4. irritate tissue pockets along the gum line.

Mr. Yee says he feels "down and worried" about his illness. Diazepam (Valium) is ordered for him.

72 Diazepam is classified as
  ○ 1. an antipsychotic.
  ○ 2. an antidepressant.
  ○ 3. a major tranquilizer.
  ○ 4. a minor tranquilizer.

73 Mr. Yee's diazepam is dispensed in a single-dose packet. When should the nurse open the packet in relation to the administration of the drug?
  ○ 1. When the nurse removes the prepackaged medication from the patient's drug supply
  ○ 2. After the nurse has conveniently arranged all of the patient's medications on a tray
  ○ 3. As soon as the nurse enters the patient's room.
  ○ 4. Immediately before the nurse gives the medication to the patient.

74 The nurse should understand that a danger associated with long-term use of diazepam is that Mr. Yee is likely to develop
  ○ 1. diarrhea and incontinence.
  ○ 2. illusions and hallucinations.
  ○ 3. physical and psychological dependence.
  ○ 4. intermittent hypotension and hypertension.

Mr. Yee is to receive chest percussion and vibration, and postural drainage.

75 The primary purpose for using chest percussion and vibration on Mr. Yee is to help
  ○ 1. break up sticky secretions.
  ○ 2. move residual air out of the lungs.
  ○ 3. force the patient to breathe deeply.
  ○ 4. cause the bronchioles to open more widely.

76 How should the nurse use her hands when percussing Mr. Yee's chest wall?
  ○ 1. The nurse should use the fists.
  ○ 2. The nurse should use cupped hands.
  ○ 3. The nurse should use extended fingers.
  ○ 4. The nurse should use the heels of the hands.

77 At what times in the day is it *least* desirable to carry out postural drainage on Mr. Yee?
  ○ 1. Before bedtime and naps
  ○ 2. Shortly before meals
  ○ 3. Midway between meals
  ○ 4. Shortly after meals

78 The nurse decides which positions Mr. Yee should assume for postural drainage. Her decision should be based on a knowledge of the
  ○ 1. extent of the patient's disease.

○ 2. severity of the patient's disease.
○ 3. duration of the patient's disease.
○ 4. location of the patient's disease.

79 Mr. Yee's postural drainage is scheduled for a 20-minute period. If he presents the following signs or symptoms about 10 minutes after starting the treatment, which one should prompt the nurse to *discontinue* it?
○ 1. The patient says he is feeling faint.
○ 2. The patient says the treatment is not helpful.
○ 3. The patient is expectorating large amounts of thick secretions.
○ 4. The patient's pulse rate has dropped from 80 to 72 per minute.

80 The desired effect of Mr. Yee's postural drainage is accomplished by the physical phenomenon of
○ 1. gravity.
○ 2. suction.
○ 3. surface tension.
○ 4. positive pressure.

Mr. Yee asks the nurse questions about his hospital record.

81 If the nurse makes the following statements to Mr. Yee in relation to uses of patients' records, which one is in *error*?
○ 1. "Patients' records are used for research purposes."
○ 2. "Patients' records are inadmissible in courts of law."
○ 3. "Patients' records are used for evaluating the health care patients receive."
○ 4. "Patients' records are used for exchanging information among various health workers."

82 In the hospital where Mr. Yee is receiving care, patients' records are developed and organized according to each patient's health-related difficulties. Such a record is called a
○ 1. case study record.
○ 2. traditional record.
○ 3. nursing care record.
○ 4. problem-oriented record.

83 If the nurse makes the following statements to Mr. Yee concerning a current trend in relation to patients' records, which one is correct?
○ 1. "Patients are being allowed to examine their records."
○ 2. "Patients are being allowed to make entries on their records."
○ 3. "Health workers are being discouraged from using mechanical devices to assist with record keeping."
○ 4. "Health workers are being discouraged from using records containing confidential information about the patient."

84 At one time during his hospitalization, Mr. Yee threatens to leave without his physician's consent. The nurse documents Mr. Yee's threat.

Which of the following procedures is also most often followed when an adult patient wishes to leave a hospital without a physician's consent?
- O 1. Being sure the patient leaves in an ambulance
- O 2. Having the patient sign an appropriate release form
- O 3. Having the patient discuss his decision with a hospital administrator
- O 4. Being sure the hospital bill is cared for before allowing the patient to leave

Nurses caring for Mr. Yee discuss a teaching and discharge program for Mr. Yee.

85 The nurses use the health-illness continuum to plan teaching for Mr. Yee. The continuum helps nurses most to understand that, according to the continuum, there
- O 1. is a point indicating when the patient is well or ill.
- O 2. are many nursing needs a patient has in common with other patients.
- O 3. is a wide range in which a patient can fluctuate and be considered well or ill.
- O 4. are points on a scale to indicate when a patient is unlikely to live and when recovery is occurring.

86 While planning for Mr. Yee, the nurses take into account that a patient's mind and body are interrelated and not separate from each other. This manner of viewing a person is called
- O 1. holism.
- O 2. advocacy.
- O 3. well-being.
- O 4. continuity.

87 The nurses should also take into account when planning teaching and discharge that Mr. Yee's emphysema affects the respiratory system by eventually destroying his
- O 1. alveoli.
- O 2. pleural sacs.
- O 3. bronchioles.
- O 4. pulmonary venules.

88 Part of the teaching program for Mr. Yee includes how to help further damage from his illness on his body. This teaching should be based on knowledge that a reason commonly given for the rapid rise in the incidence of chronic pulmonary diseases in this country is an increase in
- O 1. air pollution.
- O 2. sedentary living.
- O 3. eating processed foods.
- O 4. stresses in daily living.

89   A chair in Mr. Yee's room is upholstered. One *disadvantage* of using an upholstered chair for Mr. Yee, either at home or in the hospital, is that it
○ 1.   does not support the body well.
○ 2.   cannot be moved about to meet a patient's needs.
○ 3.   is difficult to get out of for persons with limited motion.
○ 4.   is uncomfortable for most persons after a period of bedrest.

90   Mr. Yee is to be taught basic knowledge concerning the physiology of respiration. A characteristic of capillaries that allows nutrients, such as oxygen, and wastes, such as carbon dioxide, to exchange easily in the body is that capillaries
○ 1.   are very elastic.
○ 2.   have very thin walls.
○ 3.   connect with arterioles and venules.
○ 4.   empty directly into body tissues and sinuses.

91   Mr. Yee is noted to have a very low pitched voice. The structure that serves primarily to determine the pitch of this voice is the
○ 1.   larynx.
○ 2.   trachea.
○ 3.   pharynx.
○ 4.   epiglottis.

A Nurse is Assigned to a Hospital Unit that Houses Adult Patients Who Are Ill With Various Respiratory Disorders.

Ms. Aguirre is suspected of having bronchiectasis. She is hospitalized for diagnostic tests and treatment.

92   Ms. Aguirre is scheduled to have a bronchoscopy. If the following orders are written for her immediately after she has had the bronchoscopy at 9 A.M., which one should the nurse question before carrying it out?
○ 1.   Fluids as desired
○ 2.   Bathroom privileges
○ 3.   Cleansing enema tonight.
○ 4.   Soft diet tonight; regular diet tomorrow.

93   Ms. Aguirre is diagnosed as having bronchiectasis, which is best defined as
○ 1.   dilatations in the walls of the bronchi.
○ 2.   constrictions causing obstructions in the bronchi.
○ 3.   grape-like growths causing occlusion of the bronchi.
○ 4.   distention of blood vessels causing varicose veins in the bronchi.

94   Ms. Aguirre's blood pressure is to be obtained twice each day. The nurse notes that the patient's blood pressure was 130/90 mm Hg. the evening before, and it is 170/100 mm Hg. when she obtains it the next morning. When should the nurse next check the patient's blood pressure?

- ○ 1. At noon
- ○ 2. At bedtime
- ○ 3. About 6 P.M.
- ○ 4. Within a few minutes

95 If Ms. Aguirre is ordered to receive an antibiotic and the patient says, "That medicine makes me sick and I am sick enough already!," the nurse's best course of action is to

- ○ 1. give half the dose but give the second half about 4 hours later.
- ○ 2. give the drug and explain to the patient how it will help her feel better.
- ○ 3. omit giving the drug but give it when the patient feels somewhat better.
- ○ 4. omit giving the drug and report the situation to the nurse-in-charge.

96 Ms. Aguirre asks for a sleeping pill and one is prescribed for her, to be used as necessary. The chief reason that nurses should discourage patients from the regular use of medications for sleep is that

- ○ 1. sleep becomes increasingly erratic.
- ○ 2. the body rids itself slowly of medications for sleep.
- ○ 3. sleep becomes associated with greater restlessness.
- ○ 4. the body becomes dependent on medications for sleep.

97 Which of the following activities, if observed in the hospital where Ms. Aguirre is a patient, violates a basic right of an alert adult patient?

- ○ 1. The patient has been told very frankly about the seriousness of her illness.
- ○ 2. The patient is allowed to refuse care when the care is not required by law.
- ○ 3. The patient has been asked to observe the hospital's regulations in relation to visiting hours.
- ○ 4. The patient is unaware that she is participating in a research project being conducted in the hospital.

Ms. Delmer has pleurisy with effusion on her right side.

98 Ms. Delmer complains of pain and she breathes shallowly and with difficulty. The preferred position in bed for Ms. Delmer is to have her lie on her

- ○ 1. back.
- ○ 2. left side.
- ○ 3. right side.
- ○ 4. abdomen.

99 Ms. Delmer is scheduled to have a thoracentesis. If the thoracentesis

accomplishes its intended purpose, what effects will it have on Ms. Delmer's vital signs?
- O 1. The patient's blood pressure will drop.
- O 2. The patient's respirations will be easier.
- O 3. The patient's body temperature will drop.
- O 4. The patient's pulse rate will become regular.

Mr. Roark has a lobectomy because of cancer of the lung.

100 How is air prevented from entering Mr. Roark's thoracic cavity postoperatively when he has a closed drainage system?
- O 1. The suction is used intermittently.
- O 2. The drainage catheter is kept under water.
- O 3. Positive pressure is maintained with an air-tight drainage bottle.
- O 4. Atmospheric pressure is maintained within the entire drainage system.

101 Immediately postoperatively, the level of water in the glass tube in the collecting bottle does not rise and fall with each of Mr. Roark's respirations. One very probable cause for this is that the
- O 1. drainage catheter is clogged.
- O 2. thoracic drainage is excessive.
- O 3. amount of suction is too small.
- O 4. water level in the collecting bottle is too high.

102 Which of the following items should be kept ready in Mr. Roark's room, to be used if the closed drainage setup is accidently broken?
- O 1. A trocar
- O 2. A rib retractor
- O 3. A tongue blade
- O 4. A surgical clamp

103 The structure in the lower respiratory tract where Mr. Roark's malignancy most likely originated is in his
- O 1. alveoli.
- O 2. bronchi.
- O 3. bronchioles.
- O 4. pleural spaces.

Mr. Union has pulmonary tuberculosis.

104 The most likely type of therapy the nurse can anticipate being used for Mr. Union is
- O 1. diet therapy.
- O 2. drug therapy.
- O 3. radiation therapy.
- O 4. electrolyte therapy.

105 Mr. Union's family members have Mantoux tests. Tuberculin is injected intradermally. The site most often selected for injecting pharmaceutical agents intradermally is the
○ 1. outer aspect of the thigh.
○ 2. inner aspect of the forearm.
○ 3. lower third of the abdomen.
○ 4. inner aspect of the upper arm.

106 Mr. Union's mother has a positive Mantoux test result, which means that she has
○ 1. active tuberculosis.
○ 2. been exposed to tubercle bacilli.
○ 3. a natural immunity to tuberculosis.
○ 4. a predisposition to having tuberculosis.

107 When Mr. Union shows an interest, the nurse explains to him that the organism causing tuberculosis in a bacillus, which means it is shaped like a
○ 1. rod.
○ 2. berry.
○ 3. corkscrew.
○ 4. clover leaf.

108 If Mr. Union is typical of most patients with tuberculosis, in which of the following communities does he most likely live?
○ 1. In a rural community
○ 2. In an urban community
○ 3. In a suburban community
○ 4. In a cold-weather community

Mr. Ivar is 92 years old and has influenza.

109 The organism causing Mr. Ovar's influenza is a
○ 1. virus.
○ 2. fungus.
○ 3. streptococcus.
○ 4. staphylococcus.

110 Most microorganisms, including the one causing Mr. Ovar's illness, need *all* of the following conditions to survive *except*
○ 1. warmth.
○ 2. oxygen.
○ 3. sunlight.
○ 4. moisture.

111 Mr. Ovar's sleep patterns are compared with those of younger adults. It has been found that in such a comparison, elderly persons tend to
○ 1. need more sleep.
○ 2. sleep more soundly.

O 3. awaken earlier in the morning.

O 4. change sleeping habits less easily.

112 Mr. Ovar is given a throat lozenge when he complains of "scratching in my throat." The nurse should explain to him that, while he uses the lozenge, he should *avoid*

O 1. talking.

O 2. drinking fluids.

O 3. sitting up in bed.

O 4. moving about in bed.

Correct Answers and Rationales

Two numbers appear in parentheses following each rationale. The first number identifies the testbook listed in the references, page 649, and the second number identifies the page(s) in that textbook where the correct answer can be verified. Occasionally, two textbooks are given for verifying the correct answer.

The Nursing Care of Patients With Disorders of the Respiratory System

Caring for a patient with lobar pneumonia

1 4. A temperature of 105.8°F is the same as 41°C. The formula to convert a Farenheit temperature to centigrade is as follows:

$$F - 32 \times \frac{5}{9} = C$$
$$105.8°F - 32 = 73.8$$

$$73.8 \times \frac{5}{9} = \frac{369.0}{9} = 41°C$$

The formula to convert a centigrade temperature to Farenheit is as follows:

$$C \times \frac{9}{5} + 32 = F$$

$$41 \times \frac{9}{5} = \frac{369}{5} = 73.8$$

$$73.8 + 32 = 105.8°F$$

(9:186)

2 1. The word, acute, when used to refer to a disease, means the illness's onset and progress are rapid. Acute in this context does not refer to the seriousness of a disease, its prognosis, the patient's convalescence, or possible complications. (15:47)

3 3. Tachypnea means rapid respirations. Dyspnea is a term to describe labored or difficult respirations. Noisy respirations are referred to as stertorous breathing. There is no term for describing shallow respirations. (9:199)

4 4. A constitutional sign is an observation that is the result of a disease affecting the entire body. It is also sometimes called a systemic sign. An elevated temperature is such a sign. Abdominal distention and edema are local signs. Pain is a subjective sign, usually called a symptom, and for the patient described in this item, is located in his chest.   (9:214, 216)

5 2. A patient acutely ill with a respiratory infection, such as the patient described in this situation, is in critical need of an adequate oxygen supply. Fluids, electrolytes, and vitamins are important, but at this time, upon admission, oxygen is often critical for the patient's survival.   (15:296)

6 2. The order for codeine sulfate described in this item is satisfactory *except* for one omission: the route of administration is not given. Although codeine sulfate is often given by mouth, it may also be administered intramuscularly, subcutaneously, or intravenously. Therefore, the nurse should consult the nurse-in-charge before proceeding, to clarify any doubts concerning the route of administration.   (9:539)

7 1. Pain is subjective in nature, that is, only the patient can describe his pain. Pain may occur without tissue damage, an example being the pain persons suffer at the death of a loved one. Pain does not necessarily occur in relation to the amount of tissue damage occurring in the body. For example, a bunion can cause excruciating pain, but the condition does not destroy large amounts of tissue, nor is it life-threatening. The experience of pain has cultural influences. For example, in some cultures, stoicism is valued and the person is expected to tolerate pain without complaining of it.   (9:132-133)

8 2. Diffuse pain covers a large part of the body, such as the chest, abdomen, or back. Pain that comes and goes is intermittent pain. Pain that moves from one part of the body to another is shifting, or migrating, pain. Pain that is felt in a part of the body removed from the diseased part is called referred pain.   (9:134)

9 3. If a patient in the back-lying position requires some support under his knees, a *small* pillow or rolled towel may be placed slightly above the knees. Placing a pillow directly under the knees tends to cause pressure on blood vessels and nerves. Placing a pillow below the knees tends to cause hyperextension of the knees.   (9:335)

10 1. A toe pleat should be used in top linens on a patient's bed. The pleat allows room for the patient's feet and prevents forcing them into a foot-drop position. Practices such as using a square corner to secure linens on a bed, placing top linens even with the bottom of the mattress, and allowing a bedspread to fall free at the foot of the bed do not provide extra room for the feet in bed.   (9:167)

11 4. The best way to define good alignment when referring to posture is that the body parts are positioned so that they are in proper relationship to each other, regardless of whether the person is lying down, sitting, or standing. The center of gravity changes, depending on the body's position. The joints are not necessarily extended; for example, the knees are flexed when in a sitting position.   (9:116, 118)

12 3. The strongest muscles are in the legs. The smaller back muscles frequently are injured because excess strain is placed on them.   (9:118)

13 3. Nursing care plans are prepared primarily to ensure that a patient receives total patient care. Without plans, care tends to become fragmented and incomplete. Nursing care that the patient receives and his responses to therapy and care are documented in nurses' notes. (9:39–40)

14 1. Sticky secretions that are difficult to raise often will become less tenacious when the patient's fluid intake is generous and when moisture is added to inspired air. Roughage in the diet, using the side-lying position, and providing rest are often legitimate measures, but they will not help make sputum less tenacious. (9:606)

15 4. Secretions tend to accumulate in the respiratory tract during the night. Therefore, it is usually easier to obtain a sputum specimen when the patient awakens in the morning rather than at other times in the day. (9:610)

16 2. The characteristic color of sputum of patients with lobar pneumonia is rusty. This is due to oozing of blood from irritated mucous membranes in the respiratory tract. The blood mixes with the sputum to give it a rusty color. (15:299)

17 4. Alcohol evaporates more quickly than water, causing more rapid cooling of the skin's surfaces. Alcohol has a tendency to toughen the skin and can be used as an antiseptic. However, these are not reasons for adding it to water used for a temperature-reducing bath. (12:324)

18 3. A warm-water bag (or its equivalent if the agency does not allow the use of warm-water bags) should be placed at the patient's feet when giving a cool-water sponge bath. The bag prevents the patient from feeling chilly. If he is allowed to shiver, his temperature is likely to increase, because shivering is one of the body's mechanisms to produce and conserve heat. (12:324)

19 4. The abdomen and anterior chest are not sponged when giving a patient a cool-water sponge bath. The patient is likely to feel chilly when these areas are sponged, and shivering is likely to cause the patient's temperature to go even higher. The arms, legs, back, neck, and face ordinarily are bathed. (12:324)

20 1. Penicillin is bactericidal, that is, it acts to destroy organisms when given in large enough doses to reach and concentrate in the area of infection. If the causative organism is not particularly sensitive to penicillin, or if the drug does not reach and concentrate in infected tissues, it is more likely to be bacteriostatic, that is, the penicillin then inhibits the growth or multiplication of organisms. Penicillin does not act to stimulate antitoxin production or immunity, nor does it increase white blood cell production. (14:140)

21 1. It is recommended that the patient point his toes inward when the dorsogluteal or ventrogluteal site is injected while the patient is on his abdomen. This technique helps relax muscles and makes the injection less uncomfortable for the patient. (9:563)

22 4. To locate the ventrogluteal site properly, the palm of the nurse's hand should be placed on the trochanter of the patient's femur. Her index finger should be on the anterior superior iliac spine. She should then move her middle finger away from the index finger as far as possible along the iliac crest and inject the site in the center of the angle formed by her index and middle finger.   (9:566)

23 1. Cleansing the skin before giving an injection should begin at the point of entry. The nurse should move the pledget in a circle away from the injection site for several inches. This technique prevents bringing organisms around the entry site to the point where the needle will enter the skin.   (9:563)

24 3. The primary reason for applying pressure at the injection site while removing the needle is to decrease the discomfort of pulling skin with the needle. The technique is not intended to prevent bleeding, prevent organisms from entering the injection site, or decrease the escape of solution through the needle tract.   (9:563)

25 1. The primary reason for massaging the area where an injection has been given is to help spread the medication in tissues and hasten the absorption of the medication. Often, discomfort also is relieved with massage because spreading the medication helps to reduce pressure on pain receptors. The area where a medication is given should *not* be massaged if the manufacturer of the medication advises against it.   (9:564)

26 4. The primary reason for seeing to it that contaminated needles and syringes are cared for in a way so that they cannot be reused is to prevent their use by persons who abuse drugs. Careful disposal of contaminated needles and syringes helps prevent the spread of such diseases as autoimmune deficiency syndrome (AIDS) and hepatitis.   (9:564)

27 2. A skin rash, sometimes accompanied by itching, is a common sign of an allergic reaction to penicillin. A rash does not *always* indicate an allergy to penicillin; another agent may be causing the rash. Nevertheless, penicillin should be withheld until the cause of a rash is determined.   (9:140)

28 2. Marked dyspnea is a common sign of systemic shock. Systemic shock was formerly called anaphylactic shock. The dyspnea is due to swelling in the respiratory passages, making it difficult for the patient to exchange air with each respiration. Other signs of shock include diaphoresis and a drop in blood pressure. In some instances, circulatory collapse may occur. Shock is an emergency situation and the nurse-in-charge should be notified promptly when symptoms occur.   (12:813; 14:140)

29 4. The distance a nasal cather used for oxygen administration should be inserted is most nearly equal to the distance from the patient's nostril to an earlobe. After the catheter is inserted, the nurse should inspect the back of the patient's throat to see to it that the catheter is properly placed.   (9:631)

30 4. Oxygen should be humidified before administering it. This helps prevent drying and irritation of mucous membranes. Humidifying oxygen is done by allowing it to pass through a container of water. (9:626)

31 3. It is generally recommended that a nasal catheter be changed at least every 8 hours, or three times in every 24 hours. If it remains in place longer, secretions are likely to accumulate and irritate mucous membranes. (9:631)

32 3. Back rubs, rest periods, oral hygiene, and range-of-motion exercises are important nursing measures for a patient acutely ill with pneumonia. However, it is particularly important that a patient receiving oxygen therapy have oral hygiene at regular, frequent intervals to avoid the drying and irritating effects of the therapy. (9:630)

33 1. Oils should be avoided around equipment used for administering oxygen. Oil may ignite spontaneously and cause a fire. (9:626)

34 3. Oxygen supports combustion and therefore, creates a fire hazard where it is being used. Special precautions should include NO SMOKING signs and signs indicating oxygen is in use. (9:626)

35 2. The household equivalent of i3 is 1 teaspoon. This is an approximation because household teaspoons vary in size. Calibrated spoons, often called dosing spoons, or calibrated medicine cups, both of which are available in most pharmacies, are recommended. (9:539)

36 2. When a label comes off a container of medication, the best procedure is to send the container to the pharmacy for relabeling. It is not considered safe to replace a label that has come off, fasten it to the container with a rubber band, or ask another nurse to help replace the label. (9:546)

37 3. Codeine is an antitussive and acts in the body to depress the cough center to control coughing. In addition to its ability to control coughing, codeine is also an analgesic and often is used to help control pain. (14:65)

38 1. Common adverse effects to codeine include nausea, vomiting, constipation, and excitement. Dizziness (vertigo), dyspnea, and headaches are not associated with the use of codeine. (14:65)

39 4. Only after other nursing measures have failed should a medication to promote sleep be used. Nursing measures to promote sleep, such as giving the patient a backrub and offering the patient a bedpan or beverage, are often successful and help decrease dependency on the use of hypnotics. (9:143)

40 4. Many persons find it most relaxing when they alternately contract and relax muscles in the body for promoting sleep. This type of activity should begin with the feet and proceed up the entire body for best results. (9:139)

41 4. The sense of smell is more difficult to stimulate to the point of arousal during sleep than the senses of pain, touch, and hearing. This fact helps explain why many people are burned when a fire occurs while they are sleeping. They do not smell the burning and smoke and awaken after it is too late. Pain and hearing fall to the least depth during sleep.   (9:139)

42   3.   Somnambulism is used to describe sleepwalking. Bed-wetting is called enuresis. Early awakening from sleep is a symptom of insomnia.   (9:144)

43   2.   External respirations take place within the lungs. Internal or cellular respirations take place in body cells.   (10:236)

44   1.   The movement of cilia is chiefly responsible for removing debris from the respiratory tract. The opening and closing of the epiglottis help keep food out of respiratory passages when swallowing.   (10:33, 38)

45   3.   The phrenic nerve arises from the cervical spine and is the chief nerve supplying the diaphragm. The sciatic nerve arises in the lumbosacral plexus and supplies the muscles and skin of the lower extremities. The vagus nerve is the tenth cranial nerve and supplies the pharynx, larynx, lungs, stomach, and heart. The accessory nerve is the eleventh cranial nerve and supplies the trapezius and sternocleidomastoid muscles.   (10:242)

46   3.   The thoracic and abdominal cavities are separated by the diaphragm. The pleurae are sacs that cover the lungs. The sternum often is called the breastbone, and most ribs are attached to it in the front of the body. The mediastinum is a space between the lungs that contains the heart and other organs.   (10:238)

47   2.   Diplococci are organisms arranged in pairs. *Diplo* means two, or double, and hence the prefix is used to describe the organism causing this patient's illness. The prefix for one is *uni*, as in the word unicellular, which means one cell. *Tri* stands for three, as in the word triangle. *Tetra* means four, as in tetralogy of Fallot, a condition in which the heart has essentially four anomalies.   (10:49)

48   1.   It is unsafe to use electrical appliances, such as an electric radio, in the bathroom. If the appliance is touched while a person is wet or in a shower or tub, he may receive a serious electrical shock. Shower curtains, ceiling heat lamps, and plastic glasses are not contraindicated in a bathroom.   (9:177)

49   1.   Growth is very rapid during adolescence, that is, during the teenage years, up to about age 18. Between approximately ages 18 and 20 years, a slow, barely perceptible decline in most physical abilities begins.   (15:23)

50   4.   Plastic lenses in eyeglasses should be handled carefully because they are very easily scratched. The lenses should be cleaned under running water, soap should be used as necessary, and the lenses should be well rinsed and wiped with a cotton cloth, such as a cotton handkerchief. The lenses should not be cleaned while they are dry because the dirt on the lenses is likely to scratch them. Tissues made from wood products are not recommended for wiping plastic lenses because the tissues may scratch the lenses.   (9:77)

51   2.   It is generally the best policy to say nothing and allow an angry patient to express his anger. Leaving the patient, trying to teach him when he is angry, and humoring him will probably accomplish little and may make him even more angry.   (9:20–21)

52   3.   When call lights are not answered with reasonable promptness, a nurse risks being legally accused of negligence. Libel refers to an untruthful written statement about a person that subjects him to ridicule or contempt. An assault is a threat or an attempt to make bodily contact with another person without his consent; battery is an assault that is carried out. False imprisonment is unjustifiable restraint of a person without his consent. Negligence is defined as performing an act that a reasonable and comparable person under similar circumstances would not do, or failing to perform an act that a reasonable and comparable person under similar circumstances would do.   (9:50)

Caring for a patient with emphysema and asthma

53   3.   Epinephrine is an adrenergic drug and is often used when a patient has an acute attack of asthma. The drug acts quickly to relax smooth muscles in the bronchi, thus giving the patient more room for the passage of air into and out of the respiratory tract.   (14:229)

54   3.   COPD means chronic obstructive pulmonary disease and represents a way of classifying respiratory diseases that cause obstruction in the respiratory passageways without regard for a specific diagnosis as to cause. Some persons use the abbreviation COLD, which means chronic obstructive lung disease.   (15:307)

55   3.   When the blood's carbon dioxide level is elevated, the patient is said to be in a state of respiratory acidosis. When the carbon dioxide level is low, respiratory alkalosis is present. Respiratory acidosis and alkalosis are determined on the basis of carbon dioxide levels in the blood. The bicarbonate level is used to indicate whether the patient is in a state of metabolic acidosis or alkalosis. Respiratory acidosis is common in patients with COPD.   (8:296; 15:297)

56   3.   The normal pH of blood is between 7.35 and 7.45, that is, it is slightly alkaline. A neutral substance has a pH of 7.00. A person whose pH falls below 7.35 is considered to be in acidosis, or acidemia, although the extracellular fluids have not actually fallen to below the neutral 7.00 level. Blood pH rarely falls below 7.00, except in severely ill patients, in whom the level may fall as low as 6.8. Death is most likely to occur when the blood pH falls to 6.8 or rises to 7.8.   (11:10–11; 15:298)

57   1.   It is most convenient to have a patient sit up, if possible, when an examiner wishes to use aucultation to examine the chest. It is comfortable for the patient and convenient for the examiner.   (9:239)

58   2.   The most common early sign of emphysema is shortness of breath that occurs with exertion. This type of breathing is called exertional dyspnea. Eventually the shortness of breath may be present even during rest. A chronic productive cough is also almost always present.   (15:313)

59   3.   Clubbing of the fingers is a characteristic change in persons with chronic respiratory and certain heart diseases. The sign is believed to be due to poor oxygenation of the blood.   (15:368)

60   1.   Patients who are in acute need of oxygen feel as though they are suffocating and most often will demonstrate fear, worry, and restlessness. Anger, depression, hysteria, illusions, euphoria, and excitement are unlikely to occur.   (9:625)

61   2.   After starting the flow of oxygen, the nurse should place the prongs in a glass of water. This technique is used to check that the equipment is functioning properly before placing the prongs in the nostrils and fastening the tubing around the patient's head.   (9:630)

62   2.   The amount of oxygen a patient with COPD receives is usually between 2 liters and 3 liters per minute. Patients with COPD have a chronically high level of carbon dioxide in the blood. The level of oxygen then becomes important to regulate respirations because the body becomes insensitive to prolonged high levels of carbon dioxide. Therefore, if a large amount of oxygen is given to a patient with COPD, his body will respond by decreasing the rate of respirations. This eventually can lead to the cessation of breathing and death.   (8:283; 15:314)

63   3.   Veins in the inner side of the elbow should be chosen last for intravenous therapy. It is best to start using veins that are as low on the arm or hand as possible. If veins in the elbow area are damaged, veins lower on the arm usually cannot then be used for intravenous therapy.   (9:516)

64   2.   The gauge of a needle describes the needle's diameter. The smaller the number, the larger is the diameter of the needle. The bevel is the slanted edge at the end of the needle and is not described by the term gauge.   (9:514)

65   3.   The patient is to receive 150 ml of solution per hour in the situation described in this item:

$$1,200 \text{ ml} \div 8 \text{ hours} = 150 \text{ ml per hour}$$

The number of drops the patient should receive each minute is calculated as follows:

$$\frac{150 \text{ ml} \times 15 \text{ (drop factor)}}{60 \text{ minutes}} = \frac{2250}{60} = 37.5 \text{ drops per minute}$$

(9:517)

66   4.   Intravenous solutions enter the vein of a patient by gravity. The greater the height of the bag of solution above the patient's vein, the faster the fluid will enter the vein. In the situation described in this item, when the bed was raised, the distance decreased between the solution bag and the vein and the solution will then enter the patient's vein more slowly. If the intravenous pole is fastened to the patient's bed, raising and lowering the bed would not influence the rate of flow because the distance between the infusion bag and the patient's vein would remain the same. Most hospitals use infusion pumps that automatically regulate the flow of intravenous solutions at a pre-set rate.   (9:524)

67   1.   The inflammation of a vein is called phlebitis. Infiltration is the escape of intravenous solution into tissues surrounding the needle. Inunction means to rub substances into the skin. A thrombosis is a blood clot.   (9:527–528)

68   3.   Aminophylline is a solution form of theophylline and is a xanthine derivative. It is classified as a bronchodilator because it relaxes smooth muscles in the bronchi to give the patient more room for the exchange of air in the respiratory tract. The desired action of the drug for the patient described in this item is to relieve respiratory distress.   (15:224–225)

69   2.   An intravenous needle, angiocath or catheter should be brought straight back while following the course of the vein as it is being removed, to prevent injuring the vein. Twisting and turning it may cause injury. Placing pressure over the intravenous needle before removing it minimizes discomfort by preventing pulling the skin while removing the needle. Applying pressure over the site of entry helps prevent bleeding. The arm can also be raised while one is applying pressure over the entry site to help prevent bleeding.   (9:529)

70   4.   A hydrogen peroxide solution helps break up dried and sticky secretions in the patient's mouth. The solution releases oxygen, which causes a froth that breaks up debris. Salt and sodium bicarbonate solutions and mouthwash do not effectively remove dried and sticky secretions from the mouth.   (9:76)

71   2.   Glycerine is hydrolytic, that is, it absorbs water. Therefore, when it is used over a period of time, it causes oral tissues to become dry. This may occur within 2 to 3 days of regular use.   (9:76)

72   4.   Diazepam (Valium) is classified as a minor tranquilizer and often is used for the treatment of mild anxiety states, tension, neuroses, and psychosomatic disorders. The effects of minor tranquilizers are similar to those of a major tranquilizer, except minor tranquilizers in proper doses are much less potent.   (14:219)

73   4.   Prepackaged single-dose medications should not be opened until immediately before the nurse gives the medication to a patient. Medications are expensive! If for some reason the medication is not used, it need not be destroyed if the single-dose package has not been opened.   (9:548)

74   3.   Diazepam can cause physical and psychological dependence. The drug should not be stopped suddenly when patients have used it for a prolonged period of time. Other effects of the drug include drowsiness, fatigue, constipation, hypotension, and confusion.   (14:215)

75   1.   Using percussion and vibration helps to break up sticky secretions so that the patient can more readily raise and move them out of the respiratory tract. These techniques do not move residual air out of the lungs, force deep breathing, or cause bronchioles to dilate.   (9:607)

76 2.   The nurse should use cupped hands when percussing a patient's chest wall for safety and for the most effective results. Using fists or the heels of the hand may injure tissues. The fingers cannot be used for percussion with any degree of effectiveness.   (9:607)

77 4.   The least desirable time in the day to have a patient use postural drainage is shortly after meals, because some of the positions may cause nausea and precipitate vomiting when a patient has recently eaten.   (9:608)

78 4.   The location of the disease helps to determine the position a patient should assume for postural drainage. For example, if the upper lobes of the lungs are to be drained, the patient uses a sitting position. The lower lobes are drained when using a modified jackknife position.   (9:608)

79 1.   Postural drainage should be discontinued when a patient states that he is feeling faint or very fatigued from the treatment. The better the ventilation becomes due to postural drainage, the more normal the pulse rate. It accelerates with respiratory distress. However, the drop in the pulse rate described in this item is probably unrelated to postural drainage. Any significant change in pulse rate or any vital sign is considered important. Patients sometimes become impatient and wish to see results faster than can be expected. In the situation described in this item, the patient is producing sputum, which is desired. He needs an explanation of the desired results of postural drainage.   (9:609)

80 1.   The desired effect of postural drainage is accomplished by gravity. The area of the lungs to be drained is placed at a level higher in relation to other parts of the body to promote drainage by gravity.   (9:607)

81 2.   Patients' records are admissible in courts of law. Patients' records are also used for research, evaluating health care, and exchanging information among health personnel.   (9:254–255)

82 4.   Problem-oriented records are developed and organized according to a patient's health problems. Traditional records are organized according to the source of information.   (9:255)

83 1.   One trend apparent in relation to patients' records is that patients are being allowed to see them. All information on patients' records should be treated as confidential by health workers and handled accordingly. Patients do not make entries on their records. Mechanical devices are being used increasingly to assist with record keeping.   (9:256–257)

84 2.   When a patient leaves a hospital without a physician's consent, hospitals require that the patient sign an appropriate form. The form indicates that the patient will not hold the hospital, its employees, or the physician responsible if his leaving has adverse effects on him.   (9:158)

85 3.   The health-illness continuum is helpful to use when planning nursing care, because the continuum illustrates a wide range in which patients can fluctuate and be considered well or ill. There are no specific points on the health-illness continuum. Patients may have nursing needs in common, but the health-illness continuum does not necessarily indicate this. Rather, it helps individualize nursing care. (9:30)

86 1. Viewing man as a whole rather than as parts separated from each other is called holism. Advocacy means working on behalf of another. Well-being is experiencing health and happiness. Continuity refers to a continuum of health care offered whether the patient is healthy or ill. (9:13)

87 1. In a patient with emphysema, the alveolar sacs overdistend, eventually rupture, and destroy the capillary beds in the alveoli. Destroyed tissues are replaced by fibrous scarring, which further prevents proper exchanges of gases in the lungs. (15:313)

88 1. Essentially three factors appear to predispose to chronic pulmonary disease: air pollution, a familial tendency, and smoking, especially cigarettes. (8:312)

89 3. Upholstered chairs are difficult to get out of for persons with limited motion. They are, however, usually very comfortable, can be moved about, and are capable of supporting the body well. (9:169)

90 2. Capillaries have very thin walls, which allow for easy exchange of nutrients and wastes in the body. Capillary walls are only one cell in thickness. No blood empties directly into body tissues except in the spleen. Capillaries connect with arterioles and venules, but this is not directly related to the exchange of nutrients and wastes in the body. (10:196, 207)

91 1. The larynx, often called the voice box, influences the pitch of the voice. Because a man's larynx is ordinarily larger than a woman's larynx, his voice is lower in pitch. (10:237)

Caring for patients with various respiratory disorders

92 1. A patient who has had a bronchoscopy ordinarily has the throat anesthetized with a local surface anesthetic. Until the anesthetic wears off, the patient cannot eat or take fluids without risk of choking. The nurse should question the order indicating that a patient may have fluids as desired immediately after a bronchoscopy. The anesthetic wears off usually in a matter of hours. (9:249)

93 1. Bronchiectasis is characterized by dilatations in the walls of the bronchi. Copious sputum is associated with the disease. These dilatations cause sacs that accumulate secretions, and chronic infections tend to develop. (15:317)

94 4. Because the two readings of the patient's blood pressure are considerably different, as described in this item, the nurse should check the patient's blood pressure again within a few minutes. The nurse should allow time between readings so that circulation in the arm can return to normal before obtaining the blood pressure a second time. (9:206)

95 4. If a patient describes reacting unfavorably to a drug the nurse is about to give, the nurse should omit giving the drug and report the situation to the nurse-in-charge. The patient may have an allergy and then it would be dangerous to give the medication. (14:407)

96 4. The body tends to become dependent on the use of medications for sleep when they are used regularly. Increasingly large doses usually then become necessary to promote sleep. The body eventually rids itself of medications and sleep does not necessarily become errative or restless with the regular use of hypnotics. (9:143)

97 4. A patient has a right to be told about a research project involving his care and has the right to refuse to participate in the project. A patient has a right to refuse care when the care is not required by law, to know about a hospital's regulations and rules, and to be told of his prognosis. (9:46-47)

98 3. A patient who has pleurisy with effusion should be positioned on her affected side in bed. For the patient described in this item, this would be on her right side. This positioning helps to splint the area and allows for greater expansion for breathing on the unaffected side. (15:303)

99 2. A thoracentesis is done on a patient with dyspnea due to pleurisy with effusion primarily to ease respirations. The pulse rate may be affected when respirations ease, but a thoracentesis is not done to change a pulse. The procedure is unlikely to alter blood pressure and body temperature. (15:303)

100 2. When a patient has a closed (underwater) drainage system following chest surgery, air cannot enter the thoracic cavity when the drainage tube is kept under water. (15:324)

101 1. In a closed drainage system, when the water level in the glass tube does not rise and fall with each respiration, a very probable cause is that the drainage catheter is clogged. Another cause could be that the remaining lung tissue has completely re-expanded, but this tends to occur later in the postoperative course. Also, the water will not rise and fall properly if the catheter has slipped out of the thoracic cavity. (15:325)

102 4. A surgical clamp should be kept ready in the room of a patient on closed underwater drainage following chest surgery. If the closed system is broken accidently, the clamp is used to close off the drainage tube. If this is not done, air from the environment will enter the thoracic cavity through the tube. If the entire tube slips out, an occlusive airtight covering with the cleanest material available should be placed over the area where the tube had entered the body, to prevent air from entering the thoracic cavity and causing the lung to collapse. (15:325)

103 2. Most malignancies in the lower respiratory tract originate in the epithelial lining of the bronchi. (8:319; 15:320)

104 2. Drug therapy is used most often for patients with tuberculosis. Some drugs being used include aminosalicylic acid, isoniazid, streptomycin, rifampin, and ethambutol. If a patient is malnourished or has an electrolyte imbalance, appropriate therapy to correct these conditions is necessary, but such therapies are not used to destroy the causative organisms of tuberculosis.   (14:322)

105 2.   Most often, intradermal injections are given into the inner aspect of the forearm. The back may also be used but the thigh, abdomen, or upper arm are rarely if ever used.   (9:581)

106 2.   A positive Mantoux test result means that the person has been exposed to tubercle bacilli but does not necessarily mean that the person has active tuberculosis. The Mantoux test does not help in determining immunity nor is it used in determining a predisposition to the disease.   (12:672)

107 1.   The bacillus is shaped like a rod. A coccus is shaped like a berry. A spirochete is curved or shaped like a corkscrew. Additional characteristics of the tubercle bacillus is that it is very hard, is acid-fast and gram negative, can survive for long periods of time, and is resistant to many disinfectants. It is very vulnerable to sunlight.   (10:49; 15:321)

108 2.   The incidence of tuberculosis is highest in large urban cities, especially in areas of those cities where the standard of living in low.   (8:318)

109 1.   Influenza is caused by one of several related but distinct viruses.   (12:688; 15:303)

110 3.   Most organisms survive in the presence of moisture, warmth, darkness, and oxygen. Exposure to sunlight and air destroys many organisms. Only a few types of organisms survive where there is no free oxygen. Knowledge of these characteristics is helpful in developing techniques that destroy organisms causing disease and that prevent their spread.   (9:273)

111 4.   The elderly tend to find it more difficult to change sleeping patterns than younger adults do. It is not necessarily true that the elderly need more sleep, awaken earlier, or sleep more soundly than younger adults.   (9:145)

112 2.   While using lozenges to soothe irritated throat membranes, the patient should avoid drinking fluids because they will wash the medication away from the irritated area. Talking need not necessarily be avoided, but the patient is usually more comfortable if talking is kept to a minimum. A patient using a lozenge may sit up and move about.   (9:554)

Classification of Test Items

Directions: *Each item in the previous review test is classified here according to the subject area it tests. Place a check mark after each item you answered **correctly** by referring to your answers. Total the number of items you answered correctly in each area and enter the numbers in the correct places on pages 553–556.*

Clinical: Medical/Surgical Nursing (Adults)

5 ✓	56 ✓	62 ✓	93 _____	102 ✓	109 ✓
16 ✓	57 ✓	87 ✓	98 ✓	103 ✓	
54 ✓	58 ✓	88 ✓	99 ✓	106 ✓	
55 ✓	59 ✓	92 _____	101 ✓	108 _____	

TOTAL _17_

Biological/Physical Sciences

43 _____	45 ✓	47 ✓	66 ✓	90 ✓	107 ✓
44 ✓	46 ✓	49 _____	80 ✓	100 _____	110 ✓

TOTAL _9_

Fundamentals of Nursing

1 _____	13 _____	26 _____	41 ✓	71 _____	91 ✓
2 ✓	14 ✓	29 ✓	42 _____	75 ✓	94 ✓
3 ✓	15 ✓	30 ✓	48 ✓	76 ✓	96 ✓
4 ✓	17 ✓	31 _____	50 ✓	77 ✓	105 ✓
6 ✓	18 ✓	32 ✓	60 ✓	78 ✓	111 _____
7 ✓	19 ✓	33 ✓	61 _____	79 ✓	112 ✓
8 ✓	21 ✓	34 ✓	63 ✓	82 _____	
9 _____	22 ✓	35 _____	64 ✓	83 ✓	
10 ✓	23 _____	36 _____	67 ✓	85 ✓	
11 ✓	24 ✓	39 ✓	69 ✓	86 ✓	
12 ✓	25 ✓	40 ✓	70 ✓	89 ✓	

TOTAL _47_

Pharmacology

20 ✓   37 ✓   53 ✓   68 ✓   73 ✓   95 ✓

27 ✓   38 ✓   65 ✓   72   74 ✓   104 ✓

28 ✓

TOTAL __12__

Psychosocial Sciences

51 ✓   52 ✓   81   84 ✓   97 ✓

TOTAL __4__

Review Test 11

The Nursing Care of Patients With Disorders of the Reproductive System

Caring for a Patient With Breast Cancer
Caring for a Patient With Benign Prostatic Hypertrophy
Caring for a Patient With Cancer of the Prostate Gland
Caring for Patients With Sexually Transmitted Diseases
Caring for Patients With Various Gynecological Disorders

The Nursing Care of Patients With Disorders of the Neurological System

Caring for Patients With Various Neurological Disorders

Correct Answers and Rationales
Classification of Test Items

Directions: *With a pencil, blacken the circle in front of the option you have chosen for your correct answer.*

The Nursing Care of Patients with Disorders of the Reproductive System

Ms. Stein seeks health care because she feels a lump in her breast. She fears she has breast cancer.

1 If the following findings are noted by the nurse in Ms. Stein's health history, the one that is most likely to have predisposed her to having breast cancer is that she
○ 1. nursed her three babies.
○ 2. had her last baby at 40 years of age.
○ 3. has a history of fibrocystic breast disease.
○ 4. has a history of having had several breast abscesses.

A biopsy indicates that Ms. Stein has a malignant tumor in her breast. A right radical mastectomy is done. Ms. Stein returns from surgery for postoperative care.

2   The nurse positions Ms. Stein in bed with her right arm supported
above the level of the surgical area primarily to help prevent
○ 1. edema in the arm.
○ 2. infection in the wound.
○ 3. separation of the wound.
○ 4. ankylosis of the joints in the arm.

3   Ms. Stein has a drain in her operative area primarily for the purpose of
○ 1. preventing too rapid closure of the wound.
○ 2. providing easy access for viewing the wound.
○ 3. allowing the escape of drainage from the wound.
○ 4. permitting introducing antibiotics into the wound.

4   Which of the following nursing measures is *contraindicated* for Ms.
Stein during the postoperative period?
○ 1. Reinforcing the dressings
○ 2. Having the patient cough and deep breathe
○ 3. Positioning the patient in a low-Fowler's position
○ 4. Introducing intravenous solutions into veins in the right arm

5   For several days postoperatively, Ms. Stein's temperature fluctuates
several degrees between normal and 101°F (38.4°C). This type of
temperature is called
○ 1. an inverse temperature.
○ 2. a remittent temperature.
○ 3. a continued temperature.
○ 4. an intermittent temperature.

Ms. Stein is prepared for discharge from the hospital.

6   Which of the following at-home activities is *contraindicated* for Ms. Stein?
○ 1. Knitting
○ 2. Blow-drying her hair
○ 3. Washing dishes by hand
○ 4. Tending to a rose garden

7   In relation to her right arm and hand, another activity Ms. Stein should
be taught to *avoid* is
○ 1. reaching into a hot oven.
○ 2. wearing rubber gloves to wash a floor.
○ 3. wearing a cuffed long sleeve on the arm.
○ 4. applying an emollient to the hand and arm.

About 3 weeks after the mastectomy, Ms. Stein returns to the hospital to
have a bilateral oophorectomy (removal of the ovaries) and to start
hormonal therapy.

8   Ms. Stein has a bilateral oophorectomy primarily to help
○ 1. prevent an accidental pregnancy.

    ○ 2. eliminate a common site of metastasis.
    ○ 3. decrease growth of any remaining malignant cells.
    ○ 4. promote elimination of sodium to maintain fluid balance.

9 The nurse should anticipate that the hormone most likely to be used for Ms. Stein is
    ○ 1. thyroxine.
    ○ 2. testosterone.
    ○ 3. progesterone.
    ○ 4. norepinephrine.

In time, Ms. Stein's condition worsens and she is admitted to a hospice for terminal care.

10 Before a nurse is prepared to care for Ms. Stein and other terminally ill patients, it is believed best if she first
    ○ 1. experiences the death of a loved one.
    ○ 2. takes a course in the dying and grieving processes.
    ○ 3. understands her own feelings about living and dying.
    ○ 4. develops a faith in a supreme being that is involved with life and death.

11 The nurses caring for Ms. Stein and other patients at the hospice discuss ethical dilemmas associated with death and dying. Which of the following factors, noted in the last few decades, is believed to be primarily responsible for the increased dilemmas facing health caretakers today?
    ○ 1. The increase in the number of elderly person in the population
    ○ 2. The increase in the number of persons claiming to have religious beliefs
    ○ 3. The increase in the variety and number of therapeutic pharmaceutical agents
    ○ 4. The increase in the scientific and technological advances in the health field

12 While caring for Ms. Stein, the attitude most often recommended for caretakers to reflect in their work is an attitude of realistic
    ○ 1. sorrow.
    ○ 2. sympathy.
    ○ 3. hopefulness.
    ○ 4. cheerfulness.

13 Ms. Stein tells the nurse that she wishes mammography had been available to her. Mammography is used primarily because it often helps to
    ○ 1. shrink the size of a malignant tumor.
    ○ 2. discover a malignant tumor before symptoms arise.
    ○ 3. detect evidence of metastasis from a malignant tumor.
    ○ 4. identify the type of cell present in the malignant tumor.

Modified brompton's mixture is used for Ms. Stein to control discomfort.

14 Which of the following analgesics is most commonly used in the Brompton's mixture for Ms. Stein?
  O 1. Codeine
  O 2. Morphine
  O 3. Meperidine hydrochloride (Demerol)
  O 4. Hydromorphine hydrochloride (Dilaudid)

15 An antiemetic agent is added to Ms. Stein's modified Brompton's mixture. The nurse judges that the antiemetic is accomplishing its intended purpose when Ms. Stein describes having less
  O 1. nausea.
  O 2. insomnia.
  O 3. anxiety.
  O 4. anorexia.

Ms. Stein has a Living Will.

16 Ms. Stein's Living Will is based on the principle that she has the privilege of
  O 1. choosing her caretakers during terminal illness.
  O 2. refusing therapy while she is mentally competent.
  O 3. making certain decisions concerning her own death.
  O 4. delegating decisions concerning her death to a person of her choice.

Ms. Stein is now in and out of a coma.

17 When Ms. Stein picks at her bed linens and clothing, she is most probably uncomfortable and feeling
  O 1. thirsty.
  O 2. hungry.
  O 3. too cold.
  O 4. too warm.

18 When Ms. Stein's pulse rate become irregular, the *minimum* amount of time the nurse should use to count the patient's pulse rate is
  O 1. 1 minute.
  O 2. 2 minutes.
  O 3. 3 minutes.
  O 4. 4 minutes.

19 A thermometer intended for oral use should *not* be used to obtain Ms. Stein's rectal temperature primarily because the oral thermometer
  O 1. may injure tissues in the rectum.
  O 2. tends to slip out of the rectum easily.
  O 3. becomes grossly contaminated with organisms.

    ○ 4. is likely to register an abnormally low temperature.

20 Ms. Stein develops Cheyne–Stokes respirations, which means her breathing is best characterized by

    ○ 1. intermittent deep inspirations and shallow expirations.

    ○ 2. labored respirations that are consistently rapid and shallow.

    ○ 3. slow and then fast respirations that alternate in rapid succession.

    ○ 4. increasingly deep respirations and then increasingly shallow respirations followed by a period of no breathing.

21 Of the following sensations, the one believed to be most acute as Ms. Stein's death nears is the sense of

    ○ 1. pain.

    ○ 2. touch.

    ○ 3. seeing.

    ○ 4. hearing.

Ms. Stein's husband is with her when Ms. Stein is pronounced dead.

22 Of the following signs, the one considered the most positive of Ms. Stein's death is an absence of

    ○ 1. pulse.

    ○ 2. respirations.

    ○ 3. electrical brain waves.

    ○ 4. electrical heart currents.

23 Of the following persons, which one is required to authorize approval for an autopsy on Ms. Stein's body, if one is requested?

    ○ 1. The closest relative of the patient

    ○ 2. The physician who cared for the patient

    ○ 3. The mortician who will embalm the body

    ○ 4. The pathologist who will perform the autopsy

Mr. Kelly, who is 75 years old, refuses health care when he is told that his urinary symptoms are most probably due to benign prostatic hypertrophy.

24 The symptom Mr. Kelly presented which most probably lead to the supposition that he has an enlarged prostate gland is

    ○ 1. passing bloody urine.

    ○ 2. having no urge to pass urine.

    ○ 3. having very concentrated urine.

    ○ 4. finding it difficult to start passing urine.

25 The danger of failing to have health care when Mr. Kelly has symptoms of benign prostatic hypertrophy is that the prostate may eventually

    ○ 1. become cancerous.

    ○ 2. block the exit from the bladder.

    ○ 3. obstruct circulation in the penis.

○ 4. cause a strangulated inguinal hernia.

One week after refusing health care, Mr. Kelly is hospitalized with a distended urinary bladder. A catheter is placed in Mr. Kelly's urinary bladder.

26 At what rate should Mr. Kelly's bladder be emptied when it has become distended after 22 hours of not voiding?
○ 1. As quickly as possible
○ 2. Slowly, over a period of several hours
○ 3. Very slowly, over a period of 36 hours or more
○ 4. Moderately rapidly, over a period of 30 to 60 minutes

The nurse caring for Mr. Kelly believes he may have a fecal impaction.

27 Of the following signs and symptoms, the one that Mr. Kelly most probably presented that caused the nurse to think he has a fecal impaction is having
○ 1. pus in the stool.
○ 2. excessive flatus.
○ 3. seepage of watery feces.
○ 4. strong, foul-smelling flatus.

28 Of the following measures, for which one should the nurse prepare to administer to Mr. Kelly to relieve the fecal impaction?
○ 1. A laxative
○ 2. A suppository
○ 3. A colonic irrigation
○ 4. An oil retention enema

A transurethral resection to remove excess prostatic tissue is planned for Mr. Kelly.

29 Mr. Kelly has pyelography preoperatively primarily to determine whether
○ 1. bladder mucosa is intact.
○ 2. damage has occurred in the kidneys.
○ 3. residual urine is present in the bladder.
○ 4. cancer cells are present in the prostate gland.

30 If Mr. Kelly were to have a suprapubic prostatectomy, rather than a transurethral prostatectomy, where should the nurse have expected Mr. Kelly would have an incision?
○ 1. In the perineal area
○ 2. On the abdominal wall
○ 3. In the left or right groin
○ 4. On the lower back near a kidney

Mr. Kelly has an indwelling catheter and has continuous bladder irriga-
tions postoperatively following the transurethral resection.

31   The primary purpose of Mr. Kelly's continuous bladder irrigation is to
help in
○ 1. controlling bladder spasms.
○ 2. preventing blood clot formation.
○ 3. decreasing the danger of bladder infection.
○ 4. minimizing backflow of urine into the ureters.

32   The solution of choice for irrigating Mr. Kelly's bladder is
○ 1. plain water.
○ 2. an antiseptic.
○ 3. bacteriostatic water.
○ 4. sterile normal saline.

33   The primary purpose for observing techniques of strict medical asepsis
when caring for Mr. Kelly's indwelling catheter and bladder irrigations
is to help
○ 1. limit the spread of organisms.
○ 2. destroy pathogenic organisms.
○ 3. ensure the sterility of equipment.
○ 4. help the patient to build up resistance to infections.

34   The nurse keeps a careful record of the amount of solution used for
Mr. Kelly's continuous bladder irrigation. This is done primarily to assist
in making a judgment concerning Mr. Kelly's
○ 1. urinary output.
○ 2. patency of the ureter.
○ 3. urinary blood clotting.
○ 4. postopertive bleeding.

35   Mr. Kelly is not circumcised. After cleaning Mr. Kelly's penis while
giving catheter care, the nurse should
○ 1. place the foreskin over the glans penis.
○ 2. spread an ointment over the glans penis.
○ 3. rinse the glans penis with sterile water.
○ 4. flush the foreskin with an antiseptic solution.

36   Of the following beverages, the one that will help most to keep Mr.
Kelly's urine acidic is
○ 1. grape juice.
○ 2. orange juice.
○ 3. grapefruit juice.
○ 4. cranberry juice.

37   After removing the indwelling catheter, a frequent but usually temporary
symptom Mr. Kelly may experience is
○ 1. marked thirst.
○ 2. dribbling of urine.

○ 3. scanty urine production.
○ 4. discomfort when voiding.

The remaining items in this situation are individual items related to Mr. Kelly's care.

38 Mr. Kelly receives propantheline bromide (Pro-Banthine) postoperatively, primarily to help
○ 1. relieve bladder spasms.
○ 2. prevent a bladder infection.
○ 3. promote urinary production.
○ 4. improve kidney functioning.

39 Which of the following activities is *contraindicated* for Mr. Kelly during his early postoperative period?
○ 1. Stooping
○ 2. Coughing
○ 3. Straining at stool
○ 4. Walking about out-of-doors

40 Mr. Kelly becomes angry one day and complains that he is exposed unnecessarily while receiving care. He says he also objects when people enter his room without knocking. According to Erikson's theory, Mr. Kelly is objecting to activities that threaten his psychosocial need for
○ 1. trust.
○ 2. integrity.
○ 3. autonomy.
○ 4. generativity.

41 When Mr. Kelly was 49 years old, he had a vasectomy for the purpose of sterilization. This surgical procedure interrupts the pathway of sperm by ligating or cutting the
○ 1. epididymis.
○ 2. vas deferens.
○ 3. spermatic cord.
○ 4. seminal vesicles.

42 Mr. Kelly asks the nurse how urine is moved from the kidneys to his bladder. The nurse should base her response on knowledge that urine is moved through the ureters to the bladder by
○ 1. cilia.
○ 2. gravity.
○ 3. peristalsis.
○ 4. positive pressure.

Mr. Fuller had cancer of the prostate for which he had therapy about 5 years ago. The cancer has metastasized and he is hospitalized for further care.

43 To which system in the body has Mr. Fuller's original prostatic cancer most likely spread?
    ○ 1. To the biliary system
    ○ 2. To the skeletal system
    ○ 3. To the respiratory system
    ○ 4. To the gastrointestinal system

44 What type of examination was most likely used for Mr. Fuller when he was examined for early signs of prostatic cancer?
    ○ 1. A blood examination
    ○ 2. A rectal examination
    ○ 3. A cystoscopic examination
    ○ 4. A proctoscopic examination

45 To which of the following disease conditions is Mr. Fuller's wife of many years likely to be more susceptible when compared with other women?
    ○ 1. To cystitis
    ○ 2. To endometritis
    ○ 3. To liver and lung cancer
    ○ 4. To cervical and breast cancer

46 A student, who is assisting with Mr. Fuller's care, asks the nurse-in-charge why she is legally liable for her nursing actions although she is only a student nurse. The nurse-in-charge should explain that the primary reason why student nurses are held responsible for their nursing actions is that
    ○ 1. instructors cannot be held liable for the actions of students.
    ○ 2. patients are poor judges of care, regardless of who gives it.
    ○ 3. health agencies cannot be held liable for the actions of students.
    ○ 4. patients have a right to have safe care, regardless of who gives it.

A Nurse Works in a Clinic that Includes Facilities to Care for Patients with Sexually Transmitted Diseases.

Mr. Deward has syphilis.

47 Mr. Deward's syphilis is in the primary stage, which is characterized by the patient's having a
    ○ 1. gumma.
    ○ 2. chancre.
    ○ 3. skin rash.
    ○ 4. positive blood-test result.

48 What is the most likely reason when it is determined that Mr. Deward cannot have penicillin therapy to treat syphilis?

○ 1. The patient is allergic to penicillin.
○ 2. The patient has a penicillin-resistant organism.
○ 3. The patient may need at least 2 weeks of therapy.
○ 4. The patient has recently been treated for another illness with penicillin.

49 Mr. Deward acquired syphilis through sexual contact. The organism causing syphilis is also commonly spread by
○ 1. urine.
○ 2. the placenta.
○ 3. public toilet seats.
○ 4. contaminated injection needles.

50 In relation to its form and structure, the organism causing Mr. Deward's syphilis is classified as a
○ 1. coccus.
○ 2. bacillus.
○ 3. spirochete.
○ 4. diplococcus.

Mr. Clanton and his sexual partner, Ms. Ford, have gonorrhea.

51 The first symptom that most probably would have caused Mr. Clanton to think he may have a health problem is having
○ 1. bloody urine.
○ 2. painful urination.
○ 3. swelling of the penis.
○ 4. an ulcer on the penis.

52 To confirm a diagnosis of gonorrhea by laboratory means, the nurse should be prepared to help obtain a specimen from Ms. Ford's
○ 1. cervix.
○ 2. urethra.
○ 3. blood stream.
○ 4. urinary bladder.

53 Ms. Ford has a discharge containing pus. Such a discharge from the body is described as being
○ 1. serous.
○ 2. purulent.
○ 3. putrified.
○ 4. sanguineous.

54 Of the following health problems, the one that Ms. Ford is very likely to develop if she does not obtain proper therapy for gonorrhea is
○ 1. meningitis.
○ 2. myocarditis.
○ 3. the suppression of menstruation.
○ 4. the inability to become pregnant.

It is determined at the clinic that Mr. Olson has acquired immune deficiency syndrome (AIDS). He has symptoms of pneumonia and is sent to a hospital for care and treatment.

55 It is recommended that the isolation techniques to be used while giving Mr. Olson care during hospitalization should be
   ○ 1. enteric precautions.
   ○ 2. respiratory precautions.
   ○ 3. blood and body fluid precautions.
   ○ 4. drainage and secretion precautions.

56 Mr. Olson is informed by a faculty member that she wishes to bring a group of student nurses to his room to observe an aspect of his care. Which of the following statements is most accurate in relation to Mr. Olson's rights in this situation?
   ○ 1. A patient has a right to refuse having observations of him by persons who are not directly involved in his care.
   ○ 2. It is unethical for a group of students to observe the care of a patient, even if the patient states he has no objections.
   ○ 3. When observation of a patient's care becomes a learning experience for health-care personnel, the patient is obligated to allow them to observe his care.
   ○ 4. When a patient chooses to enter a hospital, he indirectly consents to care that includes observations by students in educational programs for health-care personnel.

57 Why may Mr. Olson's present illness, which resulted from his having AIDS, be referred to as an *opportunistic* disease?
   ○ 1. AIDS causes the immune system to be selectively destroyed.
   ○ 2. AIDS is caused by a virus that finds a favorable environment to grow with unusual ease.
   ○ 3. AIDS causes a defect in the immune system which allows fatal illnesses to occur.
   ○ 4. AIDS is a selective disease in that only a few people in the general population are at risk for acquiring it.

The remaining items in this situation are individual items related to the care of patients with sexually transmitted diseases.

58 If 4 women for whom the nurse is caring have a sexually transmitted disease, the one who most certainly should be advised to have a regular checkup for signs of cervical cancer is the one who has
   ○ 1. syphilis.
   ○ 2. gonorrhea.
   ○ 3. herpes genitalis.
   ○ 4. *Trichomonas vaginalis.*

59 Which of the following statements in relation to natural immunity is most accurate for persons who have had gonorrhea and syphilis?
- O 1. A natural immunity is acquired after having gonorrhea but not after having syphilis.
- O 2. A natural immunity is acquired after having syphilis but not after having gonorrhea.
- O 3. A natural immunity is acquired after having either gonorrhea or syphilis.
- O 4. A natural immunity is *not* acquired after having either gonorrhea or syphilis.

60 It is believed that an important reason herpes genitalis is spreading in this country is primarily because
- O 1. there has been little public education on the disease.
- O 2. there is no known cure for the disease at the present time.
- O 3. the disease has no symptoms of which most infected persons may become aware.
- O 4. the disease is casually thought of by many as being no more serious than a common cold.

A Nurse Works in the Office of a Physician Whose Specialty is Gynecology.

61 The nurse should teach her patients that before coming to the office for a vaginal examination, it is recommended that they *avoid* vaginal douching for a *minimum* period of
- O 1. 1 to 3 days.
- O 2. 3 to 5 days.
- O 3. 1 week.
- O 4. 2 weeks.

62 Unless there are contraindications, in which position should the nurse place patients for a vaginal examination?
- O 1. The lithotomy position
- O 2. The left side-lying position
- O 3. The right side-lying position
- O 4. The dorsal recumbent position

63 It is important for the nurse to teach patients that the Papanicolaou (Pap) test is an important part of a woman's regular physical examination for the early detection of
- O 1. ovarian cysts.
- O 2. obstructed tubes.
- O 3. uterine infections.
- O 4. cancer of the cervix.

64 A woman in her mid-fifties says she had an artificial menopause, which means that she

    ○ 1. has had her ovaries removed.
    ○ 2. began menopause before age 35.
    ○ 3. stopped menstruation suddenly at age 48.
    ○ 4. had irregular menstrual periods all of her life.

Twenty-three-year-old Ms. Bonny has been unable to become pregnant. The decision is made to determine when she ovulates.

65 A commonly used method to determine when Ms. Bonny ovulates is to have the patient check her
    ○ 1. pulse rate, which normally drops when ovulation begins.
    ○ 2. temperature, which normally rises when ovulation begins.
    ○ 3. urinary output, which normally rises when ovulation begins.
    ○ 4. blood pressure, which normally drops when ovulation begins.

66 Approximately how many days or weeks after ovulation should Ms. Bonny normally expect menstruation to occur?
    ○ 1. About 4 days
    ○ 2. About 1 week
    ○ 3. About 2 weeks
    ○ 4. About 4 weeks

Vaginal irrigations are ordered for Ms. Cork.

67 The nurse should teach Ms. Cork that the nozzle used for a vaginal irrigation should be lubricated with
    ○ 1. petrolatum.
    ○ 2. sterile water.
    ○ 3. the irrigating solution.
    ○ 4. a water-soluble lubricant.

68 In what position should Ms. Cork be taught to be positioned when giving herself a vaginal irrigation?
    ○ 1. Lying in a bath tub
    ○ 2. Sitting on a toilet
    ○ 3. Standing in a shower
    ○ 4. The exact position has little significance

69 To flush the vaginal walls thoroughly while giving herself a vaginal irrigation, Ms. Cork should be taught to
    ○ 1. take several rapid panting breaths.
    ○ 2. hold her breath for several seconds before exhaling.
    ○ 3. alternately contract and relax her perineal muscles several times, as though she were trying to stop urinating.
    ○ 4. alternately contract and relax her abdominal muscles several times, as though she were trying to have a bowel movement.

70 After the vaginal irrigation, Ms. Cork is to introduce a cream into the vagina. When introducing the applicator for placing the cream in the

vagina, the nurse should teach Ms. Cork to direct the applicator toward
- ○ 1. her pubis.
- ○ 2. her umbilicus.
- ○ 3. the base of her spine.
- ○ 4. the trochanter of her femur.

Ms. Bard visits the office for a regularly scheduled postmenopausal examination.

71 After menstruation stops, Ms. Bard may suffer with various psychological fears, but *least* commonly, a fear of being
- ○ 1. sexually uninteresting.
- ○ 2. physically unattractive.
- ○ 3. unable to cope with life.
- ○ 4. depended upon excessively.

72 It is generally recommended that estrogen therapy after menstruation ceases must be dealt with on an individual basis for Ms. Bard, as well as for others, because research has caused some authorities to theorize that the prolonged use of estrogen may predispose to
- ○ 1. recurrence of menstruation.
- ○ 2. ovarian cysts.
- ○ 3. hypertension.
- ○ 4. malignancies.

73 Ms. Bard asks the nurse about various terms used to describe the period when menstruation ceases. Which one of the following terms is *not* used as a synonym for the other three?
- ○ 1. Climax
- ○ 2. Menopause
- ○ 3. Climacteric
- ○ 4. Change of life

Ms. Baxter is being assessed for premenstrual syndrome (PMS).

74 Ms. Baxter tells the nurse that before menstruation, she notes that she has swelling of her fingers, feet, and ankles. To help control this edema, it is recommended that the patient should first try to
- ○ 1. avoid active sports.
- ○ 2. cut down on her salt intake.
- ○ 3. plan to obtain additional rest.
- ○ 4. consider taking a mild diuretic.

75 Ms. Baxter describes feeling very irritable and often moody premenstrually. Which one of the following programs is very frequently helpful to assist in overcoming this aspect of PMS?
- ○ 1. A weight-control program
- ○ 2. A sexual-counseling program

○ 3. A stress-management program
○ 4. A menopausal group-therapy program

76 Ms. Baxter complains of severe dysmenorrhea. No pathology is found. A medication commonly used in the management of musculoskeletal disorders is ordered for her dysmenorrhea. This drug is most likely to be
○ 1. ibuprofen (Motrin).
○ 2. indomethacin (Indocin).
○ 3. penicillamine (Cuprimine).
○ 4. meclofenamate sodium (Meclomen).

The nurse teaches Ms. Quinn self-examination of her breasts.

77 When in relation to her menstrual period should Ms. Quinn be taught to examine her breasts for abnormal lumps?
○ 1. During the menstrual period
○ 2. Just before menstruation begins
○ 3. About 1 or 2 weeks after menstruation ends
○ 4. When convenient because the exact time has no particular significance

78 How often should Ms. Quinn be taught to examine her breasts?
○ 1. Every month
○ 2. Every 2 months
○ 3. Every 3 months
○ 4. Every 6 months

79 Ms. Quinn is scheduled for mammography at 9 A.M. in 1 week's time. The nurse should teach Ms. Quinn that she should prepare herself on the day she is scheduled for mammograms by
○ 1. omitting breakfast.
○ 2. taking a hot shower or bath.
○ 3. taking an analgesic, such as aspirin or Tylenol.
○ 4. avoiding the use of a deodorant or body powder.

80 Ms. Quinn asks why mammography should not be done several times a year, ". . . just to be sure." The nurse should teach Ms. Quinn that frequent mammography is *not* recommended because such a practice may cause
○ 1. cracking of the nipples.
○ 2. permanent skin staining.
○ 3. excessive radiation exposure.
○ 4. allergic reactions to roentgen rays.

Ms. Locker visits the office because of excessive bleeding during menstruation.

81 The term used to describe Ms. Locker's excessive bleeding during menstruation is

   ○ 1. amenorrhea.
   ○ 2. menorrhagia.
   ○ 3. metrorrhagia.
   ○ 4. oligomenorrhea.

82 It is decided that Ms. Locker should be hospitalized for diagnostic dilatation and curettage (D and C). Following the D and C, if the nurse notes the following going-home instructions, which one should she question as possibly being in error, before discussing it with Ms. Locker?
   ○ 1. Use perineal care as desired.
   ○ 2. Avoid taking a tub bath for 1 week.
   ○ 3. Avoid having sexual intercourse for 1 week.
   ○ 4. Take a vaginal douche every day for 3 days.

83 Ms. Locker is found to have cancer of the uterus and is readmitted to the hospital for a hysterectomy. She has a radium insert. If the following nursing orders appear on the patient's nursing care plan several days postoperatively, which one should the nurse question before caring for the patient?
   ○ 1. Wear a lead apron when giving direct care.
   ○ 2. Do not enter the patient's room unnecessarily.
   ○ 3. Save all urine in a container in the patient's bathroom.
   ○ 4. Allow the patient to ambulate in the corridor as desired.

The Nursing Care of Patients with Disorders of the Neurological System

Mr. Abby has a seizure disorder (epilepsy).

84 Mr. Abby is scheduled to have an electroencephalogram (EEG). The nurse should understand that the physical preparation for an EEG very often includes giving the patient a
   ○ 1. mild sedative.
   ○ 2. cleansing enema.
   ○ 3. contrast dye administered orally.
   ○ 4. beverage containing caffeine, such as coffee.

85 Upon which of the following statements should the nurse base her explanation of the EEG to Mr. Abby?
   ○ 1. The patient will experience no pain during the examination.
   ○ 2. The patient will experience very mild electrical shocks during the examination.
   ○ 3. The patient will have to refrain from eating before the examination.
   ○ 4. The patient will require a period of bed rest following the examination.

86 The nurse notes on Mr. Abby's record that his illness is described as idiopathic, which means that the cause of his seizure activity is

○ 1. unknown.
○ 2. psychological.
○ 3. a congenital defect.
○ 4. a central nervous system infection.

87 Mr. Abby is to receive diphenylhydantoin (Dilantin) orally. How many times a day should Mr. Abby receive diphenylhydantoin if the drug is to be given t.i.d.?
○ 1. Two times
○ 2. Three times
○ 3. Four times
○ 4. Five times

88 Mr. Abby's diphenylhydantoin is stored in his medication drawer. When the nurse prepares the medication for administration to Mr. Abby, the *minimum* number of times she should check the label on the medicine package is
○ 1. one time.
○ 2. two times.
○ 3. three times.
○ 4. four times.

89 In addition to checking Mr. Abby's identification bracelet to be sure the nurse gives the medication to the correct patient, she should also
○ 1. call the patient by name.
○ 2. ask the patient to state his name.
○ 3. request another nurse to verify the patient's identity.
○ 4. check the name plate on the door to the patient's room.

90 If Mr. Abby is aware of the fact that he is about to have a seizure, he most likely will describe having
○ 1. an aura.
○ 2. a fainting spell.
○ 3. loss of equilibrium.
○ 4. temporary blindness.

91 The nurse is present before Mr. Abby's body starts to convulse and he has a tonic–clonic (grand mal) seizure. The recommended measure before a seizure starts is for the nurse to
○ 1. hold the patient's head securely on a pillow.
○ 2. slap the patient's cheeks gently several times.
○ 3. explain to the patient that he is about to convulse.
○ 4. place a padded tongue blade between the patient's teeth.

92 Which of the following admonitions should the nurse observe during Mr. Abby's seizure?
○ 1. Never move a convulsing patient.
○ 2. Never touch a convulsing patient.
○ 3. Never use restraints on a convulsing patient.
○ 4. Never attempt to suction a convulsing patient.

93 If it is possible, in which of the following positions is it best to place Mr. Abby during a seizure?
- O 1. On his back
- O 2. On either side
- O 3. On his abdomen
- O 4. In a semi-sitting position

94 Mr. Abby asks how long he must take diphenylhydantoin. The nurse should base her response on knowledge that in most cases, a drug to control epilepsy must be continued for
- O 1. at least 10 years.
- O 2. the remainder of the patient's life.
- O 3. as long as the patient plans to work.
- O 4. as long as the patient has tonic–clonic seizures.

Ms. Axel has absence seizures (petit mal).

95 An activity that usually will bring on an absence seizure for Ms. Axel, but *not* a tonic–clonic (grand mal) seizure, is
- O 1. exercising.
- O 2. becoming angry.
- O 3. hyperventilating.
- O 4. becoming exhausted.

96 Ms. Axel is 24 years old. At what age is her type of seizure disorder most often noted?
- O 1. During childhood
- O 2. During early adulthood
- O 3. During late adulthood
- O 4. During old age

Mr. Tebo has parkinsonism.

97 A typical symptom of parkinsonism that most likely caused Mr. Tebo to seek health care is
- O 1. seizure attacks.
- O 2. crossing of the eyes.
- O 3. inability to swallow.
- O 4. tremors of the hands.

98 During a neurological examination, Mr. Tebo's Babinski reflex is tested and found to be normal. This means that when the examiner passes his fingers along the bottom of Mr. Tebo's feet, Mr. Tebo automatically responds by
- O 1. flexing his knees.
- O 2. jerking his feet upward.

○ 3. rotating his ankles outward.

○ 4. moving his toes downward.

99 Levodopa (Larodopa) is prescribed for Mr. Tebo. A relatively common adverse side-effect of the drug for which the patient should be observed closely is

○ 1. depression.

○ 2. tachycardia.

○ 3. hypertension.

○ 4. urinary retention.

100 Mr. Tebo's illness is considered chronic. The difference between a chronic illness and an acute illness depends on the

○ 1. age of the patient.

○ 2. severity of the patient's illness.

○ 3. length of time the patient has the illness.

○ 4. system of the body affected by the patient's illness.

Mr. Koski has tic douloureux (trigeminal neuralgia).

101 The cranial nerve Mr. Koski's disorder affects is the

○ 1. second cranial nerve.

○ 2. third cranial nerve.

○ 3. fourth cranial nerve.

○ 4. fifth cranial nerve.

102 Mr. Koski is a candidate for surgery, most likely because during attacks he suffers with

○ 1. excruciating pain.

○ 2. intolerable itching.

○ 3. projectile vomiting.

○ 4. agonizing dizziness.

103 Mr. Koski is 79 years old. Of the following statements, in relation to needs and behavior, which one is most likely to occur to an elderly person?

○ 1. The person's needs for calories increases.

○ 2. The person's intellectual level deteriorates.

○ 3. The person's ability to adjust to change decreases.

○ 4. The person's need for exercise becomes decreasingly important.

104 While Mr. Koski is hospitalized, which of the following practices is most likely to help him orient himself to his surroundings and prevent accidents during the night?

○ 1. Having a night light on

○ 2. Having a clock in the room

○ 3. Keeping window draperies open

○ 4. Keeping the bed in a low position

Ms. Quantino has multiple sclerosis.

105   Multiple sclerosis attacks the myelin in Ms. Quantino's body. Where in the body is myelin found?
○ 1. In the brain
○ 2. Around the spinal cord
○ 3. Surrounding nerve fibers
○ 4. In the nucleus of neurons

106   When helping to make long-term care plans for Ms. Quantino, the nurse should understand that the course of Ms. Quantino's disease is characterized by
○ 1. steady and relatively slow worsening of the disease.
○ 2. periods of remissions and exacerbations of the disease.
○ 3. slow onset of symptoms and relatively rapid worsening of the disease.
○ 4. slow worsening when treatment for the disease is followed, and rapid worsening when treatment is neglected.

107   Ms. Quantino has reached the point of being helpless and bedridden. She is hospitalized because of complications. The most frequent complication, and a common cause of death for the patient with multiple sclerosis, is
○ 1. meningitis.
○ 2. pericarditis.
○ 3. pancreatitis.
○ 4. respiratory infection.

Mr. Tunney has fallen from his bed and has struck his head on the floor.

108   After quickly assessing Mr. Tunney's condition, the first step the nurse should take is to
○ 1. call for help.
○ 2. get a stretcher.
○ 3. notify the nurse-in-charge.
○ 4. help the patient to his bed.

109   After his fall, the nurse should observe Mr. Tunney especially carefully for signs of increased
○ 1. intraocular pressure.
○ 2. intracranial pressure.
○ 3. intrathoracic pressure.
○ 4. intra-arterial pressure.

Ms. Ulrich is believed to have myasthenia gravis.

110   Which of the following symptoms related to Ms. Ulriich's eyesight most probably first brought her to seek health care?

○ 1. Double vision
○ 2. Color blindness
○ 3. Intermittent blindness
○ 4. Inability to determine depth (third dimension)

111 Which of the following drugs should the nurse have ready when studies are made to confirm Ms. Ulrich's diagnosis?
○ 1. Morphine
○ 2. Scopolamine
○ 3. Neostigmine (Prostigmin)
○ 4. Vasopressin tannate (Pitressin)

Ms. Kerr has Guillain–Barré syndrome.

112 If the following findings are noted in Ms. Kerr's health history, which one is particularly significant as a possible cause of Ms. Kerr's illness?
○ 1. The patient received a head injury.
○ 2. The patient was on an African safari.
○ 3. The patient had a respiratory infection.
○ 4. The patient took an overdose of barbiturates.

Some of the patients with neurological disorders for whom the nurse cares have discomfort from time to time.

113 Of the following statements in relation to discomforts, the one that should guide the nurse when her patients have pain is that, in general, patients tend to
○ 1. respond to pain in similar ways.
○ 2. be fearful when they experience pain.
○ 3. often use pain as an attention-getting device.
○ 4. usually describe pain as being worse than it really is.

Correct Answers and Rationales

Two numbers appear in parentheses following each rationale. The first number identifies the textbook listed in the references, page 649, and the second number identifies the page(s) in that textbook where the correct answer can be verified. Occasionally, two textbooks are given for verifying the correct answer.

The Nursing Care of Patients with Disorders of the Reproductive System

Caring for a patient with breast cancer

1   3.   It appears that fibrocystic breast disease predisposes to breast cancer. It is more common in women who have had no children or did not breast-feed babies. A history of breast abscesses and having children late in life do not appear to predispose to breast cancer. The disease is more common in women who have had a relative, such as a mother or an aunt, with breast cancer, or who started menstruating relatively early in life.   (8:580; 12:752)

2   1.   Following a radical or modified radical mastectomy, the patient's arm on the affected side should be supported on pillows above the level of the breast to promote circulation and prevent edema. The surgical procedure interferes with the circulation and lymphatic system in the area, which predisposes to lymphedema.   (15:586)

3   3.   A drain often is placed in the operative site when a patient has a radical or modified radical mastectomy to facilitate drainage from the wound. Drainage, usually serosanguineous in nature, that collects in the wound interferes with wound healing and predisposes to infection. Drains in the wound are not used to prevent rapid closure of the wound, provide easier viewing of a wound, or provide means to introduce antibiotics into a wound.   (15:587)

4   4.   A patient should not receive intravenous therapy in the arm on the affected side following a radical or modified radical mastectomy because there is interference with normal lymphatic and blood circulation resulting from the surgical procedure. Intramuscular and subcutaneous injections also should be introduced into the arm on the unaffected side. The blood pressure should not be obtained on the affected side. Reinforcing a dressing, having the patient cough and deep-breathe, and positioning the patient in a low- or semi-sitting position are appropriate nursing measures for patients following a mastectomy.   (15:587)

5   4.   An intermittent temperature fluctuates above normal and at or below normal. An inverse temperature is higher in the morning than it is in the evening. A remittent temperature remains above normal but fluctuates several degrees. A continued temperature remains above normal but fluctuates very little.   (9:184–189)

6   4.   Following a mastectomy, persons must be very careful of injuries to the hand and arm on the affected side. An injury may be serious because of the danger of infection. Tending a cactus and a rose garden are among activities the patient should avoid because of the danger of pricking the skin. The patient should be taught to use great care when tending to fingernails to avoid injuring the skin. Precautions are guided by knowledge that intact skin and mucous membranes offer an excellent defense against infections. Knitting, washing dishes by hand, and blow-drying the hair are not contraindicated for a post-mastectomy patient.   (15:589)

7   1.   Women who have had a mastectomy are advised not to reach into a hot oven because of the danger of receiving a burn. They also are advised not to expose the affected arm to direct sunlight because of the danger of burning the skin. Activities such as wearing gloves while cleaning, wearing long sleeves, and applying an emollient to the hand and arm are appropriate.   (8:583)

8   3.   An oophorectomy following a mastectomy is done when there has been metastasis of malignant cells and laboratory examination indicates that the cancer cells are estrogen-recipient, that is, stimulated by estrogen. Estrogen appears to enhance tumor growth in certain instances. Occasionally, the adrenal glands are also removed because the adrenal cortex manufactures certain sex hormones. An oophorectomy is not done to eliminate a common site of metastasis, prevent an accidental pregnancy, or promote sodium excretion to maintain fluid balance.   (15:585)

9   2.   It is most common to use testosterone when breast cancer has metastasized. The hormone does not "cure" cancer but often offers the patient relief from symptoms. Also, this therapy (androgen therapy) may prolong life when testosterone delays the growth and spread of malignant cells in a "hormone-dependent" tumor, that is, a tumor influenced by the female hormone, estrogen.   (14:179)

10   3.   It generally is agreed that a nurse is not well prepared to care for terminally ill patients until she understands her own feelings about death and dying. This is of primary importance, although she may have a better understanding if she experiences the death of a loved one and takes a course in the dying and grieving processes. Developing a religious faith is an individual matter but it may help a person understand feelings about living and dying.   (9:649)

11   4.   Dilemmas in health care have increased and caught the attention of both professional and lay persons in the last few decades. Almost always, these dilemmas can be traced to the marked advance in scientific and technological advances. A few of these advances deal with life support systems, organ transplants, and the development of numerous types of sophisticated equipment used in health care today.   (6:19)

12   3.   It is generally agreed that health workers should reflect realistic hopefulness as they work with a terminally ill patient. The patient and his family are likely to experience despair and depression when all hope is abandoned. Also, medical advances can be made and errors in judgment occasionally occur, so that the patient may live. Attitudes reflecting sorrow, sympathy, and cheerfulness are less effective when caring for a terminally ill patient.   (9:656)

13   2.   Mammography is used to examine breasts, primarily because it helps to discover a breast tumor before symptoms arise. It consists of a soft-tissue x-ray examination of the breast. No contrast media is used for this examination.   (8:529)

14   2.   Morphine is the analgesic used most often in Brompton's mixture. This liquid mixture is often referred to as "oral morphine." The nurse should use the same precautions when using Brompton's mixture as when administering morphine by other methods. Methadone has been used in some modified Brompton's mixtures.   (14:59)

15   1.   An antiemetic relieves nausea and vomiting and often is added to Brompton's mixture for relieving these distressing symptoms. Sedatives and hypnotics promote sleep. Tranquilizers help to relieve anxiety.   (14:239)

16   3.   The Living Will is based on the principle that a person has the right to make certain decisions and to indicate wishes concerning his terminal care and his death.   (9:650-651)

17   4.   The terminally ill and partially comatose patient is most probably too warm when picking at bed linens and clothing. A sponge bath and changing linens as necessary often help to relieve the discomfort of feeling too warm.   (9:660)

18   1.   When the pulse is irregular, the nurse should count the pulse for a minimum of one minute. She may have to continue counting even longer in some instances to obtain an accurate rate.   (9:198)

19   1.   A thermometer intended for oral use is long and slim. It may easily damage tissues in the rectum and therefore, only a rectal thermometer, which has a blunt-shaped bulb, should be used to obtain a rectal temperature.   (9:186)

20   4.   The patient with Cheyne–Stokes respirations breathes by taking respirations of gradually increasing and then gradually decreasing depths, followed by a period of no breathing.   (9:200)

21   4.   It is believed that the sense of hearing remains most acute as death approaches. For this reason, persons working with terminally ill patients should be mindful of what they say, even when the patient appears very near death. Also, it is kind and thoughtful to speak to the patient until death occurs because the patient might well hear what is being said.   (9:661)

22   3.   The most positive sign of death is considered to be the lack of electrical brain waves. Definitions of death have been studied extensively. One definition indicates death is present when there is irreversible cessation of all functions of the brain, including the brain stem, and of circulatory and respiratory functioning.   (9:663)

23   1.   The closest relative of a person who has died is the one who authorizes an autopsy. In the situation described in this item, the husband would need to give permission. A coroner can authorize an autopsy over a relative's objections in certain cases when the death may not have been due to natural causes.   (9:663)

Caring for a patient with benign prostatic hypertrophy

24   4.   Among the first symptoms of benign prostatic hypertrophy is difficulty in starting to pass urine, because the prostate is encroaching on the urethra. Other symptoms include a decreasing force and size of the urinary stream, and frequency of urination, expecially a frequent need to void during the night.   (12:756; 15:571)

25   2.   When a man ignores signs of prostatic hypertrophy, the gland may eventually encroach on the urethra so that he will not be able to pass urine. The gland is capable of blocking the entire exit from the bladder.   (15:571)

26   2.   A very distended bladder should be emptied slowly, over a period of hours. Rapid emptying of an over-extended bladder may cause a rupture of stretched blood vessels in the bladder mucosa. Also, typically, diuresis occurs when the obstruction is released, with a marked loss of water and sodium that can cause the patient to go into shock.   (15:572)

27   3.   Very often, watery feces will pass by an impaction with the result that the seepage of feces becomes apparent. Pus in the stool, excessive flatus, and strong, foul-smelling flatus are not associated with fecal impaction.   (9:468)

28   4.   An oil retention enema frequently is ordered when a patient has a fecal impaction, because the oil helps lubricate and soften the impacted feces. Following an oil retention enema, a cleansing enema is frequently given.   (9:469)

29   2.   Pyelography is done primarily to determine whether damage to kidney cells has occurred. Either an intravenous or a retrograde pyelogram, or both, are done. These examinations are unrelated to determining whether bladder mucosa is intact, residual urine is present, or cancer cells are present in the prostate gland.   (15:571)

30   2.   A suprapubic incision is made on the abdominal wall so that the surgeon can approach the prostate gland through the urinary bladder. The perineal area is the site of entry for a radical prostatectomy. A retropubic prostatectomy approaches the prostate gland through an incision in the lower abdomen, but the bladder is not entered. (8:588)

31 2. When continuous irrigation of an indwelling catheter is ordered following a prostatectomy, the primary purpose is to help prevent the formation of blood clots in the bladder. These clots, if allowed to form, clog the indwelling catheter and then prevent proper drainage of urine. Clots may cause bladder spasms but medication, not irrigation, is ordinarily used to control spasms. Irrigation does not decrease the likelihood of bladder infection or minimize the backflow of urine from the bladder into the ureters. (15:757)

32 4. Sterile normal saline is the solution of choice for irrigating an indwelling catheter. Plain water, an antiseptic solution, and bacteriostatic water tend to irritate bladder mucosa because they do not resemble normal body fluids as normal saline does. (9:452)

33 1. The primary purpose for observing medical asepsis is to limit the spread of organisms by breaking the infectious process cycle. Techniques of medical asepsis do not necessarily destroy pathogenic organisms, ensure sterility, or build up resistance to infections. Some typical techniques of medical asepsis include handwashing, covering the mouth and nose when coughing and sneezing, using pasteurized milk, and using individual personal care items. (9:274–275)

34 1. To determine urinary output accurately, the amount of solution used for irrigating the bladder on a continuous basis is subtracted from the total output. This amount is the patient's total urinary output. (12:757)

35 1. When giving catheter care, the nurse should retract the foreskin of an uncircumcised patient back over the glans penis in order to be able to clean the area well. After cleaning the area, the foreskin should be replaced over the glans penis. If this is not done and swelling of the glans occurs, injury to the penis could result. (9:67)

36 4. Cranberry juice helps keep the urine acid. It is often given to patients with an indwelling catheter because the acidity of the urine helps to decrease the likelihood of a urinary tract infection. Ascorbic acid (vitamin C) also is often used for the same purpose. (9:449)

37 2. A relatively common but usually temporary symptom that a patient experiences after an indwelling catheter is removed is dribbling of the urine. The dribbling is believed due to the stretching of the urinary sphincter during the time the indwelling catheter was in place. Scanty urine production, thirst, and dysuria are not associated with the removal of an indwelling catheter. (12:757)

38 1. Propantheline bromide (Pro-Banthine) is an antispasmotic agent used to help relieve bladder spasms following a prostatectomy. These spasms are very painful and are not relieved as effectively with the use of analgesics. (14:38)

39 3. To minimize the danger of prostatic bleeding, it is advised that during the early postoperative period, a patient who has had a prostatectomy avoid straining and lifting. For example, straining at stool is contraindicated and therefore, measures should be used to promote proper elimination. Activities such as coughing, stooping, and walking about are not necessarily contraindicated for the patient who has had a prostatectomy. (15:575)

40 2. The period in life after approximately age 65 is characterized by a need for integrity, according to Erikson. Older persons wish to live out their lives in dignity, and violating the patient's right to privacy infringes on a patient's sense of dignity and need for integrity. (17:86)

41 2. The vas deferens, also sometimes called the ductus deferens, is ligated when the male requests sterilization, or a portion of the vas deferens may be removed in some procedures. These procedures interrupt the movement of sperm from the testes to the seminal vesicles. The seminal vesicles produce semen, and substances in the semen help in nourishing sperm. The epididymis, located in the scrotal sac, provides temporary storage for sperm, where they mature and become motile. The spermatic cord consists of the vas deferens and blood and lymph vessels that extend from the scrotum and testes through the abdominal wall. (10:303)

42 3. Urine is normally moved through the ureters by peristalsis. There are no cilia in ureters. (10:289)

Caring for a patient with cancer of the prostate gland

43 2. Prostatic cancer, when it metastasizes, most often spreads to the skeletal system, especially to the lower veterbrae, pelvis, and hips. (15:575)

44 2. A rectal examination is used to detect signs of cancer of the prostate gland. It is recommended that men over about 45 or 50 years of age have at least one rectal examination each year for cancer detection. A blood examination often is done when cancer of the prostate is present and spreading. The blood acid phosphatase level is usually elevated in such instances. A cystoscopic examination is used primarily to study the appearance of the urethra and bladder. A proctoscopic examination is done to examine the lower colon and rectum. (15:575)

45 4. Women married to men who develop cancer of the prostate gland are more susceptible to cervical and breast cancer, according to statistics. These women should be encouraged to have regular Pap and breast examinations for early detection of abnormal cells and breast lumps. (8:589)

46 4. Patients have the right to have safe care, regardless of who is giving that care. Therefore, student nurses, as well as graduate nurses, can be held accountable for their nursing care. (9:52)

Caring for patients with sexually transmitted diseases

47 2. A chancre, or hard sore, is a typical sign in the patient with primary syphilis, especially the male. Skin rash and a positive blood test result are common during the secondary stage of the disease. A gumma is typical during the tertiary stage of syphilis.   (12:752)

48 1. The most likely reason when a person cannot have penicillin is an allergy to the drug. No evidence to date shows that the organism causing syphilis becomes penicillin-resistant; certain gonococci, however, have become penicillin-resistant. The length of treatment and the person's having had penicillin in the past do not rule out using the drug in this situation.   (15:596)

49 2. Syphilis can be spread from a pregnant woman to her fetus through the placenta. One characteristic of the organism causing syphilis is that it requires wetness to stay alive. Spreading syphilis through urine, public toilet seats, and contaminated needles is unlikely.   (15:594)

50 3. The organism causing syphilis is a spirochete, which is an organism shaped like a corkscrew. A bacillus is rod-shaped, and a coccus is berry-shaped. A diplococcus is a species of bacteria that appears in circular pairs.   (8:567)

51 2. Early signs of gonorrhea, especially in the male, are painful and burning sensations with urination. A few days later, the male patient is most likely to have a urethral discharge. Gonorrhea does not cause bloody urine, a penile ulcer, or swelling of the penis.   (8:538; 15:593)

52 1. A specimen for culturing to confirm a diagnosis of gonorrhea in women is taken from the cervix. In persons engaging in oral and anal intercourse, oropharyngeal and anal specimens are obtained. A stained smear of the discharge from the penis is usually used for male patients.   (5:412)

53 2. A discharge containing pus is called purulent. A sangineous discharge contains blood. A serous discharge contains serum, the nearly colorless portion of the blood. The term putrified describes decayed animal matter.   (9:224)

54 4. When women do not receive therapy for gonorrhea, the fallopian tubes may become infected and scarred. This often results in the woman's inability to become pregnant because the scarring narrows or occludes the lumen of the tubes where fertilization normally occurs.   (8:567; 15:594)

55 3. It is recommended that health personnel who are caring for persons with acquired autoimmune deficiency syndrome (AIDS) should use blood and body fluid precautions to help prevent the spread of the AIDS virus.   (12:576; 15:724)

56 1. Various bills of rights state that patients have the right to refuse having observations of them by persons, students included, who are not directly involved in their care.   (9:48)

57 3. AIDS is caused by a virus that creates a defect in the person's entire immune system. The cause of death for persons with AIDS is due to the illnesses to which these people succumb. As one author stated, AIDS ". . . takes advantage of the opportunity" to make people ill with diseases such as infections or Kaposi sarcoma, that eventually, to date, have proven to be fatal. The AIDS virus is transmitted relatively easily under proper conditions. Persons exposed to the virus causing AIDS are at risk; those at greatest risk are male homosexuals, intravenous drug users, recipients of contaminated blood, and the fetus in utero of a woman with AIDS. However, these facts do not describe why AIDS is called an opportunistic disease. (12:576)

58 3. Studies have shown that there may be a relationship between having herpes genitalis and cancer of the cervix. Women who have had herpes genitalis are urged to have regular Pap tests. Men are also known to develop cancer after having had herpes genitalis. (8:568)

59 4. Having had gonorrhea or syphilis does not result in a natural immunity. As a result, persons having had either disease may become reinfected. (12:763)

60 2. At the present time, there is no known cure for herpes genitalis, although there are some products available that help relieve symptoms. A person infected with herpes genitalis is believed to be infected for life and can expect periods of recurrent acute episodes. Most persons have symptoms, such as a vesicle on the genitalia that may eventually ulcerate, genital discharge, local pain, fever, enlarged lymph nodes, and pain with intercourse. Few consider the disease to be no more serious than a common cold. There has been considerable public education on the disease, as well as evidence that people are fearful and therefore, are probably now beginning to use extra precautions to avoid contracting the disease. (15:597)

Caring for patients with various gynecological disorders

61 1. The nurse should consult with the physician for whom she works concerning how long before a vaginal examination he wishes patients to avoid vaginal, or internal, douches. However, it is generally recommended that a patient avoid douching for a minimum of 1 to 3 days before having a vaginal examination. The douching washes away secretions that are required for laboratory examinations. (15:553)

62 1. The lithotomy position is the position of choice when examining the vagina. This positioning allows best exposure of the vaginal orifice and is convenient for the examiner. (15:552)

63 4. The Papanicolaou (Pap) test is done primarily to detect early cancer of the cervix. (15:553)

64 1. The term artificial menopause is used to describe a condition occurring after the ovaries are removed or the ovaries have been treated with radiation therapy. Beginning menopause before age 35, stopping menstruation suddenly, and having irregular menstrual periods do not result in artificial menopause. If a woman has her uterus removed, but not her ovaries, she does not menstruate and cannot become pregnant, but she will not have other typical signs of menopause until her ovaries cease functioning.   (8:565)

65   2.   A woman's temperature normally rises within about 48 hours after ovulation begins. Obtaining the basal body temperature is not an infallible method to determine when ovulation occurs, but it is a common and convenient method that is reasonably accurate.   (15:548)

66   3.   Menstruation normally occurs about 2 weeks after ovulation. The endometrium of the uterus degenerates because the ovum has not been fertilized.   (15:544)

67   3.   The nozzle used for a vaginal irrigation is ordinarily lubricated with a little of the irrigating solution. Other lubricants are not recommended. Using a sterile solution is unnecessary because the vagina is not sterile.   (9:412)

68   1.   The patient should lie down in a bathtub when giving herself a vaginal irrigation. This positioning allows solution to reach all walls of the vagina better before it flows from the vaginal orifice.   (9:411)

69   3.   Irrigating solution will not flow readily from the vagina when the patient contracts her perineal muscles several times during a vaginal irrigation. After each contraction of perineal muscles, she then relaxes the muscles to allow the solution to escape. This technique distends the vaginal walls and makes cleansing of the vaginal walls more thorough.   (9:412)

70   3.   To follow normal anatomy, an applicator that introduces a medication into the vagina should be directed downward and backward, toward the base of the person's spine.   (9:558)

71   4.   During menopause, some women have psychological fears that include feelings of being unneeded, sexually uninteresting, physically unattractive, unfeminine, worthless, or useless.   (15:546)

72   4.   Estrogen is used carefully and under close supervision to control certain postmenopausal symptoms, because some researchers theorize that its prolonged use may predispose to endometrial cancer. If estrogen is used, it is typical to prescribe only very small doses, just enough to control symptoms, and to use estrogen for the shortest possible length of time. Estrogen is sometimes given in combination with progesterone. Estrogen has also been found to help prevent osteoporosis or slow down its progress.   (15:546)

73   1.   Menopause, climacteric, and change of life are used synonomously to describe the cessation of the menstrual cycle. Climax is not a synonym for these three terms. Climax refers to the point at which feelings reach an apex during sexual intercourse.   (15:545)

74   2.   Edema prior to menstruation is common in women with premenstrual syndrome (PMS). In most cases, it is recommended that these women cut down on their salt intake to help control edema. A diuretic may be recommended as a last resort for some women. Avoiding sports and having additional rest are not recommended for PMS.   (8:564; 15:547)

75   3.   It has been found that a stress-management program often helps women with PMS to overcome irritability and moodiness. When such programs are unsuccessful and symptoms are severe and persistant, psychotropic therapy and psychotherapy may be used.   (12:748; 15:547)

76   1.   Ibuprofen (Motrin), indomethacin (Indocin), penicillamine (Cuprimine) and meclofenamate sodium (Meclomen) are used in the treatment of rheumatoid arthritis. However, ibuprofen has also been found to be very beneficial in the management of dysmenorrhea. The exact mode of action is not clear but it is thought the drug has an antiprostaglandin effect.   (14:70)

77   3.   The breasts should be examined for abnormal lumps about 1 to 2 weeks after the menstrual period. Some lumps with no clinical significance may appear during other times in the menstrual cycle but not usually about midway between menstrual periods.   (12:745)

78   1.   It is recommended that women perform self-examination of the breasts once a month.   (12:745)

79   4.   Women should be taught to avoid using deodorants or body powders before having mammograms. The examination is not painful; analgesics are unnecessary. Fluid and food are not withheld prior to mammography.   (12:745)

80   3.   It is recommended that mammography not be used more often than once a year to avoid risk of excessive radiation exposure. Yearly mammograms are especially recommended for persons at risk for breast cancer, and for aging women.   (9:252)

81   2.   Mennorrhagia means excessive bleeding during menstruation. Amenorrhea is absence of menstruation. Metrorrhagia refers to bleeding between normal menstrual periods. Oligomenorrhea is infrequent menstruation.   (12:747)

82   4.   An order that indicates a patient should take a vaginal douche following dilatation and curettage (D and C) should be questioned. After a D and C, it is customary to instruct a patient to avoid taking a tub bath, taking a vaginal douche, and having sexual intercourse for about a week. The cervix is dilated, and infections can easily enter the uterus through the open cervix. External perineal care is desired and indicated.   (15:555)

83   4.   Patients receiving internal radiotherapy ordinarily are confined to their rooms to minimize exposure of personnel and visitors to radioactivity. Typical orders for a patient receiving radiotherapy include wearing a lead apron when giving direct care, staying out of the patient's room as much as possible, and saving urine in a container in the patient's bathroom.   (15:151)

The Nursing Care of Patients with Disorders of the Neurological System

Caring for patients with various neurological disorders

84 1. It is desirable for a patient to sleep when an electroencephalogram (EEG) is being done and therefore, very often, a mild sedative is prescribed before the examination. However, a sedative is not ordered for *all* patients. Stimulants, such as caffeine, are contraindicated. Eating before the examination is permissible, and encouraged to prevent hypoglycemia, which may alter test results. An enema and contrast dye are not used in preparation for an EEG.   (5:759)

85 1. The patient experiences no pain while having an EEG. No electrical shock is used. As the rationale for the previous item indicated, a patient may eat before the examination but because rest, or even sleep, is encouraged during the examination, caffeinated beverages (coffee, tea, etc.) should be omitted. Following the examination, a patient can be expected to carry out his usual activities.   (5:759; 12:621–622)

86 1. The cause of a condition that is classified as idiopathic is unknown.   (12:928)

87 2. The abbreviation t.i.d. means that the patient should receive the medication three times a day. The abbreviation b.i.d. means two times a day and q.i.d. means four times a day.   (9:541)

88 3. The nurse should check the label on a medication container at least three times while preparing it for administration: first, when she removes the package from the storage drawer; second, immediately before she removes the medication from its wrapping; and third, after she has removed the medication from its package.   (9:548)

89 2. In addition to checking the patient's identification bracelet, the safest technique for the proper identification of a patient is to ask the patient to state his name before giving him a medication. Sometimes, a patient will respond to the wrong name when the nurse states a name. It is not safe to check a patient's identity with another nurse or to use a name plate for verification.   (9:546)

90 1. Many patients can describe an aura which warns them they are going into a seizure. An aura may take on various qualities but usually involves sensations that are strange or different from normal. An aura is almost always the same for each person and often provides clues to the anatomical origin of the seizure. Seizures do no typically follow a fainting spell, loss of equilibrium, or temporary blindness.   (12:624; 15:221)

91 4. If time permits, it is best to place a padded tongue blade between the patient's teeth *before he has a seizure*. This measure helps to prevent the patient from biting and damaging tissues in the mouth. It is dangerous to try to place a padded tongue blade in the mouth after a seizure has started.

An oral airway could also be used to help prevent oral injury and to keep the airway open.   (12:626)

92   3.   Restraints should never be used on a patient who is convulsing. Using restraints is likely to cause tissue damage and possibly bone fractures. The patient should be moved to a safe position, especially if he is sitting or standing, when an attack begins. If there is considerable mucus present, suctioning a convulsing patient is indicated. There is no reason to avoid touching a convulsing person while giving him necessary care.   (15:223)

93   2.   It is best that a patient be on either side when he has a seizure. There is usually frothing in his mouth and the person is less likely to choke on his secretions when in the side-lying position. It is possible to flip back the tongue but impossible to swallow it. It is inconvenient to care for a patient having a seizure when he is on his abdomen.   (15:223)

94   2.   In most instances, a medication to control epileptic seizures must be continued for the rest of the patient's life. It is important for the patient to know that he must take his medication regularly, even though he is experiencing no seizure attacks, and to avoid changing dosages of his medication without his physician's order.   (15:223)

95   3.   A diagnostic tool to determine whether a patient has absence (petit mal) or tonic – clonic (grand mal) seizures is to have a patient hyperventilate. This activity will produce an absence seizure in a susceptible person, but not a tonic – clonic seizure.   (8:276)

96   1.   Absence seizures (petit mal) are most often noted during childhood but they *may* occur at any time during life.   (12:625; 15:221)

97   4.   A typical sign of parkinsonism is tremors of the hands. The movement is described as "pill-rolling" because of the rhythmic motion of the thumb against the fingers. Other signs include stiffness of the body with rigidity of movements, a stooped posture, and a shuffling gait.   (15:217)

98   4.   The patient moves his toes downward when the Babinski reflex is normal, or negative. He will move his great toe backward and upward and the other toes will fan outward when the Babinski reflex is positive.   (8:239)

99   1.   Patients taking levodopa (Larodopa) often become depressed, and some may have suicidal tendencies. Other troublesome side-effects include a dry mouth, nausea, anorexia, headaches, choreiform movements, confusion, and grinding of the teeth.   (14:213)

100   3.   The criterion used to classify a patient as acutely or chronically ill is the length of time the patient has the illness. Acute illnesses are ordinarily of short duration when compared with chronic illnesses.   (9:31)

101   4.   Tic douloureux (trigeminal neuralgia) affects the fifth cranial (trigeminal) nerve. The nerve is a sensory and a motor nerve and is important for proper chewing and facial movement and sensation.   (10:124, 126)

102   1.   A typical symptom of tic douloureux is excruciating pain during attacks, pain so severe that some persons become suicidal. When conservative measures fail, the treatment of choice usually is surgery when pain is excrutiating.   (15:227)

103   3.   A characteristic of the elderly is that they adjust to change more slowly than younger persons. Unless an illness that influences intellectual ability is present, this ability does not necessarily decrease with age, although it may take an elderly person longer to accomplish an intellectual feat. Exercise remains important throughout life and its needs do not decrease, although the amount generally does. The body's needs for calories tends to decrease with age as general activity and the body's metabolic rate decrease.   (8:26)

104   1.   There are advantages to having a clock in a room and keeping the bed in a low position to prevent accidents. But to help patients orient themselves, having a night light is likely to help most because during nighttime hours, many persons, especially the elderly, become disoriented in a strange environment. Keeping windows and draperies open is generally not recommended because outdoor and early morning lights may disturb sleep.   (9:181)

105   3.   Myelin is similar to an insulating sheath and is found surrounding many nerve fibers. Myelin is light in color and often is called white matter, in contrast to darker brain cells that are often referred to as grey matter. The destruction of myelin in the person with multiple sclerosis occurs in nerves in the central and peripheral nervous system.   (12:632)

106   2.   Multiple sclerosis is characterized by periods of remission and exacerbation. The onset is usually slow, as is the progress of the disease. There is no known curative treatment for multiple sclerosis at the present time, but a multitude of agents have been used to try to help relieve symptoms.   (12:632)

107   4.   A patient with multiple sclerosis is generally very susceptible to respiratory infections because he is debilitated, inactive, and breathes shallowly as the disease progresses. A respiratory infection is a frequent cause of death in persons with multiple sclerosis.   (15:224–225)

108   1.   The first step a nurse should taken when she finds that a patient has fallen is to assess the patient's condition quickly and then call for help. Assessment is important so that the nurse is ready to describe the patient's condition accurately and promptly. The patient should not be moved until it is safe to do so. The nurse-in-charge can be called after help is summoned and the patient's condition is evaluated.   (9:178)

109   2.   When a patient is suspected of having a head injury, the nurse should observe him carefully for signs of increased intracranial pressure.   (8:259)

110   1.   A typical sign of myasthenia gravis is double vision, called diplopia. The disease is characterized by extreme muscle weakness. Ptosis, that is, a drooping of the eyelids, is another early symptom. General fatigue, with progressive weakening of the arms and legs, is typical.   (15:225)

111   3.   The drug often used to confirm a diagnosis of myasthenia gravis is neostigmine (Prostigmin), a cholinergic agent. It gives dramatic relief of symptoms after administration if the disease is present.   (8:274)

112 3.   The exact cause of Guillain–Barré syndrome is unknown, but it is common to find that a person had a respiratory infection before becoming ill with the disease. Although a clear-cut cause and effect relationship does not exist, it was observed several years ago that many patients who developed the syndrome had influenza vaccine a short time before becoming ill with the illness.   (8:258)

113 2.   Most patients in pain are fearful and anxious. Patients respond to pain in their own unique way. Patients generally do not describe pain as being worse than it really is, although some patients may. Also, some patients may use pain as an attention-getting device.   (9:132–133)

Classification of Test Items

Directions: *Each item in the previous review test is classified here according to the subject area it tests. Place a check mark after each item you answered **correctly** by referring to your answers. Total the number of items you answered correctly in each area and enter the numbers in the correct places on pages 553–556.*

Clinical: Medical/Surgical Nursing (Adults)

1 ✓	30 ____	51 ✓	71 ✓	83 ✓	97 ✓
2 ✓	31 ✓	52 ____	72 ✓	84 ____	102 ✓
3 ✓	34 ✓	54 ✓	74 ✓	85 ✓	106 ✓
4 ✓	35 ____	57 ✓	75 ✓	86 ✓	107 ✓
6 ✓	39 ✓	58 ✓	77 ✓	90 ✓	108 ✓
7 ____	43 ____	60 ____	78 ✓	91 ____	109 ✓
8 ____	44 ✓	61 ✓	79 ✓	92 ✓	110 ✓
24 ✓	45 ____	63 ✓	80 ✓	93 ✓	112 ____
25 ✓	47 ✓	64 ✓	81 ____	95 ____	
29 ✓	49 ____	65 ✓	82 ✓	96 ✓	

TOTAL 46

Biological/Physical Sciences

41 ✓	50 ✓	66 ✓	98 ____	101 ____	105 ✓
42 ____	59 ✓	73 ✓			

TOTAL 7

Fundamentals of Nursing

5 ✓	19 ____	27 ✓	53 ✓	69 ✓	100 ✓
12 ____	20 ✓	28 ✓	55 ✓	70 ____	104 ✓
13 ✓	21 ✓	32 ✓	62 ✓	87 ✓	113 ____
17 ✓	22 ✓	33 ✓	67 ____	88 ✓	
18 ✓	26 ✓	37 ✓	68 ✓	89 ✓	

TOTAL 24

Diet Therapy/Nutrition

36 __✓__

TOTAL __)__

Pharmacology

9 __✓__   15 __✓__   48 __✓__   94 __✓__   99 _____   111 __✓__
14 __✓__   38 __✓__   76 __✓__

TOTAL __8__

Psychosocial Sciences

10 __✓__   16 _____   40 _____   46 __✓__   56 __✓__   103 _____
11 __✓__   23 __✓__

TOTAL __5__

Review Test 12

The Nursing Care of Patients With Disorders of the Cardiovascular System

Caring for a Patient With a Myocardial Infarction

Caring for a Patient With Congestive Heart Failure

Caring for a Patient Who Has a Health Evaluation That Reveals the Presence of Primary Hypertension

Correct Answers and Rationales
Classification of Test Items

Directions: *With a pencil, blacken the circle in front of the option you have chosen for your correct answer.*

The Nursing Care of Patients with Disorders of the Cardiovascular System

Mr. Roth, a 53-year-old businessman, is admitted to a hospital with an acute myocardial infarction. Admission orders include a medication for the relief of pain, heparin therapy, and blood analysis.

1 Which of the following medications should the nurse be prepared to administer to Mr. Roth for the relief of discomfort?
- ○ 1. A nonsteroid, such as ibuprofen (Advil)
- ○ 2. A nonsalicylate, such as acetaminophen (Tylenol)
- ○ 3. A salicylate, such as acetylsalicylic acid (aspirin)
- ○ 4. A narcotic, such as meperidine hydrochloride (Demerol)

2 Which of the following questions is *least* appropriate when seeking information from Mr. Roth about his pain?
- ○ 1. "How long have you been in pain?"
- ○ 2. "Where is your pain most severe?"
- ○ 3. "What were you doing when your pain started?"
- ○ 4. "Is your pain so severe that you need an injection for it?"

3 Which of the following descriptions of pain should the nurse expect that Mr. Roth is most likely to use?
- ○ 1. The pain comes and goes.
- ○ 2. The pain comes on slowly.

    ○ 3. The pain is tingling in nature.

    ○ 4. The pain is continuous despite rest.

4 Mr. Roth's pain is caused by heart muscle tissues suffering from

    ○ 1. a poor blood supply.

    ○ 2. an electrolyte imbalance.

    ○ 3. inadequate electrical stimulation.

    ○ 4. an accumulation of lymph in capillary beds.

5 Mr. Roth tells the nurse he was not alarmed about what were no doubt early symptoms of a myocardial infarction. It is very likely that Mr. Roth thought he was suffering with

    ○ 1. bursitis.

    ○ 2. neuritis.

    ○ 3. influenza.

    ○ 4. indigestion.

6 Heparin is administered to Mr. Roth primarily because it acts on a thrombus by helping to

    ○ 1. shrink it.

    ○ 2. dissolve it.

    ○ 3. prevent it from becoming larger.

    ○ 4. prevent it from becoming dislodged.

7 The drug that should be kept in readiness in case it becomes necessary to overcome the effects of the heparin that Mr. Roth is receiving is

    ○ 1. calcium lactate.

    ○ 2. sodium benzoate.

    ○ 3. protamine sulfate.

    ○ 4. aluminum phosphate.

8 While giving heparin therapy, the nurse should judge that Mr. Roth may be receiving too much heparin if he

    ○ 1. produces little urine.

    ○ 2. becomes unduly lethargic.

    ○ 3. develops a rapid pulse rate.

    ○ 4. shows signs of bleeding easily.

9 If the following blood studies are done with blood samples taken from Mr. Roth at the time of his admission, the test that can be expected to reveal a normal level is the one that measures

    ○ 1. coagulation time.

    ○ 2. white blood count.

    ○ 3. sedimentation rate.

    ○ 4. serum enzyme levels.

The nurse obtains Mr. Roth's vital signs.

10 Mr. Roth's vital signs are as follows: oral temperature of 99.7°F (37.6°C); pulse rate of 50 beats per minute; respiratory rate of 20 respirations per minute; and blood pressure of 140/96/70 mm Hg.

Which vital sign should the nurse report to the nurse-in-charge promptly?

- ○ 1. The pulse rate
- ○ 2. The temperature
- ○ 3. The blood pressure
- ○ 4. The respiratory rate

11   When the nurse records Mr. Roth's blood pressure as 140/96/70, the number 70 represents the point at which the nurse first heard

- ○ 1. no sound.
- ○ 2. muffled sound.
- ○ 3. an irregular heartbeat.
- ○ 4. one distinct tapping sound.

12   The nurse obtains Mr. Roth's pulse rate at his radial artery. This site is commonly selected because the vessel is accessible and

- ○ 1. is close to the heart.
- ○ 2. can be seen to pulsate.
- ○ 3. is protected by subcutaneous tissue.
- ○ 4. lies over a bone near the skin surface.

13   If the nurse uses her thumb to obtain Mr. Roth's pulse rate, she is very likely to

- ○ 1. feel her own pulse.
- ○ 2. obtain a pulse rate that is too rapid.
- ○ 3. injure the wall of the patient's blood vessel.
- ○ 4. cut off circulation in the patient's blood vessel.

14   When the nurse obtains Mr. Roth's vital signs, when should she count his respiratory rate?

- ○ 1. Immediately before pumping up the blood pressure cuff
- ○ 2. Immediately after obtaining the blood pressure, while the blood pressure cuff remains in place
- ○ 3. Immediately before obtaining the temperature and pulse rate
- ○ 4. Immediately after obtaining the pulse rate, while keeping her fingers on the pulse

15   In relation to the effect on Mr. Roth's vital signs, early in its course, acute pain is most likely to cause his

- ○ 1. temperature to rise.
- ○ 2. pulse rate to become rapid.
- ○ 3. respiratory rate to become slow.
- ○ 4. blood pressure to fall precipitously.

After initial care, Mr. Roth is transferred to a cardiac care unit.

16   A dangerous time for Mr. Roth occurs several days after he has the myocardial infarction because there is a possibility that he may develop an aneurysm. An aneurysm is best defined as

- ○ 1. a rupture in the wall of the heart.
- ○ 2. a wrinkling in the wall of the heart.

    ○ 3. a herniation in the wall of the heart.

    ○ 4. an inflammation in the wall of the heart.

17 Mr. Roth has been receiving oxygen therapy. Of the following blood tests, the one most useful in helping the nurse judge the effectiveness of Mr. Roth's oxygen therapy is to observe the patient's blood

    ○ 1. hematocrit.

    ○ 2. gas studies.

    ○ 3. bleeding time.

    ○ 4. plasma volume.

18 Which of the following nursing measures should appear on Mr. Roth's care plan as being *contraindicated* while caring for the patient's legs?

    ○ 1. Washing the legs

    ○ 2. Elevating the legs

    ○ 3. Powdering the legs

    ○ 4. Massaging the legs

19 To prevent strain on his heart, Mr. Roth should be taught that while he is moving about in bed, he should

    ○ 1. exhale.

    ○ 2. swallow.

    ○ 3. hold his breath.

    ○ 4. pinch his nose shut.

20 When Mr. Roth refers to his myocardial infarction, he is most likely to call it

    ○ 1. a stroke.

    ○ 2. a heart attack.

    ○ 3. high blood pressure.

    ○ 4. leakage of the heart.

21 Mr. Roth says one day, "This scares me. I'm concerned about what could happen to me." Of the following comments, which one is best for the nurse to make in this situation?

    ○ 1. "In what ways are you concerned?"

    ○ 2. "Why are you scared when your progress is good?"

    ○ 3. "I talked to your doctor. He says you are doing just fine."

    ○ 4. "We will do the worrying. You must work at getting well."

Mr. Roth is transferred to a medical care unit for the rehabilitation phase of his illness.

22 The guide most often used during the rehabilitation phase to judge how much exercise Mr. Roth should be allowed is based on the

    ○ 1. patient's physical reaction to activity.

    ○ 2. amount of damaged tissue in the patient's heart.

    ○ 3. length of time since the patient had the infarction.

    ○ 4. patient's emotional responses to possible permanent heart damage.

23 Mr. Roth begins isometric exercises to help prepare him for ambulation. Because Mr. Roth's exercises will place certain muscles in a state of tension without changing the length of the muscles very much, the nurse should teach him to *avoid* exercising when he

○ 1. has a closed glottis.

○ 2. is sitting up in bed.

○ 3. has just eaten a snack.

○ 4. is about to begin ambulating.

24 A rectal tube is ordered for Mr. Roth when he complains of abdominal distention. The patient experiences no relief after the tube has been in place for about 20 minutes. The best course of action in this situation is for the nurse to

○ 1. rotate the tube in place several times.

○ 2. insert the rectal tube farther into the rectum.

○ 3. remove the tube and reinsert it in 2 to 3 hours.

○ 4. remove the tube and obtain orders for a different measure to relieve the distention.

25 Mr. Roth develops a skin rash and is placed on isolation until it is determined that the rash is not infectious. Which of the following statements best describes how Mr. Roth's soiled linen should be double-bagged?

○ 1. The soiled linen should be bagged twice in the patient's room.

○ 2. The soiled linen should be bagged once in the patient's room and a second nurse bags it again in the utility room.

○ 3. The soiled linen should be bagged once in the patient's room and again in a bag held by a second nurse at the door of the patient's room.

○ 4. The soiled linen should be bagged once in the patient's room and the nurse caring for the patient places it in a second bag in a utility room.

26 Mr. Roth is studied as a candidate for cardiac surgery. An echogram is done. This examination depends on the heart's ability to reflect

○ 1. heat waves.

○ 2. sound waves.

○ 3. radiation waves.

○ 4. electrical waves.

27 Mr. Roth refuses his breakfast because he is served bacon. Avoiding pork in the diet is most commonly observed by religious persons who are

○ 1. Jews.

○ 2. Quakers.

○ 3. Mormons.

○ 4. Jehovah's Witnesses.

28 Mr. Roth is taking the types of oral medications given below. The one that should be administered without offering him fluids to drink is the medication that acts to

○ 1. decrease the patient's pain.
○ 2. control the patient's coughing.
○ 3. strengthen the patient's heartbeat.
○ 4. increase the patient's urinary output.

29 The nurse observes that Mr. Roth's behavior strongly suggests that he is concerned with generativity, a typical developmental task for a person of Mr. Roth's age. Which of the following behaviors best illustrates generativity?
○ 1. The patient expresses fear of having further illnesses of any kind.
○ 2. The patient wishes to know the purpose of each medication he takes.
○ 3. The patient says his wife is unable to manage financial affairs without him.
○ 4. The patient is eager to return to writing a book about how economic theory influences small businesses.

As part of an educational program, Mr. Roth views a videotape that includes diagrams of the heart and factors predisposing to a myocardial infarction.

30 Arteries that supply heart-muscle tissues receive their oxygenated blood, Mr. Roth learns, from the
○ 1. carotid arteries.
○ 2. ascending aorta.
○ 3. intercostal arteries.
○ 4. left subclavian artery.

31 Mr. Roth is correct when he says that the chamber of the heart from which blood that needs oxygen leaves to go to the lungs is the
○ 1. left atrium.
○ 2. riight atrium.
○ 3. left ventricle.
○ 4. right ventricle.

32 Of the following factors, Mr. Roth learns that the one believed to predispose to an acute myocardial infarction is
○ 1. phlebitis.
○ 2. hypotension.
○ 3. atherosclerosis.
○ 4. varicosities of blood vessels.

33 The structure in his heart that Mr. Roth learns is frequently called the pacemaker is the
○ 1. bundle of His.
○ 2. sinoatrial node.
○ 3. Purkinje's fibers.
○ 4. atrioventricular node.

34 If Mr. Roth has observed the following activities of daily living, the one *least* likely to have predisposed him to having a myocardial infarction, according to the videotape, is
  ○ 1. smoking cigarettes.
  ○ 2. working under emotional stress.
  ○ 3. eating a diet that is high in cholesterol.
  ○ 4. having an alcoholic beverage before lunch.

Mr. Roth complains of having chronic constipation.

35 The nurse prepares a teaching plan to help Mr. Roth overcome constipation. She bases the plan on knowledge concerning bowel elimination. Which of the following statements is *least* accurate in relation to bowel elimination?
  ○ 1. It is important to have a daily bowel movement.
  ○ 2. Gravity plays a role in the ease of elimination.
  ○ 3. It is important to observe the urge to defecate.
  ○ 4. The volume of the stool is minimally affected by the amount of food consumed.

36 Mr. Roth should be taught that a danger in the regular use of laxatives for constipation is that the practice may cause the intestinal tract to
  ○ 1. develop small herniations.
  ○ 2. become dependent on their use.
  ○ 3. eliminate more natural intestinal bacteria than is safe.
  ○ 4. absorb more chemicals from the laxatives than is desirable.

37 Mr. Roth is taught about diet and intestinal elimination. When used on a regular basis, which of the following foods help most to promote intestinal elimination?
  ○ 1. Lean meats
  ○ 2. Whole-grain cereals
  ○ 3. Enriched white bread
  ○ 4. Fortified dairy products

38 The nurse should teach Mr. Roth that many persons relieve constipation when they start each day with a glass or cup of
  ○ 1. yogurt.
  ○ 2. warm milk.
  ○ 3. hot water.
  ○ 4. carbonated soda water.

39 If Mr. Roth is typical of most persons in this country in relation to bowel elimination, he is likely to have greatest concern about the
  ○ 1. amount of stool.
  ○ 2. consistency of the stool.
  ○ 3. time of a bowel movement.
  ○ 4. regularity of bowel movements.

Mr. Roth receives warfarin sodium (Coumadin) and will take it at home after discharge.

40 In view of his taking warfarin sodium (Coumadin), Mr. Roth should most certainly be taught what steps to take if he begins to
  ○ 1. bleed.
  ○ 2. cough.
  ○ 3. feel dizzy.
  ○ 4. have palpitations.

41 Which of the following medications should Mr. Roth be instructed to *avoid* while taking warfarin sodium at home?
  ○ 1. Aspirin
  ○ 2. Ferrous sulfate
  ○ 3. Milk of magnesia
  ○ 4. Multivitamin preparations

Ms. Nesbitt, who is 75 years old, is admitted to the hospital with congestive heart failure and pulmonary edema.

42 Ms. Nesbitt says to the admitting nurse, "I am suffocating." Ms. Nesbitt's psychological response to feelings of suffocation is typically one of feeling
  ○ 1. depressed.
  ○ 2. exhilarated.
  ○ 3. disoriented.
  ○ 4. apprehensive.

43 The admitting nurse notes that Ms. Nesbitt is dyspneic. The position in which Ms. Nesbitt is most likely to feel comfortable is the
  ○ 1. back-lying position.
  ○ 2. face-lying position.
  ○ 3. side-lying position.
  ○ 4. semi-sitting position.

44 Because of pulmonary edema, the nurse can expect that the nature of Ms. Nesbitt's respirations are likely to be
  ○ 1. grunting.
  ○ 2. very deep.
  ○ 3. moist-sounding.
  ○ 4. intermittently absent.

45 Ms. Nesbitt is to receive oxygen by mask and the nurse prepares to start its administration. After the nurse attaches the mask to the oxygen supply, when should she start the flow of oxygen to Ms. Nesbitt's mask?
  ○ 1. Before applying the mask to the patient's face
  ○ 2. As soon as the mask is placed on the patient's face
  ○ 3. After the mask is in place and properly secured to the patient's face

○ 4. When the patient states that she is breathing easily after the mask is in place

Admission assessments are made on Ms. Nesbitt.

46 When obtaining a health history from Ms. Nesbitt, the nurse is most likely to find that when the patient's illness began, Ms. Nesbitt first noticed that she had
○ 1. anorexia and fever.
○ 2. dyspnea and fatigue.
○ 3. headaches and periods of dizziness.
○ 4. shortness of breath and poor equilibrium.

47 The nurse notes that Ms. Nesbitt has edema. In which part of the body is Ms. Nesbitt most likely to report that she noticed the swelling (edema) first?
○ 1. In her back
○ 2. In her abdomen
○ 3. In her face and neck
○ 4. In her ankles and feet

48 The nurse observes Ms. Nesbitt for cyanosis. The area of the patient's body where cyanosis is most likely to become conspicuous first is on the
○ 1. scalp.
○ 2. nailbeds.
○ 3. white of the eyes.
○ 4. palms of the hands.

49 An electrocardiogram (ECG) is done on Ms. Nesbitt, primarily to study electrical activity in Ms. Nesbitt's heart
○ 1. valves.
○ 2. muscle.
○ 3. arteries.
○ 4. chambers.

50 Ms. Nesbitt complains to the nurse of pain that "comes and goes." Which of the following questions will help the nurse most to assess the patient's pain?
○ 1. "Where are you feeling pain?"
○ 2. "Are you sure the pain comes and goes?"
○ 3. "What can I do to help lessen the pain?"
○ 4. "Would you like a medication to relieve your pain?"

51 A blood sample is obtained from Ms. Nesbitt for determining electrolyte levels. The nurse can expect that Ms. Nesbitt is likely retaining excessive amounts of the electrolyte
○ 1. calcium.
○ 2. sodium.
○ 3. potassium.

○ 4. magnesium.

52 Two nurses obtain Ms. Nesbitt's apical–radial pulse rate. If the nurses use the following techniques, which one is in *error*?

○ 1. The patient's chest wall exposed.

○ 2. The patient is positioned on her back.

○ 3. Each nurse uses her own watch while counting the rate.

○ 4. One nurse uses a stethoscope to obtain the apical pulse rate.

53 The nurses note that Ms. Nesbitt's apical and radial heart beats per minute are not identical. When this occurs, the difference between the two rates is called the pulse

○ 1. stroke.

○ 2. deficit.

○ 3. volume.

○ 4. differential.

54 When the nurse obtains Ms. Nesbitt's blood pressure, it is noted to be 160/95 mm Hg. Ms. Nesbitt's pulse pressure is

○ 1. 65.

○ 2. 95.

○ 3. 160.

○ 4. 255.

55 The nurse washes her hands after obtaining Ms. Nesbitt's vital signs. She then carries out the following assignment without interruption:

—Emptying Mr. Groton's bedpan after he has expelled an enema

—Giving Mr. Groton a bath in bed

—Making Ms. Story's bed (the patient is ambulatory)

—Preparing and giving a medication to Ms. Taylor

How many times should the nurse wash her hands in this situation?

○ 1. One time, after giving Ms. Taylor her medication

○ 2. Two times, after bathing Mr. Groton and after making Ms. Story's bed

○ 3. Three times, after emptying Mr. Groton's bedpan, after bathing Mr. Groton, and after giving Ms. Taylor her medication

○ 4. Four times, after emptying Mr. Groton's bedpan, after bathing Mr. Groton, after making Ms. Story's bed, and after giving Ms. Taylor her medication

Ms. Nesbitt is to receive furosemide (Lasix).

56 The nurse should judge that the desired effect of the drug is being obtained when she observes that Ms. Nesbitt's

○ 1. apppetite is improved.

○ 2. pulse is less irregular.

○ 3. urinary output is increased.
○ 4. blood pressure has returned to normal.

57 Ms. Nesbitt's furosemide is dispensed in an ampule. To remove medication from the stem of an ampule before breaking it off, the nurse should
  ○ 1. allow the ampule to stand undisturbed for a few minutes.
  ○ 2. tap the stem of the ampule with the fingernail several times.
  ○ 3. hold the ampule upside down before flipping it right side up.
  ○ 4. roll the ampule between the palms of her hands several times.

58 If the nurse uses the following techniques to open the ampule containing Ms. Nesbitt's furosemide and to remove the drug, which one is in *error*?
  ○ 1. The nurse scores the stem with a file where the stem will be broken.
  ○ 2. The nurse cleans the stem with a pledget moistened with an antiseptic where the stem will be broken.
  ○ 3. The nurse uses a sterile gauze pledget to protect her fingers when breaking the stem.
  ○ 4. The nurse steadies the needle on the edge of the broken stem while removing the drug.

59 The electrolyte for which Ms. Nesbitt should be observed carefully for its serum level while she receives furosemide is
  ○ 1. calcium.
  ○ 2. chloride.
  ○ 3. potassium.
  ○ 4. bicarbonate.

Ms. Nesbitt is to have digoxin (Lanoxin).

60 If Ms. Nesbitt is to receive 0.5 mg of digoxin orally once a day and each tablet contains 0.25 mg of the drug, how many tablets should the nurse give Ms. Nesbitt each day?
  ○ 1. ½ tablet
  ○ 2. 2 tablets
  ○ 3. 3 tablets
  ○ 4. 4 tablets

61 The vital sign the nurse should most certainly check before administering digoxin to Ms. Nesbitt is her
  ○ 1. pulse rate.
  ○ 2. temperature.
  ○ 3. blood pressure.
  ○ 4. respiratory rate.

62 The hospital where Ms. Nesbitt is a patient observes a policy that states that a drug to be given once a day is to be administered at 9 A.M.

According to most agency policies, during which of the following time spans is the drug allowed to be given?
- ○ 1. Between 9:00 and 10:00 A.M.
- ○ 2. Between 8:00 and 9:00 A.M.
- ○ 3. Between 8:30 and 9:30 A.M.
- ○ 4. Between 8:45 and 9:15 A.M.

63 The nurse monitors Ms. Nesbitt for symptoms of digoxin toxicity. Two common early symptoms are
- ○ 1. nausea and anorexia.
- ○ 2. dizziness and insomnia.
- ○ 3. constipation and flatulence.
- ○ 4. ringing in the ears and itchy skin.

64 Ms. Nesbitt receives digoxin primarily because the drug acts to
- ○ 1. increase the rate of the heartbeat.
- ○ 2. dilate the arteries supplying heart muscles.
- ○ 3. improve the functioning ability of heart valves.
- ○ 4. strengthen the force of heart muscle contractions.

An abdominal paracentesis is scheduled for Ms. Nesbitt because she has excessive fluid in her abdominal cavity.

65 The position of choice when performing an abdominal paracentesis is to have Ms. Nesbitt positioned so that she is
- ○ 1. sitting up.
- ○ 2. standing up.
- ○ 3. lying on her back.
- ○ 4. lying on either side.

66 Ms. Nesbitt angrily and purposefully pushes away the tray of equipment for the paracentesis, and it falls to the floor. In this situation, it would be best for the nurse to
- ○ 1. clean up the equipment from the floor and say nothing.
- ○ 2. explain that she will now have to get a new sterile setup.
- ○ 3. leave the room and allow the patient privacy to work out her emotions.
- ○ 4. indicate that she understands and give her an opportunity to talk about her anger.

67 Fluid in Ms. Nesbitt's body that is located in her vascular (circulatory) system is called
- ○ 1. water.
- ○ 2. plasma.
- ○ 3. cellular fluid.
- ○ 4. interstitial fluid.

Ms. Nesbitt's central venous pressure (CVP) is measured.

68 The chamber in Ms. Nesbitt's heart into which a catheter is threaded to measure venous pressure is the
- O 1. left atrium.
- O 2. left ventricle.
- O 3. right atrium.
- O 4. right ventricle.

69 When obtaining a CVP, Ms. Nesbitt should be positioned in bed so that she is
- O 1. lying flat on her back.
- O 2. lying on her right side.
- O 3. in a low-Fowler's position.
- O 4. in a modified Trendelenburg position.

70 What effect, if any, will Ms. Nesbitt's disease typically have on her CVP?
- O 1. The patient's venous pressure will be increased.
- O 2. The patient's venous pressure will be decreased.
- O 3. The patient's venous pressure will fluctuate above and below normal.
- O 4. The patient's venous pressure is unlikely to be influenced by congestive heart failure.

Rotating tourniquets are applied to Ms. Nesbitt.

71 Which of the following observations most accurately indicates that, while applying a tourniquet, it is being applied too tightly on Ms. Nesbitt's arm?
- O 1. The patient's nailbeds are cyanotic.
- O 2. The patient's hand becomes swollen.
- O 3. The patient's radial pulse is not palpable.
- O 4. The patient complains of discomfort while the tourniquet is applied.

72 If tourniquets are rotated on a 15-minute schedule, how long in an hour's time is there a tourniquet on each of Ms. Nesbitt's extremities?
- O 1. 15 minutes
- O 2. 30 minutes
- O 3. 45 minutes
- O 4. 60 minutes

73 The primary purpose for using rotating tourniquets on Ms. Nesbitt is to help
- O 1. increase venous blood pressure.
- O 2. decrease arterial blood pressure.
- O 3. limit the amount of blood returning to the heart.
- O 4. retard the progression of edema in the extremities.

Nurses responsible for Ms. Nesbitt's care have prepared a nursing care plan for Ms. Nesbitt.

74 The care plan for Ms. Nesbitt illustrates that the nurses are taking Ms. Nesbitt's age into account when nursing care is planned in a way so that
  ○ 1. periods of activity are followed by naps.
  ○ 2. personal hygiene is provided early in the day.
  ○ 3. extra time is made available for usual activities of daily living.
  ○ 4. nursing measures do not interfere with her physician's visits.

75 The nursing care plan indicates that Ms. Nesbitt requires help to be placed on a bedpan. Which of the following techniques will help most to prevent injury to Ms. Nesbitt's skin as the nurse slides a bedpan under the patient?
  ○ 1. Placing a towel on the shelf of the bedpan
  ○ 2. Moistening the shelf of the bedpan with water
  ○ 3. Placing cornstarch on the shelf of the bedpan
  ○ 4. Wrapping the shelf of the bedpan with toilet tissues

76 Nursing measures described in the care plan are used to avoid having Ms. Nesbitt develop hypostatic pneumonia. The most common cause of this illness is
  ○ 1. poor nutrition.
  ○ 2. lack of activity.
  ○ 3. abnormal blood pressure.
  ○ 4. overload of the circulatory system.

77 Ms. Nesbitt's nursing care plan indicates that the patient's fluid intake is to be limited. A nursing measure often recommended when caring for a person on limited fluid intake to help control thirst is to
  ○ 1. serve the patient crackers instead of bread.
  ○ 2. only partly fill the patient's water pitcher.
  ○ 3. offer the patient chips of ice instead of water.
  ○ 4. serve the patient small sips of artificially sweetened beverages.

78 The nurse evaluates nursing care that Ms. Nesbitt receives, as described in the nursing care plan. Evaluation is best described as
  ○ 1. reassessing data collected from the patient.
  ○ 2. documenting nursing care that has been implemented.
  ○ 3. measuring the work performance of the patient's nursing personnel.
  ○ 4. comparing the results of nursing care with the objectives of nursing care.

79 Of the following proverbs, the one which is likely best to serve the nurses caring for Ms. Nesbitt in helping to develop and maintain a good nurse–patient relationship with her is the one that states,
  ○ 1. Little strokes fell great oaks.
  ○ 2. Every cloud has a silver lining.
  ○ 3. God helps those who help themselves.
  ○ 4. Do unto others as you wish them to do to you.

Ms. Nesbitt responds to therapy and is prepared for discharge.

80 The nurse teaches Ms. Nesbitt how to take her digoxin at home. Which of the following types of information is generally *least* important to teach the patient?
   - ○ 1. The purpose for taking the medication
   - ○ 2. The name of the manufacturer of the medication
   - ○ 3. What time of the day it is best to take the medication
   - ○ 4. What symptoms are likely to develop if the patient reacts unfavorably to the medication

81 Ms. Nesbitt is to have a low-sodium diet. She should be taught that a fish she is allowed in her diet is
   - ○ 1. shrimp.
   - ○ 2. lobster.
   - ○ 3. smoked fish.
   - ○ 4. fresh oysters.

82 When seasoning her food, Ms. Nesbitt should be taught to *avoid*
   - ○ 1. garlic.
   - ○ 2. catsup.
   - ○ 3. onion juice.
   - ○ 4. dry mustard.

83 Ms. Nesbitt is to have a less-than-average daily intake of sodium. How many grams of sodium does a healthy adult need each day?
   - ○ 1. 1.5 g to 2.5 g
   - ○ 2. 4.5. g to 6.5 g
   - ○ 3. 10 g to 12 g
   - ○ 4. 15 g to 20 g

84 Ms. Nesbitt says she uses tap-water enemas at home for constipation. She says, "Several at a time if I need them." The nurse's teaching concerning this practice should be based on knowledge that one of the greatest dangers of the repeated use of tap-water enemas is that they may cause the patient to develop
   - ○ 1. a rectal infection.
   - ○ 2. a fluid imbalance.
   - ○ 3. fecal incontinence.
   - ○ 4. abdominal distention.

85 If Ms. Nesbitt describes having the following items in her home, the nurse should teach her that the one presenting the greatest safety hazard is a
   - ○ 1. television set in the bedroom.
   - ○ 2. shower rather than a bath tub.
   - ○ 3. throw rug in front of the kitchen sink.
   - ○ 4. three-prong electrical outlet in the bathroom.

86 Which of the following reasons explains why teaching patients, such as Ms. Nesbitt, about healthful living has taken on greater importance today than in the past?
   - ○ 1. Curative measures in health care have increased markedly.

○ 2. Health promotion has become an important part of health care.

○ 3. Patients today tend to be older when hospitalized than they were in the past.

○ 4. Patients today tend to be sicker when hospitalized than they were in the past.

Ms. Zeck, a 42-year-old homemaker, visits a physician's office for an evaluation of her health status after a screening examiner in a shopping-mall health fair indicates that Ms. Zeck's blood pressure is above normal.

87 When Ms. Zeck arrives for the appointment, the nurse prepares her for the examination by

○ 1. having the patient void.

○ 2. giving the patient an enema.

○ 3. giving the patient a mild sedative.

○ 4. having the patient drink several glasses of water.

The nurse obtains Ms. Zeck's blood pressure.

88 Where in relation to the heart should the nurse position Ms. Zeck's arm when she obtains the patient's blood pressure at the brachial artery?

○ 1. At the level of the heart

○ 2. Below the level of the waistline

○ 3. Slightly above the level of the heart

○ 4. Slightly below the level of the heart

89 In the manometer being used to obtain Ms. Zeck's blood pressure, the top of the curved surface on the mercury is about 6 inches (15 cm) above the nurse's eye level. What difference, if any, will this have on the blood pressure reading the nurse obtains?

○ 1. A distance of 6 inches (15 cm) is too little to be significant.

○ 2. The blood pressure reading will be lower than it actually is.

○ 3. The blood pressure reading will be higher than it actually is.

○ 4. The blood pressure reading will be at least 25 mm Hg in error.

90 Before placing the bell of her stethoscope over Ms. Zeck's brachial artery to obtain the blood pressure, the nurse should first

○ 1. feel for the patient's pulse at the radial artery.

○ 2. pump up the pressure cuff on the patient's arm.

○ 3. feel for the patient's pulse at the brachial artery.

○ 4. raise the patient's arm above her head momentarily.

91 When obtaining Ms. Zeck's blood pressure, the first clear tapping sound the nurse hears is called the

○ 1. venous pressure.

○ 2. systolic pressure.

○ 3. diastolic pressure.

    ○ 4. intraventricular pressure.

92 Of the following factors, the one that has the *least* effect on Ms. Zeck's blood pressure is
    ○ 1. her age.
    ○ 2. her sex.
    ○ 3. whether she is angry or fearful when obtaining the blood pressure.
    ○ 4. whether she is sitting or lying down when obtaining the blood pressure.

93 When in a 24-hour period is Ms. Zeck's blood pressure most likely to be at its lowest?
    ○ 1. Upon arising in the morning
    ○ 2. About noon
    ○ 3. In the early evening
    ○ 4. At bedtime

The nurse prepares to assist the physician with Ms. Zeck's examination.

94 The nurse has surface (topical) anesthesia ready for use on Ms. Zeck when the examiner wishes to
    ○ 1. test the patient's reflexes.
    ○ 2. examine the patient's eardrums.
    ○ 3. determine pressure within the patient's eyes.
    ○ 4. take a specimen of the patient's vaginal secretions.

95 While examining Ms. Zeck, the physician uses the initials RUQ, LUQ, RLQ, and LLQ as abbreviations to describe parts of Ms. Zeck's
    ○ 1. head.
    ○ 2. back.
    ○ 3. chest.
    ○ 4. abdomen.

96 The nurse has an ophthalmoscope in readiness. Which of the following anatomical structures of each of Ms. Zeck's eyes will be examined with the ophthalmoscope?
    ○ 1. The retina
    ○ 2. The sclera
    ○ 3. The lacrimal sac
    ○ 4. The conjunctival sac

97 Which of the following instruments should the nurse have in readiness for examining Ms. Zeck's vagina?
    ○ 1. An otoscope
    ○ 2. A speculum
    ○ 3. A tonometer
    ○ 4. A largyngoscope

98 The nurse should be prepared to assist Ms. Zeck to assume a knee-chest position for an examination of the patient's
    ○ 1. spine.

○ 2. vagina.
○ 3. rectum.
○ 4. urinary bladder.

99 Which of the following positions that Ms. Zeck should be helped to assume during the examination requires the nurse to have stirrups in readiness?
○ 1. The Sim's position
○ 2. The lithotomy position
○ 3. The dorsal recumbent position
○ 4. The horizontal recumbent position

100 What method of gathering information will be used to examine Ms. Zeck for lumps or masses in her breasts?
○ 1. Palpation
○ 2. Percussion
○ 3. Inspection
○ 4. Auscultation

101 If an abnormal mass or lump is found in Ms. Zeck's breast tissues, it will be correctly referred to as
○ 1. a crater.
○ 2. an ulcer.
○ 3. a tumor.
○ 4. a fissure.

102 If the examiner suspects that Ms. Zeck has an organic heart murmur, the cause of such a murmur would be a defect in the
○ 1. oxygenation of the blood.
○ 2. ability of the heart to pump.
○ 3. capacity of coronary arteries.
○ 4. action of the valves of the heart.

103 If Ms. Zeck reports having had the following illnesses earlier in life, which one would most likely have predisposed her to an organic heart murmur?
○ 1. Measles
○ 2. Mononucleosis
○ 3. Rheumatic fever
○ 4. Infectious hepatitis

104 Further examination reveals that Ms. Zeck's heart murmur is most probably functional in nature, which means that the murmur is most likely caused by
○ 1. anxiety.
○ 2. an injury.
○ 3. hypertension.
○ 4. an infection.

105 When Ms. Zeck's feet are being examined, Ms. Zeck complains of having frequent ingrown toenails. Ms. Zeck should be taught that ingrown toenails often occur when the nails are

○ 1. trimmed with a file.
○ 2. cut deeply at the sides.
○ 3. cleaned with an orange stick.
○ 4. groomed with heavy liquid nail polish.

106 After the examination, if the nurse makes the following documentations in Ms. Zeck's health record, which entry is *inappropriate?*
○ 1. The name of the examiner
○ 2. The time of the examination
○ 3. The positions that the patient assumed during the examination
○ 4. The types of specimens collected from the patient during the examination

It is determined that Ms. Zeck has primary (essential) hypertension.

107 If the following items appear in Ms. Zeck's health history, which one is most probably significant in terms of predisposing her to hypertension?
○ 1. Having had 3 children in less than 4 years
○ 2. Having two grandparents who died of the disorder
○ 3. Having been underweight all of her life, including during pregnancies
○ 4. Having had most childhood communicable diseases, including German measles

108 A sign of Ms. Zeck's primary hypertension that makes it different from other kinds of hypertension is prolonged elevation of the
○ 1. pulse pressure.
○ 2. systolic pressure.
○ 3. diastolic pressure.
○ 4. intraventricular pressure.

109 When Ms. Zeck learns that she has hypertension, she appears extremely worried and fearful. At such times it is best for the nurse to
○ 1. teach the patient how she can control hypertension.
○ 2. listen to the patient's expression of feelings about her hypertension.
○ 3. explain to the patient how well many others adjust to having hypertension.
○ 4. eliminate the subject of hypertension until the patient has regained her composure.

Ms. Zeck is to take 1 g of methyldopa (Aldomet) daily.

110 Each tablet of methyldopa contains 250 mg. How many tablets should Ms. Zeck take each day?
○ 1. 2 tablets
○ 2. 4 tablets
○ 3. 6 tablets

○ 4. 10 tablets

111 Which of the following precautions should Ms. Zeck observe to overcome a common side-effect of methyldopa?
○ 1. Getting up from a bed or chair slowly.
○ 2. Eating the heaviest meal of the day at noon.
○ 3. Taking the medication with generous amounts of water
○ 4. Lying or sitting down for a few minutes immediately after taking the medication

Dietary restrictions are discussed with Ms. Zeck.

112 The type of diet that is most likely to be ordered for Ms. Zeck is a
○ 1. bland diet.
○ 2. low-sodium diet.
○ 3. minimum fat diet.
○ 4. high-carbohydrate diet.

113 If Ms. Zeck tells the nurse that she enjoys eating the foods given below for snacking, which one should the nurse teach Ms. Zeck to *avoid*?
○ 1. Carrots
○ 2. Pretzels
○ 3. Oranges
○ 4. Plain gelatin

114 Ms. Zeck says she does not want to gain weight and asks the nurse, "What is a calorie?" The nurse should respond that a calorie is best defined as the amount of heat necessary to raise the temperature of 1 kilogram of water to the extent of
○ 1. 1°C.
○ 2. 1°F.
○ 3. 10°C.
○ 4. 10°F.

Ms. Zeck is taught that her health care will be directed toward controlling her disease and helping to prevent complications.

115 Ms. Zeck should be taught that one relatively common complication of uncontrolled hypertension is
○ 1. thrombophlebitis.
○ 2. herniation of the aorta.
○ 3. destruction of valves in the venous system.
○ 4. hemorrhaging of blood vessels in the brain.

116 Ms. Zeck will monitor her disease at home, in which case the nurse should be prepared to teach her how to obtain
○ 1. her blood pressure.
○ 2. her apical pulse rate.
○ 3. her apical–radial pulse rate.
○ 4. the specific gravity of her urine.

Correct Answers and Rationales

Two numbers appear in parentheses following each rationale. The first number identifies the textbook listed in the references, page 649, and the second number identifies the page(s) in that textbook where the correct answer can be verified. Occasionally, two textbooks are given for verifying the correct answer.

The Nursing Care of Patients with Disorders of the Cardiovascular System

Caring for a patient with a myocardial infarction

1 4. The pain associated with a myocardial infarction is very severe. A narcotic analgesic is used, usually meperidine hydrochloride (Demerol) or morphine. If pain is not relieved, an arrhythmia or shock may occur. Also, the narcotic helps relieve the patient's fears and anxieties. (15:654–655)

2 4. The question, "Is your pain so severe that you need an injection for it?", which can be answered with a simple *yes* or *no*, usually solicits little information from a patient. Also, a nurse should make the decision concerning whether a patient needs a p.r.n. medication for the relief of pain after consulting with the patient. Other questions posed in this item are likely to give the nurse information that she needs to make a sound judgment concerning the patient's discomfort. (9:134)

3 4. The pain associated with a myocardial infarction is ordinarily described with such terms as stabbing, grinding, suffocating, and crushing. The pain comes on suddenly, does not subside, and is not relieved with rest. A characteristic of the type of pain associated with an acute myocardial infarction that is *not* typical of angina pectoris is that in the latter case, the pain is relieved with rest. Angina pectoris is also relieved by using nitroglycerine or amyl nitrite; the pain of a myocardial infarction is not relieved by either of these pharmaceutical agents. (12:652; 15:654–655)

4 1. The characteristic pain associated with a myocardial infarction is due to a poor blood supply reaching heart-muscle tissues. Narcotics usually are required to overcome discomfort because of the severity of the pain. Unrelieved pain may cause shock and arrhythmias. The pain associated with a myocardial infarction is unrelated to an electrolyte imbalance, inadequate electrical stimulation, or an accumulation of lymph in capillary beds. (15:654)

5 4. Many patients who have had a myocardial infarction believe that their first symptoms were due to indigestion. Symptoms may also be similar to gallbladder disease. (12:653)

6 3.   Heparin delays blood clotting and therefore will act in the body to help prevent a thrombus that caused the patient's infarction from becoming larger. The drug is classified as an anticoagulant.   (14:94)

7 3.   Protamine sulfate is the most commonly used drug to overcome heparin effects. It is given intravenously.   (14:95)

8 4.   The chief complication when a patient is receiving heparin is that he develops bleeding tendencies with the result that he may hemorrhage. The nurse should observe the patient closely for such common signs as bleeding of oral tissues, a nose bleed, blood in the stool or urine, a tendency to bruise easily, and prolonged bleeding following injections. Convalescing patients or at-home patients taking anticoagulants may report that they bleed excessively when they nick themselves with a razor. Any signs of bleeding should be reported promptly.   (14:94)

9 1.   The patient who has had a myocardial infarction most often has an elevated sedimentation rate, white blood count, and serum enzyme level. Examples of serum enzyme tests include the CPK (creatine phosphokinase), LDH (lactic acid hydrogenase), and SGOT (serum glutamic oxaloacetic transaminase). No one test is in itself diagnostic of a myocardial infarction but all are used collectively as tools to assist with making a diagnosis.   (15:657–658)

10 1.   A pulse rate of 50 should be reported promptly because this rate is considerably lower than normal. A slow pulse rate suggests involvement of the S–A or A–V node or marked vagal tone. It can lead to poor oxygen supplies to heart muscle and to further heart damage. Arrhythmias are also ominous signs.   (15:655, 658)

11 1.   When a patient's blood pressure is recorded as 140/96/70, the number 70 represents the point at which the nurse first heard no noise or sound. This number is sometimes referred to as the second diastolic pressure and begins phase V of Korotkoff sounds. A distinct muffled sound represents the diastolic pressure, which in the example in this items is 96.   (9:207, 210)

12 4.   The radial artery usually is used for obtaining a patient's pulse rate because the artery is near the skin's surface and it lies over a bone on which the nurse can rest her fingers to feel the pulse. These two conditions make the radial artery an excellent site to obtain a pulse rate in most patients. Furthermore, the radial site is most often a very convenient site.   (9:196)

13 1.   The only danger of using the thumb to obtain a patient's pulse rate is that the nurse may feel her own pulse in her thumb rather than that of the patient.   (9:198)

14 4.   The respiratory rate should be counted after obtaining the pulse rate while keeping fingers in place on the pulse. In contrast to other techniques, this one usually does not cause the patient to know that his respiratory rate is being counted. When the patient is aware that his respiratory rate is being counted, he may alter his rate voluntarily.   (9:201)

15 2. A patient in acute pain is most likely to have rapid respiratory and pulse rates and a rising blood pressure. The blood pressure will fall if the patient goes into shock due to pain, but it is not likely to fall precipitously. By itself, pain is least likely to influence body temperature. (9:133)

16 3. An aneurysm is a sac or out-pouching that may occur in the heart following a myocardial infarction. A herniation, or aneurysm, may also occur in blood vessels elsewhere in the body. (15:391, 658)

17 2. Blood gas studies are the best way to determine the effectiveness of oxygen therapy. If therapy is effective, blood gas studies will indicate that carbon dioxide levels have decreased and that oxygen levels have increased in the blood. (8:361; 11:320)

18 4. Massaging the legs is contraindicated for the patient with myocardial infarction. If a blood clot is present, massage may cause it to break away from the vessel wall and circulate in the bloodstream. Washing, powdering, and elevating the legs are not necessarily contraindicated for the patient described in this item. (9:376)

19 1. To prevent activity occurring against a closed glottis (Valsalva's maneuver), the pateint should be taught to exhale as he moves himself. By doing this, he cannot close his glottis. Moving, exercising, or straining when stooling puts extra strain on the heart. (15:660)

20 2. Lay persons often call a myocardial infarction a heart attack. Other synonyms include MI and coronary thrombosis. A stroke is a lay term for a cerebrovascular accident (CVA). High blood pressure is hypertension. Leakage of the heart usually refers to a heart valve problem. (12:652)

21 1. The worried patient needs an opportunity to express his concerns and is most likely to do this when the nurse attempts to explore in what way the patient is concerned. (15:659)

22 1. When planning a patient's physical activities after a myocardial infarction, it is common to study the effect of activity on him. If activity causes fatigue, it should be cut back. If it does not, activity can be maintained and increased gradually. Selecting the amount of activity following a myocardial infarction is not guided by amount of heart damage, length of time since the attack, or the emotional responses to possible permanent heart damage. (15:661)

23 1. Persons should not use isometric exercises against a closed glottis. This practice affects the heart in some instances, causing it to beat irregularly or erratically fast. This guide to action becomes especially important when the patient has a heart disease. (9:346)

24 3. Part of the effectiveness in using a rectal tube to relieve abdominal distention is that it acts as a foreign body and stimulates peristalsis, thus moving gas along the gastrointestinal tract and through the rectal tube. After about 20 minutes, the tube loses its effectiveness as a stimulant to peristalsis. Therefore, if the patient has experienced no relief after about 20 minutes, it is best to remove a rectal tube and reinsert it again in about 2 to 3 hours. (9:471)

25 3. Double-bagging contaminated linen means that the nurse caring for a patient first places soiled linen in a bag in the patient's room. She then places it in a second bag being held by a nurse at the door to the patient's room. This technique prevents contamination of the outside of the second bag so that it can be cared for without contaminating persons handling laundry bags. (9:306, 310)

26 2. An echogram uses ultrasonic (sound) waves to study the heart's structure. Sound waves are reflected back in various ways, depending upon the density of the body tissues, to produce a replication of the heart that can be studied for the presence of pathology. (9:248)

27 1. Most persons practicing Judaism and Islam, and some Seventh Day Adventists, avoid pork in their diets. Mormons, Quakers, and Jehovah's Witnesses do not shun pork for religious reasons. (9:88)

28 2. Fluids should be restricted when a patient is administered an oral medication to control coughing. Because the fluids wash the medication from the throat, the local effect of the medication would be lost. (9:549)

29 4. Erik Erikson describes generativity as a concern for leaving something of worth to society. Generativity is a developmental task of persons in the middle of adult years, between about ages 40 and 65, and is best illustrated in this item when the patient is described as being eager to write a book related to business theories. (17:84)

30 2. Oxygenated blood for heart muscles is received from the ascending aorta. The carotid arteries carry blood to the head. The intercostal arteries carry blood to the chest wall. The left subclavian artery carries blood to the upper left extremity. (10:184)

31 4. Blood is pumped from the right ventricle into the lungs. Blood is received from the body in the right atrium. The left atrium receives oxygenated blood from the lungs, and oxygenated blood leaves the heart from the left ventricle. (10:182)

32 3. Atherosclerosis, in which vessels have fatty deposits of plaque on them, is believed to be the factor most often predisposing to an acute myocardial infarction. (12:648)

33 2. The sinoatrial node is often called the heart's pacemaker. It is abbreviated S–A. (10:186)

34 4. Of the factors given in this item, having an alcoholic beverage before lunch each day is least likely to predispose to myocardial infarction. Smoking, working under stress, and eating food high in cholesterol content are believed to predispose to the illness. Certain recent research has questioned the importance of cholesterol levels and heart attacks, but most authorities still believe that high cholesterol diets tend to predispose to infarction problems. (8:355)

35 1. Bowel elimination usually follows a cycling pattern, that is, the frequency of having a bowel movement differs among healthy persons. Gravity plays a role in ease of elimination. For example, most persons find it difficult while lying down and easier to stool when sitting or squatting.

Observing an urge to defecate helps overcome constipation; ignoring the urge predisposes to constipation. The amount of stool is affected by the amount persons eat.   (9:466)

36   2.   A danger in the regular use of laxatives is that the body becomes dependent on them. Eventually, the person may not be able to have a bowel movement without using a laxative because of a loss of the defecation reflex and a decrease in normal peristalsis. Laxatives are not associated with the development of hernias, elimination of normal intestinal bacteria, and the absorption of chemicals from the laxatives.   (14:234)

37   2.   Intestinal elimination is promoted when the diet contains sufficient bulk and roughage, which whole-grain cereals help provide. Such foods as lean meats, enriched white breads, and dairy products do not provide much bulk and roughage. Fresh fruits and vegetables are also good sources of roughage in the diet.   (9:468)

38   3.   Many persons find that drinking a cup of hot water each morning helps prevent constipation. Cold or cool fluids do not ordinarily have the same effect. Hot water may be made more palatable with a wedge of lemon or lime and honey to flavor it. Prunes or prune juice and a raw apple each day often relieve constipation also.   (9:490)

39   4.   In relation to intestinal elimination, people in this country appear to be most concerned with the regularity of bowel movements. Because much advertising is directed toward irregularity, many persons use laxatives more often than is good for health or is necessary. There is much less concern about the amount of stool, consistency of the stool, and the time of a bowel movement.   (9:467)

40   1.   Warfarin sodium (Coumadin) delays the time it takes for blood to clot. If a person is taking the drug, he should most certainly be taught what steps to take if he starts to bleed, because even a small injury can become a major problem if bleeding starts. Coughing, feeling dizzy, and having palpitations are not associated with the administration of warfarin sodium.   (15:96)

41   1.   Patients receiving an anticoagulant, such as warfarin sodium, should be instructed to avoid taking aspirin, as well as products containing aspirin, such as Alka-Seltzer. Aspirin is an anticoagulant and taking it may influence the prescribed anticoagulant dosages. Aspirin substitutes can be used to control minor discomforts. Ferrous sulfate, milk of magnesia, and multivitamin preparations are not necessarily contraindicated for patients taking anticoagulants.   (12:399)

Caring for a patient with congestive heart failure

42   4.   Patients who lack sufficient oxygen intake and feel as though they are suffocating typically feel apprehensive, anxious, and fearful. They are much less likely to be depressed, exhilarated, or disoriented. A prescribed medication, usually morphine or meperidine hydrochloride, may be used to help relieve anxiety and the nurse should offer appropriate emotional support as well.   (15:359)

43 4.   A patient with dyspnea is usually most comfortable and has the least amount of difficulty with breathing when placed in either a semi-sitting (mid-Fowler's) position, sitting (high-Fowler's) position, or a standing position. The condition in which breathing is easier when the patient is sitting or standing is called orthopnea. Sitting and standing positions cause organs to fall away from the diaphragm, giving more room for the lungs to expand easily.   (9:184, 200; 15:356)

44 3.   A patient with pulmonary edema typically has moist-sounding, or "gurgling" respirations and productive coughing because of the accumulation of fluid in the lungs.   (15:359)

45 1.   Oxygen should be started before applying a mask to the patient's face. The patient is less likely to feel as though he is suffocating than he would if oxygen were started after the mask is in place on the face.   (9:632)

46 2.   Early signs of congestive heart failure include dyspnea and fatigue. Edema with weight gain is also an early symptom, and a cough is not uncommon.   (15:354)

47 4.   Fluid may be retained in larger-than-normal amounts in almost all parts of the body. Most people first notice edema in their feet, ankles, and fingers. Fluids tend to accumulate quickly in these areas because of gravitational pooling of fluid in the tissues.   (15:354)

48 2.   Cyanosis is usually easiest to detect first where the body's vessels are near the surface. These areas are the nailbeds, the lips, the earlobes, and the oral mucous membranes. In the person with dark skin, cyanosis usually is observed best in the oral mucosa.   (9:225)

49 2.   An electrocardiogram (ECG) is used primarily to study electrical activity of the heart's muscle. An electrocardiograph is the machine used to measure and record the electrical currents.   (15:347)

50 1.   When assessing a patient's pain, the nurse should begin by asking the patient where he feels the pain. Although the patient should be consulted concerning measures to relieve pain, the nurse plays the primary role in assuming responsibility for judging whether an analgesic is indicated. Assessment for pain is unlikely to be complete and accurate when the nurse questions the patient concerning whether he is describing his discomfort accurately. However, she may wish to validate the patient's comments in some instances.   (9:134)

51 2.   A patient with congestive heart failure tends to retain excessive amounts of sodium. Edema is usually also present. There is an accurate saying which states, "Water goes where salt is."   (11:37–38; 15:358)

52 3.   The two nurses should use one watch when obtaining apical–radial pulse rates. They should have a signal so that each knows when the other starts counting. This technique results in a more accurate determination of the apical–radial pulse rates. Uncovering the chest wall so that clothing and linens do not interfere with hearing the heart beat, positioning the patient on her back, and using a stethoscope to obtain the apical pulse rate are appropriate techniques.   (9:196, 199)

53 2. The difference between an apical and a radial pulse rate is called the pulse deficit. The terms *stroke* and *differential* are not used to describe a pulse. If there is a pulse deficit, the beats at the heart's apex will be more than at the radial artery. The apical pulse rate is more significant than the radial pulse when a difference in the rates is noted.   (15:197)

54 1. The pulse pressure is the difference between the patient's systolic and diastolic pressure. A wide pulse pressure often suggests rigid arteries, which occur in arteriosclerosis. A narrow pulse pressure often indicates weakness, which occurs in shock.   (15:375)

55 4. To minimize the spread of organisms, the nurse should wash her hands four times in the situation described in this item. A 30-second scrub is appropriate when exposure to contamination is minimal. Hands should be washed before and after care is given. They need not be washed when a caretaker goes directly to another patient when there is no contamination of hands between patients. The importance of hand-washing cannot be overemphasized because it is believed that most organisms are spread in health agencies by the hands of health workers.   (9:275, 280)

56 3. Furosemide (Lasix) is a diuretic used to stimulate the body to get rid of excess fluids. The patient's urinary output increases when the desired effect of furosemide is being attained.   (15:113)

57 2. The best technique for bringing medication to the basin of an ampule from its stem is to tap the stem several times with a fingernail. Allowing the ampule to stand upright, flipping it right side up, and rolling the ampule will not bring medication trapped in the stem of an ampule into its basin.   (9:560–561)

58 4. The nurse contaminates the needle if she rests it on the side of the ampule where the stem has been broken. Scoring the ampule's stem with a file, cleaning the stem with an antiseptic, and protecting the fingers when breaking the stem off are appropriate techniques.   (9:560–561)

59 3. Usually, the patient receiving a diuretic loses large amounts of potassium through the urinary tract and will suffer from hypokalemia. To help prevent hypokalemia, a patient receiving a diuretic ordinarily has levels of potassium in blood serum monitored and receives potassium supplements as indicated. Signs of potassium deficit include cramping and weakness of muscles, an irregular pulse rate, postural hypotension, thirst, anorexia, and vomiting.   (14:114)

60 2. The patient described in this item should receive 2 tablets of digoxin (Lanoxin) daily. The formula for determining the correct number of tablets is as follows:

$$\frac{\text{Dose desired}}{\text{Dose on hand}} = \text{Dose to administer}$$

$$\frac{0.50}{0.25} = 2 \text{ tablets}$$

(14:10)

61 1. The pulse rate should be checked carefully before administering digoxin, which is a cardiotonic. If the pulse rate per minute is 60 beats or less, the nurse should omit giving the medication and report her action promptly to the nurse-in-charge. The exception to this rule is when there is a specific order that indicates a lower pulse rate is satisfactory.   (14:84)

62 3. Most health agencies state that unless specified to the contrary, drugs may be administered between one half hour before and one half hour after the time specified on a medication card or Kardex. In this situation, the time span would be between 8:30 and 9:30 A.M. It is considered a medication error not to give the drug within the hour's time span.   (9:545)

63 1. Common symptoms of digitalis toxicity include anorexia and nausea. Other symptoms related to the gastrointestinal tract may also occur, such as vomiting, diarrhea, and epigastric distress. Changes in pulse rates and rhythms and a slow or fast rate may be signs of toxicity to digitalis preparations. Visual disturbances are also reported.   (14:83)

64 4. Digitalis preparations strengthen the force of the heart muscle contractions and thereby improve circulation of blood throughout the body. With the increase in heart muscle contraction, cardiac output is increased and the pulse rate slows.   (14:82–83)

65 1. The position of choice when an abdominal paracentesis is performed is the sitting position. Fluid leaves the abdominal cavity by gravity, and drainage is promoted when the patient is sitting. The standing position is uncomfortable and unsatisfactory for an acutely ill patient.   (9:250–251)

66 4. When a patient is emotionally upset, it is usually best for the nurse to indicate that she accepts and understands her behavior, and allow her to express her feelings. Reprimanding her or saying nothing usually is of little help because it offers the patient no understanding and support and may make the patient feel that she is being scolded.   (9:23)

67 2. The fluid part of blood is called plasma or serum. Cellular fluid is found within cells, and interstitial fluid is found surrounding cells or between cells in the body's tissues.   (9:493)

68 3. When central venous pressure (CVP) is measured, a catheter is threaded through a large vein, usually the jugular vein, and into the patient's right atrium.   (15:346)

69 1. It is essential that the zero mark on the manometer measuring CVP be at the level of the patient's right atrium to obtain an accurate reading. Therefore, the patient should lie flat on her back when a CVP measurement is obtained. Between CVP readings, the patient may lie in a position of comfort, such as a low-Fowler's position.   (15:346)

70 1. The venous pressure is typically elevated in patients with congestive heart failure. Blood is backing up in the venous system because the heart is not pumping effectively. (15:346)

71 3. A tourniquet should not be applied so tightly on an extremity that a peripheral pulse is not palpable. A tourniquet should be applied tightly enough to ensure that a venous return is limited but that arterial blood passes through the arteries of the extremities. There will be some swelling in the hands and feet when rotating tourniquets are used, but this is more likely to occur after the tourniquets have been in place a while, not while they are being applied. The procedure normally causes no discomfort while tourniquets are applied. (15:360)

72 3. In an hour's time, each extremity has a tourniquet in place for 45 minutes and is free of a tourniquet for 15 minutes. In some situations, the tourniquets may be ordered to be rotated more frequently, but using 15-minute intervals is common. (15:360)

73 3. The primary purpose for using rotating tourniquets is to limit the amount of blood returning to an already overburdened and diseased heart. Rotating tourniquets are not used to increase venous pressure, decrease arterial blood pressure, or retard edema progression. (15:360)

74 3. Elderly persons in general are slower in their movements and responses than younger persons. The nurse should take this into account when planning nursing care for usual activities of daily living, such as eating, toileting, dressing, undressing, ambulating, preparing for sleep, and the like. Unless the patient is weak, it is unlikely that periods of activity need to be followed by napping, although elderly persons nap more than younger adults do. (15:27–29)

75 3. It would be best to place cornstarch (or powder) on the shelf of a bedpan before the nurse slides it under a helpless patient. The cornstarch reduces friction and thereby reduces the danger of injury to the patient's skin. Such techniques as placing a towel on the bedpan's shelf, moistening the shelf, or wrapping it with toilet tissue will not help reduce friction on the patient's skin as effectively as cornstarch when placing the patient on a bedpan. (9:436)

76 2. Lack of activity predisposes to hypostatic pneumonia. Secretions tend to accumulate in the respiratory tract where an infection is likely to develop, and respiratory efforts will then become inefficient. The patient described in this item should have as much activity as permitted, and her position in bed should be changed regularly and frequently. (15:318)

77 3. Offering a patient ice chips instead of water is recommended when a patient's fluid intake is restricted. Other recommended techniques include serving fluids in small containers, avoiding dry, salty foods that increase thirst, and avoiding sweetened beverages and foods that also increase thirst. (9:503)

78 4. When nursing care is evaluated, the results of care that has been given are compared with the objectives of nursing care that are stated in a patient's plan of care. The evaluation should tell the nurse the degree of success or failure for each nursing measure implemented for the patient. It is one step in the nursing process.   (9:41)

79   4.   All of the proverbs given in this item may help to develop a good nurse–patient relationship at some time. The Golden Rule, that is, doing onto others as you would wish them to do to you, is most likely to be the best when helping to develop good relationships with others.   (13:122–123)

80   2.   In general, it is least important to teach a patient the name of the manufacturer of a medication he is to take. It is important to teach the patient the purpose of the medication, when to take the medication, and symptoms of adverse effects. It has been found that noncompliance is greatest when patients are poorly taught concerning their drug regimes.   (9:586–587)

81   4.   Fresh oysters and freshwater fish are allowed in a low-sodium diet. Smoked fish and saltwater fish, such as shell fish, lobster and shrimp, should be avoided.   (16:270)

82   2.   Catsup (unless it is prepared with no salt) has a very high sodium content and should be avoided by a patient on a low-sodium diet. (16:270)

83   1.   It has been estimated that the body needs a daily intake of about 2 g of sodium each day, with a range of 1.5 to 2.5 being safe. Most Americans have a much higher intake, from 3 g to 20 g with an average of about 10 g daily. Patients should be taught to read labels on food to determine the quantity of salt in each item.   (16:104)

84   2.   A fluid imbalance is likely to result when a person repeatedly uses tap-water enemas. The tap water used for cleansing the colon is likely to be absorbed by the body in larger amounts than is desirable for maintaining fluid balance. A rectal infection, fecal incontinence, and abdominal distention are not associated with the repeated use of tap-water enemas.   (9:473)

85   3.   Throw rugs present a safety hazard because of the danger of slipping or tripping on them. This is especially true for elderly persons. Having a television set in a bedroom, showering rather than bathing in a tub, and using three-prong electrical outlets are not safety hazards.   (9:174)

86   2.   Health teaching has become an essential part of health care because of the emphasis today on helping persons stay well by promoting good health. Curative measures are increasing, and hospitalized patients tend to be older and sicker than in the past, but these findings do not explain why health teaching has taken on greater significance in nursing today.   (9:28–30)

Caring for a patient who has a health evaluation that reveals the presence of primary hypertension

87 1. Preparing for a complete examination most often is limited to having the patient void immediately before the examination. Voiding before the examination helps to put the patient at ease and makes palpation of the abdomen easier and more comfortable for the patient than when the bladder is full. Giving the patient an enema, giving the patient a sedative, and having the patient drink fluids before an examination are used only for preparing a patient who is having certain tests that require special preparation. (9:221)

88 1. The arm should be placed about level with the heart when obtaining the patient's blood pressure at the brachial artery. This positioning helps to obtain the most accurate readings of blood pressure because the arm will be neither congested with blood nor drained of normal amounts. (9:208)

89 3. When the top of the curved surface (the meniscus) on the mercury in the manometer is above the nurse's eye level, the nurse is going to read the patient's blood pressure at an abnormally high level. Her error will not be as much as 25 mm Hg but the error will be great enough so that the blood pressure will not be considered accurate. If the meniscus is below the nurse's eye level, the reading will be abnormally low. For a most accurate reading, the meniscus on the mercury should be at the nurse's eye level. (9:204, 208)

90 3. When obtaining the blood pressure, before adjusting the bell of the stethoscope, the nurse should feel for the patient's pulse at the brachial artery. This technique allows the nurse to place her bell directly over the artery where she will listen for characteristic sounds when obtaining blood pressure. (9:208)

91 2. The first appearance of faint but clear tapping sounds that slowly increase in intensity is called the systolic pressure. The nurse should read the level of mercury in the manometer carefully when she hears the first sound and record this as systolic pressure. (9:209)

92 4. The factor that least affects the blood pressure is the patient's position. The difference when the person is sitting or lying down is very small and usually is considered clinically insignificant. The person's age, sex, and emotional status affect blood pressure. (9:201)

93 1. Blood pressure tends to fall during sleep and is ordinarily at its lowest level when the person awakens and before he starts the day's activities. (9:201)

94 3. Surface (topical) anesthesia is required when an examiner wishes to measure pressure within the patient's eyes. The anesthesia, placed by drops on the surface of the lower conjunctival sac, makes it possible to place a tonometer on the eye without the patient feeling as if something is touching the eye. Topical anesthesia is not used when testing reflexes, examining the eardrums, or taking a specimen of vaginal secretions. (9:236)

95 4. RUQ, LUQ, RLQ, and LLQ are abbreviations describing the quadrants of the abdomen. The abbreviations stand for right upper quadrant, left upper quadrant, right lower quadrant, and left lower quadrant. (9:228)

96 1. An ophthalmoscope is used primarily to examine the retina of each eye. (9:237)

97 2. A speculum is used to visualize the interior surface when a body cavity is opened. (9:237)

98 3. The knee–chest position is often used for examining a patient's rectum. This is especially true if an instrument is used to examine the rectum. (9:241)

99 2. Stirrups are used for the lithotomy position. (9:240)

100 1. Gathering information through the sense of touch is called palpation. Percussion involves striking the body, either with fingers or with a percussion hammer. Inspection uses the senses of seeing, hearing, and smelling. Auscultation is listening to sounds within the body, usually with a stethoscope. (9:218)

101 3. An abnormal mass or lump is called a tumor. The tumor may be benign or malignant. An ulcer is an open lesion on the skin or mucous membrane. A crater is a lesion that has some depth or forms a depressed area. A fissure is a groove-like lesion. (12:940)

102 4. An organic heart murmur is caused by a defect in the action of heart valves. The defect does not allow the affected valve to close properly. Heart murmurs are unrelated to oxygenation of blood, the heart's ability to pump, or the capacity of coronary arteries. (10:187)

103 3. Patients who have had rheumatic fever often have heart valve problems, such as mitral stenosis, later in life. Complications involving the heart are not associated with measles, mononucleosis, and infectious hepatitis. (15:188)

104 1. A functional heart disorder, in contrast to an organic heart disease, is a disturbance in function with no organic cause. A functional heart murmur is often caused by emotional problems, such as those causing anxiety. (15:202–203)

105 2. Cutting nails deeply at the side most often causes ingrown toenails to develop. Toenails should be trimmed straight across with a file or nail scissors to prevent ingrown toenails. (9:82)

106 3. The name of the examiner, the time of the examination, and specimens collected are appropriate types of information to document in a patient's record. It is not necessary to describe various positions used during an examination because the information is irrelevant. (9:259, 261–262)

107 2. The exact cause of primary hypertension is unknown. However, heredity appears to play an important role, because strong familial tendencies are often noted. Other factors that appear to bring on hypertension include obesity, emotional stress, smoking, and high blood sodium and cholesterol levels. (15:376)

108 3. A chronically elevated diastolic pressure is a typical sign of primary hypertension and helps differentiate it from other types of hypertension. A diastolic pressure of 90 mm Hg often is used as the cut-off point to determine hypertension.   (15:376)

109 2.   When a patient seems worried and fearful, the nurse should give the patient opportunity to express her feelings first while the nurse listens. Teaching is usually not helpful when a patient is anxious. Eliminating the subject of worry is avoiding the problem and may have the patient feeling that the nurse does not care.   (8:391)

110 2.   Using the following formula, the nurse determines that the patient described in this item requires 4 tablets, each containing 250 mg, daily in order to obtain 1 g each day:

$$\frac{\text{Dose desired}}{\text{Dose on Hand}} = \text{Dose to administer}$$

A gram is equal to 1000 mg

$$\frac{1000}{250} = 4 \text{ tablets}$$

(14:10)

111 1.   Antihypertensive drugs tend to cause postural hypotension, and the patient therefore should be instructed to get up from a bed or chair *slowly*. Dizziness and light-headedness may result when this precaution is not observed. If postural hypotension does occur, the patient should be instructed to sit down and to avoid walking about. The patient should also be cautioned about driving a car in the presence of postural hypotension.   (14:117; 15:377)

112 2.   Patients with primary hypertension tend to retain fluids and sodium. A moderate- to low-sodium diet is most often prescribed for these patients.   (4:312)

113 2.   Pretzels are high in salt content and should be avoided by the patient described in this item. Snacks, such as oranges, carrots, and plain gelatin are not necessarily contraindicated because they are very low in sodium content.   (4:395–405)

114 1.   A calorie is a measure of heat that derives from the food we eat. It is defined as the amount of heat necessary to raise the temperature of 1 kilogram of water 1°C. Nutritionists also refer to a calorie as a kilocalorie, or the so-called big calorie. It may be abbreviated Kcal. The "small" calorie, which is 1/1,000 of a large calorie, is used in the science of chemistry and physics.   (4:44; 16:42)

115 4.   Hemorrhaging and occlusion of blood vessels in the body are relatively common complications of uncontrolled hypertension and occur in various places in the body, but most often in the brain (stroke), the eyes, the heart (myocardial infarction), and the kidneys.   (15:376)

116 1.   The nurse should teach the patient how to obtain her blood pressure when the patient is to monitor her disease (primary hypertension) at home. If the patient is unable to do this herself, a family member may be instructed to do so.   (15:377)

Classification of Test Items

Directions: *Each item in the previous review test is classified here according to the subject area it tests. Place a check mark after each item you answered* **correctly** *by referring to your answers. Total the number of items you answered correctly in each area and enter the numbers in the correct places on pages 553–556.*

Clinical: Medical/Surgical Nursing (Adults)

3 ✓	18 ✓	32 ✓	68 ✓	101 ✓	115 ✓
4 ✓	19 ✓	34 ✓	69 ✓	102 ✓	116 ✓
5 ✓	20 ✓	44 ✓	70 ✓	103 ✓	
9 ___	22 ___	46 ✓	71 ___	104 ___	
10 ✓	23 ___	49 ✓	72 ___	107 ✓	
16 ✓	26 ✓	51 ✓	73 ✓	108 ✓	

TOTAL 25

Biological/Physical Sciences

30 ✓	31 ✓	33 ✓	67 ✓

TOTAL 4

Fundamentals of Nursing

2 ✓	28 ✓	50 ✓	75 ✓	88 ___	97 ✓
11 ✓	35 ___	52 ✓	76 ✓	89 ___	98 ✓
12 ✓	38 ✓	53 ✓	77 ✓	90 ✓	99 ✓
13 ✓	39 ___	54 ✓	78 ✓	91 ✓	100 ✓
14 ✓	42 ✓	55 ✓	80 ✓	92 ___	105 ✓
15 ✓	43 ✓	57 ✓	84 ✓	93 ✓	106 ___
17 ✓	45 ✓	58 ✓	85 ✓	94 ✓	
24 ✓	47 ✓	62 ✓	86 ✓	95 ✓	
25 ✓	48 ✓	65 ___	87 ✓	96 ✓	

TOTAL 44

Diet Therapy/Nutrition

27 _____ 81 _____ 83 _____ 112 _____ 113 _____ 114 _____

37 _____ 82 _____

TOTAL __8__

Pharmacology

1 _____ 8 _____ 41 _____ 60 _____ 63 _____ 110 _____

6 _____ 36 _____ 56 _____ 61 _____ 64 _____ 111 _____

7 _____ 40 _____ 59 _____

TOTAL __15__

Psychosocial Sciences

21 _____ 29 _____ 66 _____ 74 _____ 79 _____ 109 _____

TOTAL __5__

Review Test 13

The Nursing Care of Patients With Disorders of the Cardiovascular System (Continued)

    Caring for a Patient With Angina Pectoris

    Caring for Patients With Various Peripheral Vascular Disorders

    Caring for a Patient Who Has Had a Cerebrovascular Accident (CVA)

The Nursing Care of Patients With Disorders of the Eye, Ear, and Nose

    Caring for Patients With Various Disorders of the Eye, Ear, and Nose

The Nursing Care of Patients With Disorders of the Endocrine System

    Caring for a Patient With Hyperthyroidism (Exophthalmic Goiter)

Individual Items
Correct Answers and Rationales
Classification of Items

Directions: *With a pencil, blacken the circle in front of the option you have chosen for your correct answer.*

The Nursing Care of Patients with Disorders of the Cardiovascular System (Continued)

Sixty-three-year-old Ms. Lee is hospitalized because of angina pectoris. She is to receive nitroglycerine.

1 Nitroglycerine is used for Ms. Lee because of the drug's ability to
    ○ 1. delay the blood-clotting process.
    ○ 2. increase the force of muscle contractions in the heart.
    ○ 3. relax smooth muscle in arterial blood vessels in the heart.
    ○ 4. promote the excretion of excess serum sodium through the kidneys.

2 Ms. Lee is to receive nitroglycerine as necessary (p.r.n.). Which of the following symptoms should cause the nurse to administer the nitroglycerine to Ms. Lee?

○ 1. Chest pain
○ 2. Facial edema
○ 3. Heart palpitations
○ 4. An irregular heart beat

3 The oral nitroglycerine for Ms. Lee is not to be swallowed. Where in her mouth should Ms. Lee hold the nitroglycerine tablet?
○ 1. Under the tongue
○ 2. Between the teeth and the upper gum
○ 3. Between the teeth and the lower gum
○ 4. Over the tongue against the hard palate

4 Ms. Lee should be taught that nitroglycerine deteriorates when exposed to air, especially in the presence of
○ 1. cold.
○ 2. heat.
○ 3. light.
○ 4. humidity.

The nurse goes to Ms. Lee's room to obtain her vital signs and to give her prescribed propoxyphene (Darvon).

5 Ms. Lee says to the nurse when she offers the patient the propoxyphene, "If that's Darvon, I don't want it. It makes me sick to my stomach and dizzy." The nurse's best course of action in this situation is to
○ 1. tell the patient that she has confused the drug with another.
○ 2. explain that the nurse is obligated to give the drug to the patient.
○ 3. teach the patient that she will not have these symptoms if she takes the drug with generous amounts of water.
○ 4. omit giving the drug to the patient and report the situation promptly to the nurse-in-charge.

6 Ms. Lee has just finished drinking hot tea when the nurse wishes to obtain Ms. Lee's oral temperature. For how long is it recommended that obtaining the oral temperature be delayed if the patient has recently been drinking a hot (or cold) beverage?
○ 1. 2 to 3 minutes
○ 2. 5 to 10 minutes
○ 3. 15 to 30 minutes
○ 4. 45 to 60 minutes

7 While obtaining her temperature, Ms. Lee tells the nurse that she notices weather makes a difference in relation to symptoms due to angina pectoris. Where in this country is year-round-living likely to aggravate Ms. Lee's illness most?
○ 1. In the New England states
○ 2. In Florida and coastal California
○ 3. In the Appalachian plateau states
○ 4. In Texas along the gulf and Mexican border

A Nurse works in a Health Maintenance Organization Where She Helps with the Care of Patients with Various Peripheral Vascular Disorders.

Ms. Eggers has surgery for the ligation and stripping of varicose veins in her leg.

8 Ms. Eggers asks the nurse how circulation will be provided in her leg after surgery. The nurse should base her response on knowledge that
   ○ 1. certain arteries begin to function as veins.
   ○ 2. new veins develop to replace the removed veins.
   ○ 3. veins deep in the leg take over the work of the removed veins.
   ○ 4. the end of ligated veins are anastomosed for continuity of veins.

9 Which of the following faults in her veins most likely caused Ms. Eggers to develop varicosities?
   ○ 1. Blood clots in the venous system
   ○ 2. An inflammation of walls in the veins
   ○ 3. A thickening of the walls of the veins
   ○ 4. An incompetency of the valves of the veins

Ms. Adler has Raynaud's disease.

10 A plan of teaching for Ms. Adler should include explaining that it is important for her to *avoid*
   ○ 1. wearing gloves.
   ○ 2. smoking cigarettes.
   ○ 3. drinking alcoholic beverages.
   ○ 4. washing with perfumed soap.

11 Ms. Adler can expect that the discomfort in her fingers will be made *worse* if she
   ○ 1. exercises her hands.
   ○ 2. allows her hands to become cold.
   ○ 3. washes her hands in warm water.
   ○ 4. holds her hands in a dependent position.
   ○

12 Ms. Adler's Raynaud's disease becomes worse with time. It can be anticipated that with disease progression, the patient's fingers are very likely to develop
   ○ 1. contractures.
   ○ 2. chronic swelling.
   ○ 3. thickened fingernails.
   ○ 4. ulcers with superficial gangrene.

Mr. Bostrum suffers with thromboangitis obliterans (Buerger's disease) and has a leg ulcer.

13 Because of the nature of his illness, which of the following pharmaceutical regimens is *contraindicated* for Mr. Bostrum?
  ○ 1. Enzymes to help clean the leg ulcer
  ○ 2. Antibiotics to control infection in the leg ulcer
  ○ 3. Adrenergic-blocking agents to dilate blood vessels
  ○ 4. Narcotics to help control the attacks of discomfort

14 In relation to its manner of healing, Mr. Bostrum's leg ulcer can be expected to
  ○ 1. require a long period of time to heal.
  ○ 2. heal with large amounts of scar tissue.
  ○ 3. heal from the center rather than from the edges.
  ○ 4. require repeated surgical incisions to promote drainage.

Mr. Baum is a 74-year-old gentleman who has had a cerebrovascular accident (CVA). His right side is paralyzed.

15 The hospital's admitting officer tells the nurse, "I think Mr. Baum is having delusions." If the officer is using the word *delusions* correctly, it means that the patient is demonstrating
  ○ 1. false beliefs.
  ○ 2. distrust of others.
  ○ 3. imagined sensory impulses.
  ○ 4. incorrectly perceived sensory impulses.

16 A health problem that is most likely described in Mr. Baum's health summary is a history of having
  ○ 1. varicosities.
  ○ 2. indigestion.
  ○ 3. hypertension.
  ○ 4. chronic gallbladder disease.

17 The type of paralysis that Mr. Baum has is called
  ○ 1. uniplegia.
  ○ 2. paraplegia.
  ○ 3. hemiplegia.
  ○ 4. quadriplegia.

18 Mr. Baum is wearing a pullover sweater when he enters the hospital. Which of the following steps should the nurse take first to remove the sweater?
  ○ 1. Remove the sleeve from the left arm.
  ○ 2. Remove the sleeve from the right arm.
  ○ 3. Remove both sleeves together, after slipping the sweater over the patient's head.

    ○ 4. Remove both sleeves, before slipping the sweater over the patient's head.

19 Mr. Baum tells the admitting nurse that he has "awful palpitations." If he is using the word *palpitations* correctly, he is describing that he

    ○ 1. is aware that he has high blood pressure.

    ○ 2. is aware of his heartbeat without feeling for a pulse.

    ○ 3. can feel at an artery that he has a very irregular heartbeat.

    ○ 4. can see arteries on his forearm without closing off circulation.

20 After completing admission procedures, the nurse positions Mr. Baum on his left side. If the nurse uses the following techniques while positioning Mr. Baum, which one is in *error*?

    ○ 1. The nurse supports the patient's right arm on pillows.

    ○ 2. The nurse places a small pillow under the patient's neck and head.

    ○ 3. The nurse allows the patient's right leg and foot to rest flat on the mattress.

    ○ 4. The nurse flexes the patient's left arm and rests the arm alongside the patient's head.

21 Mr. Baum tells the nurse that he is hungry but refuses food and points to his water pitcher. This inability to use the correct word for a thought is called

    ○ 1. aphasia.

    ○ 2. delirium.

    ○ 3. neologism.

    ○ 4. incoherence.

22 Mr. Baum is to have a subcutaneous injection. The nurse should *avoid* giving the injection into Mr. Baum's

    ○ 1. back.

    ○ 2. left arm.

    ○ 3. right arm.

    ○ 4. abdomen.

Mr. Baum develops an infection and his temperature rises to 106° F (41° C).

23 A hypothermic blanket is used to help reduce Mr. Baum's temperature. The cooling device on a hypothermic blanket should be *shut off* when Mr. Baum's temperature is

    ○ 1. at the desired temperature.

    ○ 2. a degree or two above the desired temperature.

    ○ 3. a degree or two below the desired temperature.

    ○ 4. about four degrees below the desired temperature.

24 While Mr. Baum's temperature is elevated, of the following signs or symptoms, he is *unlikely* to demonstrate

    ○ 1. restlessness.

    ○ 2. a flushed skin.
    ○ 3. feelings of thirst.
    ○ 4. a slow respiratory rate.

25 When Mr. Baum's body temperature is elevated, his pulse rate, when compared with normal, will most likely be
    ○ 1. weak.
    ○ 2. irregular.
    ○ 3. alternating.
    ○ 4. accelerated.

Mr. Baum is to have a soft (bland) diet and his intake and output are to be measured.

26 If the nurse notes the following foods on one of Mr. Baum's dinner trays, which one should she question as having been prepared in *error* for Mr. Baum?
    ○ 1. Rice
    ○ 2. Postum
    ○ 3. Southern fried chicken
    ○ 4. Sweetened canned peaches

27 When served his special diet, Mr. Baum says angrily, "Whoever could eat such poorly seasoned food!" Of the following comments the nurse could make, it would be best for her to say,
    ○ 1. "Do you want me to take your food away?"
    ○ 2. "This special diet will help you get well faster."
    ○ 3. "Your doctor ordered the diet for your own good."
    ○ 4. "It is difficult when you can't eat what you like, isn't it?"

28 Mr. Baum says he has no appetite. A loss of appetite is called
    ○ 1. alopecia.
    ○ 2. anorexia.
    ○ 3. dyspepsia.
    ○ 4. malnutrition.

29 If Mr. Baum has the following nourishment during the course of a day, which one ordinarily is *not* recorded as fluid intake?
    ○ 1. Gelatin
    ○ 2. Iced tea
    ○ 3. Malted milk
    ○ 4. Strained fruit

Mr. Baum's blood tests show that he is anemic. He is to have a regular diet that is high in iron content.

30 If Mr. Baum enjoys the following foods, which are foods he should be taught are high in iron?
    ○ 1. Citrus fruits

    ○ 2. Milk and cheese
    ○ 3. Most gelatin desserts
    ○ 4. Most meats and poultry

31 Mr. Baum needs a well-balanced diet but when compared with younger adults, his diet should have a higher-than-average amount of
    ○ 1. fats.
    ○ 2. liquids.
    ○ 3. proteins.
    ○ 4. carbohydrates.

32 One day Mr. Baum, who is of the Jewish religion, orders fish for dinner. Which of the following sea foods would be *unacceptable* to him?
    ○ 1. Tuna
    ○ 2. Trout
    ○ 3. Salmon
    ○ 4. Shrimp

33 Mr. Baum refuses to eat certain food on his tray because the food is not prepared according to his religious beliefs. In this situation, it would be best for the nurse first to
    ○ 1. notify the agency's dietician.
    ○ 2. call the physician for a change in orders.
    ○ 3. ask a friend to bring food from home for the patient.
    ○ 4. teach the patient the importance of eating in order to get well.

The nurse gives Mr. Baum oral hygiene after he eats.

34 The nurse should use warm water rather than hot water to clean Mr. Baum's dentures because hot water is likely to
    ○ 1. warp the dentures.
    ○ 2. loosen teeth in the dentures.
    ○ 3. alter the color of the teeth in the dentures.
    ○ 4. break the plates in which the teeth are anchored.

35 The loss of Mr. Baum's permanent teeth is most likely due to his having had
    ○ 1. gum disease.
    ○ 2. dental caries.
    ○ 3. poor occlusion of his teeth.
    ○ 4. early loss of his deciduous ("baby") teeth.

Mr. Baum is bedridden and inactive.

36 The nurse performs range-of-motion exercises for Mr. Baum and after being taught, Mr. Baum performs some exercises for himself. The primary goal of these exercises is to help
    ○ 1. stimulate circulation.
    ○ 2. prevent muscle atrophy.

○ 3. improve transmission of nerve impulses.
○ 4. decrease the likelihood of pathological fractures.

37 Because Mr. Baum is at risk for developing decubitus ulcers, the nurse considers various methods to prevent them. Which of the following devices is likely to *predispose* to decubitus ulcer formation?
○ 1. A flotation pad
○ 2. A water mattress
○ 3. An air-inflated doughnut
○ 4. An alternating pressure pad

38 The nurse should observe Mr. Baum carefully for the earliest sign of a decubitus ulcer, which is present when the color of the skin over a body part becomes
○ 1. bluish.
○ 2. whitish.
○ 3. purplish.
○ 4. yellowish.

39 Because Mr. Baum is at risk for developing decubitus ulcers, it is recommended that he should have his position changed as frequently as every
○ 1. ½ to 1 hour.
○ 2. 1 to 2 hours.
○ 3. 3 to 4 hours.
○ 4. 4 to 6 hours.

40 If Mr. Baum develops a decubitus ulcer, of the following factors, the one chiefly responsible for its development is
○ 1. a poorly balanced diet.
○ 2. an inadequate fluid intake.
○ 3. lack of feeling in a body part.
○ 4. pressure on an area of the body.

41 The best general treatment for a decubitus ulcer is to use
○ 1. gelatin foam.
○ 2. karaya powder.
○ 3. tannic acid spray.
○ 4. preventive measures.

Mr. Baum has not had a bowel movement for three days.

42 Mr. Baum is to receive the bulk-forming laxative, psyllium (Metamucil). When administering this laxative, the nurse should be sure she gives it to Mr. Baum with
○ 1. milk.
○ 2. a meal.
○ 3. any acidic fruit juice.
○ 4. generous amounts of fluid.

43 Mr. Baum refuses the psyllium and insists on having milk of magnesia

for constipation. The order is changed accordingly. The nurse should question the order unless the dosage for Mr. Baum is between
○ 1. 2 ml and 4 ml.
○ 2. 5 ml and 10 ml.
○ 3. 15 ml and 30 ml.
○ 4. 45 ml and 60 ml.

Mr. Baum is to be out of bed.

44 Mr. Baum is helped to sit up in a wheelchair. Before moving him from his bed to the wheelchair, for safety purposes, the nurse should prepare the chair by
○ 1. removing its arm rests.
○ 2. extending its foot and leg rests.
○ 3. locking its wheels and lifting the foot rests.
○ 4. placing small pillows on the seat and against the chair's backrest.

45 Mr. Baum's physical condition improves enough so that he can use a walker. If he uses the following techniques when using the walker, which one is in *error*?
○ 1. The patient looks at the floor as he walks.
○ 2. The patient's elbows are flexed about 30 degrees.
○ 3. The patient walks with his feet about 6 inches apart.
○ 4. The patient lifts the walker slightly as he moves it forward.

The nurse who has been caring for Mr. Baum most often is about to leave on vacation.

46 Mr. Baum's nurse sees to it that while she is away, the nurse who will be responsible for her patients is familiar with the care they require. This type of planning is generally called
○ 1. holistic care.
○ 2. preventive care.
○ 3. continuity of care.
○ 4. comprehensive care.

Mr. Baum is transferred to a nursing home. The report from the hospital nurses indicates that Mr. Baum " . . .is often difficult because of personality changes that reportedly occurred when he became ill."

47 If a nurse makes the following four comments to Mr. Baum when admitting him to the nursing home, which one is *least* likely to promote a helping nurse–patient relationship?
○ 1. "Hello, Mr. Baum. I am Ms. Bolting, a practical nurse."
○ 2. "Let's get you settled, shall we? I want to bathe you before going off duty."

○ 3. "Your roommate's name is Mr. Ardon. Would you like to meet him now?"

○ 4. "You press this button on this signal device here on your bed if you want a nurse for something."

48 Mr. Baum tells his admitting nurse at the nursing home, "You are really a dummy. How do you think you can help me?" In this situation, it would be best for the nurse to

○ 1. ask the patient to describe why he dislikes her.

○ 2. question whether anyone can really help this patient.

○ 3. allow the patient to express his dislike in a nonjudgmental atmosphere.

○ 4. request an assignment change because of the patient's hostility toward her.

49 Mr. Baum is discussed in a nursing conference. One nurse says, "He always wants something and wants to change everything. He never seems satisfied." Of the following suggestions that are offered concerning reasons for Mr. Baum's behavior, the one which is probably most appropriate is that the patient is very likely

○ 1. seeking emotional support.

○ 2. suffering from heart damage.

○ 3. showing distrust of his caregivers.

○ 4. trying to use authority he once had.

50 After his daughter visits Mr. Baum one day, she tells the nurse that her father is showing behaviors described below, none of which was typical of her father before he was hospitalized. Of these behaviors, the most common sign of cerebrovascular disease is

○ 1. forgetting recent events.

○ 2. insisting that he is well.

○ 3. wanting to find a new hobby.

○ 4. refusing to take medications.

51 Mr. Baum mutters dejectedly one day, "I wish I would die. I'm worth absolutely nothing anymore." In this situation, it would be best for the nurse to

○ 1. call the patient's daughter.

○ 2. change the subject of conversation.

○ 3. silently ignore the patient's comment.

○ 4. indicate that she cares for the patient.

52 Some of Mr. Baum's behaviors are believed due more to functional senility (senile-like behaviors that are not based on pathological changes) than to behaviors that are based on pathological changes. The nurse helps prepare a care plan for Mr. Baum that includes remotivation and behavior modification to help change certain aspects of Mr. Baum's behavior. Which of the following techniques is *least* likely to assist in reaching that goal?

○ 1. Encouraging the patient to join an arts and craft group

    ○ 2. Making the patient aware of behaviors that are unsatisfactory

    ○ 3. Using group therapy to bring about meaningful conversation among patients

    ○ 4. Allowing the patient to make as many choices as possible in his activities of daily living

53 Those personality changes that Mr. Baum is experiencing and that are believed to be associated with cerebrovascular disease, are primarily due to

    ○ 1. destruction of brain cells deprived of oxygen.

    ○ 2. degeneration of brain neurons and nerve fibers.

    ○ 3. decreased efficiency in the pumping ability of the heart.

    ○ 4. poor exchanges of oxygen and carbon dioxide in the lungs.

54 The primary reason that cerebrovascular disease is seen in this country more now than in the past is that

    ○ 1. living alone has increased.

    ○ 2. life expectancy has increased.

    ○ 3. care of the elderly has been neglected.

    ○ 4. stresses of daily living have increased.

The Nursing Care of Patients with Disorders of the Eye, Ear, and Nose

A nurse is newly assigned to care for patients with eye, ear, and nose disorders. In preparation for her new assignment, the nurse studies the anatomy and physiology of these organs before starting care of patients with various disorders.

55 The nurse reviews the functions of the eye's vision receptors which are located in the

    ○ 1. sclera.

    ○ 2. cornea.

    ○ 3. retina.

    ○ 4. choroid.

56 The nurse learns that the structure in the eye that changes the size of the pupil to control the amount of light entering the eye is the

    ○ 1. iris.

    ○ 2. lens.

    ○ 3. optic disc.

    ○ 4. fovea centralis.

57 According to her review, the nurse determines that another word for nearsightedness is

    ○ 1. myopia.

    ○ 2. hyperopia.

    ○ 3. presbyopia.

    ○ 4. astigmatism.

58 The nurse learns that the nerve that carries visual impulses from the eye to the brain is the

    ○ 1. optic nerve.
    ○ 2. trochlear nerve.
    ○ 3. abducens nerve.
    ○ 4. ophthalmic nerve.

59 The nurse's examination of the model of a human ear illustrates that the two structures connected by the eustachian tube are the

    ○ 1. outer and inner ear.
    ○ 2. middle and inner ear.
    ○ 3. inner ear and the pharynx.
    ○ 4. middle ear and the pharynx.

60 Which of the structures in the ears should the nurse examine when she studies sensory cells related to the body's sense of equilibrium?

    ○ 1. The stapes
    ○ 2. The eustachian tubes
    ○ 3. The tympanic membranes
    ○ 4. The semicircular canals

61 The nurse's review recalls for her that an important function of the sinuses in bones of the skull is to

    ○ 1. give resonance to the voice.
    ○ 2. add humidity to inhaled air.
    ○ 3. filter impurities from inhaled air.
    ○ 4. produce secretions to lubricate nasal mucosa.

62 Ms. Etinger has chronic glaucoma. When Ms. Etinger first seeks health care concerning her eyes, she is most likely to complain of

    ○ 1. having double vision.
    ○ 2. having excessive tearing.
    ○ 3. seeing floating objects.
    ○ 4. seeing halos around lights.

63 Which of the following drugs is *contraindicated* for Ms. Etinger because of her glaucoma?

    ○ 1. Atropine sulfate
    ○ 2. Morphine sulfate
    ○ 3. Physostigmine (Eserine)
    ○ 4. Acetazolamide (Diamox)

64 Ms. Etinger should be taught that of the following activities, the one that tends to aggravate glaucoma is

    ○ 1. crying.
    ○ 2. chewing.
    ○ 3. laughing.
    ○ 4. frowning.

65　Ms. Etinger is receiving eyedrops in both eyes. The correct abbreviation for both eyes is
　　○　1.　OD.
　　○　2.　OS.
　　○　3.　OP.
　　○　4.　OU.

66　Where in Ms. Etinger's eyes should eyedrops be placed?
　　○　1.　On the eyeball
　　○　2.　At the inner canthus
　　○　3.　At the outer canthus
　　○　4.　In the lower conjunctival sac

67　Ms. Etinger uses a miotic eyedrop. A miotic acts in the eyes to
　　○　1.　dilate the pupils.
　　○　2.　constrict the pupils.
　　○　3.　stimulate the production of tears.
　　○　4.　paralyze the muscles of accommodation.

68　When Ms. Etinger questions the nurse about glaucoma, the nurse should base her response on knowledge that glaucoma is best described as
　　○　1.　acute irritation of the cornea.
　　○　2.　chronic inflammation of the retina.
　　○　3.　excess pressure of fluid within the eye.
　　○　4.　diminished response of the eye to extremes of light.

69　Mr. Maloney has a foreign body in his eye and is to have his eye irrigated. The solution of choice when irrigating Mr. Maloney's eye is sterile
　　○　1.　water.
　　○　2.　normal saline.
　　○　3.　bacteriostatic water.
　　○　4.　sodium bicarbonate solution.

70　When irrigating Mr. Maloney's eye, where should the nurse direct the solution?
　　○　1.　Toward the inner canthus
　　○　2.　Toward the outer canthus
　　○　3.　Onto the lower conjunctival sac
　　○　4.　Onto the upper conjunctival sac

71　Because improper emergency care was given when swimming-pool acid splashed into his eye at another time, Mr. Maloney has a corneal ulcer. Proper emergency care for Mr. Maloney should have included
　　○　1.　placing ointment in the eyes.
　　○　2.　flushing the eyes with tap water.
　　○　3.　applying a dressing over the eyes.
　　○　4.　placing drops of boric acid solution in the eyes.

72 Mr. Myer uses an artificial eye. When removing Mr. Myer's artificial eye, it is best to do so by
  ○ 1. lifting the upper eyelid.
  ○ 2. inverting the upper eyelid.
  ○ 3. separating the two eyelids.
  ○ 4. depressing the lower eyelid.

73 It is generally recommended that it is best to clean Mr. Myer's artificial eye in a solution of water and
  ○ 1. salt.
  ○ 2. soap.
  ○ 3. sodium bicarbonate.
  ○ 4. hydrogen peroxide.

74 Mr. Yulanski has had surgery for a detached retina. Unless orders to the contrary are given, an important aspect of Mr. Yulanski's care during the early postoperative period is
  ○ 1. keeping the patient quiet in bed.
  ○ 2. restricting the patient's fluid intake.
  ○ 3. having the patient in a sitting position.
  ○ 4. providing bright light in the patient's room.

75 Mr. Shower has had a cataract removed and is being observed postoperatively for symptoms of hemorrhaging. A very common symptom Mr. Shower is likely to present when there is excessive bleeding in the eye after cataract removal is
  ○ 1. double vision.
  ○ 2. protracted nausea.
  ○ 3. severe pain in the operated eye.
  ○ 4. a sensation of rapid eye movement in the operated eye.

76 During the early postoperative period, Mr. Shower should be taught to *avoid* activity that includes
  ○ 1. turning in bed.
  ○ 2. taking very deep breaths.
  ○ 3. flexing his knees to stoop to floor level.
  ○ 4. straining when he has a bowel movement.

77 Of the following patients with eye disorders for whom the nurse is caring, which one should the nurse teach that the condition is more common among people who have a history of the disease in the family?
  ○ 1. Mr. Shower, who has a cataract
  ○ 2. Ms. Etinger, who has glaucoma
  ○ 3. Mr. Maloney, who has a corneal ulcer
  ○ 4. Mr. Yulanski, who has a detached retina

78 Ms. Zimmer has Meniere's disease. Symptoms of which Ms. Zimmer is most likely to complain include ringing in the ears and sporadic attacks of
  ○ 1. dizziness.
  ○ 2. deafness.

     ○ 3. blackouts.
     ○ 4. blindness.

79 Ms. Zimmer is to have ear drops instilled into her ears. Sterile technique should be used when instilling drops into Ms. Zimmer's ears if the patient has
     ○ 1. a loss of hearing.
     ○ 2. a ruptured eardrum.
     ○ 3. an inner ear infection.
     ○ 4. a foreign object in the ear canal.

80 In what direction should the nurse pull on Ms. Zimmer's ear when introducing eardrops?
     ○ 1. Upward and backward
     ○ 2. Downward and forward
     ○ 3. Toward the side of the head
     ○ 4. Away from the side of the head

81 Ms. Wrenn seeks health care because of severe sinusitis. Ms. Wrenn's illness is treated seriously because a complication of severe sinusitis is
     ○ 1. tonsillitis.
     ○ 2. laryngitis.
     ○ 3. endocarditis.
     ○ 4. otitis media.

82 Care for Ms. Wrenn includes using nosedrops. The preferred position when introducing nosedrops is to have Ms. Wrenn
     ○ 1. on either side with her head tilted back.
     ○ 2. on her back with her head over a pillow.
     ○ 3. in a sitting position with her head held straight.
     ○ 4. in a semi-sitting position with her head resting on the mattress.

83 Ms. Wrenn is to use Neo-Synephrine nosedrops at home. She should be taught that one danger of over-medicating with nosedrops for a "stuffy" nose is that the
     ○ 1. sinuses eventually will become irritated.
     ○ 2. nasal tissues eventually will become even more congested.
     ○ 3. throat membranes eventually will be infected wih organisms from the nose.
     ○ 4. nasal turbinates eventually will be robbed of necessary blood supplies.

84 Ms. Wrenn is to use a steam humidifier in her bedroom to help relieve congestion. Ms. Wrenn should be warned that a risk when using a steam humidifier is that the equipment can cause
     ○ 1. a fire when the water reservoir runs dry.
     ○ 2. excess saturation of moisture in the room.
     ○ 3. burns to a person when it becomes very hot.
     ○ 4. rapid growth of organisms in the environment.

The Nursing Care of Patients with Disorders of the Endocrine System

Ms. Penner has been treated for hyperthyroidism (exophthalmic goiter). She has failed to respond to conservative therapy and is admitted to a hospital for a thyroidectomy.

85   Ms. Penner's hyperthyroidism is an endocrine disorder. A characteristic of the anatomy of endocrine glands is that they are without
○ 1. ducts.
○ 2. nerve supplies.
○ 3. blood vessels.
○ 4. epithelial tissues.

86   Upon admission to the hospital, the nurse learns that radioactive iodine (^{131}I) has been used to treat Ms. Penner's hyperthyroidism. A danger in using this agent is that it may
○ 1. affect other healthy glands.
○ 2. cause cancer of the thyroid gland.
○ 3. present a radiation threat to others.
○ 4. tend to predispose to hypothyroidism.

87   Of the following signs and symptoms, the one Ms. Penner is *least* likely to present upon admission is
○ 1. hand tremors.
○ 2. emotional listlessness.
○ 3. an elevated pulse rate.
○ 4. an elevated systolic blood pressure.

88   In terms of weather conditions, it is typical when Ms. Penner tells the admitting nurse that she *cannot* tolerate weather that is
○ 1. cold.
○ 2. warm.
○ 3. windy.
○ 4. humid.

89   Upon admission, the type of diet most likely ordered for Ms. Penner is
○ 1. high in iron.
○ 2. low in sodium.
○ 3. low in protein.
○ 4. high in calories.

90   The nutrient most likely to be in short supply in Ms. Penner's diet, if she had been found to have nontoxic (endemic, simple, or colloid) goiter, rather than exophthalmic goiter is
○ 1. iron.
○ 2. iodine.
○ 3. calcium.
○ 4. potassium.

91 If Ms. Penner had a deficiency in the normal production of thyroxine over a prolonged period, rather than an over-production of thyroxine, she would now be likely to be suffering with
   O 1. cretinism.
   O 2. myxedema.
   O 3. Graves' disease.
   O 4. Addison's disease

Ms. Penner is to have iodine (Lugol's) solution.

92 The dosage of iodine solution that Ms. Penner is to receive is stated in drops. The most commonly accepted abbreviation for a drop is
   O 1. dr.
   O 2. gr.
   O 3. gtt.
   O 4. drp.
93 When giving Ms. Penner the iodine solution, the nurse should administer it while using a
   O 1. dosing spoon.
   O 2. medicine dropper.
   O 3. straw (drinking tube).
   O 4. glass (not plastic) medicine cup.

The nurse plans Ms. Penner's preoperative care while taking her surroundings into account.

94 In relation to her surroundings, the goal of Ms. Penner's preoperative nursing care should be to
   O 1. keep the patient occupied and active.
   O 2. provide a restful and relaxing atmosphere.
   O 3. encourage visiting with family and friends.
   O 4. have thought-provoking and stimulating leisure activities.
95 Ms. Penner's preoperative care is planned in terms of the definition, "Everything surrounding and influencing one's (that is, Ms. Penner's) life." This quoted definition best describes the word,
   O 1. society.
   O 2. ecology.
   O 3. stimulus.
   O 4. environment.

Ms. Penner returns to her room after initial postoperative care in the recovery room.

96 The position of choice for Ms. Penner when she arrives in her room following surgery is

     ○ 1. on either side.
     ○ 2. flat on her back.
     ○ 3. in a semi-Fowler's position.
     ○ 4. in a modified Trendelenburg position.

97 Ms. Penner's head should be firmly supported by having her neck in a position of
     ○ 1. extension.
     ○ 2. slight flexion.
     ○ 3. slight rotation.
     ○ 4. hyperextension.

98 Which of the following equipment should be kept readily available for emergency use during Ms. Penner's postoperative period?
     ○ 1. Equipment to control bleeding, such as a tourniquet
     ○ 2. Equipment to interrupt cardiac fibrillations, such as a defibrillator
     ○ 3. Equipment to provide for an open airway, such as a tracheostomy set
     ○ 4. Equipment to give rescue breathing, such as a self-inflating breathing mask and bag

99 Where should the nurse check Ms. Penner especially carefully postoperatively when assessing for excessive bleeding from the operative site?
     ○ 1. On the patient's neck under her chin
     ○ 2. On bed linens under the patient's neck
     ○ 3. On the uppermost gauze in the patient's dressing
     ○ 4. On adhesive strips used to secure the patient's dressing

100 Postoperatively the nurse asks Ms. Penner to speak from time to time. The purpose of this assessment is to help determine whether
     ○ 1. the respiratory passageways are open.
     ○ 2. the laryngeal nerve was damaged during surgery.
     ○ 3. excessive thyroid tissue was removed during surgery.
     ○ 4. excessive bleeding is occurring in the operative site.

101 If Ms. Penner's parathyroid glands are accidently damaged or removed during surgery, she may develop tetany, due to a disturbance in the body's regulation of the mineral
     ○ 1. zinc.
     ○ 2. copper.
     ○ 3. calcium.
     ○ 4. magnesium.

102 The nurse should observe Ms. Penner postoperatively for evidence of a thyroid crisis. Two common signs of this complication are
     ○ 1. muscle cramps and twitching.
     ○ 2. difficulty with swallowing and breathing.
     ○ 3. a reduction in urine production and albuminuria.
     ○ 4. an elevated body temperature and a rapid pulse rate.

103 The nurse should teach Ms. Penner to move in bed to a full sitting position postoperatively by
○ 1. supporting her head with her hands as she moves to a sitting position.
○ 2. reaching toward her toes with her hands as she moves to a sitting position.
○ 3. turning to the side and then pushing herself up with her hands and arms to a sitting position.
○ 4. turning onto her abdomen, pushing herself up with her hands and arms, and then turning herself to a sitting position.

104 Ms. Penner uses an incentive spirometer. Most incentive spirometers are designed to encourage the patient to breathe by
○ 1. inhaling deeply.
○ 2. inhaling quickly.
○ 3. exhaling slowly.
○ 4. exhaling forcibly.

The Remaining Items are Individual Items Dealing with Medical-Surgical Nursing Care.

105 A patient has a severe nosebleed that cannot be stopped with external pressure. A packing is inserted into the patient's nostril and moistened with epinephrine (adrenalin). In this situation, epinephrine is used because of its ability to
○ 1. control infection.
○ 2. hasten blood clotting.
○ 3. constrict blood vessels.
○ 4. increase pressure in the nostril.

106 A nurse cares for two patients, both of whom have respiratory infections and are on types of isolation that require using masks. She gives medications to these two persons, returns to the nurses' station to record giving the medications, and then returns to give each patient a bed bath. How many masks will the nurse need in this situation?
○ 1. One
○ 2. Two
○ 3. Three
○ 4. Four

107 If a patient has a gastrostomy tube, where is the tube inserted into the body?
○ 1. Through the nose
○ 2. Through the mouth
○ 3. Through an opening in the stomach
○ 4. Through an opening in the small intestine

108 The most typical characteristic of atherosclerosis that distinguishes it from other blood vessel conditions is that atherosclerotic arteries
  O 1. are rigid.
  O 2. are enlarged.
  O 3. contain fatty plaques.
  O 4. have small, herniated areas.

109 The substance in the body that begins the blood-clotting mechanism is called
  O 1. thrombin.
  O 2. fibrinogen.
  O 3. prothrombin.
  O 4. thromboplastin.

110 Bacterial endocarditis frequently is noted to be a complication of the illness
  O 1. meningitis.
  O 2. rheumatic fever.
  O 3. infectious hepatitis.
  O 4. herpes zoster (shingles).

111 A person learns from his health caretakers that he has been having TIAs (transient ischemic attacks). The sympoms of TIAs are due primarily to
  O 1. rapid dilatation of cerebral arterioles.
  O 2. poor supply of oxygen to a part of the brain.
  O 3. successive periods when the blood pressure falls quickly.
  O 4. partial blockage in the flow of fluid through the brain's ventricles.

112 A nurse is caring for a person with paralytic ileus. Of the following signs, the one most characteristic of this disorder is
  O 1. diarrhea.
  O 2. vomiting of blood.
  O 3. abdominal distention.
  O 4. diaphragmatic spasms.

113 Trichinosis most often is transmitted to humans by eating improperly cooked
  O 1. fish.
  O 2. pork.
  O 3. rabbit.
  O 4. poultry.

Correct Answers and Rationales

Two numbers appear in parentheses following each rationale. The first number identifies the textbook listed in the references, page 649, and the second number identifies the page(s) in that textbook where the correct answer can be verified. Occasionally, two textbooks are given for verifying the correct answer.

The Nursing Care of Patients with Disorders of the Cardiovascular System

Caring for a patient with angina pectoris

1 3. Nitroglycerine is a vasodilator. It is used commonly for persons with angina pectoris to dilate arterial blood vessels in the heart by causing smooth muscles in blood vessels to relax. This results in improved circulation to the heart's myocardium. Cardiotonic agents increase the force of the ventricular heart beat; an example is digitalis. Diuretics promote urinary excretion, including excretion of excess sodium; an example is furosemide (Lasix). Anticoagulants delay the bloodclotting process; an example is warfarin sodium (Coumadin). (14:98)

2 1. Nitroglycerin is administered for anginal chest pain. The pain ordinarily comes on suddenly and often radiates to the shoulders and arms. The drug normally acts rapidly to relieve the pain. (15:373)

3 1. Nitroglycerine is placed under the tongue when it is administered sublingually. The blood vessels are close to the surface in this area, which makes absorption into the bloodstream relatively easy. If the drug is to be administered sublingually and is swallowed instead, its effectiveness is destroyed and it may cause gastric distress. There are presently some nitroglycerine preparations that can be swallowed and that have sustained-action properties. Another way to administer nitroglycerine is transdermally. (9:540)

4 3. Nitroglycerine exposed to air, and especially to light, deteriorates rapidly. Persons taking the drug should be taught that nitroglycerine should be kept in a dark container with a firmly fitted cap. For best results, it is advised that persons taking nitroglycerine replace their supply approximately every 3 months to be assured that their supply is fresh and free of deterioration. (14:101)

5 4. When a patient states that she has unfavorable reactions to a particular medication, the nurse should not give the medication and should report the situation to the nurse-in-charge. Common adverse effects to propoxyphene hydrochloride (Darvon) include gastrointestinal disturbances, dizzi-

---

ness, headaches, and skin rash. It is inappropriate to give a medication to a patient who complains that the drug makes her ill.   (9:546)

6   3.   Obtaining a patient's oral temperature should be delayed 15 to 30 minutes when the patient has recently had hot or cold fluids, for accuracy of thermometer readings. A longer period may be used but it is unnecessary, and during a longer delay, the patient may again take fluids.   (9:192)

7   1.   Cold weather tends to constrict blood vessels, and the patient with angina pectoris is already suffering from constricted vessels. Therefore, angina victims would find cold New England weather likely to aggravate their illness. Florida, coastal California, Appalachian plateau states, and southern Texas have relatively mild and warm weather.   (8:366)

Caring for patients with various peripheral vascular disorders

8   3.   When veins are ligated and stripped, the affected veins are severed and removed. The blood then returns through veins deeper in the leg so that return circulation continues. New veins do not replace those removed, nor do arteries take over the functions of veins. Entire veins often are removed and their ends are ligated, not anastomosed.   (12:386)

9   4.   Unlike arteries, most veins have one-way valves that function to allow blood to flow in only one direction. These valves become incompetent and the veins then become dilated and tortuous when varicosities are present. Veins are thinner when compared with comparable arteries. They do not tend to thicken or fill with deposits as arteries do. Blood clots and inflamed veins do not predispose to varicosities.   (12:385)

10   2.   Raynaud's disease typically attacks fingers and toes. The affected areas feel cold, numb, and prickly due to poor circulation, probably because of vasospasms. Because nicotine in cigarettes causes vasoconstriction, cigarette smoking should be avoided by the person with Raynaud's disease. Drinking alcoholic beverages, wearing gloves, and washing with perfumed soaps are not necessarily contraindicated for the patient with Raynaud's disease.   (15:384–385)

11   2.   The discomfort associated with Raynaud's disease occurs intermittently but almost always when there is exposure to cold because cold causes constriction of arteries. Exercising, washing the hands in warm water, and holding the hands in a dependent position are not associated with attacks of pain.   (15:384–385)

12   4.   Ulcers and superficial gangrene are typical as Raynaud's disease progresses. The lesions are easily infected and healing is slow. Thickening of fingernails, chronic swelling of the fingers, and contractures of the fingers are not associated with Raynaud's disease.   (15:383)

13   4.   Buerger's disease is a chronic condition and attacks of acute discomfort are common. Because of its chronic nature, narcotics for the control of pain are contraindicated to avoid the danger of addiction. Adrenergic-blocking agents, antibiotics, and enzymes frequently are used to help to control the disease and leg ulcers that often develop.   (15:385)

14   1.   When the patient has Buerger's disease, it is characteristic for leg ulcers to heal very slowly due to insufficient blood supplies to the tissue. It requires patience and ingenuity to promote healing and to support the patient suffering with a leg ulcer. Healing is not associated with inordinate amounts of scar tissue. The slow healing process ordinarily occurs from the edges and the ulcer does not typically require frequent incisions to promote healing.   (12:663)

Caring for a patient who has had a cerebrovascular accident (CVA)

15   1.   A delusion is best defined as a false belief. Paranoia is distrust of others. A hallucination is an imagined auditory, tactile, or visual perception that occurs without a stimulus. An illusion is an incorrectly perceived sensory impulse.   (12:846)

16   3.   A history of hypertension is typical in the patient who has had a cerebrovascular accident (CVA). Such illnesses as having indigestion, varicosities, and chronic gallbladder disease do not predispose to cerebrovascular accidents.   (12:628)

17   3.   Hemiplegia is defined as paralysis on one side of the body. Paraplegia is a paralysis of the lower extremities. Quadriplegia is a paralysis of all four extremities. The prefix *uni* means one, but a paralysis is not described as uniplegia.   (12:628)

18   1.   It is recommended that a sleeve of a pullover garment be removed from the unaffected arm first. In the situation described in this item, the unaffected side of the patient is his left side. The garment then should be slipped over the patient's head. Last, the sleeve on the affected side should be removed. This technique gives best protection to a paralyzed arm. The technique also is recommended when an arm has been injured.   (9:154)

19   2.   Palpitations means that the patient is aware of his heartbeat without feeling for his pulse over an artery.   (12:933)

20   3.   When a patient is lying on the left side, the right leg should be supported on pillows to prevent pull and poor alignment on the right hip and leg. When using the side-lying position, it is appropriate to support the arm opposite the side on which the patient is lying on a pillow to provide the greatest amount of room for proper chest expansion during respirations. A small pillow is used under the head to keep the spinal cord in alignment. The arm on the side on which the patient lies is usually most comfortable when the elbow is flexed and the arm rests alongside the patient's head.   (9:336)

21   1.   Aphasia is defined as the loss of ability to use spoken or written language. One type, called expressive aphasia, is characterized by the person's using a word in a manner so that its meaning is entirely different from the word's real meaning. Auditory aphasia means that the person hears words spoken to him but does not comprehend their meanings. Delirium is characterized by bewilderment and disorientation. Neologism means making up new words. Incoherence means using disjointed sentences and words. (15:235)

22 3.   Injections should not be given into a paralyzed arm, where circulation is likely to be poor. A subcutaneous injection can be given into an unparalyzed arm, the back, or the abdomen. (15:576–577)

23 2.   When a hypothermic blanket is used to lower a patient's temperature, the patient's temperature will normally drop a couple of degrees after the cooling device is removed. Therefore, the device should be shut off when the patient's temperature is a degree or two above the desired temperature. (9:424)

24 4.   A patient with an elevated temperature is likely to be thirsty, restless, and flushed. His respiratory rate most probably will be accelerated, a phenomenon that helps the body rid itself of some of its excess heat and that also results from an elevation in the body's metabolic rate. (9:188)

25 4.   When the body's temperature is elevated, the pulse rate is accelerated, a mechanism that helps to meet increased metabolic demands. In addition, an increased rate of circulation brings more blood to superficial vessels, where excess heat can be dissipated from the skin's surface more readily. (9:188)

26 3.   Fried foods are contraindicated on a soft or bland diet. Postum, rice, and canned peaches are not contraindicated on a soft or bland diet. Other contraindicated foods include highly spiced or seasoned foods, coarse-fiber meats, foods high in residue, and coffee, colas, and alcohol. (4:344; 9:99)

27 4.   Patients who must have special diets often complain because the food usually is not the kind that they enjoy or it is not seasoned to their liking. A comment that shows understanding of the patient and gives support is recommended. Asking if the food should be removed, telling the patient that the physician ordered the diet, and saying the diet will hasten recovery are of little help in supporting the patient. (9:100)

28 2.   A loss of appetite is called anorexia. A synonym for dyspepsia is indigestion. Malnutrition is a condition that occurs from the lack of proper food nutrients in the diet. Alopecia is hair loss. (9:96)

29 4.   Strained fruit is not recorded as fluid intake. Iced tea, gelatin, and malted milk are recorded as fluid intake. (9:97–98)

30 4.   Most meats and poultry are high in iron content. Citrus fruits, cheese, and gelatin fruits are low in iron. (4:142)

31 3.   In late life there is diminished absorption from the gastrointestinal tract, and the elderly become particularly prone to protein deficiency. Therefore, their diets should be rich in protein content. For the same reason, their diets should be rich in minerals and vitamins. (4:217)

32   4.   People who practice certain forms of Judaism observe dietary laws stating that only fish with fins and scales are acceptable to eat. Shell fish, such as shrimp and lobster, are unacceptable. Fish such as tuna, trout, and salmon are acceptable.   (16:186)

33   1.   In the situation described in this item, it ordinarily is best to notify the dietician when the patient is refusing to eat the food he is served. Often the dietician can make necessary changes to accomodate the patient. Many hospitals do not allow food to be brought in from the home. It is usually useless to try to teach the patient to eat foods when his religious faith teaches him otherwise.   (9:100–101)

34   1.   Hot water should not be used to clean dentures and bridges because hot water tends to warp plastic materials. Many dentures and bridges contain plastic materials. Hot water will not loosen teeth in dentures, alter their color, or break the plates in which the teeth are anchored.   (9:75)

35   1.   The most frequent cause of the loss of permanent teeth in adults is the gum disease, periodontitis. Pyorrhea is a synonym. Good oral hygiene and dental care can prevent or forestall the disease and the loss of teeth. Dental caries, that is cavitation of teeth or tooth decay, is another disorder that can be largely prevented with proper care. However, dental caries is not a frequent cause of the total loss of teeth in adults.   (9:73)

36   2.   Exercising has various effects on the body. Following a stroke, exercising parts of the body that are partially paralyzed is used primarily to prevent muscle atrophy and to maintain muscle tone and functioning.   (12:629)

37   3.   An air-inflated doughnut is not recommended to help prevent decubitus ulcers. The doughnut helps keep pressure off a circular part of the body, but the ring of the doughnut tends to decrease circulation within the circle. This effect defeats an important purpose for using it in the first place. Flotation pads, water mattresses, and alternating pressure pads often are used with success to help prevent decubitus ulcers.   (9:402–404)

38   2.   The *earliest* sign that a patient is at risk for developing a decubitus ulcer is present when the skin over an area becomes pale and whitish in color. This sign indicates that blood has been squeezed out of the area. In a relatively short period of time, the skin turns bright red, and finally a dark, angry red. The reddish color of the skin occurs when the body tries to oversupply the part with blood to make up for poor circulation.   (9:399)

39   2.   A patient who may develop a decubitus ulcer should have his position changed often, as frequently as every 1 to 2 hours. Changing the position more often disturbs the patient and is not necessary. Allowing the patient to lie in one position for 3 hours or more is likely to cause a decubitus ulcer to develop.   (9:402–404)

40   4.   A poorly balanced diet, an inadequate fluid intake, lack of feeling in a body part, and pressure on an area of the body all may play a part in the development of a decubitus ulcer. However, the factor that is primarily responsible is prolonged pressure on an area of the body, which in turn causes poor circulation to the area, poor cell nourishment, and finally tissue breakdown. (9:398)

41 4. The best way to treat a decubitus ulcer is to prevent it in the first place. Many types of treatments have been used, but none has received widespread acceptance. The old adage, "An ounce of prevention is worth a pound of cure," is very apropos in relation to preventing a decubitus ulcer. (9:399)

42 4. The bulk-forming laxative, psyllium (Metamucil) should be administered with generous amounts of fluid while taking the laxative as well as following its administration. Psyllium consists of fibers that are nondigestible and that absorb water, creating bulk in the form of a soft mass in the intestine. If an insufficient amount of fluid is taken with the laxative, the psyllium may clump to form a partial obstruction in the gastrointestinal tract. (14:237)

43 3. The average adult dosage of milk of magnesia, when it is used as a laxative, is 15 ml to 30 ml (½ to 1 ounce). In lesser amounts, it sometimes is used as an antacid. (14:238)

44 3. For safety purposes, the wheelchair should be prepared by locking its wheels and lifting the foot rests so that the chair does not roll and the patient will not stumble on the foot rests. Arm rests in place are handy for the patient to assist lowering himself into the chair when he is able to do so. (12:307)

45 1. While using a walker, a patient should be taught to look forward as he walks. Holding his head up and looking forward prevents curving and straining the back. Patients who cannot lift their walkers slightly to move them forward can slide them, although this technique tends to wear out the nonskid protectors on the end of a walker's legs. Or, better still, such patients should be provided with walkers that have wheels on the front legs. Walking with the feet about 6 inches (15 cm) apart is appropriate to provide a wide base of support. The elbows should be flexed about 30 degrees for greatest comfort. (9:358)

46 3. Continuity of care is a continuum of care provided for the patient. In the situation described in this item, the nurse is seeing to it that her patients have continuity of care, that is, appropriate care without interruption when she is away as well as when she is on duty. (9:33)

47 2. The comment that suggests that the nurse is busy and in a hurry shows the least amount of interest in the patient as a person. Introducing oneself and roommates to a patient and explaining how a signal device works are more likely to help the nurse build a helping nurse–patient relationship, because the nurse is sharing information with the patient. This helps the patient feel welcomed and shows respect for the patient as a person. The use of the plural first person pronoun (we) is not recommended to describe work the nurse will do. (9:152–153)

48 3. It is best to allow a patient to express his dislikes in an atmosphere in which he can feel secure and free of judgments. Asking the patient why he dislikes the nurse, questioning whether anyone can help the patient, or requesting a change in assignment is unlikely to help the patient or help discern if a problem exists.   (9:21)

49   1.   A person who is used to being independent and then becomes dependent because of illness often feels insecure and frightened. This person usually needs considerable emotional support as well as physical care, and this patient is very probably seeking attention by his demanding behavior. It is less likely that the patient's demanding behavior is due to heart damage, trying to use authority, or distrust of his caretakers.   (15:233, 40–41)

50   1.   Cerebrovascular disease changes a patient's behavior in many ways, and much of the behavior is difficult to predict. However, a common sign of cerebrovascular disease is the patient's inability to recall recent events. Usually a patient can recall events from the past with relative ease.   (15:232–233)

51   4.   Because the dejected, elderly patient often feels lonesome and uncared for, the nurse should use techniques to demonstrate that the patient is not worthless and that health workers do care for him. Changing the subject of conversation, silently ignoring a patient's comments, and calling a family member offer the patient no emotional support.   (15:41)

52   2.   While it is true that limits on behavior must sometimes be set for safety and therapeutic reasons, it is generally believed that ignoring unsatisfactory behavior and praising satisfactory behavior are generally productive to promote remotivation and behavior modification. Helpful measures also include using group therapy, allowing the patient to make decisions to the extent of his ability, and encouraging the patient to participate in such activities as arts and crafts.   (12:842–843, 823)

53   1.   In persons with cerebrovascular disease, arteries are unable to carry blood in a satisfactory manner to brain cells. This condition destroys the brain cells because they are deprived of oxygen.   (1:155–156)

54   2.   Cerebrovascular disease is a disease of the elderly. Because life expectancy in this country is increasing, the incidence of the disease has also increased.   (8:261; 15:231)

The Nursing Care of Patients with Disorders of the Eye, Ear, and Nose

Caring for patients with various disorders of the eye, ear, and nose

55   3.   Rods and cones, the receptors for vision, are located in the retina. The sclera is connective tissue that forms the white of the eye. The choroid is the dark, middle layer of the eye. The cornea is transparent, colorless part of the sclera on the front of the eye. The cornea is often called the window of the eye. (10:134)

56   1. The iris is responsible for changes in the size of the pupil. The optic disc is a blind spot in the retina where there are no rods and cones. The fovea centralis is the area in the retina where vision is clearest. The lens focuses light rays entering the eye onto its retina. (10:137)

57   1. A term for nearsightedness is myopia. Hyperopia is farsightedness. Presbyopia is a type of farsightedness caused by loss of elasticity in the lenses of elderly persons. Astigmatism is an irregularity in the curvature of the cornea and lens that causes refraction errors. (10:140)

58   1. The optic nerve carries impulses to the brain. The ophthalmic nerve, which is a branch of the trigeminal (fifth) cranial nerve, carries impulses of pain, touch, and temperature. The trochlear and abducens nerves supply voluntary muscles in the eyes. (10:138)

59   4. The eustachian tube connects the middle ear and the pharynx. (10:143)

60   4. Sensory cells located in the semicircular canals alert the body to its position, especially to the position of the head. The stapes, eustachian tubes, and the tympanic membranes are not involved in the ability to maintain equilibrium. (10:143)

61   1. The sinuses give resonance to the voice. The sinuses also make the skull lighter in weight than if it were solid bone. Sinuses do not humidify inhaled air, filter air, or produce secretions to lubricate the nasal mucosa. (10:77)

62   4. A typical symptom of glaucoma is seeing halos around lights. Blurred vision is more typical of a cataract. Other symptoms of glaucoma include aching eyes, some blurring of vision, decreasing peripheral vision, and frequent need for eyeglass changes. (15:268)

63   1. Atropine sulfate is contraindicated for a patient with glaucoma because it dilates the pupils, which further decreases drainage of intraocular fluid. Morphine tends to constrict pupils, which would not be contraindicated for a person with glaucoma. Acetazolamide (Diamox) and physostigmine (Eserine) are used in the treatment of glaucoma. The first drug is a diuretic; the second constricts pupils. (15:269)

64   1. Crying tends to cause the intraocular pressure to increase. So also do straining, such as straining while stooling, and heavy lifting. (15:269)

65   4. The correct abbreviation for both eyes is OU. The abbreviation for the right eye is OD, and for the left eye, OS. OP does not represent an acceptable abbreviation. (9:541)

66   4. Eye drops and ointments should be placed in the exposed lower conjunctival sac. If they are placed on the eyeball, the cornea may be injured. Debris may be carried into the lacrimal ducts when drops and ointments are placed at the inner canthus. Placing drops and ointments on the outer canthus makes it difficult to distribute them in the eye. (9:553)

67 2. A miotic (may be spelled myotic) constricts the pupils. A mydriatic acts in the eyes to dilate the pupils. (15:281)

68 3. Glaucoma is characterized by excessive pressure of the fluid within the eyes. Excessive pressure causes destruction of the optic nerves and will lead to blindness if left untreated. Glaucoma may be either acute or chronic. (15:265, 267)

69 2. The solution of choice when irrigating the eyes is sterile normal saline. The solution is most nearly like tissue fluid and is therefore less irritating than other solutions. (15:259)

70 3. Irrigating solution should be directed onto the lower conjunctival sac when irrigating the eye. (9:412)

71 2. When a chemical has entered the eyes, emergency treatment should include generous flushing of the eyes with water to dilute and wash away the chemical. Normal saline is preferred, but water will do in an emergency. Applying a dressing, placing ointment in the eyes, and using drops of boric acid solution are improper emergency measures to use in the situation described in this item. (15:260)

72 4. The best way to remove an artificial eye is to depress the lower eyelid. The eye should then be allowed to drop from the socket into the nurse's hand. (9:78)

73 2. An artificial eye should be cleaned with a mild soap and water solution. Other substances, such as salt, sodium bicarbonate, and hydrogen peroxide, do not cleanse as well as soap and water and may damage the surface of the eye. (9:78)

74 1. When a detached retina is repaired, most authorities recommend that the patient be kept quiet in bed. He should not be turned unless specifically ordered. Care should be taken that the bed is not jarred. It is best to keep the patient's room darkened because treatment to dilate the pupil often is used, and bright lights irritate the eyes when the pupils are dilated. If the physician allows the patient to be active, he will write orders accordingly. (15:270)

75 3. Two very common symptoms of excessive bleeding following cataract removal are pain and pressure in the operated eye. Restlessness may also be present, especially if the patient is confused. (15:265)

76 4. Straining and coughing should be avoided during the immediate postoperative period after the removal of cataracts. Lowering the body while flexing the knees is appropriate, but bending over should be avoided. (15:265)

77 2. Persons with glaucoma tend to have a history of the disease in their family. Patients with glaucoma should be aware of this so that their children will have regular eye examinations. If discovered early, most cases of glaucoma can be controlled and blindness can then be prevented. (15:267)

78 1. Two common symptoms of Meniere's disease are ringing in the ears and dizziness. Dizziness is called vertigo. The disease usually involves one ear only. The attacks are sudden and may last from a few minutes to several weeks.   (15:280)

79   2.   Sterile technique should be used when instilling eardrops if the patient's eardrum is not intact because the eardrops will pass into the middle ear where an infection could develop. Sterile technique is not necessarily required if the patient has a hearing loss, an inner ear infection, or a foreign object in the ear canal, as long as the eardrum is intact.   (9:552)

80   1.   In an adult, the ear canal is best straightened by pulling the ear upward and backward. In an infant or young child, the ear needs to be pulled downward and backward to straighten the canal.   (9:555)

81   4.   A complication of sinusitis is otitis media, which is an infection in the middle ear. Microorganisms from the nasal, oral, and pharyngeal areas can extend to the middle ear through the eustachian tube. The infection may also spread to the brain.   (15:285)

82   2.   The preferred position when giving nosedrops is to have the patient on his back with his head resting over a pillow. Or, he may sit up with his head tilted back. These positions allow for the best distribution of the medication and help to prevent medication from running from the nares (nostrils).   (9:556)

83   2.   A rebound action often occurs when nosedrops are used indiscriminately. After congestion is relieved, the body rebounds and floods the area with blood, causing even more congestion.   (15:285–286)

84   3.   Steam humidifiers become very hot when in use and have caused serious burns when proper precautions have not been taken to handle the equipment carefully. Many agencies no longer allow hot steam inhalators to be used bcause of the danger of burns but they are still often used in home situations. Cold steam humidifiers are preferred.   (9:643)

The Nursing Care of Patients with Disorders of the Endocrine System

Caring for a patient with hyperthyroidism (exophthalmic goiter).

85   1.   Endocrine glands are ductless glands. They are richly supplied with blood vessels, are innervated, and are made up of epithelial tissues.   (10:152)

86   4.   A danger in the use of radioactive iodine is that it tends to predispose to hypothyroidism. This complication may not appear until long after ^{131}I is used and therefore, the patient's health status should be monitored for years. Radioactive iodine has not been found to cause cancer, to affect healthy glands, or to present a radiation hazard to others.   (15:516)

87 2. Patients with hyperthyroidism tend to be emotionally unstable and tend to overreact to emotional situations. Typical signs and symptoms of hyperthyroidism include hand tremors, elevated pulse rates and systolic blood pressure, restlessness, palpitations, intolerance to heat, and weight loss despite eating well. Protruding eyeballs (exophthalmus) are noted in about one third of patients with hyperthyroidism. (12:769)

88 2. Because of an increased metabolic rate, a patient with hyperthyroidism feels most uncomfortable when the weather is warm. Indoors, what may be a comfortable temperature for a patient with hyperthyroidism causes another person to feel cold. (15:517)

89 4. A patient with hyperthyroidism needs a diet high in calories, proteins, and vitamins and should eat enough to compensate for the elevated metabolic rate that is typical in the presence of hyperthyroidism. (12:770)

90 2. Iodine is most likely to be lacking or in short supply in the diet of a person with nontoxic goiter. This type of goiter is usually without signs and symptoms of hyperthyroidism. The thyroid gland enlarges because the body is attempting to meet its demand for thyroid hormones. The condition most often is seen in areas of the country where soil and water are low or lacking in iodine. The condition is particularly common in the midwest and Great Lakes area, an area often referred to as the "goiter belt." Using iodized salt helps to prevent nontoxic goiter. (12:772; 15:518)

91 2. A deficiency of thyroxine in adults causes myxedema. This condition causes the adult to become mentally and physically sluggish. The skin and hair are dry. Myxedema ordinarily is treated with thyroid extract or hormone. If a deficiency in thyroxine production occurs from the beginning of life, cretinism develops. Graves's disease also is called hyperthyroidism, exophthalmic or toxic goiter, or thyrotoxicosis. Hypofunctioning of the adrenal cortex causes Addison's disease. (15:519)

92 3. The accepted abbreviation for a drop is gtt. Dr. is an abbreviation for dram. Gr. is an abbreviation for grain. Drp. is not an accepted abbreviation. (9:538)

93 3. Lugol's solution stains the teeth and therefore, should be administered by using a straw (drinking tube) so that the medication does not come in contact with the teeth. The medication should be given in milk or fruit juice to help disguise its salty, strong taste. (12:770)

94 2. The atmosphere around a patient being prepared for a thyroidectomy should be relaxing and restful. Visitors ordinarily are allowed, but visiting should be brief and restful in nature. Physical and mental rest are especially important to help decrease thyroid activity. (8:535)

95 4. Environment is defined as everything surrounding and influencing one's life. The environment includes society, which is defined as a group of people joined together in some way for a common purpose or interest. Ecology is defined as dealing with the relation of living things with their environment. A stimulus is any change in one's environment sufficient enough to cause a response. When the patient described in this situation is to have a restful environment, her surroundings and anything influencing her life are taken into account.   (9:162–163)

96   3.   Following a thyroidectomy, the position of choice for the patient is a semi-Fowler's position. This promotes respiratory functioning and helps minimize swelling in the operative site.   (12:770)

97   1.   Following a thyroidectomy, the head should be supported firmly so that the neck is in a position of extension. If the neck is hyperextended, rotated, or flexed, strain and twisting on the surgical wound or pressure on the operative site may interfere with breathing and proper wound healing.   (15:515)

98   3.   Because of swelling or possible bleeding in the operative site, the patient may have respiratory obstruction following a thyroidectomy. Therefore, a tracheostomy set or an endotracheal tube should be kept readily available. Suctioning equipment should also be readily available for the patient who has a thyroidectomy.   (12:771)

99   2.   Postoperatively, the patient who has had a thyroidectomy is placed in a low or mid-Fowler's position in bed. If the patient has excessive bleeding postoperatively and blood leaves the operative incision, it normally will flow by gravity along the side of the neck onto bed linens under the patient's neck. Top layers of gauze dressing and adhesive strips are likely to become soiled with blood at a much later time than are linens under the patient's neck.   (9:386; 15:517)

100   2.   The purpose of asking a patient who has had a thyroidectomy to speak from time to time postoperatively is to help determine whether the laryngeal nerve was damaged during surgery. If it was, the patient will have difficulty speaking. Signs of obstruction indicate that respiratory passageways possibly are blocked. Excessive bleeding is likely to cause the pulse to become rapid and cause blood to drain from the operative site.   (12:771)

101   3.   Parathormone, which is secreted by the parathyroid glands, plays a major role in the body's regulation of calcium and phosphorus. The patient ordinarily complains of numbness and tingling of the extremities and muscle cramps as calcium utilization becomes poor.   (10:158)

102   4.   Common signs of a thyroid crisis include an elevated temperature, rapid pulse rate, and marked restlessness and anxiety. The signs are exaggerations of hyperthyroidism. Edema or hemorrhaging at the site of surgery is most often responsible for difficulty in swallowing and breathing. Tetany, which is characterized by muscle cramps and twitching, may occur if the parathyroid glands are damaged during surgery.   (12:771)

103   1.   Following a thyroidectomy, the patient should use her hands, which she places behind her head, to support her head while she moves herself to a sitting position. This technique helps to avoid strain on the surgical incision and on neck muscles.   (15:517)

104 1. Most incentive spirometers are designed to encourage a patient to inhale deeply. Forced exhalations, which often have been used in the past to promote deep breathing, have been found to result in injury to respiratory tissues and collapse of bronchioles and alveoli, problems that complicate proper ventilation.

Individual Items

105 3. Epinephrine (adrenalin) constricts blood vessels and can be used topically to control bleeding. The drug does not act to hasten blood clotting, control infection, or increase pressure in the nostril.   (14:37)

106 4. Masks should be worn only once and only for one patient. In the situation described in this item, the nurse is required to use four masks.   (9:307)

107 3. A gastrostomy tube is inserted through an opening made in the stomach wall.   (15:441)

108 3. Arteries affected with atherosclerosis contain deposits of fat and minerals that are called plaques. The exact relationship between atherosclerosis and cholesterol is not clear but it appears as though cholesterol contributes to atherosclerosis.   (12:648)

109 4. Thromboplastin released from injured tissues triggers the blood to clot. Thromboplastin reacts with certain substances to form prothrombin activator, which converts prothrombin into thrombin. Thrombin converts soluble fibrinogen into an insoluble fibrin that traps red blood cells to form a clot.   (10:170)

110 2. Bacterial endocarditis very often is noted in persons whose heart valves are already damaged, and most of these persons have had rheumatic fever earlier in life. The illness may also occur in persons having a congenital defect of the heart.   (15:367)

111 2. The symptoms of transient ischemic attacks (TIAs) are due to temporary, impaired circulation to a part of the brain. Brain cells are deprived of a sufficient oxygen supply during the attacks. These attacks indicate that the patient most probably has a cerebrovascular disease, and they serve as a warning for the possibility of a cerebrovascular accident.   (15:234)

112 3. Symptoms of paralytic ileus include abdominal distention and cramping pain. When the ileum is paralyzed, contents in the intestinal tract cannot move toward the rectum and an intestinal obstruction results. Diarrhea, hemoptysis, and diaphragmatic spasms are not associated with paralytic ileus.   (15:424)

113 2. The Trichinella organism is transmitted most often to man when he eats improperly cooked pork from an infected animal.   (16:238)

Classification of Test Items

Directions: *Each item in the previous review test is classified here according to the subject area it tests. Place a check mark after each item you answered* **correctly** *by referring to your answers. Total the number of items you answered correctly in each area and enter the numbers in the correct places on pages 553–556.*

Clinical: Medical/Surgical Nursing (Adults)

7 ✓	15 ✓	54 ✓	76 ✓	94 ✓	103 ✓
8 ✓	16 ✓	62 ✓	77 ✓	96 ✓	104 ✓
9 ✓	17 ✓	64 ✓	78 ✓	97 ✓	107 ✓
10 ✓	18	68 ✓	81 ✓	98 ✓	108 ✓
11 ✓	21	71 ✓	87 ✓	99 ✓	110 ✓
12	50 ✓	74 ✓	88 ✓	100 ✓	111 ✓
14 ✓	53 ✓	75 ✓	91	102 ✓	112

TOTAL 37

Biological/Physical Sciences

55 ✓	57 ✓	59	61 ✓	70 ✓	101 ✓
56 ✓	58 ✓	60 ✓	69 ✓	85 ✓	109

TOTAL 10

Fundamentals of Nursing

6	25	36 ✓	41 ✓	66 ✓	82
19 ✓	28 ✓	37 ✓	44 ✓	72	84 ✓
20	29 ✓	38 ✓	45 ✓	73	92 ✓
22 ✓	34 ✓	39 ✓	46 ✓	79 ✓	93 ✓
23	35 ✓	40 ✓	65 ✓	80 ✓	106 ✓
24 ✓					

TOTAL 24

Diet Therapy/Nutrition

26 _____ 31 _____ 33 _____ 89 _____ 90 _____ 113 _____
30 _____ 32 _____

TOTAL __8__

Pharmacology

1 _____ 4 _____ 13 _____ 43 _____ 67 _____ 86 _____
2 _____ 5 _____ 42 _____ 63 _____ 83 _____ 105 _____
3 _____

TOTAL __12__

Psychosocial Sciences

27 _____ 48 _____ 49 _____ 51 _____ 52 _____ 95 _____
47 _____

TOTAL __7__

Review Test 14

The Nursing Care of Patients With Disorders of the Endocrine System (Continued)

    Caring for a Patient With Diabetes Mellitus

The Nursing Care of Patients With Disorders of the Urological System

    Caring for Patients With Various Urological Disorders

The Nursing Care of Patients Requiring Diagnostic Procedures

    Caring for Patients Requiring Various Diagnostic Procedures

Individual Items
Correct Answers and Rationales
Classification of Test Items

Directions: *With a pencil, blacken the circle in front of the option you have chosen for your correct answer.*

The Nursing Care of Patients With Disorders of the Endocrine System (Continued)

Mr. Locke, who is 46 years old, has recently been screened for diabetes mellitus but he ignores advice to seek health care.

  1 Mr. Locke is most likely to have noted all of the following symptoms of diabetes mellitus, if he has the disease, *except*
    ○ 1. eating excessive amounts of food.
    ○ 2. voiding excessive amounts of urine.
    ○ 3. drinking excessive amounts of fluids.
    ○ 4. sleeping an excessive number of hours.

Mr. Locke continues to ignore symptoms until he develops ketoacidosis and becomes unconscious. He is hospitalized on an emergency basis for care and treatment of diabetes mellitus.

2 Upon admission, the nurse should be prepared to help in the immediate administration of
- ○ 1. regular insulin.
- ○ 2. oxygen therapy.
- ○ 3. anticonvulsive drugs.
- ○ 4. intravenous glucose solutions.

3 The electrolyte that plays an important role in maintaining the body's acid–base balance but is now unable to do so adequately for Mr. Locke is the electrolyte
- ○ 1. sodium.
- ○ 2. potassium.
- ○ 3. magnesium.
- ○ 4. bicarbonate.

4 A blood specimen for blood sugar level is obtained upon Mr. Locke's admission. To assess results of the blood analysis, the nurse must know that the normal fasting blood sugar (glucose) level in 100 ml of venous blood is between
- ○ 1. 40 mg and 80 mg.
- ○ 2. 80 mg and 120 mg.
- ○ 3. 120 mg and 160 mg.
- ○ 4. 160 mg and 200 mg.

5 On his admission, Mr. Locke's respirations are most likely to be
- ○ 1.. rapid.
- ○ 2. shallow.
- ○ 3. irregular in terms of rate.
- ○ 4. irregular in terms of depth.

6 Mr. Locke's blood pressure was 156/100 mm Hg when admitted. The nurse wishes to obtain his blood pressure now, about 3 hours after admission. How high is it recommended that the nurse allow mercury to rise in the manometer before releasing air and listening for sounds at the brachial artery?
- ○ 1. A minimum of 200 mm Hg
- ○ 2. At the point where the previous systolic pressure was obtained
- ○ 3. About 30 mm Hg above the point at which the radial pulse disappears
- ○ 4. A minimum of 70 mm Hg above the point where the diastolic pressure was previously obtained

7 Mr. Locke is in need of oral hygiene. When the nurse gives Mr. Locke oral hygiene, if Mr. Locke is unable to cooperate, it would be best to open his mouth with
- ○ 1. a surgical clamp.
- ○ 2. a padded tongue blade.
- ○ 3. the patient's toothbrush.
- ○ 4. the nurse's gloved hand.

Mr. Locke responds to therapy for ketoacidosis and is then scheduled for further diagnostic tests.

8   How should the nurse plan to prepare Mr. Locke for a glucose tolerance test?
   ○ 1.   Giving the patient a cleansing enema
   ○ 2.   Having the patient in a fasting state
   ○ 3.   Catheterizing the patient for a sterile urine specimen
   ○ 4.   Administering a sedative the night before the examination.

9   During the glucose tolerance test, Mr. Locke's blood glucose level remains abnormally high for some time after a test meal. Approximately how much time does it normally take for the blood glucose level to return to normal after eating a full meal?
   ○ 1.   1 to 2 hours
   ○ 2.   2 to 3 hours
   ○ 3.   3 to 4 hours
   ○ 4.   4 to 6 hours

10   Mr. Locke's urine is to be tested for glucose "in the A.M." The nurse discards the first morning specimen and collects a second one on which the test is done, primarily because the first morning specimen
   ○ 1.   has been collecting in the bladder over a period of hours.
   ○ 2.   has become too concentrated for accurate glucose determination.
   ○ 3.   is ordinarily too large in amount for accurate glucose determination.
   ○ 4.   is likely to contain constituents other than sugar that will confuse test results.

11   Mr. Locke is ordered to have a postprandial glucose blood test. The time of the day when the blood sample is obtained for this test is
   ○ 1.   in the evening.
   ○ 2.   upon awaking in the morning.
   ○ 3.   immediately before the largest meal in the day.
   ○ 4.   about 2 hours after eating a high-carbohydrate meal.

12   After completing various tests, Mr. Locke is told that his examinations indicate he has diabetes mellitus. He says to the nurse, "Diabetes! I just can't live with that!" Which of the following statements offers the nurse the best guide for responding to the patient's comment?
   ○ 1.   Diabetes is nothing to fear as long as the patient sees his health caretaker regularly.
   ○ 2.   Diabetes is frequently found in older people, but it is a relatively easy disorder to control.
   ○ 3.   Diabetes is a serious illness, but good care means fewer problems are likely to arise.
   ○ 4.   Diabetes can be less frightening when health workers assume major responsibility for the patient's care.

Mr. Locke is receiving fast-acting insulin.

13 Of the following types of insulin, which type would act most rapidly
when given to Mr. Locke?
○ 1. Regular insulin
○ 2. Globin zinc insulin
○ 3. Insulin zinc suspension
○ 4. Protamine zinc insulin suspension

14 Mr. Locke suddenly becomes fearful and pulls his arm away when the
nurse is about to give him an insulin injection. Of the following possible
responses, which one is best for the nurse to make in this situation?
○ 1. "Try to relax. This will hurt very little."
○ 2. "You have been frightened. I understand that you are upset."
○ 3. "This will take only a few seconds. Try to cooperate with me,
please."
○ 4. "This is ordered so that you will get well. Your doctor wants
you to have it."

*Mr. Locke complains of constipation and is to receive an enema using
hypertonic solution.*

15 The cleansing enema is to be given "tomorrow," according to a nursing
order. In relation to meal times, when should the nurse plan to give Mr.
Locke the enema?
○ 1. Immediately after breakfast
○ 2. Immediately before breakfast
○ 3. About midmorning
○ 4. Near lunchtime

16 If the nurse uses the following techniques when giving Mr. Locke the
enema with the hypertonic solution, which one is in *error*?
○ 1. The nurse gives the solution at room temperature.
○ 2. The nurse lubricates the nozzle.
○ 3. The nurse inserts the nozzle about 3 to 4 inches (8 to 10 cm)
past the anus.
○ 4. The nurse injects the solution as quickly as possible.

Instructions begin concerning Mr. Locke about his diet.

17 Mr. Locke is taught to use the exchange system. He chooses to use
skim milk in his diet. By so doing, for every cup of milk, Mr. Locke can
alter his diet by adding two exchanges of
○ 1. fat.
○ 2. protein.
○ 3. carbohydrate.
○ 4. either protein or carbohydrate.

18 Which of the following foods will usually be *excluded* from Mr. Locke's diet?
○ 1. Salt
○ 2. Honey
○ 3. Canned fish
○ 4. Peanut butter

19 Mr. Locke should be taught that certain vegetables can be used in ordinary amounts without his having to count them as a vegetable exchange. Two examples of such vegetables are
○ 1. peas and beans.
○ 2. beets and carrots.
○ 3. pumpkin and squash.
○ 4. cucumbers and mushrooms.

20 When calculating Mr. Locke's diet, it is important to know that most meats contain *little* or *no*
○ 1. fats.
○ 2. calories.
○ 3. minerals.
○ 4. carbohydrates.

21 When calculating Mr. Locke's diet, which of the following foods should be considered in the fat exchange?
○ 1. Liver
○ 2. Avocado
○ 3. Buttermilk
○ 4. Lima beans

22 Ms. Locke asks whether her husband can have foods marketed as "dietetic." The nurse's response should be based on knowledge that these foods
○ 1. are generally better suited to obese rather than diabetic patients.
○ 2. may be eaten without necessarily adjusting other foods in the diet.
○ 3. should be avoided because they contain additives harmful to most diabetics.
○ 4. can be used when their nutrient values are included in dietary calculations.

Plans are made to teach Mr. Locke how to give himself insulin.

23 Mr. Locke asks the nurse why he cannot take insulin orally. The nurse should base her response on knowledge that insulin taken orally is
○ 1. very irritating to gastrointestinal mucosa.
○ 2. poorly absorbed from the gastrointestinal tract.
○ 3. likely to produce an allergy when taken by mouth.
○ 4. readily destroyed by digestive juices in the stomach.

24 Mr. Locke will use isophane insulin suspension (NPH insulin) at home. If he gives himself insulin at 8 A.M. each day, then eats breakfast and

later, lunch, when during the day should he be taught to observe for signs of a hypoglycemic reaction?
- ○ 1. Within an hour after breakfast
- ○ 2. Immediately before lunch
- ○ 3. Between mid- and late-afternoon
- ○ 4. At bedtime

25 Mr. Locke's vial of insulin is marked U100, which means that
- ○ 1. 1 ml contain 100 units of insulin.
- ○ 2. a typical dose of insulin is 100 units.
- ○ 3. the vial contains 100 units of insulin.
- ○ 4. a minim contains 100 units of insulin.

26 How should Mr. Locke be taught to handle his vial of NPH insulin before he draws up insulin into the syringe?
- ○ 1. The patient should be taught to shake the vial vigorously.
- ○ 2. The patient should roll the vial gently between the palms of his hands.
- ○ 3. The patient should be taught to tip the vial upside down and back upright one time.
- ○ 4. The patient should be taught to avoid agitating the vial as much as possible.

27 Mr. Locke is taught that before inserting a needle into a vial of insulin, he should prepare to inject air into the vial in an amount that is equal to
- ○ 1. the amount of insulin he will withdraw.
- ○ 2. twice the amount of insulin he will withdraw.
- ○ 3. one half the amount of insulin he will withdraw.
- ○ 4. as little as one-fifth the amount of insulin he will withdraw.

28 When giving himself insulin, Mr. Locke should be taught to inject the needle at an angle of
- ○ 1. 15 degrees.
- ○ 2. 45 degrees.
- ○ 3. 60 degrees.
- ○ 4. 90 degrees.

29 After teaching Mr. Locke, the nurse observes him giving himself insulin. She notes that he is injecting the needle at an incorrect angle. The component of the nursing process the nurse has used in this situation is called
- ○ 1. evaluation.
- ○ 2. goal-setting.
- ○ 3. data gathering.
- ○ 4. implementation.

30 Mr. Locke is taught how to rotate areas on his body where he will inject himself with insulin. He says, "That's easy. I'll use different places on one leg for a week, then the other leg for a week, next one arm for a week, and finally the other arm for a week. Then I can use my abdomen for a week." Which of the following statements best describes the patient's planned technique for rotating injection sites?

○ 1. The technique is satisfactory.

○ 2. The technique is in error. He should not include his abdomen when giving himself insulin.

○ 3. The technique is in error. He should rotate to a different extremity and his abdomen between every injection.

○ 4. The technique is in error. He should use sites on his abdomen, then one leg, then one arm, then the other leg, and finally the other arm, each for a week.

31 The nurse explains to Mr. Locke that rotating the sites where he will inject himself with insulin helps to *avoid*

○ 1. staining the skin.

○ 2. damage to subcutaneous tissues.

○ 3. accidentally injecting into a vein.

○ 4. dangerously rapid absorption of insulin.

32 Mr. Locke should be taught that of the following areas of the body, the only area that is *undesirable* for injecting insulin is the area on the

○ 1. back.

○ 2. thighs.

○ 3. forearms.

○ 4. upper arms.

33 Mr. Locke is taught common symptoms of hypoglycemia (hyperinsulinism), two of which are

○ 1. vomiting and thirst.

○ 2. drowsiness and air hunger.

○ 3. rapid pulse and flushed skin.

○ 4. excessive perspiration and excited behavior.

Mr. Locke is instructed how to use Tes-Tape at home to examine his urine for the presence of glucose.

34 The Tes-Tape test depends on dipping a piece of test tape into a sample of Mr. Locke's urine and determining glucose presence by assessing the tape with

○ 1. a color chart.

○ 2. an agglutination table.

○ 3. a percentage calculator.

○ 4. an electronic calculator.

35 Mr. Locke should be instructed to store the Tes-Tape so that it is *not* exposed to light or

○ 1. air.

○ 2. dust.

○ 3. coolness.

○ 4. freezing.

Mr. Locke purchases a blood-glucose test kit for testing his blood for its glucose level.

36 From where should Mr. Locke be taught to obtain blood from himself for the blood-glucose test?
   ○ 1. From a forearm
   ○ 2. From the abdominal wall
   ○ 3. From the tip of a finger
   ○ 4. From the fleshy part of the palm of the hand

37 Which of the following precautions should Mr. Locke be taught to observe when cleansing the puncture site with an alcohol swab before he punctures the skin where he will obtain a specimen from himself?
   ○ 1. Be sure to cleanse the area twice.
   ○ 2. Be sure to apply warmth to the area.
   ○ 3. Be sure to stretch the skin over the area.
   ○ 4. Be sure to allow the alcohol to dry on the area.

Mr. Locke and his wife ask the nurse about a variety of concerns they have in relation to diabetes mellitus and health care.

38 Mr. and Ms. Locke ask about exercising. In general, what effect, if any, will exercise have on Mr. Locke's need for insulin?
   ○ 1. Exercise increases the body's need for insulin.
   ○ 2. Exercise decreases the body's need for insulin.
   ○ 3. Exercise has little or no effect on the body's need for insulin.
   ○ 4. Exercise causes the body's need for insulin to be unpredictable.

39 Ms. Locke asks, "What if my husband becomes ill with something else, like a bad cold or the flu?" Which of the following courses of action should the Lockes be taught to take if Mr. Locke becomes ill with an infection and until he can contact his physician?
   ○ 1. The patient should increase his dosage of insulin slightly.
   ○ 2. The patient should decrease his carbohydrate intake slightly.
   ○ 3. The patient should decrease his total daily caloric intake slightly.
   ○ 4. The patient should test his urine or blood for glucose more frequently than usual.

40 Mr. Locke smokes cigarettes. When he expresses a desire to quit smoking, the nurse should suggest that a good way to begin is to change his smoking habits by
   ○ 1. carrying matches rather than a lighter.
   ○ 2. buying only cigarettes that are low in nicotine.
   ○ 3. trying to put off smoking for a few minutes when the desire to smoke is present.

    ○ 4. smoking only when the craving is associated with an activity, such as having a cup of coffee.

41 If Mr. Locke inhales while he smokes, the inhaled nicotine affects peripheral arteries in his body primarily by causing them to
    ○ 1. become fragile.
    ○ 2. decrease in size.
    ○ 3. clog with plaque.
    ○ 4. engorge with blood.

42 Mr. Locke is taught the importance of maintaining normal weight. Whether he is diabetic or not, in terms of an ideal weight for Mr. Locke, a *general* guide is that he should maintain the ideal weight for a person of similar build whose age is
    ○ 1. 20 years.
    ○ 2. 25 years.
    ○ 3. 30 years.
    ○ 4. 35 years.

43 To help health caretakers who may care for Mr. Locke in an emergency, Mr. Locke should be advised to
    ○ 1. wear an identification bracelet indicating he is diabetic.
    ○ 2. carry a description of his illness and therapy in his billfold.
    ○ 3. place a label in his outer clothing indicating that he is diabetic.
    ○ 4. travel and work with someone who is familiar with his diabetes.

44 Of the following complications, the one to which Mr. Locke is particularly prone is
    ○ 1. pancreatic tumors.
    ○ 2. gallbladder disease.
    ○ 3. blood vessel disorders.
    ○ 4. urinary tract infections.

45 Mr. and Ms. Locke raise questions about the prognosis for a person with diabetes mellitus. The nurse should explain that the prognosis is best and complications can be delayed or avoided when Mr. Locke
    ○ 1. takes insulin by injection.
    ○ 2. understands his own illness.
    ○ 3. accepts his spouse as his chief caretaker.
    ○ 4. can eventually use an oral hypoglycemic.

46 Mr. Locke asks where he can obtain more information on his diet. Of the following sources, the best one is the
    ○ 1. American Dietetic Association.
    ○ 2. American Nurses' Association.
    ○ 3. American Medical Association.
    ○ 4. American Public Health Association.

47 When Mr. Locke is ready for discharge, he asks, "Am I healthy now?" Which of the following statements best defines the term health and should guide the nurse's response to Mr. Locke's question?

○ 1. Health is not being sick.
○ 2. Health is being able to cope with work and life.
○ 3. Health is physical, emotional, and social well-being.
○ 4. Health is being born without congenital defects and hereditary diseases.

The Nursing Care of Patients With Disorders of the Urological System.

A nurse is assigned to care for patients with various urological disorders.

48 When urinary disorders are present. The nursing measure of particular importance to assist in assessing the patient's health status is to be sure that his
○ 1. activities and rest periods are carefully monitored.
○ 2. dietary intake is more than adequate to meet his needs.
○ 3. skin care includes measures to prevent decubitus ulcers.
○ 4. fluid intake and output are carefully measured and recorded.

49 Mr. Teis is scheduled to have a cystoscopy under local anesthesia. If the following orders are written for Mr. Teis prior to his cystoscopy, which one should the nurse question before carrying it out?
○ 1. Withhold food.
○ 2. Withhold fluids.
○ 3. Administer a cleansing enema.
○ 4. Administer a prescribed sedative.

50. Mr. Teis voids frequently and in large amounts. This excessive production of urine is called
○ 1. anuria.
○ 2. pyuria.
○ 3. nocturia.
○ 4. polyuria.

51 Mr. Teis is found to have no disorder. When in a 24-hour period is his urine normally likely to be most concentrated and darkest in color?
○ 1. Upon awaking in the morning
○ 2. About midday
○ 3. Early in the evening
○ 4. Before going to bed at night

52 Mr. Galt has cancer of the bladder. The first symptom that caused Mr. Galt to seek health care because of his disorder is most likely to have been
○ 1. dysuria.
○ 2. hematuria.
○ 3. urinary retention.

○ 4. urinary incontinence.

53 A urinary diversion (ileal conduit) is performed on Mr. Galt. To help prevent infection postoperatively, Mr. Galt should increase his usual daily intake of
○ 1. fluids.
○ 2. proteins.
○ 3. minerals.
○ 4. roughage.

54 Mr. Galt expresses concern about the odor of his urine. If he has eaten the following foods, the food which is no doubt responsible for causing his urine to have a strong odor is
○ 1. beans.
○ 2. cheese.
○ 3. bananas.
○ 4. asparagus.

55 Mr. Galt will wear a reusable appliance after discharge to collect urine at his stoma. It is recommended that the appliance be washed in soap and water between uses and deodorized in a solution of
○ 1. table salt.
○ 2. white vinegar.
○ 3. hydrogen peroxide.
○ 4. sodium bicarbonate.

56 Ms. Coburn is to have an indwelling catheter placed in her urinary bladder. If Ms. Coburn complains of pain after the indwelling catheter is inserted when the balloon of the catheter is being inflated, the most probable cause of the discomfort is that the balloon
○ 1. has broken.
○ 2. is in the urethra.
○ 3. contains too much fluid.
○ 4. is too high in the bladder.

57 Ms. Coburn's catheter will normally drain her urinary bladder by the action of
○ 1. suction.
○ 2. gravity.
○ 3. capillary action.
○ 4. atmospheric pressure.

58 Of the following nursing measures, the one that is most likely to appear on Ms. Coburn's nursing care plan because she has an indwelling catheter is to
○ 1. encourage a generous fluid intake.
○ 2. change the catheter every other day.
○ 3. powder the perineal area after cleaning it.
○ 4. cleanse the perineal area thoroughly once a day.

59 To help prevent infection, it is especially important that Ms. Coburn's catheter care include

○ 1. irrigating the catheter every 4 to 6 hours.
○ 2. keeping the perineal area scrupulously clean.
○ 3. emptying the collecting container at least every 4 hours.
○ 4. clamping the drainage tube whenever the patient is out of bed.

60 Mr. Yager is assessed for kidney functioning. Mr. Yager's blood is examined for its blood urea and nitrogen level (BUN). The nurse should judge that Mr. Yager's BUN is *abnormal* if it rises above a level of approximately
○ 1. 5 mg per 100 ml of blood.
○ 2. 10 mg per 100 ml of blood.
○ 3. 15 mg per 100 ml of blood.
○ 4. 20 ml per 100 ml of blood.

61 Mr. Yager's kidney function is to be evaluated. Which of the following examinations is used primarily to test the ability of the kidneys to excrete wastes?
○ 1. A renal arteriogram
○ 2. A cystoscopic examination
○ 3. A phenolsulfonphthalein (PSP) test
○ 4. An acid phosphatase blood level test

62 Mr. Yager becomes uremic. The nurse should plan that careful attention is especially important in the daily hygienic care of this patient's
○ 1. feet.
○ 2. eyes.
○ 3. skin.
○ 4. scrotum.

63 Peritoneal dialysis is used temporarily for Mr. Yager to attempt to remove wastes from his blood. A nursing measure to promote fluid to leave the peritoneal cavity during the drainage period in this procedure is to
○ 1. lower the patient's bed.
○ 2. irrigate the drainage catheter.
○ 3. elevate the drainage receptable.
○ 4. change the patient's position in bed.

64 Mr. Yager is prepared for hemodialysis. He receives heparin before therapy primarily to help
○ 1. relieve discomfort.
○ 2. prevent blood clotting.
○ 3. maintain blood pressure.
○ 4. stimulate the production of urine.

65 Mr. Jones has a stone in his ureter. Another name for a stone in the urinary tract is
○ 1. calix.
○ 2. calculus.
○ 3. calcemia.
○ 4. calcitonin.

66 The nature of pain Mr. Jones is most likely to complain of while the stone is lodged in his ureter is best described as being
○ 1. dull.
○ 2. severe.
○ 3. burning.
○ 4. referred.

67 Ms. Valdez has a neurogenic disorder affecting her urinary bladder and is learning to catheterize herself. While teaching Ms. Valdez self-catheterization, the nurse encourages the patient to try to void before catheterization. Which of the following techniques is likely to help Ms. Valdez *least* to help her start voiding?
○ 1. Using the toilet for voiding
○ 2. Pouring warm water over the perineal area
○ 3. Taking a warm bath before attempting to void
○ 4. Limiting fluid intake before attempting catheterization.

68 When teaching Ms. Valdez the techniques of at-home self-catheterization, it is appropriate for the nurse to teach her to
○ 1. use techniques of medical asepsis.
○ 2. catheterize herself while standing up.
○ 3. apply pressure to the lower abdomen after removing the catheter.
○ 4. contract her abdominal muscles while the catheter is in place.

69 Ms. Lasky is to be catheterized to determine whether urine remains in her bladder after she has voided. Urine that remains in Ms. Lasky's bladder after she voids is called
○ 1. reflux urine.
○ 2. overflow urine.
○ 3. residual urine.
○ 4. retention urine.

70 When preparing Ms. Lasky for catheterization, the nurse should explain that while she is inserting the catheter, the patient is most likely to experience a sensation of
○ 1. tickling.
○ 2. burning.
○ 3. piercing.
○ 4. pressure.

71 When cleaning the area of the meatus before inserting the catheter into Ms. Lasky's bladder, in what direction should the cotton balls be moved?
○ 1. From one side across the meatus
○ 2. From above the anus toward the meatus
○ 3. From above the meatus toward the anus
○ 4. From one side to the other and back across the meatus

72 If the catheter meets some resistance before it reaches Ms. Lasky's bladder, it is best for the nurse to ask the patient to
○ 1. take a deep breath.
○ 2. cough several times.

○ 3. swallow several times.

○ 4. hold her breath for a few seconds.

73 For approximately how far should a catheter be inserted when catheterizing Ms. Lasky?

○ 1. From ½ inch to 1 inch (1.25 cm to 2.50 cm)

○ 2. From 2 inches to 3 inches (5 cm to 7.50 cm)

○ 3. From 4 inches to 5 inches (10 cm to 12.50 cm)

○ 4. From 6 inches to 7 inches (15 cm to 17.50 cm)

74 Ms. Jackson is incontinent of urine. If the following orders appear on Ms. Jackson's nursing care plan, which one should the nurse question before carrying it out?

○ 1. Serve a regular diet.

○ 2. Offer bedpan every 4 hours.

○ 3. Limit fluid intake to 800 ml daily.

○ 4. Ambulate every morning and evening.

75 Which of the following exercises is most likely to help Ms. Jackson to strengthen muscles that control urinary elimination?

○ 1. Doing push-ups

○ 2. Running in place

○ 3. Alternately contracting and relaxing the perineal muscles

○ 4. Alternately contracting and relaxing the abdominal muscles

76 A urine specimen is collected from Ms. Jackson to determine its specific gravity. If the specimen stands and cools, the urine will normally change by becoming

○ 1. cloudy.

○ 2. odorless.

○ 3. highly acid.

○ 4. light in color.

77 Mr. Washington is ill with acute glomerulonephritis. If Mr. Washington is typical, he would indicate that before his present illness, he was sick with

○ 1. "Asian flu."

○ 2. "strep throat."

○ 3. mononucleosis.

○ 4. infectious hepatitis.

78 The color of Mr. Washington's urine is most likely to be

○ 1. smoky dark.

○ 2. cloudy white.

○ 3. greenish yellow.

○ 4. very light amber.

79 Mr. Washington has oliguria, which means that in terms of urinary production, he is excreting

○ 1. no urine.

○ 2. bloody urine.

○ 3. very little urine.

    ○ 4. excessive amounts of urine.

80 Mr. Washington is to be weighed daily, the most likely purpose being to assist in
    ○ 1. regulating his food intake.
    ○ 2. determining drug dosages.
    ○ 3. estimating kidney damage.
    ○ 4. observing for relief of edema.

81 If the nurse uses the following techniques when she weighs Mr. Washington, which one is in *error*?
    ○ 1. The nurse weighs the patient before he has breakfast.
    ○ 2. The nurse places a paper towel on the scale.
    ○ 3. The nurse helps the patient to remove his shoes before weighing him.
    ○ 4. The nurse has the patient wear his cotton bathrobe while weighing him.

82 If Mr. Washington's glomerulonephritis becomes chronic, his diet will most likely be ordered to be low in
    ○ 1. fat.
    ○ 2. iron.
    ○ 3. sodium.
    ○ 4. calcium.

83 Mr. Washington is a student and finds reading a pleasant diversion while recuperating. He studies a book that describes the urinary tract and learns that when urine leaves the kidneys, it next travels to the
    ○ 1. bladder.
    ○ 2. urethra.
    ○ 3. ureters.
    ○ 4. tubular capillaries.

84 Mr. Washington is correct when he says that the structures in the kidneys where substances useful to the body are reabsorbed rather than excreted are the
    ○ 1. hila.
    ○ 2. tubules.
    ○ 3. renal pelves.
    ○ 4. Bowman's capsules.

85 The internal sphincter in the urinary system, Mr. Washington learns, is located at the junction of the
    ○ 1. kidney and ureter.
    ○ 2. ureter and bladder.
    ○ 3. bladder and urethra.
    ○ 4. nephron and kidney pelvis.

86 In another book Mr. Washington reads, he learns about how personality normally develops. According to Freud, which of the following phases of personality development normally occurs first in life?
    ○ 1. The oral phase

    ○ 2. The latent phase
    ○ 3. The phallic phase
    ○ 4. The genital phase

87 Ms. Geist has cystitis. Vitamin C is given to Ms. Geist, the most likely reason being that Vitamin C will help
    ○ 1. increase the acidity of urine.
    ○ 2. limit the spread of infection.
    ○ 3. relieve spasms of the bladder.
    ○ 4. improve the permeability of the nephrons.

88 The nurse judges correctly that Ms. Geist's urine is normal in terms of its specific gravity, when laboratory reports indicate that several specimens ranged between about
    ○ 1. 1.000 and 1.010.
    ○ 2. 1.015 and 1.025.
    ○ 3. 1.025 and 1.050.
    ○ 4. 1.050 and 1.070.

89 The specific gravity of Ms. Geist's urine is a measurement that describes the weight of her urine when compared with the weight of
    ○ 1. plasma.
    ○ 2. mercury.
    ○ 3. normal saline.
    ○ 4. distilled water.

90 Mr. Rodier has a suprapubic catheter inserted into his urinary bladder. Mr. Rodier's catheter is introduced into his body through the patient's
    ○ 1. ureter.
    ○ 2. kidney.
    ○ 3. urethra.
    ○ 4. abdomen.

The Nursing Care of Patients Requiring Diagnostic Procedures

A nurse works in the unit of a health agency where a variety of diagnostic procedures are performed for ambulatory patients.

91 For which of the following examination is a test meal most often ordered?
    ○ 1. A radioactive scan
    ○ 2. A gastrointestinal series
    ○ 3. A glucose tolerance test
    ○ 4. An intravenous pyelogram

92 Radioactive iodine (^{131}I) is used to help in diagnosing patients suspected of having disorders of the

   O 1. thyroid gland.
   O 2. adrenal gland.
   O 3. thymus gland.
   O 4. pituitary gland.

93 Of the following procedures, the one that ordinarily requires a patient's legally witnessed signature on an informed consent form is
   O 1. an electrocardiogram.
   O 2. a glucose tolerance test.
   O 3. an abdominal paracentesis.
   O 4. an upper gastrointestinal series.

94 A patient is to have a barium enema, a gastrointestinal series, a glucose tolerance test, and an electroencephalogram. During which of the examinations is the patient likely to find the examination most tiring and uncomfortable?
   O 1. The barium enema
   O 2. The electroencephalogram
   O 3. The glucose tolerance test
   O 4. The gastrointestinal series

95 A specimen of bone marrow is to be obtained from a patient. From which of the following bones is the specimen most likely to be taken?
   O 1. A rib or a clavicle
   O 2. A vertebra or a femur
   O 3. The skull or a mandible
   O 4. The sternum or an iliac crest

96 For which of the following diagnostic tests is it most important that the patient be in a state of fasting?
   O 1. A thoracentesis
   O 2. A gastric analysis
   O 3. An electroencephalogram
   O 4. An abdominal paracentesis

97 Having the patient void before performing a diagnostic procedure is especially important when the patient will have
   O 1. a bronchoscopy.
   O 2. a thoracentesis.
   O 3. an electroencephalogram.
   O 4. an abdominal paracentesis.

98 For which of the following examinations is the patient's fluid intake ordinarily limited for about 24 hours prior to the examination?
   O 1. A cystoscopy
   O 2. A gallbladder series
   O 3. An intravenous pyelogram
   O 4. A flat plate x-ray of the kidneys

The Remaining Items Are Individual Items.

99 A nurse is reviewing basic human needs as she prepares a nursing care plan. According to Maslow's theory, which basic need will normally demand being met before others?

○ 1. The need for trust
○ 2. The need for water
○ 3. The need for acceptance
○ 4. The need for self-fulfillment

100 In terms of human values during the life span, American culture tends to focus primarily on the

○ 1. beauty of youth.
○ 2. wisdom of the elderly.
○ 3. experience of child-rearing.
○ 4. social contributions of the middle-aged.

101 Which of the following diseases has been clearly established as a genetic disorder?

○ 1. Epilepsy
○ 2. Osteoporosis
○ 3. Hydrocephalus
○ 4. Phenylketonuria (PKU)

102 A patient develops singultus postoperatively. A synonym for singultus is

○ 1. flatus.
○ 2. hiccups.
○ 3. embolus.
○ 4. distention.

103 Because the thermometer may stimulate the vagus nerve, some health agencies recommend *not* obtaining a rectal temperature from a patient ill with a medical diagnosis of

○ 1. pleurisy.
○ 2. serum hepatitis.
○ 3. myocardial infarction.
○ 4. bleeding gastric ulcers.

104 Of the following adverse effects, which one is associated with morphine sulfate?

○ 1. Headaches
○ 2. Skin rashes
○ 3. Constipation
○ 4. Tingling in the extremities

105 The nurse should withhold administering morphine sulfate and consult with the nurse-in-charge if the patient's vital signs indicate that the patient has a

○ 1. body temperature of 99.6°F (37.6°C).
○ 2. systolic blood pressure of 130 mm Hg.

○ 3. pulse rate between 80 and 90 beats per minute.

○ 4. respiratory rate between 10 and 12 per minute.

106 As a cause of death in this country, diseases of the heart rank

○ 1. first.

○ 2. second.

○ 3. third.

○ 4. fourth.

107 The American Cancer Society has a pamphlet entitled *Help Yourself To Recovery,* which is most appropriate for the patient who, due to a malignancy, has had the surgical removal of

○ 1. a lung.

○ 2. a breast.

○ 3. the uterus.

○ 4. the prostate gland.

108 When a particular population has a morbidity rate of 12 per 1,000 persons, this describes the population's

○ 1. death rate.

○ 2. illness rate.

○ 3. congenital defect rate.

○ 4. communicable disease rate.

109 The primary reason most people believe that states should require licensing nurses before they can practice is that licensure helps to

○ 1. distinguish a practical from a registered nurse.

○ 2. organize nurses for promoting better working conditions.

○ 3. protect the public from persons unable to give safe care.

○ 4. provide accurate statistics concerning the number of properly prepared health workers in the country.

110 A patient asks a nurse the difference between an LPN and an LVN. The nurse explains correctly when she states that

○ 1. an LPN has more education than an LVN.

○ 2. an LPN is qualified to give care to adults, and an LVN to children.

○ 3. there is no difference. Both are abbreviations for recognized legal titles.

○ 4. there is no difference. Both are abbreviations for students preparing to become practical nurses.

Correct Answers and Rationales

Two numbers appear in parentheses following each rationale. The first number identifies the textbook listed in the references, page 649, and the second number identifies the page(s) in that textbook where the correct answer can be verified. Occasionally, two textbooks are given for verifying the correct answer.

The Nursing Care of Patients With Disorders of the Endocrine System

Caring for a patient with diabetes mellitus

1   4.   The classical symptoms of diabetes mellitus are voiding excessively (polyuria), eating excessively (polyphasia), and being excessively thirsty (polydipsia). Because food is being metabolized improperly, the person with diabetes loses weight and becomes fatigued quickly.   (12:776)

2   1.   The patient in diabetic acidosis has an acute insulin deficiency and needs insulin. Therapy ordinarily starts promptly, and insulin is most often given intravenously. The patient also is usually in a state of fluid and electrolyte imbalance, which must be treated. Giving glucose intravenously will add to this patient's problem. Oxygen therapy may be necessary in some situations but is usually not as urgent as the need for insulin. Anticonvulsive agents are not used for treating diabetic acidosis.   (15:534)

3   4.   Bicarbonate is an important buffering agent in the body and plays a vital role in the body's maintaining an acid–base balance. Sodium is important to maintain proper osmotic pressure and muscle and nerve irritability. Potassium is important to maintain fluid balance, muscle and nerve irritability, and heart rhythm. Magnesium is important for proper muscle and nerve irritability.   (11:293)

4   2.   Normal fasting blood sugar (glucose) levels of venous blood are between 80 mg and 120 mg per 100 ml of blood.   (15:529)

5   1.   Kussmaul's respirations are typical of a person who has ketoacidosis. The respirations are rapid, deep, and labored, and demonstrate air hunger. This is in response to the body's efforts to rid itself of excess carbon dioxide, which is in the form of carbonic acid in the bloodstream.   (15:534)

6   3.   It is recommended that the mercury be made to rise about 30 mm Hg above the point at which the radial pulse disappears when the patient's blood pressure is obtained at the brachial artery. The patient's previous blood pressure reading is irrelevant in this situation.   (9:209)

7   2.   It is best to open the mouth of a patient who cannot cooperate with a padded tongue blade. A toothbrush or surgical clamp is likely to injure oral tissues and teeth. The nurse's fingers should never be used! If the patient bites down, the injury can be serious because the mouth normally harbors many organisms.   (9:76)

8   2.   The patient must fast for a glucose tolerance test. The test ordinarily is done in the morning after an overnight fasting period and includes obtaining several blood samples after the fasting sample. These later samples are obtained at ordered intervals after the patient has a high glucose liquid. A cleansing enema and a catheterized urine specimen are not required, nor is a sedative administered the night before the examination.   (12:776; 15:530)

9   2.   Normally, it takes about 2 to 3 hours for the blood glucose level to return to normal after eating a full meal. A diabetic's blood glucose level remains high throughout the test and is still elevated after 2 to 3 hours.   (15:530)

10   1.   When a morning specimen of urine is ordered for glucose determination, it is best to discard the first voiding and collect a second one 10 to 30 minutes later. This second specimen reveals the amount of glucose excreted at that time. The first morning specimen contains glucose that has accumulated in the bladder's urine throughout the night.   (15:530)

11   4.   Postprandial means after a meal. When a postprandial glucose blood test is planned, a blood sample is taken about 2 hours after the person has eaten a high-carbohydrate meal.   (15:530)

12   3.   Diabetes mellitus is a serious illness. Best policy is to be truthful and teach the patient how he can best take care of himself. Problems are fewer when the disease is kept under good control by carefully following dietary and insulin prescriptions and by observing healthful habits of daily living. It is false to tell a patient diabetes is a disease without complications or can be regulated by frequent consultations with a health caretaker only. Health workers and family members may play an important role in helping the diabetic but he will do better and maintain independence when he is taught how to help himself to the greatest degree possible.   (15:531)

13   1.   Of the insulins described in this item, regular insulin acts most rapidly.   (15:532)

14   2.   When the patient is emotionally upset, it is best to indicate you understand and offer him whatever support you can. Trying to talk him "out of his feelings" will be of no help.   (9:21)

15   3.   It is best to give treatments, such as a cleansing enema, between meals rather than close to meal hours. This plan interferes least with the meal hours and with the patient's appetite.   (9:101)

16   4.   The solution should be injected slowly when giving an enema by compressing the plastic bottle containing the hypertonic solution. It should take at least a minute, or up to 2 minutes, to introduce an adult amount, which is approximately 120 ml. Hypertonic solution is administered at room temperature, the nozzle on the bottle is lubricated before inserting it, and the nozzle is inserted about 3 to 4 inches past the anus.   (9:478)

17 1.   For each cup of skim milk, the patient with diabetes can add two exchanges of fat to his diet. The cream portion of whole milk is equivalent to two fat exchanges.   (4:442)

18 2.   Of the foods given in this item, only honey will ordinarily be excluded from the diet of a patient with diabetes. Such foods as condensed milk, soft drinks (unless they are sugar free), sugar, jams, marmalades, pie, cake, cookies, syrup, and molasses also are especially high in sugar (simple carbohydrate) content and should be restricted. Salt need not be limited in a diabetic's diet unless he suffers with another illness also. Canned fish and peanut butter can be used.   (15:531)

19 4.   Cucumbers and mushrooms can be eaten in ordinary amounts by the diabetic patient without calculating amounts in the diet because they are very low in carbohydrate and calories. If eaten in large amounts, 1 cup or more in cooked form, they must be added to the diet calculations. Any fat used on these vegetables, such as butter, margarine, or salad dressing, is taken from the daily fat allowance.   (16:413)

20 4.   Meats contain proteins, fats, certain minerals, and calories. They contain little or no carbohydrates.   (16:34)

21 2.   Avocados are rich in monosaturated fat. About one-eighth of a 4-inch avocado is equivalent to one fat exchange. Buttermilk is in the milk exchange. Lima beans are in the vegetable exchange. Liver is in the meat exchange.   (4:445)

22 4.   Foods marketed as "dietetic" can be eaten by the diabetic person when his health caretaker approves, provided the nutrients in these foods are included in dietary calculations. These foods are not without carbohydrates, proteins, and fats, and therefore, their content must be taken into account. Labels should be read carefully when selecting dietetic products. For example, the terms *low caloric* and *dietetic* do not necessarily mean that the foods contain no simple sugars.   (4:291; 15:531)

23 4.   Insulin must be given by injection because it is destroyed by digestive juices in the stomach. Hypoglycemic agents are administered orally but they function differently from insulin.   (10:159)

24 3.   Isophane insulin suspension (NPH insulin) is an intermediate-acting insulin. It peaks between about 7 and 12 hours after it is administered. Most patients who take NPH insulin in the morning experience signs of hypoglycemia between mid- and late-afternoon.   (15:532)

25 1.   An insulin vial that is marked U100 means that 1 ml of solution contains 100 units of insulin.   (15:533)

26 2.   NPH insulin is cloudy and should be mixed well before drawing it up into the syringe. This is best done by rolling the vial of insulin gently between the palms of the hands. Shaking the vial vigorously causes air bubbles to appear and makes accurate measurement of the dosage difficult. Tipping the vial once is not likely to mix the insulin sufficiently well. (12:781)

27 1.   An amount of air equal to the amount of insulin to be withdrawn should be injected into a vial. Large amounts of air will cause pressure within the vial and smaller amounts will cause a partial vacuum within the vial. Both conditions make it difficult to withdraw accurate dosages of insulin. (9:578)

28 4.   When giving themselves insulin, persons with diabetes are taught to inject the needle at an angle of 90 degrees. This ensures reaching subcutaneous tissue while still being able to use a relatively short needle. (12:781)

29 1.   In the situation described in this item, the nurse is using evaluation when she compares something a patient does with the correct or appropriate behavior or standard. One teaching objective that the nurse used in this situation was that the patient will learn to inject the needle while holding the syringe at a 90 degree angle. When the patient fails to accomplish this objective, or goal, the nurse's next step is to correct the patient's error by teaching him the technique again. (9:41)

30 3.   The patient's technique, described in this item, is in error. He should rotate to a different extremity and his abdomen between each injection to prevent tissue damage and resulting poor absorption of insulin. (9:580)

31 2.   Injection sites are rotated when persons take insulin daily in order to avoid damage to subcutaneous tissues. The damage is atrophy of subcutaneous fat which is called insulin lipoatrophy. (15:533)

32 3.   The forearms are not used for subcutaneous injections because they contain very little subcutaneous tissue. In addition to the back, thighs, and upper arms, insulin can be injected into the abdomen. (9:577)

33 4.   Although symptoms vary considerably among diabetics, symptoms most typical of hypoglycemia (hyperinsulinism) are excessive perspiration and excited behavior. Drowsiness, air hunger, a rapid pulse, flushed skin, dry skin, vomiting, and thirst are more commonly observed in a diabetic suffering with hyperglycemia (hypoinsulinism). (15:535–536)

34 1.   Tes-Tape uses a color chart. The patient can determine relative amounts of sugar in the urine by comparing the color on the tape moistened with urine with colors on a chart prepared by the manufacturer. The tape turns green or blue when there is glucose present. (15:530)

35 1.   Light and moisture from the air affect testing materials used for determining whether glucose is present in urine. This may alter test results. The container in which tape is stored should be well capped at all times and kept in a place where it is not exposed to light and air. (15:530)

36 3.   The lateral aspect of a fingertip is used to collect a specimen of blood for blood-glucose testing when commercial kits, such as Chemstrip bG, Visidex, and Dextrostic, are used. The fingertip is used because it has a good blood supply and the site is very convenient. A sharp sterile lancet is used to prick the fingertip. (12:777)

37 4.   A person using a blood-glucose testing kit should be taught to be sure to allow the alcohol used to cleanse the skin at the site of injection to dry. The accuracy of the test can be impaired when this precaution is not observed. The area is squeezed before obtaining the specimen of blood; this technique helps bring blood to the area and helps avoid striking a bone in the finger. It is not necessary to use warmth over the area to be punctured and one good cleansing is recommended. (12:777)

38 2. It has been found that the body's need for insulin decreases with exercise. The exercise uses glucose for energy, and thereby, decreases the amount of blood glucose in the body. (15:534)

39 4. For any illness, the patient should be taught to test his urine or blood more frequently for glucose and report these findings when he contacts his physician. Generally, illness increases the body's demands for insulin. Changing the diet or insulin dosage without consulting the physician is not recommended. (15:537)

40 3. The only suggestion in this item that is likely to help a person stop smoking is to teach him to begin by trying to put off smoking for a few minutes when a desire to smoke becomes apparent, and then plan to do something that will distract his attention from smoking. Low-tar and low-nicotine cigarettes ordinarily do not help the patient to stop smoking. It is best that he not smoke when doing something that he associates with smoking, such as drinking coffee. Also, he should not carry cigarettes, matches, or a lighter when trying to cut down or to stop smoking. Other suggestions to help decrease or stop smoking include getting someone to stop with him, buying cigarettes one package at a time, keeping cigarettes in an inconvenient place, changing activities when the urge to smoke arises, and cutting down on inhaling. (8:356; 12:585)

41 2. Nicotine inhaled when a person smokes affects peripheral arteries by decreasing their size. The clogging of arteries with plaque is believed to be caused by fatty materials. Dilated veins, seen when varicosities are present, are engorged with blood. (8:387)

42 2. Determining an ideal weight is difficult. However, one very general guide for a person's best weight for life is the ideal weight of a person of similar build and the same sex at age 25. (4:265)

43 1. Persons with diabetes should wear an identification bracelet or necklace that indicates that they are diabetic. Placing a label in clothing, traveling and working with someone familiar with the disease, and carrying a description of the illness and therapy in a billfold are not as convenient, nor as effective for helping to alert others that a person is diabetic as an identification bracelet or necklace. (8:547-548)

44 3. The person with diabetes is particularly prone to various blood vessel (vascular) disorders. Any part of the body can be affected. However, the lower extremities, the kidneys, and the eyes are especially susceptible to problems. Complications are more likely to occur and become severe in the person whose diabetes is not under good control and who does not take care of himself properly. (15:536)

45 2.   For any person with diabetes, the prognosis is best and complications can be delayed or avoided when the person understands his own illness thoroughly and follows his physician's orders. For some persons, help from family members is indicated, but depending on family members completely is not advised unless the patient is unable to participate in his own care.   (15:537)

46 1.   The best sources of information concerning diets for persons with diabetes are the American Dietetic Association, the American Diabetic Association, and the Department of Health and Human Services (DHHS).   (16:146)

47 3.   The best definition of health, as authorities describe it today, is physical, emotional (including spiritual), and social well-being. It is considered to be more than merely not being sick, being free of congenital and hereditary diseases, and being able to cope with work and life.   (12:23)

The Nursing Care of Patients With Disorders of the Urological System

Caring for patients with various urological disorders

48 4.   When a urinary disorder is present, it is of utmost importance that the patient's fluid intake and output are noted and documented very carefully for assessment purposes. For some patients, but not necessarily all, dietary intake, activities, rest, and skin care may also be important.   (12:729)

49 2.   It is usual to give fluids generously and a full liquid breakfast before a cystoscopy unless the patient is going to have general anesthesia. Solid food is ordinarily withheld, because the discomfort of the procedure may cause nausea and vomiting. A sedative and an enema frequently are ordered before a cystoscopy.   (15:487)

50 4.   Polyuria is an excess production of urine. Anuria is a lack of the production of urine. Pyuria is pus in the urine. Nocturia is excessive urination during the night.   (9:433)

51 1.   Urine normally is darkest in color on awakening in the morning. Because the person ordinarily has no fluid intake during the night, the urine becomes most concentrated during the night.   (9:434)

52 2.   The most common first symptom of a malignancy of the urinary bladder is painless hematuria. Dysuria, urinary retention, and incontinence are not associated with bladder cancer.   (15:500)

53 1.   A patient with a urinary diversion should have a generous fluid intake. The fluids act as a natural irrigation in the urinary system, thus helping to prevent infections. Certain minerals are limited in the diet of a patient with a urinary diversion, primarily to help prevent the development of kidney stones.   (9:457)

54 4. Asparagus tends to give normal urine a very strong odor. (9:457)

55 2. A solution of about half white vinegar and half water is an effective deodorant for a reusable appliance worn over the stoma of an ileal conduit. Household bleach is also a good deodorizer. Solutions of table salt, hydrogen peroxide, and sodium bicarbonate are not effective deodorizing agents. (9:457)

56 2. The most probable cause of discomfort when the balloon of an indwelling catheter is being inflated is that the balloon is in the urethra. The pressure this causes on the urethra results in discomfort. Discomfort is not a probable sign if the balloon breaks, is high in the bladder, or contains too much fluid. (9:447)

57 2. An indwelling catheter normally drains the urinary bladder by gravity. The level of the bladder should be above the level of the drainage receptacle to promote drainage by gravity. (9:441)

58 1. Patients with an indwelling catheter should have a generous fluid intake. The perineal area should be cleansed thoroughly at least twice a day, more often as indicated. The perineal area should not be powdered because this measure is likely to cause local irritation. The catheter is usually changed as infrequently as possible, sometimes every week or two, or once a month for some patients. (9:449)

59 2. It is especially important to keep the perineal area scrupulously clean when a patient has an indwelling catheter. Irrigating the catheter is not done routinely unless there is a specific reason to do so. The drainage tube should not be clamped when the patient ambulates. Agency policies differ on how often the collecting container is emptied; some policies state to empty them every 8 hours, others indicate less often. However, the amount of urine excreted in every 8-hour period ordinarily is noted and recorded. (9:449)

60 4. The top level of normal for a BUN test is reported at about 18 to 20 mg per 100 ml of blood. Normal BUN findings at the lower range are at about 8 mg per 100 ml of blood. (15:485)

61 3. The phenolsulfonphthalein (PSP) test is done to study the ability of the kidneys to excrete wastes. When renal disease is present, the dye used in the test is excreted slowly, especially when kidney tubules are involved. A renal arteriogram is done to evaluate the condition of blood vessels in the kidneys. A cystoscopy examination allows the examiner to view the urethra, bladder, and ureteral openings. (15:485)

62 3. Careful care of the skin, which is usually dry and itchy, is especially important when caring for a patient with uremia. The skin can be sponged with water to which a little vinegar is added to relieve the itching (pruritus). An ointment or lotion also may be used to relieve itching but should be applied only after the skin is clean. Because edema is usually present, the patient is at risk for developing decubitus ulcers, and nursing measures should be used to help prevent them. The feet, which may be edematous, should be elevated on pillows. Oral hygiene becomes very important because the mucous membranes of the mouth are often very dry and halitosis is often present.   (15:678)

63   4.   During the drainage period when peritoneal dialysis is used, fluid instilled into the peritoneal cavity leaves by gravity. Changing the patient's position in bed and elevating the level of the bed help to promote drainage of the solution. If the catheter becomes plugged, a qualified caretaker is responsible for irrigating it. Otherwise, it is not irrigated. Elevating the drainage receptacle will slow the rate at which drainage leaves the peritoneal cavity because it decreases the distance between the patient's abdomen and the receptacle.   (15:681)

64   2.   Heparin is an anticoagulant. It is administered to a patient having hemodialysis to help prevent blood clotting. The effects of heparin are overcome following therapy by its antidote, protamine sulfate.   (15:680)

65   2.   Synonyms for a stone in the urinary tract include calculus (plural is calculi) and lithiasis. Calcemia is an excess amount of calcium in the blood. Calcitonin is a hormone from the thyroid gland. Calix, also spelled calyx, is a division of the kidney pelvis.   (15:496)

66   2.   The pain associated with a ureteral stone is best described as severe and colicky. The pain may radiate to the groin, leg, scrotum, penis, or umbilicus but ordinarily starts around the kidney and ureter on the side where the stone lodges. In most instances, a narcotic analgesic is required to promote comfort. The pain is due to contractions and spasms as the ureter tries to propel the stone toward the bladder.   (15:497)

67   4.   If a person has difficulty to start voiding, it is best to offer the person fluids to drink, have the person in a sitting position, and pour warm water over the perineal area. Taking a warm bath is also often helpful because it helps to relax the person having difficulty with voiding. Limiting fluid intake is not recommended. A distended bladder sometimes helps stimulate voiding. Allowing water to run at a nearby tap so that the patient can hear it and placing the hands in warm water are also recommended nursing measures to use when retention is a problem.   (9:438–439)

68   1.   Persons who catheterize themselves at home are taught to use techniques of medical asepsis. Infections at home have not been a problem when the person uses medical asepsis. Appropriate techniques for a woman who uses self-catheterization include catheterizing herself while sitting on a toilet and applying pressure to the lower abdomen while the catheter is in place (Credé massage). Contracting abdominal muscles during the procedure is not recommended.   (9:454)

69   3.   Urine that remains in the bladder after a person has finished voiding is called residual urine. Normally, it consists of no more than about 1 ml to 3 ml. Reflux means a backward or return flow. Overflow means a continuous escape of urine. Retention refers to the inability to void.   (9:440)

70   4.   The patient is most likely to experience pressure when a catheter is being inserted into the urethra. Normally, there should be no pain or other sensations when inserting a catheter into the urinary bladder.   (9:440)

71 3. Before a female patient is catheterized, cotton balls used for cleaning at the meatus should be moved from above the meatus toward the anus. This prevents carrying organisms from an area of more contamination to an area of less contamination. Moving cotton balls across does not clean the area below the meatus where contamination is likely. Each cotton ball should be used for one swabbing movement only.   (9:444)

72 1. When a catheter meets resistance before it reaches the urinary bladder during catheterization of a female patient, it is often helpful to have the patient take several deep breaths. This helps the patient to relax, and the sphincter offering resistance also relaxes, allowing the catheter to be passed with ease. Never force a catheter! Coughing, swallowing, and holding the breath do not help to promote relaxation of the sphincter.   (9:445)

73 2. The catheter should be inserted about 2 to 3 inches (5 to 7.5 cm) in a female. The female urethra is about 1½ to 2½ inches (3.75 to 6.25 cm). The catheter should be passed just far enough to reach the bladder. The male urethra is considerably longer than the female urethra. The catheter should be inserted 6 to 8 inches (15 to 20 cm) in a male.   (9:445)

74 3. A patient who is incontinent should have at least an average fluid intake and preferably, an above-average fluid intake. Limiting the patient's fluid intake would be an unusual order and should be questioned in the situation described in this item. Such orders as serving a regular diet, offering a bedpan every 4 hours, and ambulating the patient are not necessarily inappropriate for a patient who is incontinent of urine.   (9:435)

75 3. Alternately contracting and relaxing the perineal muscles often helps the incontinent patient strengthen the muscles that control voiding. These exercises are called Kegel exercises. Doing push-ups, running in place, and alternately contracting and relaxing abdominal muscles will strengthen certain muscles but not those that help to control urinary elimination.   (9:439)

76 1. Urine that cools normally becomes cloudy and has a sediment. This occurs as the urine becomes alkaline in nature. If the specimen was clear when obtained, adding a little acid and warming the urine will clear the cloudiness.   (9:434)

77 2. A history of "strep throat," scarlet fever, or an upper respiratory infection is typical of the person with acute glomerulonephritis, although no definite cause for the disease is known. Organisms are not present in the kidneys when symptoms appear. It is suspected that the disease may be the result of an autoimmune response.   (12:735)

78 1. The urine of a patient with acute glomerulonephritis is likely to be dark and smoky owing to the presence of red blood cells in the urine. The urine will probably be positive for the presence of albumin also.   (12:735)

79 3. Oliguria means that the patient is excreting very little urine. Anuria means no urine production. Bloody urine is called hematuria. Diuresis and polyuria are terms used to describe excessive amounts of urine.   (9:433)

80 4. Edema is often present in the patient with glomerulonephritis. Therefore, daily weighing often helps caretakers to judge when edema is subsiding or worsening. Daily weighing is very unlikely to be used to help in regulating fluid intake, determining drug dosages in adults, and estimating kidney damage. (15:507)

81 4. It is common practice to weigh patients in the morning before breakfast is served. A paper towel is placed on a scale before the patient steps onto the scale with bare feet. The patient should be helped to remove a bathrobe before being weighed. (9:216)

82 3. The patient with chronic glomerulonephritis often suffers with edema, and therefore his diet is most probably best when it is low in sodium content. The diet is usually high in fat, carbohydrates, and proteins when glomerulonephritis becomes chronic. (15:508; 16:302)

83 3. Urine leaves the kidneys by the ureters, which carry urine to the urinary bladder. Urine leaves the body through the urethra and external meatus. (10:280)

84 2. Materials that the body needs are reabsorbed in the tubules of the kidneys. The renal pelvis is the basin that collects urine before it enters the ureters. Water, useful materials, and dissolved wastes flow into Bowman's capsule, which is the beginning of the tubule. The hilum is a notch in the kidney where an artery, vein, and the ureter connect with the kidney. (10:282, 287)

85 3. The internal sphincter in the urinary system is located at the junction of the bladder and urethra. This sphincter consists of circular muscle fibers that help to prevent emptying of the urinary bladder involuntarily. The sphincter functions automatically by reflex in an infant. Control is learned by training and after some physical maturation. (10:289)

86 1. Freud listed the phases of life in the following order: oral phase, occurring between birth and about 1 year of age; the anal-expulsion phase, occurring between about 1 and 3 or 4 years; the phallic phase, occurring between about 3 or 4 to 6 years; the latent phase, occurring between about 7 and 12 years; the genital or adolescent phase, occurring between about 12 and 18 years; and the adult phase, occurring after about age 18. (1:22–27)

87 1. Vitamin C frequently is used to help increase the acidity of urine in patients with cystitis. Increasing the acidity of urine helps to produce a hostile environment for bacteria, thus limiting their ability to live and sustain the infection. Cranberry juice is also often used to help maintain acidity of urine. (8:447)

88 2. The specific gravity of urine is normally considered to be between approximately 1.015 and 1.025, although some persons with readings outside of this range may have no urinary tract pathology. Even a reading of 1.035 may be normal for some persons. (15:729)

89 4. Specific gravity compares the weight of a fluid with the weight of distilled water. Normal urine is slightly heavier than distilled water because it contains dissolved substances, such as minerals and protein wastes.   (15:729)

90 4.   The prefix *supra* means above or over. A suprapubic catheter is introduced through the abdominal wall and then into the urinary bladder.   (15:504)

The Nursing Care of Patients Requiring Diagnostic Procedures

Caring for patients requiring various diagnostic procedures

91 3.   Patients having a glucose tolerance test most often are ordered to have a test meal which is a high-carbohydrate meal. Test meals are not used for radioisotope scans, an intravenous pyelogram, or a gastrointestinal series.   (15:530)

92 1.   Radioactive iodine is used to diagnose disorders of the thyroid gland. Scanners are used to study the distribution of the isotope in the body. The preparation is also used for treating certain thyroid disorders, especially when surgery is indicated.   (15:515)

93 3.   Agency policies vary somewhat on which procedures require a patient's legally witnessed signature. However, a signature most often is required when the skin or parts of the body are entered, such as occurs during a thoracentesis and an abdominal paracentesis. One is almost never required prior to performing an electrocardiogram, a glucose tolerance test, or an upper gastrointestinal series.   (9:235)

94 1.   Most patients find a barium enema to be very tiring and uncomfortable and should be prepared accordingly. Some patients may dislike the taste of the barium they must drink when having a gastrointestinal series, but discomfort is not associated with the examination. Discomfort is also not associated with an electroencephalogram or a glucose tolerance test.   (9:245)

95 4.   The two most commonly used sites for obtaining a bone marrow specimen are the sternum and a posterior iliac crest.   (12:663)

96 2.   It is important that the patient is in a state of fasting when he is being prepared for a gastric analysis. Food in the stomach increases the risk of vomiting and distorts laboratory findings on gastric contents.   (12:696)

97 4.   It is especially important that a patient void before an abdominal paracentesis is performed. A full bladder may be punctured when the trocar and cannula are introduced through the abdominal wall. The patient is ordinarily more comfortable if his bladder is empty during other examinations, but voiding remains especially important before an abdominal paracentesis.   (12:697)

98 3.   The patient's fluid intake should be limited for about 24 hours before an intravenous pyelogram. This preparation causes urine and the contrast medium used in the examination to become concentrated to a maximum degree.   (12:730)

The Remaining Items Are Individual Items

99   2.   According to psychologists, including Maslow, humans normally meet physiological needs for water, food, oxygen, and elimination before other human needs are met. Humans then pursue such needs as trust, acceptance, safety, self-fulfillment, and esthetic needs.   (12:21)

100   1.   The culture of this country places value and emphasis on the beauty of youth. This preoccupation with youth helps explain why many people in this country use special efforts to try to remain young and young-looking.   (8:30)

101   4.   It has been clearly demonstrated that phenylketonuria (PKU) is a genetic disorder. Hydrocephalus is due to an accident in the development of the fetus and is called a congenital defect. Epilepsy is caused by trauma, infection, or a tumor although some persons believe it may have a hereditary tendency. Osteoporosis is due to demineralization of bone tissue and tends to occur late in life; it may occur as a result of inactivity and of taking certain drugs, such as corticosteroids.   (8:79, 172, 276)

102   2.   Singultus is hiccups. Flatus is gas in the intestinal tract. An embolus is a blood clot. Distention, sometimes called tympanites, is a swelling of the abdomen due to accumulations of gas in the intestinal tract.   (9:387)

103   3.   Some agencies do not recommend obtaining a rectal temperature on patients who have had a myocardial infarction. The thermometer may stimulate the vagus nerve and cause the heart's rhythm to become irregular.   (15:658)

104   3.   Constipation is a common side-effect of morphine sulfate. Additional adverse effects to morphine include nausea, vomiting, euphoria, and dependency. Another adverse effect is a decrease in the respiratory rate, as the next item illustrates.   (14:65)

105   4.   Morphine sulfate tends to depress respirations. The drug should not be used until the nurse-in-charge is notified if a patient's respiratory rate is below 10 to 12 respirations per minute.   (14:61)

106   1.   Diseases of the heart rank first as the cause of death in this country. Malignancies rank second, cerebrovascular diseases rank third, and accidents rank fourth.   (15:345)

107   2.   The pamphlet *Help Yourself To Recovery* has been prepared by the American Cancer Society for patients who have had a breast removed because of a malignancy.   (15:588)

108   2.   The word morbidity means illness or sickness. A population's morbidity rate refers to the illness rate. Death rates are described as mortality rates.   (15:48)

109   3.   The primary purpose of licensure is to protect the public from persons unqualified to give safe health care. Licensing also may serve other purposes, but preventing unfit persons to practice is its primary purpose.   (12:162)

110   3.   The abbreviations LPN and LVN are abbreviations for recognized legal titles. They stand for licensed practical nurse and licensed vocational nurse. LPNs and LVNs are graduate practical or vocational nurses who have completed educational programs that qualify them to care for persons of all ages.   (12:8)

Classification of Test Items

Directions: *Each item in the previous review test is classified here according to the subject area it tests. Place a check mark after each item you answered **correctly** by referring to your answers. Total the number of items you answered correctly in each area and enter the numbers in the correct places on pages 553–556.*

Clinical: Medical/Surgical Nursing (Adults)

1 ✓	34 ✓	41 ✓	53 ✓	77 ✓	95 ✓
2 ✓	35 ✓	43 ✓	60 ___	78 ✓	96 ___
5 ✓	36 ✓	44 ✓	61 ___	80 ✓	97 ✓
8 ✓	37 ✓	45 ✓	62 ___	88 ✓	98 ___
10 ___	38 ✓	48 ✓	63 ___	90 ✓	103 ✓
11 ✓	39 ✓	49 ✓	65 ✓	91 ✓	106 ✓
12 ✓	40 ___	52 ✓	66 ✓	94 ___	107 ✓

TOTAL ___33___

Biological/Physical Sciences

3 ✓	9 ___	57 ✓	83 ✓	84 ✓	85 ✓
4 ✓					

TOTAL ___6___

Fundamentals of Nursing

6 ___	29 ✓	51 ✓	67 ✓	73 ___	89 ✓
7 ___	30 ___	54 ✓	68 ✓	74 ✓	102 ___
15 ✓	31 ✓	55 ✓	69 ✓	75 ✓	108 ___
16 ✓	32 ✓	56 ✓	70 ___	76 ✓	
27 ✓	47 ✓	58 ✓	71 ✓	79 ✓	
28 ✓	50 ✓	59 ✓	72 ___	81 ✓	

TOTAL ___26___

Diet Therapy/Nutrition

17 ✓   19 ✓   21 ✓   42 _____   46 ✓   82 ✓

18 ✓   20 _____   22 ✓

TOTAL 7

Pharmacology

13 ✓   24 _____   26 ✓   64 ✓   92 ✓   105 ✓

23 ✓   25 ✓   33 _____   87 _____   104 _____

TOTAL 8

Psychosocial Sciences

14 ✓   93 ✓   100 ✓   101 ✓   109 ✓   110 ✓

86 ✓   99 ✓

TOTAL 8

Summary: Classification of Test Items

Enter your individual scores for each review test in the spaces provided below. When you have completed the 14 review tests and entered your results, follow the directions at the end of this form to determine how well you did in each subject area.

Test	Clinical Nursing		Biological/ Physical Sciences		Fundamentals of Nursing		Diet Therapy/ Nutrition		Pharmacology		Psychosocial Sciences	
	Number of Items Answered Correctly	Total Number of Items in Test	Number of Items Answered Correctly	Total Number of Items in Test	Number of Items Answered Correctly	Total Number of Items in Test	Number of Items Answered Correctly	Total Number of Items in Test	Number of Items Answered Correctly	Total Number of Items in Test	Number of Items Answered Correctly	Total Number of Items in Test
Test 1 Mental Health Nursing	60	77		None	3	3	1	1	16	20	13	16
Test 2 Maternity Nursing and Care of Newborns	55	71	19	20	2	4	13	14	1	2	2	2
Test 3 Maternity Nursing and Care of Newborns	62	92	8	10	4	5	2	2	4	4	6	7
Test 4 Nursing Care of Children	57	78	1	2	5	6	3	4	6	10	15	16
Test 5 Nursing Care of Children	43	50	5	6	6	8	2	4	22	26	21	26
Test 6 Medical/ Surgical Nursing (Adults)	35	41	2	4	30	39	5	7	10	11	13	13

(continued)

553

Summary: Classification of Test Items (continued)

Enter your individual scores for each review test in the spaces provided below. When you have completed the 14 review tests and entered your results, follow the directions at the end of this form to determine how well you did in each subject area.

Test	Clinical Nursing		Biological/Physical Sciences		Fundamentals of Nursing		Diet Therapy/Nutrition		Pharmacology		Psychosocial Sciences	
	Number of Items Answered Correctly	Total Number of Items in Test	Number of Items Answered Correctly	Total Number of Items in Test	Number of Items Answered Correctly	Total Number of Items in Test	Number of Items Answered Correctly	Total Number of Items in Test	Number of Items Answered Correctly	Total Number of Items in Test	Number of Items Answered Correctly	Total Number of Items in Test
Test 7 Medical/Surgical Nursing (Adults)	39	45	12	13	25	33	6	8	3	6	7	8
Test 8 Medical/Surgical Nursing (Adults)	40	46	4	4	44	56	0	None	1	2	5	6
Test 9 Medical/Surgical Nursing (Adults)	16	23	7	10	34	47	2	5	14	17	7	9
Test 10 Medical/Surgical Nursing (Adults)	17	21	9	12	47	61	0	None	12	13	4	5

	(hw)	(print)	(hw)	(print)	(hw)	(print)	(hw)	(print)	(hw)	(print)	(hw)	(print)
Test 11 Medical/Surgical Nursing (Adults)	46	58	7	9	24	28		1	8	9	5	8
Test 12 Medical/Surgical Nursing (Adults)	25	32	4	4	44	51	8	8	15	15	5	6
Test 13 Medical/Surgical Nursing (Adults)	37	42	10	12	24	31	8	8	12	13	7	7
Test 14 Medical/Surgical Nursing (Adults)	33	42	6	7	26	33	7	9	8	11	8	8
ALL TOTALS	565	718	94	113	318	405	58	71	133	159	118	137

Mental Health Nursing (Test 1) — 60

Maternity Nursing and Care of Newborns (Tests 2 and 3) — 117

Nursing Care of Children (Tests 4 and 5) — 100

Medical/Surgical Nursing (Adults) — 286

137/603
1285
are 80%

Summary: Classification of Test Items

After completing the above form, you will know how many items dealing with each subject area that you answered correctly. To determine the percentage of items you answered correctly, divide the number of items you answered correctly by the total number of items in each subject area, as follows:

Number of items testing clinical content in Test 1 $\dfrac{60}{77}$ = 80 %   Percentage of items you answered correctly in Mental Health Nursing

Number of items testing clinical content in Test 2-3 $\dfrac{119}{163}$ = 72 %   Percentage of items you answered correctly Maternity Nursing and Care of the Newborn

Number of items testing clinical content in Test 4-5 $\dfrac{100}{128}$ = 78 %   Percentage of items you answered correctly in Nursing Care of Children

Number of items testing clinical content in Test 6-14 $\dfrac{280}{350}$ = 80 %   Percentage of items you answered correctly in Medical/Surgical Nursing (Adults)

Number of items in all tests: Biological/Physical Science $\dfrac{94}{113}$ = 83 %   Percentage of items you answered correctly in biological/physical sciences

Number of items in all tests: Fundamentals of Nursing $\dfrac{318}{405}$ = 78 %   Percentage of items you answered correctly in fundamentals of nursing

Number of items in all tests: Diet Therapy/Nutrition $\dfrac{58}{71}$ = 82 %   Percentage of items you answered correctly in diet therapy/nutrition

Number of items in all tests: Pharmacology $\dfrac{130}{159}$ = 82 %   Percentage of items you answered correctly in pharmacology

Number of items in all tests: Psychosocial Sciences $\dfrac{118}{137}$ = 86 %   Percentage of items you answered correctly in psychosocial sciences

Interpretation: If you answered more than about 75% to 90% of the items correctly, yuou are probably prepared for the state licensure examination. However, if you answered less than 75% of the items correctly, it is suggested that you review your tests, class notes, and this review book again to prepare for the licensing examination. Studying the percentage of items you answered correctly in each subject area helps identify subjects in which you did well and subjects in which you are especially in need of further review.

COMPREHENSIVE EXAMINATION

Parts I and II

General Instructions for the Comprehensive Examination

A two-part comprehensive examination that resembles NCLEX-PN as closely as possible is presented next. Each part consists of 120 items. Follow these instructions for both parts of the comprehensive examination:

—Each item consists of 4 possible answers, or options. (The item is described more fully on page xx in the Introduction.) Read each item carefully and then select the one correct or best answer for each item.

—Indicate your choice for the correct or best answer by blackening the circle *completely* next to your choice for the correct answer in this book or on the appropriate answer sheet at the end of this book.

—There is only one correct answer for each item. If you think the correct answer for an item is not among the options, choose the option that you believe is the best possible answer.

—Work systematically and proceed steadily. Do not spend too much time on any one item.

—Time your progress occasionally so that you know you will finish the entire Part on which you are working in 2-hours' time.

—Correct answers and rationales are provided for both parts of the comprehensive examination so that you can determine how well you scored. If you gave correct answers to about 180 to 190 items or more of the 240 items in the examination (75 to 80%), you are probably prepared to write your state licensing examination. However, if you answered fewer than 180 to 190 items correctly, it is suggested that you continue with your reviewing. It is also suggested that you concentrate your review on subject matter on which you tested poorly in the review tests. The table on pages 553–556, when completed, will help you identify your areas of weaknesses and strengths.

—Proceed to the next page for Part I of the comprehensive examination.

Part I
of the Comprehensive Examination

Allow yourself 2 hours to complete Part I. Start this part now.

Sixty-One-Year-Old Mr. Roy Beven Has a Laryngectomy for Removal of a Malignant Tumor. He Has a Tracheostomy.

1 The symptom that most probably caused Mr. Beven to seek health care is
○ 1. a brassy cough.
○ 2. excessive sputum.
○ 3. a chronic sore throat.
○ 4. persistent hoarseness.

2 If Mr. Beven presents the following signs, which one is *least* likely to be present if his tracheostomy needs suctioning?
○ 1. The patient has dyspnea.
○ 2. The patient has noisy respirations.
○ 3. The patient has a decreased pulse rate.
○ 4. The patient has an increased respiratory rate.

3 If the nurse is suctioning Mr. Beven's tracheostomy and uses the following techniques, which one is in *error*?
○ 1. The nurse lubricates the catheter with normal saline.
○ 2. The nurse instills a few milliliters of sterile normal saline into the tracheostomy.
○ 3. The nurse suctions while inserting the catheter.
○ 4. The nurse handles the catheter with surgical aseptic techniques.

4 The nurse wishes to clean Mr. Beven's left bronchus when suctioning his tracheostomy. For best results, she should ask Mr. Beven to position his head by
○ 1. looking toward his chest.
○ 2. looking toward the ceiling.
○ 3. turning his head to the left.
○ 4. turning his head to the right.

5 The maximum recommended time to do continuous suctioning of the tracheostomy while the catheter is in Mr. Beven's respiratory passageway is
○ 1. 5 to 10 seconds.
○ 2. 10 to 15 seconds.
○ 3. 15 to 20 seconds.
○ 4. 20 to 25 seconds.

6   If Mr. Beven starts to cough while the nurse is suctioning his tracheostomy, it is best for the nurse to
○ 1. remove the catheter.
○ 2. rotate the catheter.
○ 3. increase the amount of suction that is being used.
○ 4. turn the suction off but leave the catheter in place.

7   Mr. Beven's outer tracheostomy tube comes out accidentally. Until a physician arrives, the nurse should
○ 1. try to insert the tube gently.
○ 2. start administering oxygen by mask.
○ 3. place dressings on the tracheostomy incision.
○ 4. hold the tracheostomy open with a surgical dilator.

8   The nurse accidentally spills water near the portable electric suctioning machine that she has used to suction Mr. Beven's tracheostomy. In this situation, it is safest for the nurse to unplug the machine and
○ 1. move the machine from the water.
○ 2. post a sign warning of a wet floor.
○ 3. wipe up the water that was spilled.
○ 4. call the housekeeping department for prompt assistance.

Mr. Beven has a gavage tube in place through which he is given nourishment four times a day.

9   The nourishment used for Mr. Beven's gavage is prepared by the dietary department of the hospital. At approximately what temperature should the nourishment be introduced?
○ 1. Cold, about 40°F (5°C)
○ 2. Cool, about 60°F (16°C)
○ 3. Warm, about 100°F (38°C)
○ 4. Near room temperature

10   Which of the following methods is considered most accurate for determining whether Mr. Beven's gavage tube is in the stomach before nourishment is introduced?
○ 1. Aspirating stomach contents through the tube
○ 2. Feeling for the tube through the abdominal wall
○ 3. Observing for bubbles appearing regularly when the end of the tube is under water
○ 4. Hearing air sounds with a stethoscope placed over the stomach while introducing air into the tube

11   After the position of the tube is established but before introducing nourishment through Mr. Beven's gavage tube, the nurse's next course of action should be to
○ 1. help the patient to a supine position in bed.
○ 2. irrigate the tube with about an ounce of water.
○ 3. undo adhesive strips used to fasten the tube to the patient's face.

    ○ 4. aspirate nourishment remaining in the stomach from the patient's previous feeding.

12 After introducing Mr. Beven's nourishment and before clamping the gavage tube, the nurse should then inject a small amount of

    ○ 1. air.

    ○ 2. water.

    ○ 3. a mild antiseptic solution.

    ○ 4. a sodium bicarbonate solution.

A Nurse Is Helping with the Care of Betsy Cramer, a 16-Year-Old Who Is Attending a Prenatal Clinic. Betsy Is Unmarried and Pregnant.

13 To better understand Betsy's emotional needs, the nurse should obtain a nursing history that includes learning

    ⊘ 1. who the father of the baby is.

    ○ 2. what the patient knows about the use of contraceptives.

    ○ 3. why the patient became sexually active at a relatively early age.

    ○ 4. how the patient's family feels about the fact that she is having a baby.

14 Betsy is more apt to have complications during pregnancy than most older women. It is generally agreed that the primary reason for this phenomenon is that, in contrast to older women, Betsy is likely to have *less* healthful

    ◑ 1. eating habits.

    ○ 2. leisure activities.

    ○ 3. sleeping patterns.

    ○ 4. exercise programs.

Betsy telephones about a week after her initial visit to tell the nurse that she has a severe headache that has lasted for two days.

15 In the situation described above, it would be best for the nurse to advise Betsy to

    ○ 1. increase her exercise and fluid intake.

    ○ 2. add fresh fruits and vegetables to her diet.

    ○ 3. take two aspirins and lie down for an hour or two.

    ◐ 4. come to the physician's office and be checked that day.

16 During the telephone conversation with Betsy, she asks the nurse if she can safely exchange reconstituted nonfat dry milk for whole milk in her diet. The nurse should explain that reconstituted nonfat dry milk can be safely substituted for whole milk if the dry milk is

    ○ 1. not used to cook foods.

○ 2. not stored before being reconstituted.
○ 3. reconstituted with distilled water.
⊘ 4. fortified with appropriate vitamins.

Mr. George Connor Has a Fractured Mandible that Is Immobilized with Wires.

17 The piece of equipment that should be kept readily available at Mr. Connor's bedside for emergency use is a
  ○ 1. forceps.
  ○ 2. tourniquet.
  ○ 3. wire cutter.
  ⊘ 4. tracheostomy set.

18 Before caring for Mr. Connor, the nurse studies his medication orders. Which medication should the nurse be ready to use immediately if Mr. Connor requires it?
  ○ 1. A hypnotic
  ○ 2. A laxative
  ○ 3. An analgesic
  ⊘ 4. An antiemetic

19 The type of diet Mr. Connor will require is a
  ○ 1. light diet.
  ○ 2. bland diet.
  ⊘ 3. full liquid diet.
  ○ 4. mechanical soft diet.

The nurse obtains Mr. Connor's blood pressure.

20 The readings the nurse obtains are likely to be *falsely* high if the cuff used for Mr. Connor is
  ○ 1. too wide.
  ○ 2. too narrow.
  ○ 3. applied too tightly.
  ⊘ 4. applied too low on the arm.

Mr. Barry Jones, a 20-Year-Old College Student Is Hospitalized Following a Visit to the College's Health Office Where He Described "Hearing Voices."

21 Mr. Jones tells the nurse, "The voices are telling me I'm wicked and must be punished." Of the following possible responses, it would be best for the nurse to say,

   ◯ 1. "Don't be silly. There are no voices."
   ◯ 2. "If you are going to talk about voices, I'll leave and return later."
   ⊘ 3. "I don't hear voices but what you hear must be frightening to you."
   ◯ 4. "How can you be hearing a voice when you can see there's nobody here but you and me?"

22 After several days, Mr. Jones appears fearful and says the voices he hears are threatening him. He sits for long periods in one place and must be fed. The nurse's initial goal in interacting with Mr. Jones should be to help the patient develop a feeling of
   ⊘ 1. trust.
   ◯ 2. autonomy.
   ◯ 3. sociability.
   ◯ 4. independence.

Ms. Nell Jenner, Who Is 81 Years Old, Has a Cerebrovascular Accident (CVA), or Stroke, Due to a Cerebral Thrombus. Ms. Jenner Is Started on Parenteral Heparin Therapy.

23 The drug that should be kept readily available to give to Ms. Jenner to reduce the effects of heparin, if it becomes necessary, is
   ◯ 1. furosemide.
   ◯ 2. amyl nitrite.
   ◯ 3. protamine sulfate.
   ◯ 4. epinephrine hydrochloride.

Nurses responsible for Ms. Jenner's care prepare a nursing care plan for Ms. Jenner who is conscious but has paralysis on her right side.

24 Which of the following nursing measures in relation to positioning Ms. Jenner's bed should be described on her nursing care plan?
   ◯ 1. The foot of the bed should be slightly elevated.
   ⊘ 2. The head of the bed should be slightly elevated.
   ◯ 3. The bed should be flat with neither the head nor foot elevated.
   ◯ 4. The position of the bed should be one of comfort for the patient as long as the patient is conscious.

25 Ms. Jenner's nursing care plan should be based on knowledge that the best nursing measure to help prevent Ms. Jenner from developing a decubitus ulcer is to
   ◯ 1. bathe the patient daily.
   ◯ 2. see that the patient's fluid intake is generous.
   ⊘ 3. change the patient's position in bed frequently.
   ◯ 4. carry out range-of-motion exercises with the patient several times a day.

26   Which of the following nursing orders best describes care to help
     prevent contractures in Ms. Jenner's right hand?
     O 1. Elevate the patient's hand on pillows.
     Ø 2. Secure a handroll in the patient's hand.
     O 3. Keep the patient's hand in a supine position.
     O 4. Apply warm compresses to the patient's hand several times a day.

27   Trochanter rolls will be used for Ms. Jenner when she is on her back,
     the primary purpose being to help prevent
     O 1. flexion of the knees.
     O 2. contractures of the hips.
     O 3. hyperextension of the feet.
     O 4. external rotation of the legs.

28   As she rehabilitates following the stroke, Ms. Jenner is encouraged by
     her nurses to compensate for the partial paralysis in her right arm and
     hand by learning to use her left arm and hand for certain activities of
     daily living. She does so only after much encouragement. Her seeming
     reluctance to try to compensate for paralysis in her right arm and hand
     should be judged as very probably the result of
     O 1. loss of adaptability because of aging and disease.
     O 2. inability to follow instructions because of limited intellect.
     O 3. stubbornness because of brain tissue injury and destruction.
     O 4. feelings of doubt because of lack of confidence in her caregivers.

Seven-Year-Old Donald Cory Is Hospitalized. He Has Nephrotic Syndrome. An Admission Order Indicates that Donald's Fluid Intake Is to Be Restricted.

29   When the admitting nurse interviews Ms. Cory, it would be most typical
     if Donald's mother says of Donald, "I first became aware that
     something was wrong when I noticed that Donald had . . .
     O 1. a staggering gait."
     O 2. dark urine, especially at night."
     O 3. a hoarse voice and profuse sweating."
     O 4. swelling at his ankles and around his eyes."

30   Donald complains of thirst when his fluid intake is restricted. Which of
     the following items, offered in small amounts, most often helps relieve
     thirst effectively?
     O 1. Ice chips
     O 2. Ice cream
     O 3. Ginger ale
     O 4. Lemonade

The nurse caring for Donald notes that he shows signs of regression.

31 Of the following behaviors, the one that illustrates best that Donald is demonstrating regressive behavior is when this child refuses to
○ 1. feed himself.
○ 2. speak to the nurses.
○ 3. play with a roommate.
○ 4. read for his own amusement.

Donald receives the glucocorticoid, prednisone (Meticorten).

32 The nurse observes Donald carefully for signs of adverse effects to the prednisone therapy. Of the following observations, the one *least* likely to be related to prednisone therapy is
○ 1. diarrhea.
○ 2. muscle weakness.
○ 3. increased perspiration.
○ 4. excessive body hair growth.

33 The nurse evaluates the results of prednisone therapy and judges correctly that the first desired effect occurs when Donald shows signs of
○ 1. an increase in appetite.
○ 2. a decrease in pulse rate.
○ 3. a decrease in blood pressure.
○ 4. an increase in urinary output.

34 After about a month of prednisone therapy, the drug is given in decreasing amounts over time before it is discontinued. This regime of tapering off is followed primarily to help prevent
○ 1. bladder spasms.
○ 2. metabolic acidosis.
○ 3. cardiac arrhythmias.
○ 4. adrenal insufficiency.

Ms. Rosa Marino, 77 Years Old, Has Artrial Fibrillations and Arrhythmia for Which She Has Been Receiving Drug Therapy. She Is Hospitalized for Surgery to Remove an Embolus Lodged in an Artery in Her Left Leg Near the Knee.

35 Ms. Marino is describing her arrhythmia correctly to the nurse when she says she has
○ 1. a very slow heart beat.
○ 2. an irregular heart beat.
○ 3. a heart beat that cannot be felt at the radial artery.
○ 4. a heart beat of which she is aware without feeling her pulse.

36 Ms. Marino complains of pain in her left lower leg. The nurse should expect that Ms. Marino will most probably indicate that pain in her leg is brought on by

    ○ 1. stress.
    ○ 2. walking.
    ○ 3. wearing stockings.
    ○ 4. elevating her leg.

37 In which position should Ms. Marino's left leg be placed by the nurse upon the patient's admission?
    ○ 1. In any position that affords comfort
    ○ 2. Well elevated on pillows
    ○ 3. Flat on the surface of the bed
    ○ 4. In a supportive position that keeps the knee flexed

Nursing care is planned for Ms. Marino while keeping her age in mind.

38 A common effect on elderly patients, such as Ms. Marino, when they are in a strange environment is that they are most often likely to become
    ○ 1. combative.
    ○ 2. disoriented.
    ○ 3. overly sleepy.
    ○ 4. overly hungry.

A blood clot is removed surgically from an artery near Ms. Marino's left knee. She is to take the drug, warfarin sodium (Coumadin), while hospitalized and after discharge at home.

39 An important postoperative nursing measure is to check Ms. Marino's left leg frequently for skin temperature and for
    ○ 1. edema.
    ○ 2. skin color.
    ○ 3. muscular spasms.
    ○ 4. purulent discharge from the surgical incision.

40 Which of the following over-the-counter medications should Ms. Marino be taught to *avoid* while taking warfarin sodium?
    ○ 1. The antacid, calcium carbonate (Tums)
    ○ 2. The analgesic, acetylsalicyclic acid (aspirin)
    ○ 3. The laxative, magnesium hydroxide (Milk of Magnesia)
    ○ 4. The decongestant, phenylephrine hydrochloride (Allerest)

A Nurse who Works through a Local Registry Accepts the Care of Ms. Ann Stuart who Will Be Delivered at Home by a Midwife. This Will Be the Stuart's Second Child. Mr. and Ms. Stuart Have Had Prenatal Teaching. The Nurse Goes to the Stuart Home when the Midwife Calls Her to Say that Ms. Stuart Is in the First Stage of Labor.

41 Upon her arrival at the Stuart home, the nurse assesses the fetal heart rate and notes that the rate gradually slows and reaches its lowest point during a contraction and then returns to normal near the end of the contraction. Which of the following courses of action should the nurse take in this situation?

  ○ 1. Notify the midwife.
  ○ 2. No action is indicated at this time.
  ○ 3. Turn the patient onto her back in bed.
  ○ 4. Elevate the head of the patient's bed.

42 After the nurse assesses Ms. Stuart, Mr. Stuart asks what he can do to help. Which of the following responses the nurse could make is most appropriate?

  ○ 1. "There is really nothing to do now. Possibly you may like to watch television for a while."
  ○ 2. "Now that I am here, it would be better for you to relax in the living room. We may need you later."
  ○ 3. "You may sit near your wife, hold her hand, and help her with breathing during contractions if you like."
  ○ 4. "The midwife has asked that I give your wife an enema. It would be helpful if you prepare supplies for me so that I can stay with your wife."

Ms. Stuart's membranes rupture.

43 When Ms. Stuart's membranes rupture, the nurse should first take prompt steps to

  ○ 1. notify the midwife.
  ○ 2. check the fetal heart rate.
  ○ 3. elevate the head of the patient's bed.
  ○ 4. place the patient in a side-lying position.

44 The nurse cleans Ms. Stuart and changes bed linens after the membranes rupture. Which of the following actions is recommended that the nurse take next?

  ○ 1. An underpad may be placed under the patient's buttocks.
  ○ 2. A perineal pad may be placed over the patient's perineal area.
  ○ 3. A terry cloth towel may be placed under the patient's buttocks and draped over the perineal area.
  ○ 4. It is recommended that nothing be placed under or on the patient because of the danger of contamination.

The midwife is present when Ms. Stuart enters the second stage of labor.

45 As soon as Baby Stuart's head is delivered, the piece of equipment the midwife is most likely to request of the nurse is a

  ○ 1. forceps.

   ○ 2. catheter.
   ○ 3. bulb syringe.
   ○ 4. fresh pair of sterile gloves.

46 The midwife assesses Baby Stuart's condition shortly after birth according to the Apgar scoring chart. A score of 8 is obtained, which means that Baby Stuart's condition is correctly judged to be
   ○ 1. poor.
   ○ 2. fair.
   ○ 3. good.
   ○ 4. critical.

47 If Ms. Stuart's membranes had ruptured very early in labor, the nurse should be especially alert for signs that indicate Ms. Stuart may have developed
   ○ 1. uterine inertia.
   ○ 2. a prolapsed cord.
   ○ 3. uterine hemorrhage.
   ○ 4. a premature separation of the placenta.

48 The nurse should understand that an important aspect in planning care that will help the Stuarts develop a newborn – parent interaction and attachment is to allow Mr. and Ms. Stuart to
   ○ 1. touch their newborn.
   ○ 2. talk to their newborn.
   ○ 3. hear their newborn cry.
   ○ 4. watch the newborn being cared for.

The nurse attends to Baby Stuart.

49 The most often recommended technique to determine the patency of Baby Stuart's anal opening soon after delivery is for the nurse to
   ○ 1. obtain a rectal temperature.
   ○ 2. perform a digital rectal examination.
   ○ 3. observe for the presence of meconium.
   ○ 4. auscultate the abdomen for bowel sounds.

50 An ointment containing an antibiotic is placed in Baby Stuart's eyes shortly after birth. The reason for placing the ointment in the newborn's eyes is to destroy organisms that cause
   ○ 1. syphilis.
   ○ 2. gonorrhea.
   ○ 3. genital herpes.
   ○ 4. trichomoniasis.

51 When secretions accumulate in Baby Stuart's mouth and throat, the nurse suctions him with a bulb syringe. Before inserting the syringe into the infant's mouth, the nurse should prepare it by
   ○ 1. lubricating the syringe's tip with saline.
   ○ 2. deflating the bulb of the syringe by squeezing it.

○ 3. rinsing the bulb syringe with an antiseptic solution.

○ 4. checking to see that the bulb of the syringe is fully inflated.

52 When the nurse places Baby Stuart in his crib, it is preferable for the nurse to position him so that he is lying on

○ 1. his back.

○ 2. either side.

○ 3. his abdomen.

○ 4. his back with his head slightly elevated.

The midwife goes to a nearby restaurant to eat. While she is away, the nurse notes that Ms. Stuart has vaginal bleeding.

53 After determining that Ms. Stuart's vital signs are satisfactory, the nurse should then

○ 1. call the midwife.

○ 2. begin forcing fluids.

○ 3. start massaging the uterus.

○ 4. elevate the foot of the bed.

Ms. Emma Pitt, 76 Years Old, Has a Cataract Removed from Her Left Eye. The Procedure Is Carried out in a Surgical Center. Postoperatively, Ms. Pitt Rests at the Center for a Few Hours and Then Is Given Home-Going (Discharge) Instructions.

54 Ms. Pitt should be instructed to *avoid* all of the following activities at home *except*

○ 1. coughing.

○ 2. walking about.

○ 3. straining at stool.

○ 4. stooping over to the floor.

55 Ms. Pitt should be instructed to call her eye surgeon immediately if she experiences pain in the operative eye. This symptom is typical if Ms. Pitt's operative eye has

○ 1. excessive bleeding.

○ 2. loss of vitreous humor.

○ 3. detachment of the retina.

○ 4. injury to the optic nerve.

56 Which of the following structures is adversely affected when Ms. Pitt develops the cataract in her eye?

○ 1. The iris

○ 2. The lens

○ 3. The retina

○ 4. The sclera

Ms. Jan West Is Admitted to a Hospital With a Bipolar Disorder, Manic Phase. Ms. West Is 48 Years Old. The Nursing Process Is Used By Nurses Caring for Ms. West.

57 The nurse assigned to care for Ms. West reads the patient's health record, including notations made by the admitting nurse and physician. Next, it would be best for the nurse to assist the registered nurse supervising Ms. West's care by

○ 1. preparing a plan of care.
○ 2. establishing a nursing diagnosis.
○ 3. interviewing and observing the patient.
○ 4. setting up goals and a schedule for evaluating care.

58 The nurse helps write a nursing care plan for Ms. West. On completion of the plan, the next step in the nursing process is to

○ 1. evaluate nursing care.
○ 2. analyze admission data.
○ 3. implement nursing care.
○ 4. write a patient teaching plan.

The nurse deals with Ms. West's inappropriate behavior.

59 Ms. West is observed to be chiding and harassing another patient. The nurse can best manage Ms. West's inappropriate behavior by

○ 1. directing the patient to her room.
○ 2. reminding the patient that she will be disciplined.
○ 3. diverting the patient's attention to other activity.
○ 4. explaining to the patient that her behavior will not be tolerated.

60 Because Ms. West's behavior is observed to be characteristic of manic-type behavior, an important aspect of her nursing care is to see to it that the patient receives adequate amounts of

○ 1. praise.
○ 2. exercise.
○ 3. food and fluids.
○ 4. socializing and interpersonal interactions.

61 The word that describes typical feelings Ms. West is demonstrating by her behavior is exaggerated

○ 1. panic.
○ 2. euphoria.
○ 3. compulsion.
○ 4. disorientation.

62 One day, Ms. West announces emphatically, "This dayroom stinks! I am an interior decorator and the furniture simply must be rearranged. Help me move this television set." In this situation, it would be best for the nurse to

○ 1. consult with the nurse-in-charge about a possible need to increase drug therapy.

○ 2. let the patient expend excess energy and assist her with moving some of the furniture.

○ 3. tell the patient that she will have to return to her room if she moves any of the furniture.

○ 4. explain that the furniture cannot be moved and engage the patient in a game of ping pong.

63 The nurse overhears the following comments made by patients in a group of which Ms. West is a member. Which comment is most likely to have been made by Ms. West?

○ 1. "That man talking to the nurse is an FBI agent."

○ 2. "No matter how hard I try, I never seem to get it right."

○ 3. "Some day I want to be a counselor so that I can help people like me."

○ 4. "There is no place I travel without being hounded for a photograph of myself."

Ms. Amy Shelley, Who Is 42 Years Old, Is to Have Her Gallbladder Removed (Cholecystectomy) Under General Anesthesia. After Ms. Shelley's Admission To a Hospital, Preoperative Teaching Is Begun.

64 Ms. Shelley is taught how to cough properly so that she can raise secretions from her respiratory passages postoperatively. To decrease discomfort in the area of her incision, she should be taught to cough while she

○ 1. lies in bed on either side.

○ 2. applies pressure over the surgical area.

○ 3. takes several panting breaths between coughs.

○ 4. keeps abdominal muscles tense in the surgical area.

65 While the nurse teaches Ms. Shelley deep-breathing exercises, the patient complains of feeling dizzy and light-headed. It is most probable that Ms. Shelley is experiencing these symptoms because she is breathing too

○ 1. slowly.

○ 2. deeply.

○ 3. rapidly.

○ 4. irregularly.

66 Ms. Shelley is taught how to exercise her feet and legs. These exercises help primarily to prevent

○ 1. footdrop.

○ 2. venous stasis.

○ 3. pitting edema.

○ 4. varicose veins.

Ms. Shelley returns to her room from the recovery room and her postoperative care begins. She has an indwelling catheter in place and may have a clear liquid diet as tolerated.

67 Ms. Shelley's vital signs are checked frequently. If Ms. Shelley begins to bleed excessively, the two most typical signs she is likely to display are
   ○ 1. a rapid pulse rate and a drop in blood pressure.
   ○ 2. a slow pulse rate and an elevated body temperature.
   ○ 3. a slow respiratory rate and a drop in body temperature.
   ○ 4. an irregular pulse rate and a slowly increasing blood pressure.

68 If Ms. Shelley is served the following items for one of her meals, the one that is *inappropriate* for her is
   ○ 1. tea.
   ○ 2. ice cream.
   ○ 3. apple juice.
   ○ 4. chicken broth.

69 Of the following activities scheduled for Ms. Shelley during her early postoperative period, which one is she likely to find most uncomfortable?
   ○ 1. Breathing deeply and coughing
   ○ 2. Dangling on the edge of the bed
   ○ 3. Performing leg and foot exercises
   ○ 4. Being turned from side to side in bed

70 The management of Ms. Shelley's indwelling catheter is planned while taking into account that, of the following conditions, the one most frequently associated with the use of an indwelling catheter is
   ○ 1. urinary incontinence.
   ○ 2. an ulcer in the urethra.
   ○ 3. a urinary tract infection.
   ○ 4. injury to bladder mucosa.

71 A urine specimen is to be obtained from Ms. Shelley while her indwelling catheter is in place. The recommended technique to obtain a specimen from Ms. Shelley is for the nurse to
   ○ 1. clean an area of entry on the catheter and use a sterile needle and syringe to aspirate a specimen of urine.
   ○ 2. separate the catheter from the drainage tube and allow urine to drop directly from the catheter into a sterile specimen container.
   ○ 3. open the spigot on the drainage receptacle and allow urine to empty from the receptacle into a sterile specimen container.
   ○ 4. clamp the drainage tube, separate it from the drainage receptacle, and then open the clamp to allow urine to flow from the drainage tube into a sterile specimen container.

72 Ms. Shelley's indwelling catheter is to be removed. The first step for the nurse to take when removing it is to

○ 1. clamp the tubing.
○ 2. deflate the balloon.
○ 3. irrigate the catheter.
○ 4. elevate the collecting receptacle.

Ms. Angela Lopez, Who Is 22 Years Old and Pregnant for the First Time, Is Admitted to a Hospital In Labor. She Says She Is Sure That "This Is the Real Thing," and Describes How Her Uterus Dropped in Her Abdomen a Couple of Weeks Ago. The Fetus's Head Is Presenting.

73 The phenomenon Ms. Lopez describes concerning how her uterus dropped is called
○ 1. show.
○ 2. quickening.
○ 3. lightening.
○ 4. Hegar's sign.

74 Upon admission, Ms. Lopez says that she has been timing her contractions, which she states are occurring every 10 minutes. If she is timing her contractions correctly, the 10-minute time interval is equivalent to the time between the
○ 1. beginning and end of one contraction.
○ 2. end of one contraction and the beginning of the next.
○ 3. beginning of one contraction and the end of the next.
○ 4. beginning of one contraction and the beginning of the next.

A registered nurse assesses Ms. Lopez for station.

75 After an examination of Ms. Lopez, she is described as being at "plus 2 station." This means that the
○ 1. cervical canal is 2 inches long.
○ 2. the cervical opening is 2 cm in diameter.
○ 3. fetus's body is 2 degrees removed from a longitudinal lie.
○ 4. fetus's head is 2 cm below the level of the mother's ischial spines.

The nurse monitors the fetal heart rate with a fetoscope when Ms. Lopez's membranes rupture.

76 This is an important time to obtain the fetal heart rate because, if an abnormally slow rate is detected, a very possible complication is that the
○ 1. uterus has inverted.
○ 2. umbilical cord has prolapsed.

    ○ 3. intensity of labor is diminishing.

    ○ 4. fetus has aspirated amniotic fluid.

Ms. Lopez is transferred to the delivery room.

77 The nurse places Ms. Lopez's legs in stirrups on the delivery table. The recommended technique to place the legs in stirrups is to put

    ○ 1. either leg in a stirrup, then the other leg.

    ○ 2. the right leg in a stirrup, then the left leg.

    ○ 3. the left leg in a stirrup, then the right leg.

    ○ 4. both legs in the stirrups at the same time.

78 After the placenta is delivered, the nurse should be prepared to administer a drug to Ms. Lopez, the most common one being a drug classified as

    ○ 1. an oxytocic.

    ○ 2. a cardiotonic.

    ○ 3. an anticoagulant.

    ○ 4. an antihistamine.

Mr. Andrew Carney, Who Is 68 Years Old, Is Hospitalized Because of Pulmonary Emphysema Complicated With a Respiratory Tract Infection. He Is Receiving Intravenous Therapy.

79 Pulmonary emphysema is a respiratory disease that interferes with the proper functioning of Mr. Carney's

    ○ 1. alveoli.

    ○ 2. pleurae.

    ○ 3. diaphragm.

    ○ 4. surfactant.

80 Aminophylline, 250 mg, is added to 500 ml of 5% dextrose in water and is administered to Mr. Carney intravenously over an 8-hour period. If the drop factor on the intravenous equipment is 20 drops per ml, about how many drops per minute should Mr. Carney receive?

    ○ 1. 11 drops

    ○ 2. 21 drops

    ○ 3. 31 drops

    ○ 4. 41 drops

81 The nurse compares Mr. Carney's condition at the time of admission with his condition after he receives aminophylline. She should judge that the desired effect of the drug is being achieved if Mr. Carney demonstrates less

    ○ 1. dyspnea.

    ○ 2. coughing.

○ 3. tenacious sputum.
○ 4. respiratory congestion.

Mr. Carney uses percussion and vibration and receives oxygen therapy continuously through a nasal cannula.

82 Mr. Carney's wife has been using percussion and vibration over Mr. Carney's chest wall. The primary purpose of this therapy is to help
○ 1. force deep breathing.
○ 2. move residual air out of lung tissues.
○ 3. break up tenacious respiratory secretions.
○ 4. prevent air sacs in the lungs from collapsing.

83 The nurse caring for Mr. Carney should be sure he is *not* receiving oxygen in larger amounts than ordered, because excessive amounts may lead to
○ 1. respiratory arrest.
○ 2. respiratory alkalosis.
○ 3. excessively dry respiratory mucosa.
○ 4. sudden constriction of respiratory airways.

Fifteen-Year-Old Mark Horton Comes to the Office of a School Nurse. He Has Sustained Numerous Bruises About the Face and Shoulders In a Fight With a Classmate Who Made Fun of Mark for Being Obese.

84 Mark says to the nurse, "My parents are fat and I guess that's why I am fat too." Before responding to Mark's comment, the nurse should be aware that most authorities agree that obesity is most probably caused by
○ 1. genetic factors.
○ 2. metabolic factors.
○ 3. psychological factors.
○ 4. numerous factors.

85 Which of the following courses of action would most probably provide the best psychological help for Mark in his effort to lose weight?
○ 1. Have the patient eat small meals at frequent intervals.
○ 2. Encourage the patient to join a group of dieting teenagers.
○ 3. Suggest that the patient start dating girls who are also obese.
○ 4. Arrange for the patient to go off his reducing diet periodically.

Mark's mother comes to the health office to talk to the school nurse about her son.

86 Ms. Horton tells the nurse, "I cook only foods that are good for Mark.

What more can I do to help him?" Which of the following possible responses by the nurse demonstrates the best understanding of how Mark and his mother can be helped?

○ 1. "It is reassuring to know that you want to help Mark. Have you ever put him on a reducing diet?"

○ 2. "It is good that you are concerned about Mark's nutrition. Tell me about the foods that he likes most to eat."

○ 3. "Mark is fortunate to have a mother who is a good cook. Are you able to prepare foods for a strict low-calorie diet?"

○ 4. "This is a difficult time for Mark. You might like to consider sending him to a doctor who specializes in gastrointestinal problems."

87 Adolescents often want between-meal snacks. The nurse should be prepared to offer Mark and his mother suggestions for nutritious but low-calorie snack foods, such as

○ 1. crackers with cheese.

○ 2. a glass of chocolate milk.

○ 3. a dish of buttered popcorn.

○ 4. a serving of a fresh fruit.

Mr. Harold Daly, Who Is 68 Years Old, Is Hospitalized and Is Being Prepared for Surgery. He Knows He Has a Malignant Growth in the Colon and Is to Have a Colostomy.

88 A few days before surgery, Mr. Daly tells the nurse, "I am scared. This operation worries me." In this situation, it would be best for the nurse to say,

○ 1. "There is no need for fear and worry, trust me."

○ 2. "You said you were scared and worried about your surgery?"

○ 3. "Do you know, as I do, that your surgeon is very good and very competent?"

○ 4. "Try to relax because fear and worry may make you feel worse after the surgery."

89 Mr. Daly tells the nurse that he prepared a Living Will before coming to the hospital. This type of will describes a person's wishes in relation to

○ 1. who is to be responsible for the disposition of the person's body.

○ 2. how the person wants personal belongings distributed after his death.

○ 3. the person with whom caregivers should consult concerning his terminal care.

○ 4. the type of care the person wishes when his illness is judged to be terminal.

90 During their conversation, Mr. Daly also tells the nurse, "Our youngest daughter, who is 27 years old, is working and shares an apartment with several friends. I want her to live with my wife and me until she marries but she refuses." Which of the following statements is most probably the best explanation for the daughter's behavior?

O 1. The daughter is unwilling to have her parents learn of her life-style.
O 2. The daughter is forgetful of her parents' need to continue to be close to her.
O 3. The daughter is striving to accomplish developmental tasks typical of her age.
O 4. The daughter is showing lack of appreciation for parental concerns for their children.

Mr. Daly makes satisfactory progress following surgery and a colostomy irrigation is planned for him.

91 While his colostomy is irrigated, Mr. Daly complains of severe cramping. The nurse's best course of action in this situation is to
O 1. remove the irrigating cone for a few minutes.
O 2. ask the patient to take several panting breaths.
O 3. stop administering irrigating solution temporarily.
O 4. decrease the rate of administering the irrigating solution.

92 Mr. Daly's colostomy is located in the descending colon. The location of the colostomy makes it relatively easy to manage and regulate fecal discharge because the major function of the large intestine is to
O 1. neutralize acidic digestive juices.
O 2. complete digestion of fibrous foods.
O 3. absorb water from the fecal material.
O 4. destroy organisms found in the small intestine.

About 6 months after surgery, Mr. Daly is hospitalized to begin chemo-therapy with fluorouracil (Adrucil).

93 The drug, fluorouracil acts in the body to
O 1. destroy the walls of malignant cells.
O 2. halt the division of malignant cells.
O 3. interfere with the growth of malignant cells.
O 4. stimulate the body's anticancer immune system.

Betsy Lamar, Who Is 2½ Years Old, Has Cystic Fibrosis. Her Health Care Is Obtained at a Community Health Clinic.

94 Betsy's cystic fibrosis is due to abnormal functioning of glands in her body that produce

O 1. bile.
O 2. lymph.
O 3. mucus.
O 4. cerumen.

95 Betsy's mother describes a typical sign of cystic fibrosis when she tells the nurse that she became disturbed when she first noticed Betsy's perspiration to be abnormally
O 1. salty.
O 2. scanty.
O 3. excessive.
O 4. tan or brown in color.

The nurse helps implement a teaching program for Betsy.

96 Betsy's mother should be taught that of special importance in the care of Betsy to forestall complications is to use every effort to prevent Betsy from developing
O 1. contractures.
O 2. muscle atrophy.
O 3. respiratory infections.
O 4. urinary tract infections.

97 The nutrient in Betsy's diet that the nurse can anticipate should be restricted is
O 1. fat.
O 2. protein.
O 3. mineral.
O 4. carbohydrate.

98 Ms. Lamar says Betsy is a "typical toddler" when feeling well. The mother should be taught that during the toddler stage (1 to 3 years of age), Betsy's need to develop self-assurance and autonomy is best met when Betsy is
O 1. cared for by a variety of caregivers.
O 2. cared for primarily by the parent of the same sex.
O 3. allowed to do things for herself to the extent possible.
O 4. allowed to carry out activities of daily living whenever she wishes.

Mr. Archer, 82 Years Old, Is Admitted to a Nursing Home Following Hospitalization for a Urinary Tract Disorder.

99 Of the following techniques, the one that is *least* likely to promote communication when the nurse is talking with Mr. Archer upon admission is for the nurse to
O 1. use eye-to-eye contact.

 ○ 2. sit down while conversing.

 ○ 3. write notes on what the patient says.

 ○ 4. explain that things will be better soon.

100 Of the following measures, the first one the nurse should take when planning Mr. Archer's nursing care when he is admitted is to

 ○ 1. ask the patient his opinion of a nursing care plan.

 ○ 2. determine how nursing care for the patient can best be evaluated.

 ○ 3. state nursing measures that may be used with success in the patient's plan of care.

 ○ 4. identify goals that the nurse believes can be met with nursing measures administered to the patient.

Mr. Archer is to be catheterized for a urine specimen and is to have a 24-hour urine specimen obtained.

101 The position of choice when catheterizing Mr. Archer is the

 ○ 1. back-lying position.

 ○ 2. semi-sitting position.

 ○ 3. left side-lying position.

 ○ 4. right side-lying position.

102 If resistance is met in the area of the prostate gland when inserting the catheter to catheterize Mr. Archer, the nurse should place slightly more tension on the penis and

 ○ 1. drop the penis toward the toes.

 ○ 2. have the patient flex his knees a bit.

 ○ 3. place more lubricant on the catheter.

 ○ 4. ask the patient to take panting breaths.

103 Mr. Archer is to have the 24-hour urine specimen as follows: 10 A.M., September 6 – 10 A.M., September 7. Which of the following of Mr. Archer's voidings during the 24-hour period should the nurse discard?

 ○ 1. Urine passed at 10 A.M. on September 6

 ○ 2. The last urine passed before bedtime on September 6

 ○ 3. The first urine passed upon awakening on September 7

 ○ 4. Urine passed at 10 A.M. on September 7

The nurse assigned to care for Mr. Archer prepares to give the patient a bath and backrub.

104 The following statements describe certain actions the nurse takes when preparing to bathe Mr. Archer and to give him a backrub. Which statement describes the nurse at work while using *poor* body mechanics?

 ○ 1. The nurse bends over to obtain clean linens for the patient's bed on a bottom shelf, near floor level, in the linen closet.

 ○ 2. The nurse pushes a laundry hamper that is mounted on wheels to the patient's room.

○ 3. The nurse loosens soiled top linens while walking around the patient's bed.

○ 4. The nurse positions the patient near the side of the bed where she stands to rub his back.

105 While bathing Mr. Archer, the patient says he wishes to tell the nurse something but she must promise not to tell anyone. Which of the following comments is best for the nurse to make in this situation?

○ 1. "I can keep the information between the two of us, if you wish."

○ 2. "I would rather you did not tell me whatever it is you have on your mind."

○ 3. "I will call the nurse-in-charge because it would be better for you to tell her."

○ 4. "I will have to share whatever you tell me with other caretakers if I think it is in your best interest."

Fifty-Eight-Year-Old Mr. Jerry Brown Is Admitted to a Hospital for Surgery Because of a Bleeding Peptic Ulcer.

106 Mr. Brown says he has frequently taken baking soda in water after meals at home for heartburn-type discomfort. One danger of this practice is that it may cause

○ 1. an electrolyte imbalance.

○ 2. an increase in bile secretions.

○ 3. a decrease in cell wall permeability.

○ 4. a decrease in gastric juice secretions.

107 Mr. Brown tells the admitting nurse that he uses the following nonprescription (over-the-counter) preparations relatively frequently. The nurse should judge that the one that most likely contributes most to Mr. Brown's stomach irritation and discomfort is

○ 1. aspirin.

○ 2. vitamin C.

○ 3. Pepto-Bismol.

○ 4. milk of magnesia.

108 If the nurse uses the following techniques when recording admission information on Mr. Brown's record, the one that is in *error* is when the nurse

○ 1. uses the abbreviation c/o for "complains of."

○ 2. prints the information that she enters in the nurses' notes.

○ 3. erases a mistake when she writes that the patient is not responding.

○ 4. draws a line through a blank area in the nurses' notes when the area is not filled with information.

Mr. Brown's diet is high in protein.

109 Protein is important for Mr. Brown primarily because this nutrient acts to
○ 1. slow the speed of digestion.
○ 2. protect an ulcer from irritation.
○ 3. depress secretions of gastric acids.
○ 4. promote healing of an ulcerated area.

Mr. Brown is scheduled for surgery.

110 The evening prior to surgery, Mr. Brown repeatedly turns on his call light, complains of minor discomforts, asks for fresh water, and wants his pillow adjusted. He is most probably illustrating feelings of
○ 1. panic.
○ 2. anxiety.
○ 3. hostility.
○ 4. loneliness.

111 The most therapeutic comment that the nurse could make to Mr. Brown in this situation is saying,
○ 1. "You seem to be concerned about something. Would you like to talk about it?"
○ 2. "It is important that you get some sleep. Would you like a sleeping pill to help you relax?"
○ 3. "You really have nothing to worry about. You will be just fine after you have had your surgery."
○ 4. "You must realize that I have other patients. Please don't turn on your light unless you really need something."

The nurse helps with Mr. Brown's postoperative care.

112 The nurse assists Mr. Brown with deep-breathing exercises, knowing that these exercises help most to prevent Mr. Brown from developing postoperative
○ 1. nausea.
○ 2. hiccups.
○ 3. phlebitis.
○ 4. atelectasis.

113 Mr. Brown uses an incentive spirometer to help with deep-breathing exercises. Between each deep breath, when using incentive spirometry, Mr. Brown should be taught to
○ 1. cough 2 or 3 times.
○ 2. rest about 1 minute.
○ 3. take about 5 normal breaths.
○ 4. hold his breath about 10 seconds.

114 The nurse observes sterile techniques when changing Mr. Brown's dressings to help prevent a wound infection. Before most organisms can spread from an area where they are growing to another area where they can also grow to cause an infection, the organism ordinarily must
- 1. have living spores.
- 2. be producing a toxin.
- 3. have time to reproduce.
- 4. be transported by some means.

Carla Ortega, a 15-Month-Old Child, Has Dyspnea and Tires Easily. She Has Patent Ductus Arteriosus and Is Admitted to a Hospital to Prepare Her for a Surgical Repair of the Defect.

115 While admitting Carla, her parents ask about visiting hours. Unless contrary to hospital policy, it would be best for the nurse to suggest that the parents
- 1. stay with Carla as much as possible.
- 2. visit with Carla for a short time once a day.
- 3. limit their visits with Carla to morning hours.
- 4. plan visits with Carla so that only one parent is present.

116 Which of the following activities is an appropriate form of amusement for Carla before surgery is performed?
- 1. Crawling about in her crib
- 2. Pushing herself in a walker
- 3. Playing a game of pat-a-cake
- 4. Tossing a small ball about in her crib

117 Carla's mother asks plaintively, "Why was our little girl born with a heart problem?" On which one of the following statements should the nurse base her response to the mother?
- 1. The cause of patent ductus arteriosus is due to a placental defect.
- 2. The cause of patent ductus arteriosus is a hereditary factor.
- 3. The cause of patent ductus arteriosus is an intrauterine injury.
- 4. The cause of patent ductus arteriosus is unknown at the present time.

Carla's defect is corrected surgically.

118 If the nurse notes the following immediate postoperative orders on Carla's nursing care plan, which one should she question before carrying it out?
- 1. Suction as necessary.
- 2. Change position every 2 hours.
- 3. Measure urinary output for 24 hours.
- 4. Begin offering milk as soon as awake.

The Remaining Items Are Individual Items Related to the Care of Adults With Medical–Surgical Disorders.

119 An 86-year-old patient is receiving intravenous therapy. When the patient tries to remove the intravenous needle, the nurse restrains the patient. If the nurse uses the following measures related to restraining the patient, which one is in *error?*
○ 1. The nurse applies restraints at her discretion.
○ 2. The nurse places restraints on both of the patient's wrists.
○ 3. The nurse places stockinette under the restraints where they encircle the wrists.
○ 4. The nurse gives the patient passive arm exercises when she removes the restraints.

120 A 30-year-old person becomes ill with hepatitis A (infectious or epidemic hepatitis). Of the following ways in which a pathogen can be spread, which one is most often responsible for a person's acquiring hepatitis A?
○ 1. Having eaten contaminated food
○ 2. Having been bitten by an infected mosquito
○ 3. Having an injection with a contaminated needle
○ 4. Having sexual intercourse with an infected person

Correct Answers and Rationales

Two numbers appear in parentheses following each rationale. The first number identifies the textbook listed in the references, page 649, and the second number identifies the page(s) in that textbook where the correct answer can be verified. Occasionally, two textbooks are given for verifying the correct answer.

Caring for a Patient Who Has a Laryngectomy

1 4. The characteristic early symptom of cancer of the larynx is persistent hoarseness that does not respond to conservative therapy. Difficulty with swallowing and pain when talking are also symptoms of laryngeal cancer. Excessive sputum, a brassy cough, and a chronic sore throat are not associated with laryngeal cancer. (15:289)

2 3. Typical signs that indicate a tracheostomy needs suctioning include dyspnea, noisy respirations, and increased respiratory and pulse rates. Auscultation of the chest helps most to determine when suctioning of a tracheostomy should be done. (9:620)

3 3. Suctioning should *not* be allowed to occur until the catheter is situated about 10 to 12 inches (25 to 30 cm) into the respiratory passageway for a patient with a tracheostomy. If it is turned on earlier, the suctioning will remove oxygen and the patient may then suffer from a lack of sufficient oxygen. The suctioning also may tear or injure mucous membranes. Appropriate techniques when suctioning a tracheostomy include lubricating the catheter with normal saline, instilling a few milliliters of sterile normal saline into the tracheostomy (especially if mucus is tenacious), and handling the catheter while using surgical aseptic techniques. (9:620–621)

4 4. For suctioning the left bronchus when a patient has a tracheostomy, it is best to have the patient turn his head to the right, and for the right bronchus, turn the head to the left. These maneuvers make entry of the catheter into the bronchi relatively easy. (9:620)

5 2. The maximum amount of time that a tracheostomy should be suctioned continuously is 10 to 15 seconds. If suctioning continues longer, so much oxygen will be removed that the patient may suffer from an oxygen shortage, and respiratory arrest could occur. (9:620)

6 1. When a patient coughs while his tracheostomy is being suctioned, the nurse should remove the catheter. The patient can then raise secretions through his tracheostomy. (9:620)

7 4. The patient cannot get air to his lungs when the outer tube of a tracheostomy slips out. Therefore, until a physician arrives to replace it, a surgical dilator should be used to keep the tracheostomy open. The nurse should not try to insert the tube because of possible injury that may lead to still further complications. A dilator, as well as an entire sterile tracheostomy set or laryngectomy set, should be kept in the room of a patient with a tracheostomy at all times so that if an emergency arises, equipment to handle it is readily available.   (15:290)

8   3.   When water is spilled near an electrical machine, it is safest for the nurse to wipe up the water promptly herself. The machine should also be unplugged. Severe electrical shock is possible when standing in water while using a machine. Asking someone else to wipe up the water, moving the machine, and posting a sign do not solve the problem of electrical shock nearly as quickly, conveniently, and, most importantly, as safely.   (9:177)

9   4.   When giving large amounts of nourishment in single feedings through a gavage tube, it is recommended that the nourishment be given at about room temperature. This helps to prevent the patient from becoming chilled. When nourishment is being given continuously, drop by drop, the nourishment ordinarily is not warmed to help prevent its souring. The nourishment warms sufficiently as it slowly passes through the tube so that the patient does not feel chilly.   (9:106)

10   1.   The most accurate method for determining whether a gastric tube is in the stomach is to aspirate stomach contents through the tube. Observing for bubbles when the end of the gavage tube is under water and hearing air sounds with a stethoscope over the stomach while introducing air also are used but are not considered as accurate as aspirating stomach contents, and in some agencies, they are not recommended.   (9:104)

11   4.   Before introducing additional nourishment when it is being given in large single quantities, the stomach should be emptied to prevent overfilling it with additional nourishment. No new nourishment ordinarily is introduced if 100 ml to 150 ml or more from a previous feeding remain in the stomach; the exact amount depends on agency policy. The tube is not irrigated before introducing nourishment nor should the tube be unfastened from the face. It is best when the patient is in a mid-Fowler's position when being gavaged to help prevent nourishment from being regurgitated.   (9:106)

12   2.   A small amount of water, usually 1 to 2 ounces, should be injected into the gavage tube after the liquid nourishment has been introduced. This practice helps "wash" nourishment from the tube into the stomach. Air, an antiseptic, or sodium bicarbonate solution are not advised.   (9:107)

Caring for a Teenager Who is Pregnant

13   4.   An unmarried teenager who is pregnant usually needs considerable emotional support. Therefore, it is helpful when the nurse knows about the type of support the patient is receiving at home and from her peers. If the patient has good support and is accepted by her family and friends, the nurse can often build on this strength. If this type of support is absent, the nurse must plan her care accordingly and be ready to offer the patient as much emotional support as possible. Learning who the father is, why the patient was sexually active, and what she knows about contraceptives are less important while giving prenatal care to this patient. Also, the patient may become resentful if the nurse raises questions that appear to pry into her private life.   (2:138–140)

14   1.   It is generally believed that teenagers have more complications during pregnancy than older women, and less healthy babies, because teenagers have poorer eating habits. Their diets are generally not balanced, and usually contain many foods that are not particularly nutritious. In general, teenagers are reluctant to change these habits when advised to do so by authority figures.   (2:112–113)

15   4.   A patient complaining of a persistent headache should be advised to see her physician promptly, the same day if at all possible. The symptom *may* be insignificant but it may be an early sign of a complication. Other danger signs that require immediate health care include persistent vomiting, visual disturbances, dizziness, rapid change in weight, edema, and bleeding or discharge of fluid from the vagina.   (2:101)

16   4.   If it is fortified with appropriate vitamins, reconstituted nonfat dry milk can be safely substituted for whole milk. The only nutrient in milk missing in reconstituted nonfat dry milk is fat because the cream has been removed during the drying process. Most nonfat dry milk is presently fortified with appropriate vitamins.   (2:111)

Caring for a Patient Who Has a Fractured Mandible

17   3.   A danger when the upper and lower jaws are wired together to immobilize a fractured mandible is that the patient may aspirate if he vomits. Therefore, it is important to keep a wire cutter at the bedside so that the wires can be cut if necessary to prevent aspiration of vomitus.   (15:174)

18   4.   A nurse caring for a patient whose jaws are wired should be particular aware of a medication to use as necessary for nausea. If the patient vomits, he is likely to aspirate vomitus which could be a threat to life. Therefore, if nausea is present, an antiemetic should be administered promptly.   (15:174–175)

19   3.   For a patient whose jaws are wired, a full liquid diet is ordinarily used because the patient is unable to move his jaws to chew.   (15:175)

20   2.   If a blood-pressure cuff is too narrow, the blood-pressure readings are likely to be falsely high. If the blood-pressure cuff is too wide, the blood-pressure readings are likely to be falsely low. The width of the blood-pressure cuff should be no more than ⅔ the length of the upper arm. Another guide is that the cuff should be about 20% wider than the diameter of the limb being used.   (9:203)

Caring for a Patient Who Is "Hearing Voices"

21 3. The nurse presents reality by saying that she does not share the patient's perceptions but does accept the patient's feelings. The patient needs to feel free to express himself. Denying the patient's perceptions, not accepting the patient's feelings, and using logic when the patient is unable to respond to logic are of no help to the patient described in this item.   (1:88–89, 91–92)

22 1. The patient described in this item is fearful of others and is isolating himself as much as possible. His outstanding need is to have a relationship in which he feels secure. If he can learn to trust one person, he can then learn to trust others. The need for trust is essential for the development of a therapeutic relationship between a nurse and a patient. Feelings of ability and autonomy function independently of each other. Socializing effectively with others depends first on a sense of trust.   (1:89)

Caring for a Patient Who Has a Cerebrovascular Accident (CVA)

23 3. Protamine sulfate is a heparin antagonist. When the cause of a cerebrovascular accident (CVA) is a cerebral hemorrhage, heparin would be contraindicated because of the danger of increasing the hemorrhaging. Epinephrine hydrochloride is used commonly when shock and cardiac arrest are present. Amyl nitrite is used to help overcome attacks of pain in a patient with angina pectoris. Furosemide is a diuretic.   (14:15; 15:235)

24 2. The preferred position of the bed after a patient has had a CVA is a position in which the head of the bed is slightly elevated to help prevent increased intracranial pressure. Lowering the head of the bed may further increase pressure within the brain. The patient is ordinarily placed on his side if unconscious to facilitate drainage from the nose and mouth.   (15:238)

25 3. A person with partial paralysis is at risk for developing bedsores. The best nursing measure to help prevent bedsores from developing is to change the patient's position in bed at least every two hours. It is important that range-of-motion exercises be used, that personal hygiene needs be attended to, and that fluid and dietary needs be well met. These measures, however, are not as immediately critical for preventing decubitus ulcers as seeing to it that the patient does not have pressure over bony prominences for long periods of time. (15:238-239)

26 2. A handroll should be secured in a patient's hand to help prevent contractures. Keeping the hand elevated, applying warm compresses, and positioning the hand in supination will not help to prevent contractures. (9:322; 15:239)

27 4. Trochanter rolls are placed along a patient's hips and thighs to help prevent the femurs from rotating outwardly. They are ineffective in preventing other types of musculoskeletal complications, such as footdrop and knee and hip contractures. (9:322; 15:239)

28 1. Many elderly people with cerebrovascular disease lose adaptability to follow suggested changes in their usual way of living. With age, adapting to a new way of life also becomes difficult because of an unwillingness to give up the older ways of doing things. If the elderly do work toward change, it requires more time for them to change than it does for a younger adult. Caregivers who take the effects both of aging and of cerebrovascular disease into account need to demonstrate great patience and should recognize the effects of aging as well as disease on their elderly patients. (15:30-31)

Caring for a Patient Who Has Nephrotic Syndrome

29 4. The first noted symptom when nephrotic syndrome is present is almost always edema, ordinarily first noticed around the eyes and ankles. Typical laboratory examination of urine demonstrates proteinuria (albuminuria). Blood in the urine is uncommon early in the disease but may be present later if kidney damage occurs. A staggering gait, hoarseness, and profuse perspiration are not associated with nephrotic syndrome. (3:211)

30 1. Ice chips often help to relieve thirst and provide a minimum of fluid intake when offered judiciously. Lemonade, ginger ale, and ice cream are sweet and are likely to increase thirst. (9:503)

31 1. Regression is characterized by reverting to behavior that is typical of an earlier age. A 7-year-old child who refuses to feed himself is an example. Less typical of regression would be refusing to read, play with a roommate, or speak to the nurse. (9:23)

32 1. There are numerous side-effects that may result when prednisone therapy is used, excessive body hair growth (hirsutism), muscle weakness, and increased perspiration being common. Some others include signs and symptoms related to fluid, electrolyte, musculoskeletal, neurological, and endocrine disturbances. Diarrhea is not associated with adverse effects to prednisone therapy. (14:173)

33 4. An early desired effect of prednisone therapy in the presence of nephrotic syndrome is an increase in urine production. The therapy usually has a diuretic effect beginning about 1 to 2 weeks after therapy starts. As urinary output increases, if the blood pressure has been elevated, it can be expected that the blood pressure will decrease but this would be a later result of prednisone therapy. Prednisone is not used to increase the appetite and decrease the pulse rate.   (3:212)

34   4.   The pituitary gland secretes ACTH, which causes the body to produce glucocorticoids. The administration of a glucocorticoid, such as prednisone, decreases ACTH secretion. Therapy with glucocorticoid is tapered off because if there is any decrease in ACTH secretion while the patient is taking the drug, sufficient amounts of glucocorticoid may not be produced normally when the drug is stopped abruptly. Adrenal insufficiency then may result. A patient receiving glucocorticoid therapy should be taught to take the drug exactly as prescribed to help avoid adverse effects.   (14:174)

Caring for a Patient Who Has Atrial Fibrillations and a Blood Clot

35   2.   The word arrhythmia means an irregular heart beat. Because the electrical conduction system is failing when a person has atrial fibrillations, the person's pulse will usually become irregular, or arrhythmic.   (9:195; 15:644)

36   2.   The type of pain cause by a blood clot lodged in an artery that supplies an extremity is typically brought on by walking and exercising; it is relieved with rest. This type of pain is called intermittent claudications. The pain is due to an insufficient blood supply to the leg to meet tissue needs when walking and exercising.   (15:382)

37   3.   The patient described in this item has an insufficient blood supply to her lower leg due to an embolus in an artery near the knee. To promote the blood supply to the affected leg, the leg should be in a dependent position and flat on the surface of the bed. Elevating the leg or flexing the knee will further compromise circulation to the leg. Pain-relieving measures should be used as necessary but positioning the leg in any position of comfort, unless that is a dependent position, is unsatisfactory.   (15:389)

38   2.   Elderly persons who are placed in a strange environment very often become disoriented, confused, and anxious. Becoming combative is uncommon but may occur. Being wakeful and having a poor appetite are more likely to occur than are being overly sleepy and hungry.   (9:160)

39   2.   Postoperative care following surgery to remove an embolus from an artery in the leg includes frequent checking of the color and temperature of the skin on the leg distal to the surgical entry. If circulation becomes impaired, the skin will feel cool and its color will be pale or bluish. These signs are serious because unless adequate circulation is established in the leg, tissues will deteriorate and the patient is at risk for losing the extremity. There may be some edema present due to the surgical procedure but this is not usually critical to circulation. The surgical incision should be watched for signs of hemorrhage. A purulent discharge would be atypical unless the wound eventually becomes infected. (15:389)

40 2. Acetylsalicyclic acid (aspirin) prolongs bleeding time by inhibiting the clumping of blood platelets. Therefore, aspirin is contraindicated for persons receiving an anticoagulant, such as warfarin sodium (Coumadin) because the combination of two anticoagulants may lead to bleeding. (14:67)

Caring for a Woman Who Delivers at Home

41 2. Early deceleration that is the result of a contraction is described in this item, that is, the fetal heart rate slows and reaches its lowest point at the height of a contraction but returns to normal at or near the end of the contraction. This is not a sign of fetal distress and no action need be taken at this time. Any other type of change could be a sign of distress. If the nurse has any questions about her findings, she should immediately notify the midwife in this situation. Auscultation for fetal heart rate is a responsibility no nurse should take lightly. When the nurse is given this responsibility, she should be well aware of signs that may indicate fetal distress and report her findings to her immediate superior promptly. (1:348–390)

42 3. When the husband of a wife in labor wishes to help and asks what he can do, it is best for him to remain with his wife and help her with her breathing with contractions. He wants to help and his support for his wife is important. To suggest that he rest or go elsewhere is inconsiderate of both his wife and him. The nurse should prepare her own equipment, such as the enema equipment. In the situation described in this item, it would be better that the husband stay with his wife while the nurse prepares the enema. (2:231–232)

43 2. When the membranes rupture, the nurse should check the fetal heart tones promptly. This will help determine whether there is pressure on the cord, which may have prolapsed when the membranes ruptured. Pressure on a prolapsed cord can lead to serious fetal distress if the pressure is not relieved. Elevating the head of the bed would represent poor judgment. If the cord has prolapsed, elevating the head of the bed would increase pressure on a prolapsed cord. After the fetal heart rate is checked, the midwife should be notified of the rupture of the patient's membranes. (2:237)

44 1. After cleaning the patient and changing bed linens following the rupture of membranes, an underpad may be safely placed *under* the patient's buttocks to prevent unnecessary soilage of bottom linens on the bed. Perineal pads or terry cloths over the perineum are not recommended because they tend to move about and may carry organisms from the anus forward toward the vaginal meatus. If the nurse does nothing, the bottom linens will become soiled and require repeated change to help prevent discomfort for the patient. An underpad can be changed as necessary with relative ease.   (2:235)

45   3.   Normally, there are accumulated secretions in the nose and mouth of the infant being delivered. As soon as the head is delivered, it is customary to use a bulb syringe to suction the mucus from the nose and mouth to prevent aspiration of secretions by the infant.   (2:243)

46   3.   The Apgar scoring chart assigns a number between 1 and 10 to a newborn within about a minute of birth, and again about 5 minutes later. Five signs are checked: heart rate, respiratory rate, muscle tone, reflex irritability, and color. A score of 10 indicates the newborn is in the best possible condition. A score between about 5 and 10 indicates that the newborn is not in need of special care. A score below 5 indicates the newborn is in need of immediate attention. The lower the score, the poorer is the newborn's condition. A score of 8, as described in this item, indicates that the newborn is in good condition.   (2:376; 12:466)

47   2.   When the membranes rupture early in labor, there is danger that the fluid will wash the cord into the birth canal before the fetus is advanced enough to close off the canal to prevent a prolapse of the cord.   (2:234)

48   1.   A newborn–parent interaction has been found to develop when the parents are allowed to touch their infant as soon after delivery as possible. This early attachment, sometimes called bonding, is believed to have an effect on the long-term parent–child relationship. Hearing the newborn cry, talking to it, and watching it receive care are not inappropriate but these activities are not as effective as touching to begin bonding. Eye-to-eye contact is also believed to enhance newborn–parent bonding.   (2:378)

49   1.   Newborns ordinarily do not pass meconium immediately after delivery. Therefore, the first body temperature of a newborn is obtained rectally primarily to determine whether the anal opening is patent. In many newborn nurseries, body temperatures of normal newborns are obtained by using the axillary method after the initial rectal temperature has been obtained. A rectal examination is not performed on a newborn by the nurse. Auscultation of the abdomen for bowel sounds will not confirm anal patency.   (2:416)

50   2.   An ointment containing an antibiotic is used in a newborn's eyes to help prevent gonococcal ophthalmia neonatorum, which is likely to occur if the mother has gonorrhea.   (12:468)

51   2.   Before inserting the tip of a bulb syringe for suctioning the newborn's mouth and nose, the nurse should be sure to deflate the bulb by squeezing it. If she does not and then deflates it after it is in place, she will force air in the bulb into the newborn's respiratory tract. The tip does not need lubricating. The bulb syringe should be sterile before using it.   (2:383)

52   2.   The preferred position in a crib for the newborn is on either side, flat or with the head slightly elevated. This positioning allows for best drainage of mucus. Placing an infant on his abdomen ordinarily is not recommended until the infant is older or at least not until the cord clamp has been removed. (2:383)

53 3. When vaginal bleeding is noted shortly after delivery, the nurse should first massage the uterus. This is often sufficient to cause contraction of the uterus which may have become relaxed and soft. Normally, with firming of the uterus, bleeding will stop. If this conservative care does not succeed, the midwife should be called promptly. (2:285, 322)

Caring for a Patient Who Has a Cataract Removed

54 2. Unless complications had occurred, a person who has had a cataract removed in a surgical center is given home-going instructions that include allowing the patient to walk about. However, the person is instructed to avoid coughing, straining at stool, stooping over to the floor and sudden, jarring motions. (12:801)

55 1. There is ordinarily no, or very minimal, pain in the operative eye following the removal of a cataract. If pain is present and severe, the symptom usually indicates that the person is hemorrhaging in the operative eye. Loss of vitreous humor, detachment of the retina, and optic nerve damage are unlikely complications following cataract removal and are conditions that do not necessarily cause pain. (12:801; 15:265)

56 2. A cataract is a condition in which the lens in the eye becomes opaque. This reduces the amount of light that can reach the retina. As a result, vision diminishes as the lens becomes more opaque with time. (15:264)

Caring for a Patient Who Has a Bipolar Disorder, Manic Phase

57 3. After gathering information from the patient's record, the nurse should next interview and observe the patient. After that, she is better able to help the nurse-in-charge to assess the patient's strengths and weaknesses, determine a nursing diagnosis, set up goals of care, and prepare a care plan and evaluation schedule. (1:106 – 108; 9:34 – 39)

58 3. There are 4 steps described in the nursing process. The first step is assessment and consists of collecting and analyzing data related to the patient's health status. (Some persons describe 5 steps in the nursing process; in those instances, the process of collecting and analyzing data are separated into 2 steps.) In the 4-step description, the second step is to plan the patient's nursing care and describe it in a nursing care plan. The third step is to implement, or carry out, the nursing care as described in the patient's nursing care plan. The last step is to evaluate the nursing care given to the patient in terms of its success or failure in meeting objectives of nursing care.   (1:106–112)

59   3.   A patient who has manic-type behavior is restless and may become increasingly aggressive. Behavior may reach a point of frenzy. Such a patient can usually be distracted and can be relatively easily diverted to nonconfrontational, satisfactory behavior. Threats, scolding, and reasoning are rarely effective methods to manage a troublesome situation because of a patient's manic-type behavior.   (1:196)

60   3.   The person demonstrating manic-type behavior is usually too busy and active to pay attention to such needs as obtaining sufficient nourishment, fluids and rest, or to attend to personal hygiene needs. A nursing care plan for such a patient should take into account these physical needs, which the patient typically ignores.   (1:196; 12:845)

61   2.   The patient with manic-type behavior typically demonstrates exaggerated elation, or euphoria, in his behavior. Compulsion is an act that a person finds himself forced to do; carrying out the act reduces his anxiety. Disorientation is being unaware of time and place. Panic is a state of extreme anxiety.   (1:196)

62   4.   In the situation described in this item, it is best when the nurse behaves in a firm and matter-of-fact way. She is responsible for setting limits for the patient but should do so without rejecting or punishing the patient for her behavior. The nurse should set limits and divert the patient's energy in a game of ping pong. Other alternatives, such as helping the patient to move furniture, threatening to punish the patient by sending her to her room, and consulting the nurse-in-charge, are not helpful to the patient who is demonstrating excessively active behavior and attempting to manipulate the environment.   (1:196; 12:845)

63   4.   The person demonstrating manic-type behavior usually has grandiose ideas of his own ability, accomplishments, and worth. He views himself as the best and the most popular. This thinking is demonstrated best by the patient in this situation who says she is always being asked for photographs of herself.   (1:196)

Caring for a Patient Who Has a Cholecystectomy

64   2.   To help decrease discomfort in the operative area while coughing postoperatively, the patient should be taught to splint the area. This is best done by having the patient apply pressure over a small pillow she holds over the operative site or over her hands placed on the site, while coughing. Lying on the side, taking panting breaths, and keeping abdominal muscles tensed will not relieve discomfort associated with coughing postoperatively.   (9:370–371)

65   3.   Dizziness and feeling light-headed are symptoms that result from hyperventilation due to excessive carbon dioxide loss from extracellular tissues. The symptoms are likely to occur if a patient is breathing too rapidly. (9:370)

66 2. Exercising the legs and feet postoperatively helps primarily to prevent venous stasis, which predisposes to thrombus formation and thrombophlebitis. These conditions can be serious, lead to further complications, and delay recovery. Footdrop is best prevented by using a footboard. The legs may be elevated if edema or varicose veins are present. (9:386; 15:123)

67 1. Two of the most typical signs of excessive bleeding are a rapid pulse rate and a drop in blood pressure. When circulating blood is decreasing in quantity, the heartbeat increases to attempt to make up for blood loss but because the circulating blood is decreased in amount, the blood pressure falls. (9:386)

68 2. Ice cream is inappropriate for a clear liquid diet. It is appropriate for a full liquid diet. A clear liquid diet includes the following items: bouillon broths, clear fruit juices, such as apple juice, plain gelatin, coffee, and tea. Carbonated beverages may or may not be permitted. (9:99)

69 1. Most activity may be uncomfortable during the early postoperative period. However, because the incision for a cholecystectomy is high on the patient's abdomen, the patient is likely to find breathing deeply and coughing especially uncomfortable. A medication to prevent the discomfort may be necessary but analgesics should not be administered so frequently that the patient is lethargic and breathes even more shallowly. (15:474)

70 3. The most frequent complication associated with the use of an indwelling catheter is a urinary tract infection. It is extremely important to use aseptic techniques when caring for a patient with an indwelling catheter, so that problems with infections can be minimized. Of special importance is that caretakers wash their hands *thoroughly* before and after care. (9:446–449)

71 1. Because of the danger of infection, it is recommended that a closed drainage system be maintained at all times when a patient has an indwelling catheter. Therefore, when a specimen is requested, the nurse should clean an area of entry on the catheter and aspirate a specimen of urine with a sterile syringe and needle. (9:459)

72 2. When an indwelling catheter is to be removed, the nurse should first deflate the balloon of the catheter. If this is not done, the bladder and urethral mucosa may be injured when efforts are used to withdraw the catheter. The tubing need not necessarily be clamped when removing the catheter. An indwelling catheter should not be irrigated unless there are specific orders to do so. The collecting receptacle should always be kept lower than the level of the bladder to prevent a backflow of urine into the bladder. (9:454)

Caring for a Woman in Labor and During Delivery

73   3.   Several weeks before delivery, many women, especially those pregnant for the first time, describe a dropping of the uterus in the abdomen. This phenomenon is called lightening. Quickening refers to the first movement of the fetus that the mother feels. Show refers to a blood-tinged mucus discharge expelled from the vagina and occurs before or during labor. Hegar's sign is a softening of the lower segment of the uterus and is noted early in pregnancy.   (2:199)

74   4.   The frequency of contractions is the time between the beginning of one contraction and the beginning of the next. The duration of a contraction is the time between the beginning and the end of one contraction. A third assessment of a contraction is its intensity. Intensity is determined by feeling for the degree of firmness of the uterus during a contraction. The firmer the uterus, the more intense the contraction.   (2:201)

75   4.   Station refers to the position of the presenting part in relation to the level of the mother's ischial spines. A plus 2 station means the presenting part is 2 cm below the level of the mother's ischial spines. If the assessment had been a minus 2 station, the presenting part would be 2 cm above the level of the mother's ischial spines. The term lie refers to the relationship of the long axis of the fetus to the long axis of the mother and is described as either longitudinal or transverse. Lie is not measured in degrees. Dilatation refers to the gradual opening of the cervix as labor progresses and is measured by determining the diameter, in centimeters, of the cervical opening. The cervical canal is obliterated gradually during labor. The amount of obliteration, called effacement, is measured in percentage and represents the portion of the canal that has obliterated. It is as thin as it will become when effacement is 100%.   (2:203)

76   2.   If the umbilical cord prolapses when the mother's membranes rupture, fetal distress occurs. This can be ascertained by a marked slowing of the fetal heart rate and an irregular heartbeat. The fetus is not breathing at the time membranes normally rupture and therefore, cannot aspirate fluid. An abnormal fetal heart rate is not related to an inverted uterus and diminishing intensity of labor.   (2:237)

77   4.   It is recommended that both legs of a person who is about to deliver be placed in stirrups on the delivery table at the same time. This technique is used to help prevent strain on ligaments in the pelvis that may occur when one leg and then the other are placed in stirrups.   (2:241)

78   1.   An oxytocic drug is used after the placenta of the mother is delivered to stimulate contractions of the myometrium in the uterus. This contraction of muscles helps to prevent hemorrhaging by closing blood vessels at the site where the placenta was attached. Examples of oxytocic drugs include ergonovine maleate (Ergotrate) and oxytocin (Pitocin, Syntocinon).   (2:243; 14:193, 196)

Caring for a Patient Who Has Emphysema

79 1. Pulmonary emphysema is the result of obstruction of bronchioles that causes an accumulation of air in lung tissue distal to the obstruction. The alveoli lose their elasticity, resulting in the trapping of air that normally should be expired. Distention of alveoli eventually causes rupture of their walls. The pulmonary pathology associated with emphysema results in poor ventilation. (15:313)

80 2. The patient described in this item is to receive 62.5 ml of solution intravenously per hour (500 ml divided by 8 = 62.5). The drop factor of the equipment is multiplied by the number of milliliters to be received every hour and then divided by 60 to determine the drops to be administered each minute:

$$\frac{20 \times 62.5}{60} = \frac{1250}{60} = 20.8 \text{ (or about 21 drops per minute)}$$

(9:517)

81 1. Aminophylline is a bronchodilating agent and acts to improve breathing and relieve dyspnea. A drug that acts as a decongestant relieves respiratory congestion. An antitussive is used to relieve coughing. Tenacious sputum is often relieved by humidification of the environment and by offering a generous fluid intake to the patient. (14:224; 15:315–316)

82 3. The primary purpose for using vibration and percussion over the chest wall is to help break up tenacious respiratory secretions. By so doing, the patient is better able to raise secretions and open airways. (9:607)

83 1. A patient with chronic obstructive pulmonary disease (COPD), such as emphysema, usually has a normally high level of carbon dioxide in blood plasma. As a result, the respiratory center loses its sensitivity to stimulating respirations as it adjusts to the higher-than-normal levels of carbon dioxide. If the patient receives high concentrations of oxygen and the carbon dioxide level drops, the respiratory center may not stimulate respirations and the patient is likely to suffer with respiratory arrest. (15:313–314)

Caring for a Teenager Who Is Obese

84 4. It is generally agreed that obesity is most probably caused not by any one group of factors but by numerous factors, including psychosocial, genetic, metabolic, and cultural. Certain research has demonstrated that obesity may be associated with an increase in both number and size of fat cells in the body. It appears that dieting may reduce fat cell size but probably not fat cell numbers. (3:274; 16:200–202)

85 2. The adolescent needs to share his feelings with peers and feel accepted by them. Encouraging the patient described in this item to join a group of dieting teenagers would probably provide the best psychological support.   (3:275)

86 2. The nurse needs to make an assessment before she is in a position to help any patient, including the obese adolescent. She should gather information first about what the patient usually eats and learn about his attitudes toward food. Learning about an adolescent's eating habits enables the nurse to offer appropriate suggestions about modifying his diet. The nurse will not gather information she needs to help the patient by inquiring from the mother about previous dieting or by suggesting that the patient see a physician. Adolescents are unlikely to be placed on a strict low-calorie diet because such a diet has been proven unsatisfactory for the young person trying to lose weight.   (3:275)

87 4. Fresh fruit is nutritious and most fruit is low in calories. Snacks such as crackers and cheese, chocolate milk, and buttered popcorn do not meet these two criteria.   (16:204)

Caring for a Patient Who Has a Colostomy Due to a Malignant Tumor in the Colon

88 2. When a patient shows emotional responses to an experience, it is best for the nurse to help him to express and describe his emotions. This helps bring them to the surface so that they can be handled. A comment such as "You said you were scared and worried about your surgery?", helps to encourage the patient to describe his feelings and while he does so, the nurse should listen to what he has to say. Telling someone not to worry or be afraid, to trust caregivers, and to try to relax are not helpful for the patient who is experiencing fear and worry.   (9:23)

89 4. A Living Will describes a person's wishes concerning the type of care the person wishes when his illness is judged to be terminal. One purpose of such a will is to spare other persons, such as relatives, friends, and caretakers, from having to make decisions concerning terminal care. A Living Will does not indicate how the person's body is to be disposed of, but in most instances, the person's wishes in this regard have been made known to family members. The more common last will and testament, which is prepared by the person's attorney in most instances, describes wishes concerning how personal belongings and assets are to be distributed after death.   (9:650)

90 3. The primary developmental task of young adults in our culture is to establish independence and develop self-esteem. This requires, among other things, differentiating between oneself and one's parents. The patient's 27-year-old daughter described in this item appears to be striving to accomplish this developmental task when she chooses to live with friends rather than with her parents. (15:24)

91 3. When a patient complains of cramping while a colostomy irrigation is administered, the nurse should stop administering the irrigating solution temporarily. Often, the cramping passes and the irrigation can be resumed. Removing the cone is not the best first course of action and may be unnecessary. Panting breaths are unlikely to help relieve cramping while administering the irrigating solution. (9:486)

92 3. A major function of the large intestine is to absorb water from feces. By the time the feces reach the lower part of the large intestine, the feces are soft and formed. This makes managing and regulating fecal discharge relatively easy. On the other hand, a colostomy located in the proximal part of the colon and an ileostomy tend to discharge feces almost continuously; the stool is liquid or semi-liquid in nature because little water has been absorbed. (10:259)

93 3. Fluorouracil (Adrucil) is an antimetabolite and acts to prevent the use of nutrients necessary for the growth of malignant cells. Certain antibiotics with antineoplastic activity act to halt the division of malignant cells. Various other agents are used in the treatment of malignant diseases with different actions, and, in some instances, with unknown ways of acting. (14:198, 203)

Caring for a Child Who Has Cystic Fibrosis

94 3. Cystic fibrosis is due to abnormal functioning of mucus-producing glands in the body. Mucus coagulates and then forms obstructions, particularly in the pancreatic ducts and in the bronchi. The liver also is often affected. About one half of all children with cystic fibrosis develop pulmonary complications. (3:158)

95 1. Children with cystic fibrosis lose abnormally large amounts of salt in their perspiration. Many times, parents report noticing the saltiness of sweat when they kiss a child with cystic fibrosis. (3:159-160)

96 3. Cystic fibrosis affects primarily the lungs, pancreas, and liver, but pulmonary complications are the most common. Every effort should be used to help a child with cystic fibrosis avoid exposure to respiratory infections, which can easily lead to further complications, such as bronchiectasis, emphysema, lung abscesses, and atelectasis. These complications are likely to cause severe respiratory inadequacy. (3:158, 160)

97 1. Fat is poorly digested by the child with cystic fibrosis because of an absence or a decreased amount of pancreatic enzymes. The result is poor absorption of fat. This leads to greasy, bulky, and foul-smelling feces.

When foods high in fat are eaten, extra amounts of pancreatic enzymes, which ordinarily are prescribed for children with the disease, are given to improve fat digestion and absorption. (3:160)

98 3. A toddler needs opportunities to develop autonomy for successful psychosocial development. This usually is best accomplished when he is allowed to do things for himself to the greatest extent possible in a safe environment. During toddlerhood, a youngster is very active while he explores his environment and himself and tries to do new things for himself. Constant thwarting of his behavior may lead to the child's feeling doubtful, ashamed of himself, and "bad." Nevertheless, the toddler still needs guidance and limits to develop respect for a family's cooperative efforts to have a schedule of activities of daily living that is within reason. (3:94)

Caring for a Patient with a Urinary Tract Disorder

99 4. Offering a comment that things will be better soon does little to promote communication between a nurse and a patient. The patient is likely to interpret the comment as showing that the nurse does not really care. Techniques such as using eye-to-eye contact (without staring), taking brief notes on what the patient is saying, and sitting while talking with the patient tend to promote communication. (9:18–22)

100 4. This item explores knowledge of the nursing process. A nurse begins planning a patient's nursing care by stating what goals she believes can be reached through the use of nursing measures. After goals are stated, the nurse lists various nursing measures that might be used to reach these goals. A nursing care plan should be discussed with the patient when possible, but this cannot be done until goals and possible nursing measures that will help to reach those goals are explored. The last step in the nursing process is evaluating care the patient receives. (9:35, 39)

101 1. The position of choice when catheterizing a male patient is the back-lying position with the legs flat on the bed. It is usually easier when the legs are together so that a sterile field can be set up next to the patient's legs. (9:442)

102 1. When catheterizing a male, if the catheter meets resistance in the area of the prostate gland, dropping the penis toward the toes and placing slightly more tension on the penis usually help the catheter slip by the area. Flexing the knees and panting do not help a catheter pass the prostatic urethra. The catheter should be lubricated generously before starting the procedure to minimize friction when the catheter is inserted. (9:445)

103 1. The patient should be asked to void at 10 A.M. on the day the collection of a 24-hour urine specimen is started, when specimen collection is ordered to start at 10 A.M. The urine is discarded because the urine has collected in the bladder before the specified time to start the 24-hour specimen. All urine is collected for the next 24-hour period, including urine the patient should be asked to void at the time the test ends, and in the situation described in this item, that is at 10 A.M. on September 7. (9:459)

104   1.   It causes less strain on the back when one stoops, rather than bends, to reach an object near the floor. Pushing a hamper and avoiding unnecessary stretching, such as walking around the bed to loosen linens and placing the patient near the nurse to rub his back, avoid twisting and stretching the body unnecessarily. Placing strain on the body while working predisposes to injury of the nurse's muscles.   (9:120–123)

105   4.   If a patient wishes to confide in a nurse, it is best to listen to the patient rather than, for example, ask the patient not to share the information or ask that he tell some other person. However, the nurse is obligated to tell the patient that she has to share the information with appropriate health personnel if the information will influence the patient's health care or status. Promising not to divulge the information puts the nurse in a difficult position if the information is important to share with other health personnel for the patient's best interests.   (9:21)

Caring for a Patient Who Has Surgery Because of a Peptic Ulcer

106   1.   Using baking soda regularly to relieve heartburn may cause an electrolyte imbalance. Sodium bicarbonate is absorbed into the bloodstream and may lead to systemic alkalosis. This is of special danger to persons with impaired kidney functioning because the kidneys normally function to excrete excess bicarbonate.   (15:415)

107   1.   Aspirin is irritating to stomach mucosa and may cause gastritis and bleeding if taken in large amounts or at frequent intervals. Factors that appear to contribute to the development of ulcers include excessive smoking, stress, and taking large amounts of aspirin.   (16:245)

108   3.   An error should not be erased. A line should be drawn through it, the word "error" should appear above it, and the nurse should identify herself by name. The abbreviation c/o is appropriate when used to mean "complains of," although some agencies prefer to use the word "states," that is, "The patient states . . ." It is appropriate to use printing, although legible writing is very acceptable. Drawing a line through a blank area in the nurses' notes when it is not filled with information is recommended technique so that there is no danger of adding information at a later time in the blank area.   (9:26)

109   4.   Diet therapy for a person with ulcers has changed over the years. However, protein continues to remain important for the person with ulcers primarily because it maintains body tissues and promotes healing of the ulcer. It also supports red blood cell formation and because of bleeding from ulcers, this benefit of a high protein diet is important.   (4:342)

110   2.   Anxiety may be caused by any threat to a person's security or survival. Most anxious persons are unable to explain why they feel uncomfortable, but they communicate anxiety in indirect ways. Hostility usually is expressed through aggressive behavior. There is no clear evidence that the patient described in this item is lonely. Panic is a state of such overwhelming anxiety that the patient displays pronounced physical signs, such as dyspnea, faintness, hot flashes, and the like.   (1:203–205)

111   1.   The nurse should focus on the feelings of an anxious patient and give him an opportunity to talk about them. A comment that acknowledges that the nurse is interested in the patient and that opens avenues to further discussion is best. It is not helpful when the nurse's comments ignore the patient's feelings, assume that the patient can control how he feels, or give false assurances.   (1:208–209; 12:246)

112   4.   Deep-breathing exercises help most to prevent atelectasis and hypostatic pneumonia.   (9:369)

— **113**   3.   A person using incentive spirometry should be taught to take about 5 normal breaths between each deep breath he takes when using a spirometer. This technique helps prevent hyperventilation and fatigue.   (9:369)

114   4.   The spread of organisms most often depends on vehicles of transmission. Such vehicles include the hands, supplies and equipment, instruments, respiratory droplets, feces, mucus, food, water, and so on. The spread of organisms is not normally dependent on the organisms' having time to reproduce, having living spores, or producing a toxin. Some organisms are spread by direct contact, such as sexually acquired infections.   (9:274)

Caring for a Child Who Has Patent Ductus Arteriosus

115   1.   Parent–child separation is very difficult for the young patient. Unless contraindicated by agency policy, it would be best if parents can visit the child as much as possible. This will aid the child to cope with illness and therapy and familiarize the parents with the child's care. Hospital regulations have changed markedly during the last few decades when research revealed the importance of the child–parent relationship and the ill effects that result when children and parents are separated.   (3:xii)

116   3.   Selecting an appropriate activity for a young child should be based on answers to these questions: What symptoms does the child have as a result of the illness? What activity is appropriate in terms of the child's developmental age? The child described in this item is dyspneic and fatigues easily. Activity should not be strenuous, such as pushing about in a walker or crawling. Tossing a ball in a crib is also too strenuous but in addition, is beyond the ability of a 15-month-old child. The child can play pat-a-cake, play "peek-a-boo," and scribble with crayons. These activities do not require strenuous activity and would therefore, be appropriate for this child. (3:75, 102, 141)

117 4. At present, the cause of patent ductus arteriosus, which is a defect that allows blood after birth to pass from the aorta into the pulmonary artery, is unknown. (3:74)

118 4. A postoperative order that indicates milk should be offered as soon as the patient is awake should be questioned. Milk is ordinarily difficult to tolerate soon after surgery and it also tends to make mucus more tenacious. Offering sips of water would be typical, and also ice chips if the child is old enough to handle them. Measuring urinary output is important to ascertain kidney functioning postoperatively. Changing position and having suction available if it becomes necessary to use are appropriate postoperative nursing orders also. (3:327)

Individual Items

119 1. Restraints should not be applied unless there is a specific order to do so. Under certain conditions, a registered nurse may apply restraints. In the situation described in this item, the nurse should report to the nurse-in-charge before applying restraints and receive specific orders. After an appropriate order is received, correct techniques for this patient include restraining both wrists after stockinette is placed at the wrists and giving passive arm exercises to the patient when the nurse removes the restraints. (12:840)

120 1. The organism causing hepatitis A is discharged from an infected person through the stool and saliva. The person also harbors the organisms in his blood. In most cases, food and water contaminated with the feces of a person with the disease spread the disease to others. In health agencies, items that may also contribute to the spread of hepatitis A include bedpans, rectal thermometers, linens soiled with feces, and the like, when these items are not properly cleaned between uses. Hepatitis A has not been found to spread by mosquitoes nor through sexual intercourse. Contaminated needles can spread hepatitis but this is not the case in *most* instances. (12:471)

Part II
of the Comprehensive Examination

Allow yourself 2 hours to complete Part II. Start this part now.

Ron Merick, 3½ Years Old and a "Near-drowning" Victim, Has Brain Damage. He is Being Cared for at Home by His Parents and a Nurse. Ron is Unable to Talk, Cannot Move Himself, and Has Trouble Focusing His Eyes. He Responds to Touch and Sound and Appears to See Some Things.

1 In view of Ron's accident, the nurse judges correctly that Ron's brain damage is most probably due to prolonged
   ○ 1. below normal blood oxygen levels.
   ○ 2. below normal blood sugar levels.
   ○ 3. above normal intracranial pressure.
   ○ 4. above normal blood potassium levels.

The remaining items in this situation deal with Ron's care.

2 Whenever the nurse begins care measures, it would be best for her first to
   ○ 1. play with the child for a short time.
   ○ 2. ask the parents to leave the child's room.
   ○ 3. explain to the child what she will be doing.
   ○ 4. decrease sound stimuli reaching the child to a minimum.

3 Ron has a tracheostomy. If the nurse uses the following techniques while suctioning the tracheostomy, which one is in *error*?
   ○ 1. The nurse gives the child oxygen therapy for a minute or two before starting to suction the airway.
   ○ 2. The nurse avoids any suctioning while inserting the catheter.
   ○ 3. The nurse suctions for approximately 20 seconds at one time.
   ○ 4. The nurse rotates the catheter while withdrawing it as she suctions.

4 Ron's mother learns to prepare a formula for Ron's gastrostomy feedings. She avoids the use of raw eggs in the formula primarily because they may cause
   ○ 1. salmonella food poisoning.
   ○ 2. high blood cholesterol levels.
   ○ 3. regurgitation of stomach contents.
   ○ 4. obstruction at the pyloric sphincter.

5 Ron is fed the formula through a gastrostomy tube that is inserted and

removed with each feeding. To protect skin from the irritating effects of stomach juices when the tube is removed, the nurse should protect the area around Ron's gastrostomy stoma with

○ 1. a lotion, such as Intensive Care.
○ 2. an ointment, such as zinc oxide.
○ 3. a paste, such as a mixture of cornstarch and water.
○ 4. an antiseptic, such as half-strength hydrogen peroxide.

6 Which of the following activities is likely to be *least* entertaining and diversional for Ron?

○ 1. Performing with hand puppets for the child
○ 2. Using flash cards to play simple number games with the child
○ 3. Opening gifts in the child's presence at holiday times
○ 4. Positioning the child so that he can watch family activities

Ms. Ruth Faust, Who is 66 Years Old, Has Osteoarthritis. She Lives at Home and Attends a Community Clinic for Health Care.

7 The symptom Ms. Faust most likely noted first when her disease started is

○ 1. general malaise.
○ 2. a low-grade fever.
○ 3. swelling of the involved joints.
○ 4. stiffness of the involved joints.

8 Ms. Faust has been using ibuprofen (Motrin) for discomfort. The most common adverse reaction to this drug is

○ 1. double vision.
○ 2. loss of equilibrium.
○ 3. irregular pulse rates.
○ 4. gastrointestinal disturbances.

The nurse teaches Ms. Faust concerning her self-care at home.

9 Ms. Faust says hot moist packs applied to her knees help relieve discomfort. The nurse should teach Ms. Faust safety measures to prevent burns when applying hot packs by explaining that an important characteristic of the body's heat receptors is that they are

○ 1. located in free nerve endings.
○ 2. absent in certain parts of the body.
○ 3. slow to respond to sudden changes in temperature.
○ 4. capable of adjusting when temperatures are moderate.

10 Ms. Faust is a vegetarian. She should be taught that, of the following foods she eats, the one *lowest* in protein content is

○ 1. nuts.
○ 2. peas.
○ 3. beans.
○ 4. potatoes.

Ms. Clara Shultz, Age 25 Years, is About 8 Months Pregnant. She Has Been Free of Complications. Ms. Shultz Attends a Prenatal Clinic where a Nurse Teaches Her About Her Prenatal Care.

11 Ms. Shultz complains of dizziness and feeling faint, especially when she first gets out of bed in the morning. "What can I do about that?" she asks the nurse. Of the following possible replies the nurse could make, which one is best?
○ 1. "Lie on your back as much as possible while in bed."
○ 2. "Drink a glass of milk or fruit juice before getting out of bed."
○ 3. "Move to a sitting position in bed and then to a standing position slowly."
○ 4. "Move from the bed to a chair quickly and remain in the chair for a few minutes."

12 Ms. Shultz says she is now often uncomfortable with heartburn. In relation to eating habits, the nurse should point out that heartburn is often relieved by
○ 1. lying down after eating.
○ 2. exercising before eating.
○ 3. omitting fluid while eating.
○ 4. eating small frequent meals.

13 At this time in her pregnancy, the nurse recommends to Ms. Shultz that she take showers rather than tub baths primarily because
○ 1. sitting in warm water is likely to induce early labor.
○ 2. taking a shower stimulates circulation in the skin, thereby helping the body rid itself of wastes.
○ 3. rinsing soap off is easy during a shower, thereby preventing soap remnants from collecting at the vaginal orifice.
○ 4. losing balance when getting in and out of a tub is likely when the abdomen becomes large late in pregnancy.

14 Ms. Shultz is to wear antiembolism stockings. When during the day should the nurse teach Ms. Shultz to put on the stockings?
○ 1. After she has had her breakfast
○ 2. After she takes a morning shower
○ 3. At bedtime, as soon as she is in bed for the night
○ 4. Upon awakening in the morning, before getting out of bed

Ms. Grace Inner is 50 Years Old. She is Hospitalized For a Biopsy of a Lump in Her Right Breast and For Surgery If the Lump Proves to Be Malignant.

15 When assessing Ms. Inner by palpating the right breast for an abnormal mass, the nurse should position the patient by having her lie down on her back and
- ○ 1. flex her neck.
- ○ 2. flex her right elbow.
- ○ 3. place a pillow under her left shoulder.
- ○ 4. place a pillow under her right shoulder.

16 After the assessment, Ms. Inner tells the nurse that she dreads the possibility of having her breast removed. The nurse should understand that a significant reason why many women are reluctant to have a breast removed is that they fear
- ○ 1. psychological inability to fight cancer.
- ○ 2. an inaccuracy in their laboratory reports.
- ○ 3. a permanent loss of their feeling feminine.
- ○ 4. a disability in the use of the arm on the affected side.

Ms. Inner has a right radical mastectomy to remove a malignant tumor.

17 To promote muscle and joint efficiency in her right arm, Ms. Inner should be taught that the best course of action postoperatively is to
- ○ 1. keep the arm abducted.
- ○ 2. keep the arm on pillows.
- ○ 3. actively exercise the arm.
- ○ 4. passively exercise the arm.

18 Ms. Inner tells the nurse caring for her, "Men are so lucky! They don't get breast cancer." The nurse should base her response to the patient's statement on knowledge that indicates the patient's comment is
- ○ 1. true; men do not develop breast cancer.
- ○ 2. true; men develop breast tumors, but they are benign.
- ○ 3. false; men develop breast cancer, but the cells do not metastasize.
- ○ 4. false; men develop breast cancer but not as frequently as women.

About a year following surgery, Ms. Inner is readmitted to the hospital. She is gravely ill with metastasis of the breast tumor.

19 Ms. Inner speaks of her impending death with the nurse. Of the following comments the nurse could make, it would be best for her to say,
- ○ 1. "For now, let's talk about something more cheerful."
- ○ 2. "You are saying that thoughts of death are frightening?"
- ○ 3. "I think we should think more positively about life and living."

    ○ 4. "Shall we delay this conversation until we have more time to be together?"

20 Life-support systems and resuscitation are *not* to be used for Ms. Inner. Withholding life-prolonging measures poses an ethical dilemma and often causes health caretakers to feel psychological discomfort primarily because withholding such measures

    ○ 1. may invade the patient's human rights.

    ○ 2. represents defeat in the minds of many health caretakers.

    ○ 3. ends the search by health caretakers for alternative methods of care.

    ○ 4. violates common religious beliefs concerning death held by most patients.

21 Ms. Inner's respirations become noisy. The so-called "death rattle" most probably is due to Ms. Inner's having

    ○ 1. swallowed her tongue.

    ○ 2. accumulated secretions in her airway.

    ○ 3. partial paralysis of her respiratory center.

    ○ 4. fluids in excess of her body's ability to use them.

22 Ms. Inner's husband says to the nurse that he cannot face the death of his wife. The nurse's best guide to her course of action during this conversation with Mr. Inner is to

    ○ 1. explain that adjustment to death comes with time.

    ○ 2. give the husband an opportunity to express his feelings.

    ○ 3. ask the husband if he would like the nurse to call a clergyman for him.

    ○ 4. encourage shifting the conversation to thoughts of the patient's remaining life.

Ten-year-old Susan Strong is Hospitalized. She is Acutely Ill With Rheumatic Fever.

23 An illness that is most likely to appear in Susan's health history is that recently she was sick with

    ○ 1. insect bites.

    ○ 2. chicken pox.

    ○ 3. a sore throat.

    ○ 4. gastroenteritis.

24 The nurse should plan Susan's nursing care during the acute phase of her illness so that Susan receives a maximum amount of

    ○ 1. rest.

    ○ 2. fluids.

    ○ 3. exercise.

    ○ 4. proteins.

Susan is started on salicylate (aspirin) therapy.

25 The nurse should judge that Susan most probably is experiencing salicylate poisoning when she tells the nurse
   ○ 1. "My nose won't stop itching."
   ○ 2. "I hear funny noises in my ears."
   ○ 3. "Look. I have a blister on my lip."
   ○ 4. "I think my hair is turning darker in color."

Susan speaks about things she enjoyed before she became ill.

26 If Susan is typical of school-age children between about 6 and 12 years of age, she is demonstrating a very common way to meet her psychosocial needs for normal development if the comment she makes to the nurse is
   ○ 1. "I like going to school."
   ○ 2. "I like being around boys."
   ○ 3. "My mother is my best friend."
   ○ 4. "I would rather play alone than on a team."

Ms. Hannah Eichler, 78 Years Old, Has Glaucoma. She Receives Care at an Eye Clinic of Her Health Maintenance Organization.

27 On each visit to the clinic, Ms. Eichler's intraocular pressure is checked with a tonometer. Before measuring the pressure, the nurse should be prepared to
   ○ 1. irrigate the eyes.
   ○ 2. dim lights in the room.
   ○ 3. turn back the upper eyelids.
   ○ 4. place a topical anesthetic in the eyes.

28 Ms. Eichler uses eye drops containing pilocarpine for her glaucoma. Pilocarpine in eye drops acts to
   ○ 1. constrict the pupils.
   ○ 2. dilate the canals of Schlemm.
   ○ 3. partially immobilize the ciliary muscles.
   ○ 4. suppress the production of the vitreous humor.

29 Ms. Eichler also uses an ophthalmic solution of timolol maleate (Timoptic) for treating her glaucoma. This eye preparation acts in the eyes to help
   ○ 1. keep the corneas clear.
   ○ 2. prevent macular degeneration.
   ○ 3. suppress the production of aqueous humor.

       ○ 4. remove crystal-like deposits in the lenses.

30 If Ms. Eichler fails to continue with health care for glaucoma, a typical symptom that is likely to occur is irreversible
       ○ 1. double vision.
       ○ 2. color blindness.
       ○ 3. impaired peripheral vision (tunnel vision).
       ○ 4. extreme intolerance of light (photophobia).

Ms. Cherok, Who is 67 Years Old, is Admitted to the Hospital Because of Behavioral Changes Characterized by Marked Depression.

31 Ms. Cherok's feelings of depression make it important for the nurse to observe Ms. Cherok often and carefully because a depressed person has a tendency to
       ○ 1. recover spontaneously.
       ○ 2. have suicidal thoughts.
       ○ 3. act out aggressively toward others.
       ○ 4. exhibit excessive psychomotor activities.

32 Ms. Cherok says to the nurse, "Why waste your time on me? It's just not worth it." This remark probably is most accurately interpreted to mean that the patient is asking for someone who will
       ○ 1. cure her.
       ○ 2. accept her.
       ○ 3. respect her privacy.
       ○ 4. tell her that she is sane.

Amitriptyline (Elavil) is prescribed for Ms. Cherok.

33 For which one of the following activities should Ms. Cherok be taught to move slowly while taking amitriptyline?
       ○ 1. When walking down a flight of stairs
       ○ 2. When walking from indoors to the outdoors
       ○ 3. When moving from her bed to a standing position
       ○ 4. When moving from a standing position to a deep upholstered chair

34 When Ms. Cherok does not respond to amitriptyline, tranylcypromine (Parnate) is prescribed. If Ms. Cherok has adverse signs after taking tranylcypromine, she will most likely demonstrate warning signs of
       ○ 1. hepatic coma.
       ○ 2. kidney failure.
       ○ 3. respiratory crisis.
       ○ 4. hypertensive crisis.

After Ms. Cherok's condition improves, her husband receives permission to take her out for dinner.

35 When Ms. Cherok learns she can go out for dinner, she winks at the nurse and says, "Good! Now I may be able to have a drink before dinner for a change." The patient and her husband should be taught that while using tranylcypromine, the patient must *avoid* drinking
- ○ 1. beer and wine.
- ○ 2. gin and vodka.
- ○ 3. bourbon and scotch.
- ○ 4. brandy and liqueurs.

36 Mr. and Ms. Cherok should also be taught that of the following foods, the only one Ms. Cherok may eat freely while taking tranylcypromine is
- ○ 1. yogurt.
- ○ 2. chocolate.
- ○ 3. aged cheese.
- ○ 4. chicken liver.

The Clothing of 51-Year-Old Mr. Hal Tyson Catches on Fire While He is Burning Rubbish Out of Doors.

37 The recommended course of action when Mr. Tyson's clothes are burning and he is out of doors is to place Mr. Tyson in a horizontal position on the ground and to
- ○ 1. wrap the victim in a blanket.
- ○ 2. quickly carry the victim indoors.
- ○ 3. place the victim in a tub of cool water.
- ○ 4. direct a fire extinguisher onto the victim.

Mr. Tyson is transported to the emergency room of a hospital where he is observed to have severe burns (second- and third-degree) on his legs and back. After emergency care, the patient is moved to a private room.

38 Mr. Tyson's blood electrolyte levels are examined. The two electrolytes most often found in *abnormal* amounts in the blood serum after a major burn are sodium and
- ○ 1. calcium.
- ○ 2. chloride.
- ○ 3. potassium.
- ○ 4. magnesium.

39 Mr. Tyson is placed in isolation. His burned areas are undressed. When feeding and bathing Mr. Tyson, in addition to wearing a cap, the nurse should also wear a

    ○ 1. mask only.
    ○ 2. gown only.
    ○ 3. gown and mask.
    ○ 4. mask and gloves.

40 A cream containing mafenide (Sulfamylon) is placed on Mr. Tyson's burns daily. The nurse should prepare Mr. Tyson before applying the cream by explaining that the cream is likely to cause a sensation of
    ○ 1. warmth.
    ○ 2. itching.
    ○ 3. burning.
    ○ 4. chilliness.

41 Mr. Tyson is scheduled for a tubbing at 10 A.M. Because of the nature of this measure, it is best to prepare the patient before the tubbing by
    ○ 1. keeping him NPO after 6 A.M.
    ○ 2. helping him to nap for about an hour.
    ○ 3. giving him a prescribed analgesic about 9:30 A.M.
    ○ 4. positioning him in a mid-Fowler's position for a few minutes.

42 Mr. Tyson receives a high protein diet. The whole milk he has with meals has been mixed with nonfat dry milk. What is the primary purpose for fortifying Mr. Tyson's milk in this manner?
    ○ 1. To increase the digestibility of the milk
    ○ 2. To increase the calories without increasing the protein content
    ○ 3. To increase the absorption of nutrients into the bloodstream
    ○ 4. To increase the protein content without increasing the fat content

43 Mr. Tyson tells the nurse that contrary to his wife's comment, his accident was *not* due to excessive use of alcohol. Admitting personnel were also of the opinion that the use of alcohol may have played a role in the accident. A recommended technique to help determine whether a patient really means what he has said when you think he may not, is first to
    ○ 1. casually question the patient about what he has said.
    ○ 2. specifically request the patient to repeat what he has said.
    ○ 3. carefully observe what the patient is communicating by nonverbal means.
    ○ 4. politely explain that you are having difficulty believing what the patient has said.

In addition to Mr. Tyson, the nurse is helping with the care of 3 other patients who are also between 50 and 65 years of age.

44 If the 4 patients made the following comments to the nurse, which comment demonstrates that the patient is probably meeting the developmental task typical of his age in the most satisfactory way?
    ○ 1. "I hope I will recover soon enough to help with our community United Way drive."

   ○ 2. "I can hardly wait to retire so that my wife and I can do the traveling we have always wanted to do."

   ○ 3. "I don't mind so much being 55 years old; it's better than 70. But my best years were those between 20 and 30."

   ○ 4. "I'm glad there is a television set in this room. I watch a lot of television since the children are grown and away from home."

A Nurse in the Labor Room Hears Ms. Stella Hardy Call, "Nurse, the Baby is Coming." The Nurse is Alone and No One is Available to Help. The Nurse Prepares to Deliver the Baby.

45 Which of the following admonitions should the nurse observe when she determines that she must deliver Ms. Hardy?

   ○ 1. Never manipulate a cord around the infant's neck.

   ○ 2. Never hold back the infant's head to prevent birth.

   ○ 3. Never aspirate mucus until after the infant is delivered.

   ○ 4. Never rupture membranes until after the infant is delivered.

46 After inspecting Ms. Hardy's perineum and determining that delivery is imminent, the nurse should then

   ○ 1. have the patient hold her legs together tightly.

   ○ 2. stretch the vaginal opening with a gloved hand.

   ○ 3. place clean linens on which the infant is to be delivered.

   ○ 4. turn the patient onto her side while she takes deep breaths.

47 In relation to Ms. Hardy's contractions, the time when it is best for the nurse to deliver the infant's head is

   ○ 1. between contractions.

   ○ 2. near the end of a contraction.

   ○ 3. at the height of a contraction.

   ○ 4. at the very onset of a contraction.

48 After the delivery of the placenta, a technique that helps to stimulate contractions of Ms. Hardy's uterus is to

   ○ 1. massage the mother's uterus.

   ○ 2. have the mother bend her knees sharply.

   ○ 3. drop the head of the bed below the level of the mother's pelvis.

   ○ 4. turn the mother to her side while she assumes a fetal position.

Soon after delivery, the nurse assesses Ms. Hardy's uterus and finds it to be displaced to one side and at a level above the umbilicus.

49 The most likely reason for the position of Ms. Hardy's uterus is that the

   ○ 1. uterus contains clots.

   ○ 2. urinary bladder is full.

○ 3. placenta was not completely expelled.
○ 4. rectum was not emptied before delivery.

Thirty-One-Year-Old Mr. Quady, Who Has Hodgkin's Disease, Receives Chemotherapy in a Health Clinic.

50 Mechlorethamine (Mustargen), an alkylating agent, is given to Mr. Quady. This pharmaceutical agent affects malignant cells by
○ 1. destroying them.
○ 2. slowing their division.
○ 3. interfering with their metabolism.
○ 4. decreasing their enzyme-producing abilities.

51 If Mr. Quady has an adverse effect to the mechlorethamine, he is most likely to experience
○ 1. double vision.
○ 2. marked depression.
○ 3. fever and dyspnea.
○ 4. nausea and vomiting.

52 During one visit, Mr. Quady tells the nurse that he is fearful of his prognosis. A guideline recommended most often to help patients who are demonstrating emotional responses to illness is for the nurse to
○ 1. attempt to direct the patient's thoughts into more constructive channels.
○ 2. reassure the patient that his feelings are typical of those of most patients.
○ 3. listen to the patient while giving him opportunities to express his feelings.
○ 4. help the patient understand that his feelings are standing in the way of recovery.

Jane Morgan Has Mononucleosis. She is at Home Where a Home-Care Nurse Visits to Discuss Jane's Care With Her and Her Parents.

53 The nurse notes on information from Jane's health record that a blood test reveals lymphocytosis. This means that Jane's blood contains
○ 1. numerous ruptured lymphocytes.
○ 2. a below-average number of lymphocytes.
○ 3. an above-average number of lymphocytes.
○ 4. numerous abnormally shaped lymphocytes.

54 What type of isolation techniques, if any, should the nurse discuss with Jane and her parents?

○ 1. Blood precautions
○ 2. Secretion precautions
○ 3. Respiratory precautions
○ 4. No isolation techniques are used

55 The nurse should teach that during her convalescence, Jane will need to cope with feeling very
○ 1. tired.
○ 2. restless.
○ 3. anorectic.
○ 4. depressed.

56 Jane's school classmates are very likely to refer to her illness as a
○ 1. "dose."
○ 2. "bad trip."
○ 3. kissing disease.
○ 4. walking disease.

57 Near the end of the nurse's visit, Jane, who is 14 years old, engages in a conversation in which she poses a variety of questions to the nurse. Which one of the following questions illustrates best that Jane is striving to meet a developmental task typical of her age?
○ 1. "Who am I?"
○ 2. "Is God real?"
○ 3. "Do my parents really love me?"
○ 4. "Is our society destroying itself?"

58 Before the nurse leaves, Ms. Morgan tells her that she is fearful that Jane's 16-year-old brother is using marijuana. The sign Ms. Morgan will most likely describe if her son is using marijuana is that he
○ 1. has very red eyes.
○ 2. complains of poor appetite.
○ 3. suffers with bouts of diarrhea.
○ 4. drinks copious amounts of water.

Mr. Gregor, Who is 60 Years Old and Has Angina Pectoris, is Hospitalized. He Complains of Severe Attacks of Pain that Are Becoming Increasingly Frequent.

59 The pain associated with angina pectoris of which Mr. Gregor complains is caused by a
○ 1. stenosis of the aorta.
○ 2. sudden rise in blood pressure.
○ 3. sudden dilatation of coronary arteries.
○ 4. lack of blood supply to heart muscles.

60 While the admitting nurse is interviewing Mr. Gregor, he describes an event to the nurse which, he states, ". . . almost always brings on an

attack of pain." The experience that is most likely to precipitate an attack is when this patient

- ○ 1. snores.
- ○ 2. skips a meal.
- ○ 3. loses his temper.
- ○ 4. stoops to put on socks.

61 When the nurse obtains Mr. Gregor's health history upon admission, Mr. Gregor describes a life-style that includes the activities given below. Which activity should Mr. Gregor be advised to *discontinue*?

- ○ 1. Driving a car
- ○ 2. Drinking beer
- ○ 3. Smoking cigarettes
- ○ 4. Working during nighttime hours

62 Mr. Gregor's pulse pressure is obtained. The pulse pressure is best defined as

- ○ 1. pressure of blood against capillary walls.
- ○ 2. pressure of blood against the wall of the aorta.
- ○ 3. difference between the venous and the arterial blood pressure.
- ○ 4. difference between the systolic and the diastolic blood pressure.

Nitroglycerin in an ointment and dispensed in a disk is applied to Mr. Gregor's skin (transdermal administration).

63 Which of the following guidelines should the nurse use when she applies the disk containing nitroglycerin to Mr. Gregor's skin?

- ○ 1. The nurse should massage the ointment into the skin.
- ○ 2. The nurse should avoid getting ointment on her skin.
- ○ 3. The nurse should keep away from fumes arising from the ointment.
- ○ 4. The nurse should place the ointment on the same area with each application.

64 The nurse should judge that the dosage of nitroglycerin is very probably too large for Mr. Gregor when the patient's skin becomes flushed and he has a

- ○ 1. fever.
- ○ 2. throbbing headache.
- ○ 3. decrease in urine production.
- ○ 4. tingling sensation in the extremities.

Ms. Doan, a Multigravida, is Admitted to a Hospital. She is in Labor But Early in the First Stage.

65 The nurse notes the following admission order for Ms. Doan: Meperidine hydrochloride (Demerol) 200 mg IM, as necessary. The nurse should question the order before administering the drug because

○ 1. meperidine hydrochloride and Demerol are not the same drug.
○ 2. the route is unusual. This drug is ordinarily given orally during labor.
○ 3. the drug is unusual. This drug is ordinarily used only late in labor.
○ 4. the dosage is unusual. The drug's usual adult dosage is between 50 mg and 100 mg.

66 The nurse assesses Ms. Doan shortly after admission and obtains the findings described below. Which one should the nurse report to the nurse-in-charge promptly?
○ 1. The patient requests that she be moved from her side to her back.
○ 2. The patient's vaginal discharge of amniotic fluid appears yellow green in color.
○ 3. The patient refuses to have a prescribed analgesic despite strong contractions.
○ 4. The patient's blood pressure has risen from 126/80 to 132/84 mm Hg in the last 30 minutes.

67 The nurse-in-charge determines that Ms. Doan's cervical dilatation is 7 cm. Which of the following nursing measures is *contraindicated* for Ms. Doan?
○ 1. Giving an enema
○ 2. Obtaining a urine specimen
○ 3. Carrying out a perineal preparation
○ 4. Listening for fetal heart tones with a fetoscope

Ms. Doan delivers a baby girl. The nurse starts Ms. Doan's postpartum care.

68 Ms. Doan's blood pressure is 130/80 mm Hg when she leaves the delivery room. If her blood pressure 45 minutes later is 106/60 mm Hg, the nurse should
○ 1. notify the nurse-in-charge.
○ 2. start oxygen therapy.
○ 3. elevate the head of the bed slightly.
○ 4. give a p.r.n. medication for discomfort.

69 The nurse checks Ms. Doan's lochia and notes that it is very scant in amount. A likely reason for Ms. Doan's scant lochia is that the patient's
○ 1. body fluids are depleted.
○ 2. uterus is filling with blood.
○ 3. placenta is partially retained.
○ 4. breasts are filling rapidly with milk.

70 Nursing measures are used to help prevent Ms. Doan from developing thrombophlebitis during the postpartum period. Which of the following measures is *contraindicated*?

  ○ 1. Elevating the legs
  ○ 2. Massaging the legs
  ○ 3. Moving the legs in bed
  ○ 4. Using antiembolism stockings

71 If Ms. Doan bleeds excessively, the nurse can expect the nature of Ms. Doan's pulse to be
  ○ 1. rapid and thready.
  ○ 2. slow and difficult to palpate.
  ○ 3. intermittently rapid and slow.
  ○ 4. near normal in rate but bounding.

The remaining items in this situation relate to the care of Ms. Doan's baby girl.

72 Ms. Doan will bottle-feed her infant. The nutrient that is *lower* in cow's milk, when compared with human milk, is
  ○ 1. fat.
  ○ 2. iron.
  ○ 3. protein.
  ○ 4. carbohydrate.

73 Ms. Doan is upset when she notices that her infant has a small bloody spot in her diaper. The nurse examines the baby and finds it to be a normal discharge. The nurse should explain to the mother that the discharge is from the infant's
  ○ 1. rectum, and is due to irritation of meconium on intestinal mucosa.
  ○ 2. rectum, and is due to capillary breaks from pressure during delivery.
  ○ 3. vagina, and is due to capillary breaks from pressure during delivery.
  ○ 4. vagina, and is due to a hormonal reaction on the infant's uterine lining.

74 Phototherapy is ordered for Baby Girl Doan. The most likely reason for this therapy is that the infant has
  ○ 1. thrush.
  ○ 2. cyanotic skin.
  ○ 3. jaundiced skin.
  ○ 4. congenital syphilis.

75 Before applying phototherapy, the nurse should prepare Baby Girl Doan by covering the infant's
  ○ 1. scalp.
  ○ 2. cord.
  ○ 3. eyes.
  ○ 4. fontanels.

Ms. Lamato, Who is 71 Years Old, Seeks Health Care When She Notices that She is Very Thirsty and Voids Frequently. It is Found that Ms. Lamato Has Diabetes Mellitus.

76 Ms. Lamato asks the nurse, "Why am I so thirsty and then have to go to the bathroom so often?" The nurse explains correctly when she tells the patient that these two symptoms illustrate the body's attempt to
○ 1. detoxify ketone bodies.
○ 2. rid itself of excess glucose.
○ 3. stimulate insulin production.
○ 4. metabolize excess fat accumulations.

Ms. Lamato is to take the oral hypoglycemic, tolbutamide (Orinase), and is to test her urine for glycosuria (glucose in the urine).

77 The pharmaceutical agent, tolbutamide, is intended to function in Ms. Lamato's body to stimulate the
○ 1. liver to store glucose.
○ 2. kidneys to excrete glucose.
○ 3. pancreas to secrete insulin.
○ 4. digestive processes to metabolize carbohydrates.

78 The nurse teaches Ms. Lamato to test a second voided specimen of urine when she is testing for glycosuria. A second voided specimen is used primarily because it is more likely to
○ 1. be free of sediment.
○ 2. be alkaline in nature.
○ 3. contain more glucose than a first voided specimen.
○ 4. demonstrate the current level of glucose being excreted by the kidneys.

A teaching plan for Ms. Lamato includes instructions concerning various aspects of her health care.

79 An example of a dietary item that Ms. Lamato should be taught to take if she develops symptoms of hypoglycemia (hyperinsulinism) is
○ 1. milk.
○ 2. honey.
○ 3. an apple.
○ 4. tomato juice.

80 Which of the following foods can Ms. Lamato eat as desired without taking the food into account when she uses an exchange diet?
○ 1. Rice
○ 2. Olives

○ 3. Watermelon
○ 4. Cranberries

81 Ms. Lamato should be taught that of the following areas of her body, the area of which she should be especially mindful to take proper hygienic care is her
○ 1. feet.
○ 2. scalp.
○ 3. hands.
○ 4. mouth.

82 Ms. Lamato is also taught early symptoms that are likely to occur in her legs when the arteries fail to supply sufficient blood to the leg muscles. One common symptom is a type of discomfort best described as
○ 1. cramping pain.
○ 2. tingling pain.
○ 3. psychogenic pain.
○ 4. phantom-limb pain.

83 The nurse stresses the importance of Ms. Lamato's continuing need for health care. The nurse bases this teaching for Ms. Lamato on knowledge that one of the greatest risks among persons using oral hypoglycemic agents is that these diabetics often tend to develop
○ 1. chronic hypoglycemia.
○ 2. severe insulin-dependent diabetes.
○ 3. sensitivities to hypoglycemic agents.
○ 4. casual attitudes toward their disease.

Mr. John Hutton, 57 Years Old, is Admitted to a Substance-Abuse Center for Help in Overcoming Alcohol Abuse.

84 The person who is usually most instrumental in convincing an alcoholic like Mr. Hutton that he needs help and must enter a substance-abuse center is the
○ 1. alcoholic's spouse.
○ 2. alcoholic's clergyman.
○ 3. alcoholic person himself.
○ 4. counselor where the alcoholic works.

85 What is the primary physical effect of alcohol on Mr. Hutton's body?
○ 1. Alcohol stimulates the cerebral cortex.
○ 2. Alcohol depresses the central nervous system.
○ 3. Alcohol decreases the irritability of muscle cells.
○ 4. Alcohol increases activity in the gastrointestinal tract.

86 The nurse learns that Ms. Hutton has taken over most of the family's home chores ordinarily done by Mr. Hutton in the past and has

purposefully avoided social gatherings while making various excuses when her husband was likely to embarrass the family. What effect, if any, does Ms. Hutton's behavior have on Mr. Hutton's alcoholism?

○ 1. The patient has been belittled by his wife's behavior.

○ 2. The patient has been enabled to continue with alcoholism because of his wife's behavior.

○ 3. The patient has been made increasingly aware of his alcoholism because of his wife's behavior.

○ 4. There is no convincing evidence that a spouse's behavior has an effect on an alcoholic's behavior.

87   Mr. Hutton tells the nurse he wishes to quit smoking but has tried in the past, only to have failed in his efforts. In this situation, it would be best for the nurse to

○ 1. take the cigarettes from the patient's room.

○ 2. describe the dangers of continuing to smoke cigarettes.

○ 3. explain how much better the patient will feel when he quits smoking cigarettes.

○ 4. provide the patient with information concerning resources for help in quitting smoking cigarettes.

Twenty-Five-Year-Old Mr. Jim Dunn is in a Motorcycle Accident. He Has a Compound Fracture of the Bone in His Right Thigh and an Open Wound on His Left Lower Leg.

88   The name of the bone that is fractured in Mr. Dunn's right leg is the

○ 1. femur.

○ 2. tibia.

○ 3. fibula.

○ 4. humerus.

89   Before moving Mr. Dunn from the site of the accident, first aid care most certainly should include

○ 1. lowering the patient's head to prevent shock.

○ 2. elevating the patient's fractured leg to prevent edema.

○ 3. splinting the patient's fractured leg to immobilize the broken bone.

○ 4. removing debris from the area of the patient's fracture to prevent infection.

90   While Mr. Dunn is being transported in an ambulance to a hospital, the open wound on his left leg begins to bleed profusely. It is best to handle the bleeding by first

○ 1. placing pressure bandages on the bleeding area.

○ 2. irrigating the wound with normal saline solution.

○ 3. splinting the leg in the area of the bleeding wound.

○ 4. applying a tourniquet above the level of the wound.

After emergency care is administered, an open reduction is done and a cast is applied to Mr. Dunn's right leg.

91 Of the following nursing measures, which one is *inappropriate* when caring for the still-wet cast on Mr. Dunn's right leg?
- ○ 1. A cradle is used to keep bed linens off the cast.
- ○ 2. An electric fan is directed onto the cast to help it dry.
- ○ 3. Waterproof material is placed around the cast to protect bed linens.
- ○ 4. The cast is elevated in bed on several pillows to prevent edema.

92 The nurse compresses the nailbeds of Mr. Dunn's toes while assessing the casted leg. The primary purpose for the nurse's action is to help determine whether
- ○ 1. the cast is too tight.
- ○ 2. an infection is developing.
- ○ 3. a pulse rate is perceptible.
- ○ 4. drainage from the wound is present.

Tim Elbert, Who is 5 Years Old, is Prepared to Have a Tonsillectomy.

93 Tim is given atropine sulfate preoperatively at 7 A.M. When surgery has to be delayed for about a half hour, Tim remains in his room. The nurse can expect that before he is transported to the operating room, he is most likely to complain of being
- ○ 1. cold.
- ○ 2. dizzy.
- ○ 3. thirsty.
- ○ 4. nauseated.

Tim's tonsillectomy is completed and he is returned to his room.

94 Tim is placed in a semi-prone position in bed. The primary reason for positioning Tim in this manner is to help
- ○ 1. minimize nausea and vomiting.
- ○ 2. relieve pressure on the operative site.
- ○ 3. promote drainage from the nose and mouth.
- ○ 4. prevent the tongue from obstructing the airway.

95 If the nurse makes the following observations about Tim during his early postoperative hours, the one that the nurse should judge as being most probably due to excessive bleeding is when the child
- ○ 1. swallows frequently.
- ○ 2. spits out dark blood.
- ○ 3. vomits mucoid material.
- ○ 4. complains of severe pain in the throat.

Mr. Charles York, 70 Years Old, is Terminally Ill with Widespread Metastasis of an Adenocarcinoma. Tumors on Vertebrae Have Caused Sufficient Pressure on Nerves So that He is Now Paraplegic (Paralyzed Below the Waist). A Nurse Plans and Administers Care to Mr. York in His Home.

96   It is particularly important that the nurse plan care for Mr. York that includes nursing measures to help prevent
- O 1. dehydration.
- O 2. pressure sores.
- O 3. bowel incontinence.
- O 4. ulceration of oral mucosa.

97   The nurse administers methadone hydrochloride to Mr. York regularly. If Mr. York presents the symptoms below, the methadone is intended primarily for the relief of
- O 1. pain.
- O 2. anxiety.
- O 3. anorexia.
- O 4. insomnia.

98   Mr. York's oral body temperature is obtained with a glass thermometer. It is recommended that the nurse clean the thermometer after each use with
- O 1. soap and water.
- O 2. hydrogen peroxide.
- O 3. a dry cotton ball.
- O 4. household bleach.

99   Mr. York complains that his feet are cold and he wishes to use a warm water bag to warm them. The nurse should use a thermometer to be sure that the water in the bag is no warmer than
- O 1. 100°F (38°C).
- O 2. 110°F (43°C).
- O 3. 115°F (46°C).
- O 4. 120°F (49°C).

100   Heparin is administered subcutaneously to Mr. York. Which of the following techniques is *contraindicated* when administering this drug to Mr. York?
- O 1. Using a pledget moistened with alcohol to cleanse the injection site before administering the drug
- O 2. Inserting the needle at a 45 to 90 degree angle when administering the drug
- O 3. Massaging the injection site after administering the drug
- O 4. Rotating the injection site between administrations of the drug

101   The nurse prepares to obtain an apical pulse rate on Mr. York. From the sketch below, select the best site for obtaining the apical pulse rate?

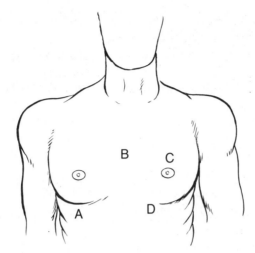

○ 1. Site A
○ 2. Site B
○ 3. Site C
○ 4. Site D

102 Mr. York's friend visits him each evening when he and she can be alone in his room and when, Mr. York tells the nurse, "We can express our love for each other." Which of the following comments would be most appropriate for the nurse to make in this situation?
○ 1. "Would you like to discuss with me what you two do?"
○ 2. "You must be very happy to be loved and to have someone to love."
○ 3. "The type of behavior you describe is unusual for a person of your age."
○ 4. "Do you think the two of you should discuss your desires for each other with your children?"

It is determined that Mr. York has urinary retention with overflow and an indwelling catheter will be used.

103 Urinary retention with overflow means that Mr. York is producing urine but
○ 1. the patient voids small amounts at frequent intervals.
○ 2. urine constantly dribbles when the bladder does not store urine.
○ 3. the patient is unable to empty the bladder completely with voidings.
○ 4. urine is retained in the bladder until small amounts of urine eventually leak through the urethra.

104 It is very important for the nurse to plan to lubricate the indwelling catheter generously before inserting it primarily because, when compared with the female urethra, the male urethra is longer and
○ 1. narrower.
○ 2. more fragile.

○ 3. more tortuous.

○ 4. part of the reproductive system.

105 Which of the following findings should indicate to the nurse that Mr. York's indwelling catheter is in need of changing.

○ 1. Urine output slowly decreases while fluid intake remains essentially unchanged.

○ 2. Urine output occurs in larger amounts during certain hours during the day than during other hours.

○ 3. Cloudiness of urine is noted in the transparent connector at the end of the indwelling catheter.

○ 4. Sandy particles are freed when the drainage tubing is rolled between the nurse's fingers.

Two-Year-Old Karl Ester Has Wilms' Tumor.

106 The area of attack by a Wilm's tumor in Karl's body is the

○ 1. brain.

○ 2. kidney.

○ 3. rectum.

○ 4. stomach.

107 Which of the following nursing measures is *contraindicated* when caring for Karl?

○ 1. Rocking the child

○ 2. Bathing the child's abdomen

○ 3. Patting the child's back.

○ 4. Taking the child's temperature rectally.

A Nurse Works in An Emergency-Care Unit and Helps With the Care of Adults Admitted to the Facility.

108 It is determined that Ms. Theresa Cleaver, 42 years old, requires cardiopulmonary resuscitation (CPR). Before the nurse starts rescue breathing, Ms. Cleaver's head should be placed so that her neck is in a position of

○ 1. extension.

○ 2. slight flexion.

○ 3. slight rotation.

○ 4. hyperextension.

109 The nurse notes that Ms. Cleaver's chest wall does not rise and fall with each rescue breath. The most probable cause is that the

○ 1. airway of the patient is not open.

○ 2. rescue efforts are no longer helpful.

○ 3. cardiac compressions are too shallow.

○ 4. rescue breaths are being given too slowly.

110 The nurse notes that the second rescuer is using the following techniques while administering cardiac compressions to Ms. Cleaver. The technique that is in *error* is when the second rescuer

○ 1. interlocks his fingers.

○ 2. brings his shoulders directly over his hands.

○ 3. places one hand directly over his other hand.

○ 4. flexes his elbows slightly while administering pressure.

111 Ms. Cleaver is to receive an intramuscular injection. The patient is now breathing easily and is conscious. The deltoid muscle will be used. Before injecting the needle, it is best for the nurse to

○ 1. bunch the muscle in her hand.

○ 2. pull the muscle taut in her hand.

○ 3. push the muscle to one side with her fingers.

○ 4. have the patient clench her fist to enlarge the muscle.

112 The nurse uses proper technique when the angle of the needle and syringe she uses to give Ms. Cleaver the medication is

○ 1. between 5 and 15 degrees.

○ 2. between 20 and 40 degrees.

○ 3. 45 degrees.

○ 4. 90 degrees.

113 Mr. Thomas Abbott is admitted following an accident that occurred while he was riding horseback. Of the following signs, the one that should most certainly suggest to the nurse that Mr. Abbott probably has a spinal cord injury is that the patient is

○ 1. unable to swallow.

○ 2. unable to move his lower extremities.

○ 3. without a pulse in his lower extremities.

○ 4. noted to have marked cyanosis of the skin of his lower body.

114 Twenty-four-year-old Ms. Sara Gander has ingested a poisonous substance. Inducing Ms. Gander to vomit is most certainly *contraindicated* if she has ingested

○ 1. alcohol.

○ 2. aspirin.

○ 3. kerosene.

○ 4. poisonous mushrooms.

115 Ms. Louise Dodd calls the emergency facility because she has found that her husband, 49-year-old Mr. John Dodd, has taken an unknown quantity of secobarbital (Seconal). Ms. Dodd asks the nurse what she should do while she waits for an ambulance to take her husband to the emergency facility. In this situation, the nurse should instruct Ms. Dodd to start first aid treatment by trying to

○ 1. induce her husband to vomit.

○ 2. make her husband eat burned toast.

    ○ 3. start artificial ventilation on her husband.

    ○ 4. give her husband copious amounts of water.

116 Twenty-six-year-old Mr. George Busher is brought to the emergency facility by ambulance. If Mr. Busher presents the following symptoms, the one having highest priority in terms of first aid care is

    ○ 1. anuria.

    ○ 2. hemorrhaging.

    ○ 3. projectile vomiting.

    ○ 4. a high body temperature.

The Remaining Items are Individual Items.

117 If a nurse is caring for the following persons, for which one should she check for cyanosis by examining the person's mucous membranes?

    ○ 1. For a redheaded person

    ○ 2. For a dark-skinned person

    ○ 3. For an unconscious person

    ○ 4. For a white-skinned (albinism) person

118 Which of the following proverbs becomes the best guide when interviewing and examining an elderly person?

    ○ 1. Haste makes waste.

    ○ 2. Every cloud has a silver lining.

    ○ 3. Cast not stones from a glass house.

    ○ 4. God helps those who help themselves.

119 Authorities believe that the single best way to prevent nosocomial infections, that is, infections acquired in a health agency, is for health caretakers to use proper

    ○ 1. sterile techniques.

    ○ 2. isolation techniques.

    ○ 3. handwashing procedures.

    ○ 4. sterilization procedures.

120 The use of which of the following pieces of patient-care equipment is most often found to predispose a patient to acquiring a nosocomial infection?

    ○ 1. A stethoscope

    ○ 2. A sphygmomanometer

    ○ 3. A urethral catheter

    ○ 4. A clinical thermometer

Correct Answers and Rationales

Two numbers appear in parentheses following each rationale. The first number identifies the textbook listed in the references, page 649, and the second number identifies the page(s) in that textbook where the correct answer can be verified. Occasionally, two textbooks are given for verifying the correct answer.

Caring for a Child Who is a "Near-Drowning" Victim

1 1.   Neurological damage results when "near-drowning" victims suffer from a prolonged below-normal blood oxygen level (hypoxemia). The damage is caused by poor nourishment of brain cells and tissues. Prolonged increased intracranial pressure and below normal blood sugar levels may lead to brain damage but these causes do not play a role in the "near-drowning" victim. The presence of high levels of blood potassium is not a factor in the care of the child described in this item.   (15:209)

2 3.   It is best for the nurse caring for a patient with neurological damage to speak to the patient before touching him and explain what she is going to do. The child described in this item responds even though he cannot talk. It is best to assume he does understand. Speaking slowly, keeping eye contact, and using simple language are recommended. Playtime is satisfactory but not necessarily indicated before giving nursing care. To promote family relationships, it is preferable to have parents at hand during care times if they wish to stay; this practice also offers good teaching opportunities for the nurse.   (9:26)

3 3.   Suctioning a tracheostomy should not be continuous for more than 10 seconds, or at most 15 seconds. Suctioning for longer periods is likely to cause respiratory distress because the suctioning removes needed oxygen along with the mucus and other debris. Some authorities recommend that the nurse use suctioning for a period no longer than she can comfortably hold her breath, which usually amounts to about 10 to 15 seconds. Correct techniques include oxygenating the patient for a minute or two before and after suctioning a tracheostomy, avoiding suctioning while inserting the catheter, and rotating the catheter when withdrawing it.   (9:620)

4 1.   Raw eggs are unsafe because they often harbor salmonella organisms that can cause serious food poisoning. Using pasteurized powdered eggs is recommended for gastrostomy feedings. Blood cholesterol levels are not of primary importance at this time for the child described in this item. Raw eggs are unlikely to cause regurgitation of stomach content or obstructions at the pyloric sphincter.   (4:360)

5 2.   To protect the skin around a gastrostomy stoma, it is recommended that an ointment, such as zinc oxide, be used. Pastes, lotions, and antiseptics do not offer firm protective coatings to withstand the irritating effects of stomach secretions.   (15:441)

6   2.   Play serves many functions for children, including for the brain-damaged child. For the child at home, including the family in appropriate ways helps strengthen family relationships and demonstrates love and caring. Using flash cards for number games is least appropriate for a 3½-year-old child with brain damage.   (12:57, 511)

Caring for a Patient with Osteoarthritis

7   4.   Unlike rheumatoid arthritis, osteoarthritis presents no systemic symptoms, such as fever and general malaise. Osteoarthritis is a degenerative joint disease that is an affliction of aging. Stiffness of joints is especially common. The joints may become painful in time.   (12:615; 15:181)

8   4.   A typical side-effect when ibuprofen (Motrin) is used is gastrointestinal disturbances. Other adverse effects include dizziness, headaches, drowsiness, tinnitus, skin rash, and fluid retention.   (14:231)

9   4.   Heat receptors, as well as cold receptors, can adjust to temperatures when the temperature is not extreme. Patients often complain that hot or cold applications are too cool or not cool enough after applications have been on for a period of time. Actually, the temperature of the application may still be satisfactory, but the patient's receptors have adjusted to the temperature. Heat and cold receptors are widely distributed in the skin and connective tissues. Pain receptors are found in free nerve endings, but this is irrelevant to the situation described in this item.   (9:420–421; 15:182)

10   4.   Potatoes are a poor source of protein. Nuts, peas, and beans are good sources of protein although they contain incomplete proteins, that is, they contain amino acids but not all the essential ones in sufficient amounts. Non-meat proteins that are complete include eggs, milk, and cheese.   (16:386)

Caring for a Woman Who is Receiving Prenatal Care

11   3.   Feeling dizziness and faintness late in pregnancy is often due to supine hypotensive syndrome, caused by a low blood pressure that occurs when the uterine contents cause pressure on large abdominal blood vessels. Moving quickly from the reclining to the sitting position and from the sitting to the standing position often causes faintness and dizziness because blood is slow to reach the head. Moving slowly from one position to another helps avoid the symptoms. Lying in bed on the left side, which moves weight of the uterus off abdominal blood vessels, often helps also to prevent this discomfort of pregnancy. (12:448)

12 4. Heartburn often can be relieved when pregnant women alter their eating habits by having small but more frequent meals. The burning sensation is caused by stomach contents spilling back into the esophagus. (2:122)

13 4. Showers are recommended late in pregnancy primarily because a pregnant woman's center of gravity changes as the uterus becomes large. This change makes it relatively easy to fall when stepping in and out of a tub. (12:445)

14 4. Antiembolism stockings should be put on the first thing in the morning, after awakening, and before starting activity for the day. This technique places support on veins before they become engorged with blood. They should be removed at bedtime. (2:125)

Caring for a Patient with Breast Cancer

15 4. During a right breast examination, the patient should be positioned by having her lie down, placing a pillow under her right shoulder, and placing her right hand under her head. This positioning helps distribute breast tissues on the chest wall evenly and makes examination of tissues convenient and more thorough. (15:582)

16 3. Many women dread having a mastectomy because of a fear of feeling less feminine and less attractive as a sex partner. Such fears as a psychological inability to fight cancer, an inaccuracy in laboratory reports, and disuse of the arm on the affected side figure less prominently but may occur in some women. (15:583)

17 3. Postmastectomy patients are taught to exercise the arm actively on the affected side. The exercises may need to be started with some help, but active exercises are recommended. Certain activities of daily living should be encouraged, such as brushing the teeth and combing the hair, to further exercise the arm. (12:754–755; 15:587)

18 4. Men develop breast cancer, just as women do, and it can metastasize. Treatment is similar as when women have breast cancer. However, the disease occurs much less frequently in men than it does in women. Men are now being advised to examine their breasts regularly for abnormal lumps, just as women are. (15:580)

19 2. A comment that reflects on the patient's words gives the patient an opportunity to express and describe feelings. In the situation described in this item, the patient can be given an opportunity to explore her feelings further. It is not helpful to the patient when a nurse suggests other topics of conversation or suggests delaying conversation, nor is it helpful to give advice when a patient is trying to express feelings. (9:658)

20 2. Health caretakers aim to conquer illness at all costs and are committed to supporting life. Therefore, when a decision is made to withdraw life-support systems and to deny attempts to resuscitate, many caretakers experience psychological discomfort. The discomfort is most often described to be the result of health caretakers' thinking they have been defeated in their work. Policies and such laws that exist that relate to stopping therapy when death appears inevitable offer health caretakers guidelines but not necessarily psychological comfort. (6:19)

21 2. The so-called death rattle is caused by the accumulation of secretions in the airway. Placing the patient in a position so that secretions can drain more easily, such as in a side-lying position, and using suction as necessary are recommended. (9:662)

22 2. In the situation described in this item, the husband is expressing grief. It is best for the nurse to allow the husband an opportunity to express his feelings. Offering explanations, suggesting that a clergyman be called, and changing the subject are poor alternative courses of action. (9:667)

Caring for a Child with Rheumatic Fever

23 3. Rheumatic fever is usually a sequela of an illness caused by a group A beta-hemolytic streptococcal infection. Most often, a youngster with rheumatic fever has had a sore throat relatively recently. Rheumatic fever is a serious disease and is the most frequent cause of acquired heart disease in children. (3:243)

24 1. It is essential that a child ill with rheumatic fever have complete bed rest to help prevent heart disease. This means that the child should do nothing for herself and should be fed, bathed, toileted, and the like. Exercise would tend to aggravate the discomfort in joints because of polyarthritis, which is common when the patient is acutely ill with rheumatic fever. (3:245)

25 2. A typical sign of toxicity when salicylate therapy is used is a ringing in the ears, called tinnitus. A child is likely to state that she hears funny noises in her ears when she has tinnitus. Other symptoms of salicylate toxicity include nausea, vomiting, and headaches. Salicylates also can cause gastric burning and even bleeding of gastric mucosa. The symptoms of toxicity should be reported promptly when they occur so that appropriate adjustments can be made in therapy. (3:245)

26 1. Between about ages 6 and 12 years, children seek success through achievement. They tend to enjoy school and competitive team activities. Without opportunities to achieve success, a youngster is likely to develop feelings of inferiority. During these years, there is a moving away from the close relationship with the primary caretaker that existed earlier in life and a "best friend" is likely to be a child of about the same age. Usually, elementary school children appear to be happier in relationships with children of their own sex than in relationships with children of the opposite sex.   (3:95)

Caring for a Patient with Glaucoma

27   4.   Before measuring intraocular pressure in the eyes with a tonometer, the nurse should be prepared to place a topical anesthetic in the eyes. The drops are placed on the exposed lower conjunctival sac. The anesthetic numbs the surface of the eyes so that the tonometer can be placed directly onto the eye surface without discomfort to the patient. No other preparation is required to obtain intraocular pressure.   (9:236)

28   1.   Pilocarpine, a cholinergic drug, acts to constrict the pupils of the eyes. This action allows better drainage of ocular fluid from the eyes, thus reducing intraocular pressure.   (14:49)

29   3.   Timolol maleate (Timoptic) is a beta-blocking agent. When used in solution for eyedrops, it is believed that this drug helps reduce intraocular pressure by reducing aqueous formation in the eyes.   (15:268)

30   3.   If a person with glaucoma does not use health care to prevent excessive pressure in the eyes, a typical symptom is impaired peripheral, or tunnel, vision. Also vision becomes blurred and halos around objects are likely to occur. Damage to the eyes due to glaucoma is irreversible. The final result of untreated or poorly treated glaucoma is blindness. Glaucoma is the second most common cause of blindness in this country.   (12:800; 15:267)

Caring for a Patient Who is Depressed

31   2.   It is particularly important to watch patients who are depressed for signs of suicidal tendencies. This is also true of dejected persons. Depressed patients are unlikely to recover spontaneously. They tend to direct feelings inwardly rather than outwardly to others. Their psychomotor activities are typically reduced.   (1:199; 12:847)

32   2.   A patient who is derogatory of herself needs someone who accepts her and can reassure her of her personal worth. Acceptance shows respect for the worth of a person; everyone, the well person as well as the ill person, needs to enjoy being accepted.   (1:199)

33   3.   Tricyclics, such as amitriptyline (Elavil), tend to cause hypotensive reactions, especially in elderly persons. The person should be cautioned not to stand up quickly after lying down because of this hypotensive side-effect.   (1:241; 14:219)

34   4.   A dangerous side-effect that may accompany the use of the drug tranylcypromine (Parnate), which is a monoamine oxidase (MAO) inhibitor, is a hypertensive crisis. Symptoms of the crisis include an elevated blood pressure and temperature, headaches, nausea, vomiting, chest pains, a slow heart rate, dilated pupils, and palpitations.   (1:241; 14:219)

35   1.   Foods containing tryamine or dopa can precipitate a hypertensive crisis in the person receiving an MAO inhibitor, such as tranylcypromine. The person should be cautioned against using beer, wine, and foods such as aged cheese, yeast products, chocolate, and chicken livers.   (1:241)

36   1.   Yogurt can be eaten safely when a patient is receiving tranylcypromine.   (1:241–242)

Caring for a Patient Who has Burns

37   1.   When a victim's clothing is on fire, it is recommended that the first course of action at the scene of the accident is to place the victim in a horizontal position on the ground and wrap the victim in a blanket or rug, or something similar, so that the fire is extinguished by smothering. The victim can also be rolled on the ground to help smother the fire if a blanket or rug is not readily available. Having the victim lie down helps to prevent fire, smoke, and hot air from entering his respiratory passages. These techniques work quickly and usually are the most convenient at the site of an accident involving burning. Rushing the victim about increases the flames. Using a fire extinguisher is likely to damage the tissue at the site of the burn even more. Placing the victim in a tub of water is too time-consuming and usually not convenient at the site of the accident.   (15:685)

38   3.   Ions of potassium tend to move from burned areas into the bloodstream with the result that serum potassium levels become elevated. Sodium levels are likely to decrease when the ion leaves the body in fluid lost at a burned site. Protein is also lost in large amounts from a burned area.   (15:686)

39   3.   When caring for the burn victim described in this item, the nurse should wear a cap, mask, and gown. Gloves are used, in addition to the cap, mask and gown, when caring for the patient's burned areas. Visitors should wear caps, masks and gowns also. These precautions are taken to help decrease problems with infection in the wounds.   (15:687)

40   3.   Typical sensations when mafenide (Sulfamylon) is applied to burned areas are burning and stinging. The patient should be prepared for this discomfort before the cream is applied.   (15:689)

41   3.   Tubbing a burned patient is ordinarily a painful procedure. Therefore, it is best to prepare a patient for tubbing by administering an analgesic about 30 minutes before the procedure, to help decrease the amount of discomfort. Preparation for tubbing does not include fasting, napping, or positioning the patient in a mid-Fowler's position.   (15:689)

42 4. Whole milk often is fortified with nonfat dry milk to increase the milk's protein content without increasing its fat content. Calories are also increased, which is ordinarily needed by a burned victim, but this is not the primary reason for giving the fortified milk in this situation. The fortified milk is no easier to digest or to absorb than whole milk.   (4:370; 16:331)

43 3. If a nurse suspects that a patient may be distorting the truth or may not be describing how he really feels about something, it is best to observe his nonverbal communication first. This type of observation can often help confirm suspicions without confronting the patient unnecessarily. It also provides time for the patient to develop confidence in the nurse–patient relationship so that he can better express himself. It may become necessary later in certain situations to follow this by asking for further explanations, but to suggest by comments or questions that you do not believe what the patient is saying is likely to destroy a helping relationship. (9:18–20)

44 1. Adults in middle age face choices and stresses just as persons of other ages do. Often, they find most satisfaction during these years when they use energies for the good of the family and also for the good of society in general. Many persons refer to this developmental task as the need for generativity, which is a need to do things worthwhile for society and of worth to those who come after them. Being concerned about helping with a community project illustrates that the person is probably meeting his needs for generativity very satisfactorily.   (15:25–27)

Caring for a Woman During an Emergency Delivery

45 2. The infant's head should not be held back to delay or prevent birth. If the cord is found to be around the infant's neck, it should be manipulated carefully and removed, if possible. The infant is receiving no blood when there is pressure on the cord, and this could threaten the infant's life. Mucus is aspirated as soon as the head is delivered. The membranes must be ruptured before birth when they have not done so spontaneously. If this is not done, the infant is likely to aspirate amniotic fluid and suffocate.   (12:494)

46 3. When an emergency delivery (also called a precipitate or spontaneous delivery) is imminent, if it is at all possible, the nurse should prepare a clean area on which to deliver the infant. This will help to prevent infection. Moving the patient to the delivery room is better, but often there is no time for this, especially when a nurse is alone.   (2:249)

47 1. To help prevent cerebral damage to the infant and lacerations in the mother, it is recommended that the infant's head be delivered between contractions. This decreases the danger of the effects of the strong expulsive force of a contraction on the baby and mother.   (2:251)

48   1.   Massaging the uterus causes contractions and helps to firm the uterus. This helps to prevent excessive bleeding following delivery.   (2:251)

49   2.   A full bladder will cause the uterus to rise above the level of the umbilicus, and it often can be found on one side of the abdomen when the mother is palpated. The uterus is unlikely to be as high as the umbilicus and displaced to one side because the uterus contains some clots, the placenta was not completely expelled, or the rectum was not emptied before delivery.   (2:285)

Caring for a Patient with Hodgkin's Disease

50   2.   Alkalyting agents are often used for a patient with certain malignant diseases, such as Hodgkin's disease, because they help slow the division of malignant cells. Antimetabolites are agents that interfere with the metabolism of malignant cells.   (14:198)

51   4.   Nausea and vomiting are commonly noted in the patient suffering with adverse effects to mechlorethamine (Mustargen). Other adverse effects include loss of hair, jaundice, skin rash, ringing in the ears, and diminished hearing.   (14:202)

52   3.   It is most often recommended that patients showing emotional responses to illness be given opportunities to bring their emotions to the surface while the nurse listens to what is being said. Techniques that are used to try to reassure the patient that his feelings are typical of others, to direct his thoughts into other channels, or to tell the patient his emotions could stand in the way of recovery tend to block communications. (9:18–20)

Caring for a Patient with Mononucleosis

53   3.   Lymphocytosis means that the number of lymphocytes in the blood is abnormally high. This finding is typical of infectious mononucleosis. A positive result for a heterophil agglutination test also is typical of the disease.   (15:342)

54   4.   No particular type of isolation techniques or precautions are ordinarily used for persons with infectious mononucleosis. However, precautions should be observed to prevent the person from acquiring a secondary infection.   (3:282; 12:557)

55   1.   Feeling tired and weak are common during convalescence following a bout with infectious mononucleosis. The patient should be prepared to take rest periods as necessary and plan to return to usual activities gradually. Restlessness, anorexia, and depression are not associated with convalescence following infectious mononucleosis.   (2:282; 12:557)

56 3. Infectious mononucleosis is often referred to as the kissing disease because it is believed that the disease is spread by direct contact with oral secretions. It also can be spread by sharing a cigarette, sharing food, and by inhaling oral droplets released with speaking and sneezing. The cause of the disease is thought to be a virus. A "bad trip" refers to symptoms occurring as a result of an overdose of certain controlled substances, such as LSD. A "dose" refers to being infected with a sexually transmitted disease, especially gonorrhea.   (3:281)

57 1. Between about 12 and 18 years of age, youngsters work to achieve self-identity and often pose the question, "Who am I?" Many physical and emotional changes normally occur during these years, and teenagers are confronted with the knowledge that they will soon be adults and responsible for their own behavior. Relationships with peers are especially important, most probably because these close relationships serve as mirrors for their own development of self-identity.   (17:78–79)

58 1. One of the most obvious physical effects when marijuana is used is a marked reddening of the eyes. Also noted are a rapid heartbeat and an increased appetite. The person also may demonstrate mood changes, light-headedness, drowsiness, and impaired motor coordination and reflex activity.   (15:94–95)

Caring for a Patient with Angina Pectoris

59 4. The pain associated with angina pectoris is caused by a lack of sufficient blood to heart muscles. The pain is characteristically over the area of the heart and under the sternum. At times, the pain may radiate to the shoulders and arms, especially on the left side, or even to the neck, jaws, and teeth. The pain is usually described as being choking in nature, squeezing, or a burning sensation. Stenosis of the aorta, a sudden rise in blood pressure, and a sudden dilatation of coronary arteries are not related to pain because of angina.   (15:373)

60 3. Attacks of pain due to angina pectoris are most likely to be precipitated by either emotional or physical stress. Losing one's temper is more likely to bring on an attack than, for example, skipping a meal, snoring, or stooping. Anger stimulates the release of adrenalin (epinephrine) which is a vasoconstrictor and further reduces the blood supply in already pathologically narrowed blood vessels. In addition, this release of adrenalin could cause serious effects for the patient with cardiovascular disease. An example of physical stress that often brings on an attack of pain is climbing stairs.   (15:373)

61 3. Cigarette smoking tends to increase the risk of coronary artery diseases. A patient with angina pectoris therefore should be encouraged to stop smoking. Nicotine in tobacco is a vasoconstrictor and decreases the lumen of the coronary arteries to precipitate angina. Nicotine has also led to arrhythmias that can be dangerous. Driving a car, drinking beer, and working night hours are not associated with coronary artery disease. (15:374)

62 4. Pulse pressure is the difference between the systolic and the diastolic blood pressure. The forcefulness and the volume of the pulse felt at an artery in the body is largely determined by the magnitude of the pulse pressure. (9:203; 15:375)

63 2. When applying nitroglycerin in an ointment to the patient's skin, a nurse should be especially careful to avoid getting any of the ointment on her skin. She also can absorb nitroglycerin through her skin and receive medication in her bloodstream in the same manner as the patient does. There are no dangerous fumes that arise from the ointment. The ointment should *not* be massaged into the skin and the area for applying the ointment should be rotated so that the skin in one area does not become irritated. (9:552)

64 2. Typical symptoms of nitroglycerin toxicity include a flushing of the skin, a throbbing headache, dizziness, nausea, and palpitations. Usual procedure is to decrease the amount of ointment applied to the skin until the patient can use an amount that does not cause adverse effects. Fever, a decrease in urine production, and a tingling sensation in the extremities are not associated with nitroglycerin toxicity. (14:102; 15:374)

Caring for a Woman During and After Delivery and Caring for Her Newborn

65 4. A dosage of 200 mg meperidine hydrochloride (Demerol) is unusual. The normal adult dosage is between 50 and 100 mg. The intramuscular route is typical and meperidine hydrochloride is the generic name of Demerol, its trade name. (14:65)

66 2. The staining of amniotic fluid that gives the fluid a yellow green color is a sign of fetal distress and should be reported to the nurse-in-charge promptly. Normally, the amniotic fluid is watery and clear. A yellow green color suggests staining with meconium. A patient has a right to refuse an analgesic if she wishes. Although it is sometimes preferable for a woman in labor to lie on her left side, the patient may lie on her back also, preferably with the head of the bed slightly elevated. An increase in blood pressure from 126/80 to 132/86 mm Hg is not alarming but it should be checked closely and regularly. (2:237; 12:457)

67 1. An enema ordinarily is contraindicated when a multigravida is in active labor and dilated more than 4 cm to 5 cm. There is danger that the infant may be born precipitously, or the remainder of the enema may be expelled while on the delivery table. Obtaining a urine specimen, doing a perineal preparation, and listening for fetal heart tones are not contraindicated for a multigravida whose cervical dilation is as much as 7 cm.   (2:228, 239)

68 1.   A blood pressure that falls after delivery, especially during the first few hours, is a sign of possible hemorrhaging. The nurse-in-charge should be notified. Other signs of hemorrhaging include a rapid pulse, cold, clammy and pale skin, and dyspnea.   (2:322)

69 2.   When lochia is scant shortly after delivery, it is likely that blood is pooling and filling the uterus. Blood in the uterus can prevent it from contracting and may lead to excessive blood loss. Normally, lochia should be moderate soon after delivery.   (2:285)

70 2.   Massaging the legs is contraindicated when helping to prevent thrombophlebitis. If a clot has developed, the massaging may cause it to break away from a vessel wall and circulate in the blood system as an embolus. Measures used to help prevent thrombophlebitis include elevating the legs, moving the legs in bed, using antiembolism stockings, and increasing fluid intake to help make the blood less viscid and less likely to clot.   (12:660)

71 1.   The pulse becomes rapid and thready when a patient bleeds excessively. A sudden increase in the pulse rate is an early sign of hemorrhage.   (2:322; 12:461)

72 4.   Cow's milk has about two-thirds as much carbohydrate as human milk. It has about 2½ times as much protein and about the same amount of fat as human milk. Neither human nor cow's milk contains iron. When formula is prepared from cow's milk, it is diluted with water. Carbohydrate is then added so that the infant will receive nutrients similar in amounts to those found in human milk. Most women use prepared formula when bottle-feeding their infants, such as Enfamil, Similac, and SMA.   (4:209; 16:146, 148)

73 4.   A small amount of bloody discharge from the vagina of a newborn is normal and due to a withdrawal of maternal hormones that are present during gestation. The reaction is believed to occur before the infant is born. The condition is often referred to as pseudomenstruation, or infantile menstruation. The condition requires no treatment.   (2:368)

74 3.   Phototherapy is used most often for infants whose skin is jaundiced. It is not used for thrush, cyanosis, or congenital syphilis. It is not known exactly how phototherapy works. One theory is that the light converts the bilirubin in the skin into a colorless, water-soluble compound that can be excreted readily through the urinary system.   (2:422–423)

75 3.   The eyes are covered while the infant is receiving phototherapy to help prevent injury to the retina from radiation. Phototherapy does not expose the infant to harmful effects on the scalp, cord, or fontanels. For male infants, most agencies cover the scrotum also because of fear of damage to the testes.   (2:422)

Caring for a Patient with Diabetes Mellitus

76 2. Polydypsia (excessive thirst) and polyuria (excessive urine production) are two typical signs of diabetes mellitus and illustrate the body's attempt to rid itself of excess glucose through the urinary system. Even though the person may eat more than he usually does, he does not gain weight in accordance with his food intake because of the changes in metabolism of all nutrients as a result of his having diabetes. (15:529)

77 3. Oral hypoglycemics, one example being tolbutamide (Orinase), function in the body by stimulating the beta cells in the pancreas to increase insulin secretion. These agents are useless unless the body can secrete at least some insulin. As a result, oral hypoglycemics are not used for person with Type I-Insulin-dependent diabetes mellitus (IDDM) because their pancreases are incapable of producing insulin. The oral hypoglycemics are used for selected persons with Type II-Non-insulin-dependent diabetes mellitus (NIDDM). (14:132)

78 4. When glucose testing is done, it is best when the specimen demonstrates the amount of glucose present in the urine at that time. A first voided specimen has accumulated over a period of time in the bladder and is less likely to demonstrate the amount of glucose being spilled into the urine at the moment it is voided. It is generally recommended that the patient save some of the first voided specimen, in case he is unable to produce a second specimen. (15:530)

79 2. A person suffering with hypoglycemia, or hyperinsulinism, requires a quick-acting carbohydrate to overcome the effects of excessive insulin. Examples of common dietary items to meet this need include honey, orange juice, a cola beverage, and a dextrose solution. Candy is also a good item to use when hypoglycemia is present but chocolate candy is not recommended. The fat in chocolate delays absorption of the sugar in the candy into the bloodstream. Milk, an apple, and tomato juice contain complex carbohydrates and enter the bloodstream as glucose too slowly at those times when the body is in desperate need of glucose. Persons using oral hypoglycemics may develop hypoglycemia just as persons who use insulin. (15:535)

80 4. The only food described in this item that can be used as desired is cranberries, because they have very limited amounts of fats, proteins, and carbohydrates. The following foods are also allowed as desired: artificial sweeteners, bouillon, fat-free broth, catsup, mustard, horseradish, meat sauce, coffee, tea, garlic, plain gelatin, herbs and spices, lemon, lime, dill or sour pickles, salt, pepper, and vinegar. (15:531)

81 1. The feet and legs are especially susceptible to problems in the diabetic patient, owing to poor circulation. Therefore, the patient should take especially good care of his feet and legs. They should be kept immaculately clean, shoes should fit properly, nails should be trimmed with extreme caution, and garters and hosiery that constrict circulation should be avoided.   (8:548)

82   1.   A common symptom when there is an inadequate blood supply to the leg muscles is cramping pain. Diabetics almost always are noted to have thickening in the walls of capillaries, arterioles and venules, the condition that brings on cramping pain in the legs, and very occasionally in the arms. Tingling pain is more common when nerve tissue is involved. Psychogenic pain is pain having a mental rather than an organic cause. Phantom-limb pain is common following an amputation when the person feels pain in the amputated limb.   (15:536)

83   4.   Many diabetics who use oral hypoglycemic agents in time tend to develop casual attitudes toward their disease. They often fail to obtain sufficient health supervision, neglect taking their medication as prescribed, erroneously come to think of their illness as being minor in nature, and forget to take care of themselves properly. These observations point up the importance of a nurse's responsibilities to teach when they are caring for patients taking oral hypoglycemic agents. These agents have not demonstrated that patients using them tend to develop severe insulin-dependent diabetes; some *may*, but many patients use them for years. They also do not predispose to chronic hypoglycemia and sensitivities to the agents.   (15:534)

Caring for a Person Who Abuses Alcohol

84   3.   Efforts to convince an alcoholic of the need for health care are nearly useless unless the alcoholic first recognizes himself that he needs help.   (15:92)

85   2.   Alcohol acts in the body by depressing the central nervous system through interference with normal transmission of nerve impulses. It acts to cause a progressive and continuous depression until the alcohol level is reduced in the body as it is excreted. Many people think alcohol is a stimulant because an intoxicated person may act stimulated. This behavior is due to a lessening in the person's normal inhibitions.   (15:90)

86   2.   Alcoholism is often treated as a "family" illness because rarely can an alcoholic continue abuse without help from others, usually family members. These family members tend to make excuses and amends for the ill person and as a result, the entire family tends to become enmeshed in the problem of alcoholism. Therefore, treatment for alcoholism generally includes help for the enablers, or co-dependents, that is, for those persons who make it possible for an alcoholic to be an alcoholic. Two national organizations, Al-Anon and Al-A-Teen, aim to help spouses and children of alcoholics who have been the alcoholic's enablers. When an alcoholic no longer has an enabler, he is forced to look at his own behavior and take responsibility for it rather than blaming others for his alcoholism.   (1:173; 12:852–853)

87   4.   The person who smokes cigarettes and wants to quit has to have a very strong desire to stop smoking. Explanations, scoldings, lectures, and the like, are very unlikely to help. Most communities have resources available to help the person who wishes to quit smoking and caretakers of smokers would be serving their patients best by referring their patients to such facilities.   (15:98)

Caring for a Patient Who has a Fractured Leg

88   1.   The femur is fractured when the bone in the thigh is broken. The tibia and fibula are bones in the lower leg. The humerus is in the upper arm.   (10:81)

89   3.   A safe admonition when giving first aid at the site of an accident if a fracture is believed to be present is to "splint them where they lie." Moving a victim may cause further damage at the site of the fracture unless the area is immobilized. *After* splinting the area, it may be appropriate to elevate the leg, although this is not always done. Removing debris from a wound can wait until a victim has been transported to a place where emergency care is available. Lowering the head if shock is threatening is seldom used; a horizontal position is preferred.   (15:158)

90   1.   It is best first to apply sterile dressings and a pressure bandage over a wound that is bleeding profusely. Only as a last resort should a tourniquet be applied to control bleeding from a wound on an extremity because of complications associated with the removal of tourniquets.   (15:157–158)

91   3.   Waterproof material should not be wrapped around a wet cast because this will delay drying of the cast. The pillows on which the casted leg is placed should have a waterproof covering. If the pillows do not, a piece of plastic can be placed *under* the cast to protect the pillows. Using an electric fan directed onto the cast, but not onto the patient, can be used to help dry a cast. A cradle can be used to keep bed linens off the cast. It is appropriate to elevate a casted extremity as high as possible, either on pillows or in a specially designed sling, to help prevent edema.   (9:593, 595)

92   1.   The primary purpose for compressing nailbeds of a patient whose extremity is casted is to determine whether the cast is too tight. If it is, the normal pinkish color of the nailbeds will not return promptly after compressing the nails, and the toes or fingers will feel cold and appear blue in color. A good way to assess the color, temperature, and size of casted fingers and toes is to compare them with uncasted fingers or toes so that deviations from normal can be determined with more accuracy. If the nurse notes signs that indicate that the cast is too tight, she should notify proper personnel immediately. The cast may need to be opened or removed to prevent damage to tissues under the cast if they are suffering from an insufficient blood supply.   (9:596)

Caring for a Child Who has a Tonsillectomy

93 3. The desired effect of atropine sulfate given preoperatively is to decrease secretions. As a result, dryness of the mouth with thirst is almost always noted after the administration of atropine.   (14:54–57)

94 3. A patient is placed in a semi-prone position after a tonsillectomy, primarily to help promote drainage from the nose and mouth.   (3:205)

95 1. Swallowing frequently and an increasing pulse rate during the postoperative period following a tonsillectomy are signs that excessive bleeding very likely is occurring. It is normal for the patient to complain of severe pain in his throat, to spit out dark blood, and to vomit mucoid material. However, if the vomitus contains bright red blood, the patient should be checked for bleeding.   (3:205)

Caring for a Patient with Metastatic Adenocarcinoma

96 2. All of the disorders described in this item are important to prevent. However, because the patient is paraplegic and is at high risk for developing decubiti, it is particularly important that the nurse caring for him use measures to prevent them. Nursing subscribes to the philosophy that it is important to help a terminally ill patient enjoy the best quality of life possible in remaining time and preventing pressure sores is certainly one way to add to quality of life. Ulceration of the oral mucosa is a likely disorder when a patient receives certain antineoplastic agents but good oral hygiene is important for every patient. Bowel incontinence is to be expected in a patient with paraplegia, although many cord-injured patients benefit from training for bowel control. This type of training is more appropriate for the cord-injured person who is not presumed to be terminally ill.   (15:251)

97 1. Methadone hydrochloride is an effective analgesic. It is addictive, a factor to be considered in its use when long-term, rather than terminal, care is anticipated. Methadone is also used in drug-abuse programs for detoxification and maintenance treatment of persons addicted to certain narcotics.   (14:60)

98 1. The recommended way to clean a glass clinical thermometer when the thermometer is being used by one person at home is to wash the thermometer with cool water and soap or detergent. It should then be rinsed well with water, dried with tissues and stored in a container between uses. It is not considered necessary to use disinfectants to clean a glass thermometer being used at home. A dry cotton ball is ineffective for cleaning a thermometer.   (9:191)

99 2.   The patient described in this item is at great risk for being burned with a hot water bag because he is elderly and because he is without feeling below the waist. Therefore, it is *especially* important that the nurse measure the temperature of the water she uses in a hot water bag and that the temperature is no higher than 110°F (43°C). Many health agencies no longer allow hot water bags because of the many problems with burning patients when the water is too hot.   (9:425–426)

100 3.   The site where heparin is injected into the body should *not* be massaged. Massage is likely to increase bleeding at the injection site. Proper techniques when giving heparin subcutaneously include rotating the injection site, inserting the needle at a 45 to 90 degree angle, and using a pledget moistened with alcohol to cleanse the injection site.   (9:579)

101 4.   The best place to obtain an apical pulse rate is at the apex, or lower tip, of the heart. The bell of the stethoscope should be placed slightly below the level of the left nipple on the chest wall and to the left of the sternum (breastbone). This area is represented in Site D in the sketch in this item.   (9:196, 199)

102 2.   The only appropriate comment/question for the nurse to make when the elderly gentleman described in this item and his friend spend time together alone in his room is a comment that is supportive. The nurse's attitude should indicate that she understands that the emotional needs of people continue until death, regardless of age. Meeting these needs adds to the elderly person's feelings of dignity, self-respect and self-worth. Probing questions or comments that suggest the nurse does not approve of sexual behavior among the elderly are inappropriate.   (12:818, 820; 15:28–29)

103 4.   Urinary retention with overflow is defined as retaining urine in the bladder until it fills to the point that small amounts of urine leak through the urethra. Residual urine is described as urine remaining in the bladder when it does not empty completely with voiding. Frequency is described as voiding small amounts of urine at frequent intervals. Urinary incontinence is described as the constant dribble of urine when the bladder is unable to store urine.   (9:433)

104 3.   The male urethra is longer and more tortuous than the female urethra and therefore, a catheter inserted in the male urethra should be generously lubricated to prevent injury. The male urethra is part of the male reproductive system but this fact in itself does not explain why it is important to lubricate a catheter very well before inserting it into the urethra. The male urethra is no more fragile than the female urethra; both can be injured by disregarding gentleness and care when inserting a catheter.   (9:443)

105 4.   The recommended technique to determine whether an indwelling catheter needs changing is to roll the drainage tubing between one's fingers; sandy particles will be freed if the catheter needs changing. Other techniques described in this item are unrelated to determining whether an indwelling catheter needs changing.   (9:451)

Caring for a Child with Wilms' Tumor

106   2.   Wilms' tumor is a malignant tumor that grows within the renal area. Ordinarily, it does not invade kidney tissue until late in the disease. A Wilms' tumor usually occurs in children under 3 years of age and usually affects only one kidney area. Surgical removal as soon as possible is recommended and postoperative care may include radiation and chemotherapy.   (3:132)

107   2.   Wilms' tumor is detected as a mass in a child's abdomen. Care should be taken not to massage, palpate, or bathe the abdomen because doing so could cause the tumor to spread.   (3:552)

Caring for Patients in an Emergency-Care Unit

108   4.   The neck should be placed in a hyperextended position during cardio-pulmonary resuscitation (CPR) because this positioning helps to keep the airway open. However, the neck should not be hyperextended to the point of occluding the airway.   (15:636)

109   1.   When the victim's chest does not rise and fall with each rescue breath during CPR, it is most likely that the victim's airway is not open. Ventilation cannot be carried out unless the airway is opened.   (9:640)

110   4.   A person giving CPR should have elbows in an extended, not flexed, position when administering cardiac compressions. The rescuer should interlock his fingers, place one hand directly over the other, and bring his shoulders directly over his hands when carrying out cardiac com-pressions.   (9:638)

111   1.   When a small muscle is to be injected, the nurse should bunch the muscle in her hand to be sure that the muscle is entered properly. Pulling the muscle taut, pushing it to one side, or having the patient clench his fist does not help to inject a small muscle.   (9:569–570)

112   4.   When injecting a medication intramuscularly, proper technique in-cludes holding the needle and syringe at a 90 degree angle for the injection.   (9:569–570)

113   2.   The most common finding when a victim suffers a spinal cord injury is that he has no feeling in his legs and cannot move them. Being unable to swallow, being unable to obtain a pulse in the lower extremities, and noting cyanosis in the lower extremities are not signs of spinal cord injury.   (8:267)

114   3.   Vomiting should not be induced when a victim has drunk any petroleum products, such as kerosene or gasoline. There would be danger of aspirating fumes and liquids, which could cause serious pneumonia. Inducing vomiting is frequently used as a first aid measure, for example, when a victim has eaten aspirin or poisonous mushrooms, or has drunk excessive amounts of alcohol.   (15:109)

115   1.   A person who has swallowed a poison that is *not* a strong acid or alkali and is *not* a petroleum product should be induced to vomit because this prevents the remaining poison in the stomach from being absorbed into the body. Giving large quantities of water or making the victim eat burned toast will not work as effectively as vomiting to limit the amount of medication that is absorbed. Artificial ventilation should be used if the victim stops breathing.   (15:109)

116   2.   In an emergency situation, of highest priority is establishing an airway. Hemorrhaging takes second priority. Either condition risks life, whereas treatment of conditions such as a high fever, anuria, and projectile vomiting ordinarily can be delayed until bleeding has been stopped or an airway has been opened.   (15:105)

Individual Items

117   2.   Cyanosis is best checked in a person with dark skin, such as a black person, by examining the oral mucous membranes. In other areas of the body, cyanosis is detectable but often is more difficult to discern in dark-skinned persons.   (15:352)

— **118**   1.   It is best to allow sufficient time so that an elderly person can set his pace. Older persons function best in an unhurried environment.   (9:231)

119   3.   Authorities generally agree that the single most effective way to prevent nosocomial infections, that is, infections acquired in health agencies, is to use proper handwashing procedures. Unfortunately, much carelessness in handwashing continues to occur. It is important to use sterile techniques, isolation techniques, and sterilization procedures properly too but they are not considered to be most responsible for decreasing the incidence of nosocomial infections.   (9:275; 12:235)

— **120**   3.   It has been found in studies conducted in health agencies that the use of a urethral catheter predisposes a patient most often to acquiring a nosocomial infection. There may be instances when a sphygmomanometer, a clinical thermometer, or a stethoscope may spread infection but not as often as a urethral catheter.   (8:444)

References

1   Barry, Patricia D, Morgan, A James. Mental Health and Mental Illness, Ed 3. Philadelphia, JB Lippincott, 1985

2   Bethea, Doris C. Introductory Maternity Nursing, Ed 4. Philadelphia, JB Lippincott, 1984

3   Broadribb, Violet. Introductory Pediatric Nursing, Ed 3. Philadelphia, JB Lippincott, 1983

4   Eschleman, Marian Maltese. Introductory Nutrition and Diet Therapy. Philadelphia, JB Lippincott, 1984

5   Fischbach, Frances Talaska. A Manual of Laboratory Diagnostic Tests, Ed 2. Philadelphia, JB Lippincott, 1984

6   Fowler, Marsha DM, Levine-Ariff, June. Ethics at the Bedside: A Source Book for the Critical Care Nurse. Philadelphia, JB Lippincott, 1987

7   Hamilton, Persis Mary. Basic Pediatric Nursing, Ed 5. St. Louis, CV Mosby, 1987

8   Keane, Claire Brackman. Essentials of Medical–Surgical Nursing. Philadelphia, WB Saunders, 1979

9   Lewis, LuVerne Wolff, Timby, Barbara Kuhn. Fundamental Skills and Concepts in Patient Care, Ed 4. Philadelphia, JB Lippincott, 1988

10 Memmler, Ruth Lundeen, Wood, Dena Lin. The Human Body in Health and Disease, Ed 6. Philadelphia, JB Lippincott, 1987

11 Metheny, Norma Milligan, Snively, WD Jr. Nurses' Handbook of Fluid Balance, Ed 4. Philadelphia, JB Lippincott, 1983

12 Rosdahl, Caroline Bunker. Textbook of Basic Nursing, Ed 4. Philadelphia, JB Lippincott, 1985

13 Ross, Carmen F. Personal and Vocational Relationships in Practical Nursing, Ed 5. Philadelphia, JB Lippincott, 1981

14 Scherer, Jeanne C. Introductory Clinical Pharmacology, Ed 3. Philadelphia, JB Lippincott, 1987

15 Scherer, Jeanne C. Introductory Medical–Surgical Nursing, Ed 4. Philadelphia, JB Lippincott, 1986

16 Williams, Sue Rodwell. Basic Nutrition and Diet Therapy, Ed 8. Philadelphia, JB Lippincott, 1988

17 Wolff, LuVerne, Weitzel, Marlene H., Zornow, Ruth Ann, Zsohar, Helen. Fundamentals of Nursing, Ed 7. Philadelphia, JB Lippincott, 1983

With a pencil, blacken the circle in front of the option you
have chosen for your correct answer.

	1 2 3 4		1 2 3 4		1 2 3 4		1 2 3 4
1	○○○○	16	○○○○	31	○○○○	46	○○○○
2	○○○○	17	○○○○	32	○○○○	47	○○○○
3	○○○○	18	○○○○	33	○○○○	48	○○○○
4	○○○○	19	○○○○	34	○○○○	49	○○○○
5	○○○○	20	○○○○	35	○○○○	50	○○○○
6	○○○○	21	○○○○	36	○○○○	51	○○○○
7	○○○○	22	○○○○	37	○○○○	52	○○○○
8	○○○○	23	○○○○	38	○○○○	53	○○○○
9	○○○○	24	○○○○	39	○○○○	54	○○○○
10	○○○○	25	○○○○	40	○○○○	55	○○○○
11	○○○○	26	○○○○	41	○○○○	56	○○○○
12	○○○○	27	○○○○	42	○○○○	57	○○○○
13	○○○○	28	○○○○	43	○○○○	58	○○○○
14	○○○○	29	○○○○	44	○○○○	59	○○○○
15	○○○○	30	○○○○	45	○○○○	60	○○○○

	1 2 3 4		1 2 3 4		1 2 3 4		1 2 3 4
61	○○○○	76	○○○○	91	○○○○	106	○○○○
62	○○○○	77	○○○○	92	○○○○	107	○○○○
63	○○○○	78	○○○○	93	○○○○	108	○○○○
64	○○○○	79	○○○○	94	○○○○	109	○○○○
65	○○○○	80	○○○○	95	○○○○	110	○○○○
66	○○○○	81	○○○○	96	○○○○	111	○○○○
67	○○○○	82	○○○○	97	○○○○	112	○○○○
68	○○○○	83	○○○○	98	○○○○	113	○○○○
69	○○○○	84	○○○○	99	○○○○	114	○○○○
70	○○○○	85	○○○○	100	○○○○	115	○○○○
71	○○○○	86	○○○○	101	○○○○	116	○○○○
72	○○○○	87	○○○○	102	○○○○	117	○○○○
73	○○○○	88	○○○○	103	○○○○		
74	○○○○	89	○○○○	104	○○○○		
75	○○○○	90	○○○○	105	○○○○		

Answer Sheet

UNIT II
Review Test 2

With a pencil, blacken the circle in front of the option you have chosen for your correct answer.

	1 2 3 4		1 2 3 4		1 2 3 4		1 2 3 4
1	○○○○	16	○○○○	31	○○○○	46	○○○○
2	○○○○	17	○○○○	32	○○○○	47	○○○○
3	○○○○	18	○○○○	33	○○○○	48	○○○○
4	○○○○	19	○○○○	34	○○○○	49	○○○○
5	○○○○	20	○○○○	35	○○○○	50	○○○○
6	○○○○	21	○○○○	36	○○○○	51	○○○○
7	○○○○	22	○○○○	37	○○○○	52	○○○○
8	○○○○	23	○○○○	38	○○○○	53	○○○○
9	○○○○	24	○○○○	39	○○○○	54	○○○○
10	○○○○	25	○○○○	40	○○○○	55	○○○○
11	○○○○	26	○○○○	41	○○○○	56	○○○○
12	○○○○	27	○○○○	42	○○○○	57	○○○○
13	○○○○	28	○○○○	43	○○○○	58	○○○○
14	○○○○	29	○○○○	44	○○○○	59	○○○○
15	○○○○	30	○○○○	45	○○○○	60	○○○○

61	1 2 3 4 ○○○○	76	1 2 3 4 ○○○○	91	1 2 3 4 ○○○○	106	1 2 3 4 ○○○○
62	1 2 3 4 ○○○○	77	1 2 3 4 ○○○○	92	1 2 3 4 ○○○○	107	1 2 3 4 ○○○○
63	1 2 3 4 ○○○○	78	1 2 3 4 ○○○○	93	1 2 3 4 ○○○○	108	1 2 3 4 ○○○○
64	1 2 3 4 ○○○○	79	1 2 3 4 ○○○○	94	1 2 3 4 ○○○○	109	1 2 3 4 ○○○○
65	1 2 3 4 ○○○○	80	1 2 3 4 ○○○○	95	1 2 3 4 ○○○○	110	1 2 3 4 ○○○○
66	1 2 3 4 ○○○○	81	1 2 3 4 ○○○○	96	1 2 3 4 ○○○○	111	1 2 3 4 ○○○○
67	1 2 3 4 ○○○○	82	1 2 3 4 ○○○○	97	1 2 3 4 ○○○○	112	1 2 3 4 ○○○○
68	1 2 3 4 ○○○○	83	1 2 3 4 ○○○○	98	1 2 3 4 ○○○○	113	1 2 3 4 ○○○○
69	1 2 3 4 ○○○○	84	1 2 3 4 ○○○○	99	1 2 3 4 ○○○○		
70	1 2 3 4 ○○○○	85	1 2 3 4 ○○○○	100	1 2 3 4 ○○○○		
71	1 2 3 4 ○○○○	86	1 2 3 4 ○○○○	101	1 2 3 4 ○○○○		
72	1 2 3 4 ○○○○	87	1 2 3 4 ○○○○	102	1 2 3 4 ○○○○		
73	1 2 3 4 ○○○○	88	1 2 3 4 ○○○○	103	1 2 3 4 ○○○○		
74	1 2 3 4 ○○○○	89	1 2 3 4 ○○○○	104	1 2 3 4 ○○○○		
75	1 2 3 4 ○○○○	90	1 2 3 4 ○○○○	105	1 2 3 4 ○○○○		

Answer Sheet

UNIT II
Review Test 3

With a pencil, blacken the circle in front of the option you have chosen for your correct answer.

	1 2 3 4		1 2 3 4		1 2 3 4		1 2 3 4
1	O O O O	16	O O O O	31	O O O O	46	O O O O
2	O O O O	17	O O O O	32	O O O O	47	O O O O
3	O O O O	18	O O O O	33	O O O O	48	O O O O
4	O O O O	19	O O O O	34	O O O O	49	O O O O
5	O O O O	20	O O O O	35	O O O O	50	O O O O
6	O O O O	21	O O O O	36	O O O O	51	O O O O
7	O O O O	22	O O O O	37	O O O O	52	O O O O
8	O O O O	23	O O O O	38	O O O O	53	O O O O
9	O O O O	24	O O O O	39	O O O O	54	O O O O
10	O O O O	25	O O O O	40	O O O O	55	O O O O
11	O O O O	26	O O O O	41	O O O O	56	O O O O
12	O O O O	27	O O O O	42	O O O O	57	O O O O
13	O O O O	28	O O O O	43	O O O O	58	O O O O
14	O O O O	29	O O O O	44	O O O O	59	O O O O
15	O O O O	30	O O O O	45	O O O O	60	O O O O

	1 2 3 4		1 2 3 4		1 2 3 4		1 2 3 4
61	○ ○ ○ ○	76	○ ○ ○ ○	91	○ ○ ○ ○	106	○ ○ ○ ○
62	○ ○ ○ ○	77	○ ○ ○ ○	92	○ ○ ○ ○	107	○ ○ ○ ○
63	○ ○ ○ ○	78	○ ○ ○ ○	93	○ ○ ○ ○	108	○ ○ ○ ○
64	○ ○ ○ ○	79	○ ○ ○ ○	94	○ ○ ○ ○	109	○ ○ ○ ○
65	○ ○ ○ ○	80	○ ○ ○ ○	95	○ ○ ○ ○	110	○ ○ ○ ○
66	○ ○ ○ ○	81	○ ○ ○ ○	96	○ ○ ○ ○	111	○ ○ ○ ○
67	○ ○ ○ ○	82	○ ○ ○ ○	97	○ ○ ○ ○	112	○ ○ ○ ○
68	○ ○ ○ ○	83	○ ○ ○ ○	98	○ ○ ○ ○	113	○ ○ ○ ○
69	○ ○ ○ ○	84	○ ○ ○ ○	99	○ ○ ○ ○	114	○ ○ ○ ○
70	○ ○ ○ ○	85	○ ○ ○ ○	100	○ ○ ○ ○	115	○ ○ ○ ○
71	○ ○ ○ ○	86	○ ○ ○ ○	101	○ ○ ○ ○	116	○ ○ ○ ○
72	○ ○ ○ ○	87	○ ○ ○ ○	102	○ ○ ○ ○	117	○ ○ ○ ○
73	○ ○ ○ ○	88	○ ○ ○ ○	103	○ ○ ○ ○	118	○ ○ ○ ○
74	○ ○ ○ ○	89	○ ○ ○ ○	104	○ ○ ○ ○	119	○ ○ ○ ○
75	○ ○ ○ ○	90	○ ○ ○ ○	105	○ ○ ○ ○	120	○ ○ ○ ○

Answer Sheet

UNIT III
Review Test 4

With a pencil, blacken the circle in front of the option you have chosen for your correct answer.

	1 2 3 4		1 2 3 4		1 2 3 4		1 2 3 4
1	○○○○	16	○○○○	31	○○○○	46	○○○○
2	○○○○	17	○○○○	32	○○○○	47	○○○○
3	○○○○	18	○○○○	33	○○○○	48	○○○○
4	○○○○	19	○○○○	34	○○○○	49	○○○○
5	○○○○	20	○○○○	35	○○○○	50	○○○○
6	○○○○	21	○○○○	36	○○○○	51	○○○○
7	○○○○	22	○○○○	37	○○○○	52	○○○○
8	○○○○	23	○○○○	38	○○○○	53	○○○○
9	○○○○	24	○○○○	39	○○○○	54	○○○○
10	○○○○	25	○○○○	40	○○○○	55	○○○○
11	○○○○	26	○○○○	41	○○○○	56	○○○○
12	○○○○	27	○○○○	42	○○○○	57	○○○○
13	○○○○	28	○○○○	43	○○○○	58	○○○○
14	○○○○	29	○○○○	44	○○○○	59	○○○○
15	○○○○	30	○○○○	45	○○○○	60	○○○○

	1 2 3 4		1 2 3 4		1 2 3 4		1 2 3 4
61	○○○○	76	○○○○	91	○○○○	106	○○○○
62	○○○○	77	○○○○	92	○○○○	107	○○○○
63	○○○○	78	○○○○	93	○○○○	108	○○○○
64	○○○○	79	○○○○	94	○○○○	109	○○○○
65	○○○○	80	○○○○	95	○○○○	110	○○○○
66	○○○○	81	○○○○	96	○○○○	111	○○○○
67	○○○○	82	○○○○	97	○○○○	112	○○○○
68	○○○○	83	○○○○	98	○○○○	113	○○○○
69	○○○○	84	○○○○	99	○○○○	114	○○○○
70	○○○○	85	○○○○	100	○○○○	115	○○○○
71	○○○○	86	○○○○	101	○○○○	116	○○○○
72	○○○○	87	○○○○	102	○○○○		
73	○○○○	88	○○○○	103	○○○○		
74	○○○○	89	○○○○	104	○○○○		
75	○○○○	90	○○○○	105	○○○○		

Answer Sheet

UNIT III
Review Test 5

With a pencil, blacken the circle in front of the option you have chosen for your correct answer.

	1 2 3 4		1 2 3 4		1 2 3 4		1 2 3 4
1	○○○○	16	○○○○	31	○○○○	46	○○○○
2	○○○○	17	○○○○	32	○○○○	47	○○○○
3	○○○○	18	○○○○	33	○○○○	48	○○○○
4	○○○○	19	○○○○	34	○○○○	49	○○○○
5	○○○○	20	○○○○	35	○○○○	50	○○○○
6	○○○○	21	○○○○	36	○○○○	51	○○○○
7	○○○○	22	○○○○	37	○○○○	52	○○○○
8	○○○○	23	○○○○	38	○○○○	53	○○○○
9	○○○○	24	○○○○	39	○○○○	54	○○○○
10	○○○○	25	○○○○	40	○○○○	55	○○○○
11	○○○○	26	○○○○	41	○○○○	56	○○○○
12	○○○○	27	○○○○	42	○○○○	57	○○○○
13	○○○○	28	○○○○	43	○○○○	58	○○○○
14	○○○○	29	○○○○	44	○○○○	59	○○○○
15	○○○○	30	○○○○	45	○○○○	60	○○○○

	1 2 3 4		1 2 3 4		1 2 3 4		1 2 3 4
61	○○○○	76	○○○○	91	○○○○	106	○○○○
62	○○○○	77	○○○○	92	○○○○	107	○○○○
63	○○○○	78	○○○○	93	○○○○	108	○○○○
64	○○○○	79	○○○○	94	○○○○	109	○○○○
65	○○○○	80	○○○○	95	○○○○	110	○○○○
66	○○○○	81	○○○○	96	○○○○	111	○○○○
67	○○○○	82	○○○○	97	○○○○	112	○○○○
68	○○○○	83	○○○○	98	○○○○	113	○○○○
69	○○○○	84	○○○○	99	○○○○	114	○○○○
70	○○○○	85	○○○○	100	○○○○	115	○○○○
71	○○○○	86	○○○○	101	○○○○	116	○○○○
72	○○○○	87	○○○○	102	○○○○	117	○○○○
73	○○○○	88	○○○○	103	○○○○	118	○○○○
74	○○○○	89	○○○○	104	○○○○	119	○○○○
75	○○○○	90	○○○○	105	○○○○	120	○○○○

Answer Sheet

UNIT IV
Review Test 6

With a pencil, blacken the circle in front of the option you have chosen for your correct answer.

	1 2 3 4		1 2 3 4		1 2 3 4		1 2 3 4
1	○○○○	16	○○○○	31	○○○○	46	○○○○
2	○○○○	17	○○○○	32	○○○○	47	○○○○
3	○○○○	18	○○○○	33	○○○○	48	○○○○
4	○○○○	19	○○○○	34	○○○○	49	○○○○
5	○○○○	20	○○○○	35	○○○○	50	○○○○
6	○○○○	21	○○○○	36	○○○○	51	○○○○
7	○○○○	22	○○○○	37	○○○○	52	○○○○
8	○○○○	23	○○○○	38	○○○○	53	○○○○
9	○○○○	24	○○○○	39	○○○○	54	○○○○
10	○○○○	25	○○○○	40	○○○○	55	○○○○
11	○○○○	26	○○○○	41	○○○○	56	○○○○
12	○○○○	27	○○○○	42	○○○○	57	○○○○
13	○○○○	28	○○○○	43	○○○○	58	○○○○
14	○○○○	29	○○○○	44	○○○○	59	○○○○
15	○○○○	30	○○○○	45	○○○○	60	○○○○

	1 2 3 4		1 2 3 4		1 2 3 4		1 2 3 4
61	○○○○	76	○○○○	91	○○○○	106	○○○○
62	○○○○	77	○○○○	92	○○○○	107	○○○○
63	○○○○	78	○○○○	93	○○○○	108	○○○○
64	○○○○	79	○○○○	94	○○○○	109	○○○○
65	○○○○	80	○○○○	95	○○○○	110	○○○○
66	○○○○	81	○○○○	96	○○○○	111	○○○○
67	○○○○	82	○○○○	97	○○○○	112	○○○○
68	○○○○	83	○○○○	98	○○○○	113	○○○○
69	○○○○	84	○○○○	99	○○○○	114	○○○○
70	○○○○	85	○○○○	100	○○○○	115	○○○○
71	○○○○	86	○○○○	101	○○○○		
72	○○○○	87	○○○○	102	○○○○		
73	○○○○	88	○○○○	103	○○○○		
74	○○○○	89	○○○○	104	○○○○		
75	○○○○	90	○○○○	105	○○○○		

Answer Sheet

UNIT IV
Review Test 7

With a pencil, blacken the circle in front of the option you have chosen for your correct answer.

	1 2 3 4		1 2 3 4		1 2 3 4		1 2 3 4
1	○○○○	16	○○○○	31	○○○○	46	○○○○
2	○○○○	17	○○○○	32	○○○○	47	○○○○
3	○○○○	18	○○○○	33	○○○○	48	○○○○
4	○○○○	19	○○○○	34	○○○○	49	○○○○
5	○○○○	20	○○○○	35	○○○○	50	○○○○
6	○○○○	21	○○○○	36	○○○○	51	○○○○
7	○○○○	22	○○○○	37	○○○○	52	○○○○
8	○○○○	23	○○○○	38	○○○○	53	○○○○
9	○○○○	24	○○○○	39	○○○○	54	○○○○
10	○○○○	25	○○○○	40	○○○○	55	○○○○
11	○○○○	26	○○○○	41	○○○○	56	○○○○
12	○○○○	27	○○○○	42	○○○○	57	○○○○
13	○○○○	28	○○○○	43	○○○○	58	○○○○
14	○○○○	29	○○○○	44	○○○○	59	○○○○
15	○○○○	30	○○○○	45	○○○○	60	○○○○

	1 2 3 4		1 2 3 4		1 2 3 4		1 2 3 4
61	○ ○ ○ ○	76	○ ○ ○ ○	91	○ ○ ○ ○	106	○ ○ ○ ○
62	○ ○ ○ ○	77	○ ○ ○ ○	92	○ ○ ○ ○	107	○ ○ ○ ○
63	○ ○ ○ ○	78	○ ○ ○ ○	93	○ ○ ○ ○	108	○ ○ ○ ○
64	○ ○ ○ ○	79	○ ○ ○ ○	94	○ ○ ○ ○	109	○ ○ ○ ○
65	○ ○ ○ ○	80	○ ○ ○ ○	95	○ ○ ○ ○	110	○ ○ ○ ○
66	○ ○ ○ ○	81	○ ○ ○ ○	96	○ ○ ○ ○	111	○ ○ ○ ○
67	○ ○ ○ ○	82	○ ○ ○ ○	97	○ ○ ○ ○	112	○ ○ ○ ○
68	○ ○ ○ ○	83	○ ○ ○ ○	98	○ ○ ○ ○	113	○ ○ ○ ○
69	○ ○ ○ ○	84	○ ○ ○ ○	99	○ ○ ○ ○		
70	○ ○ ○ ○	85	○ ○ ○ ○	100	○ ○ ○ ○		
71	○ ○ ○ ○	86	○ ○ ○ ○	101	○ ○ ○ ○		
72	○ ○ ○ ○	87	○ ○ ○ ○	102	○ ○ ○ ○		
73	○ ○ ○ ○	88	○ ○ ○ ○	103	○ ○ ○ ○		
74	○ ○ ○ ○	89	○ ○ ○ ○	104	○ ○ ○ ○		
75	○ ○ ○ ○	90	○ ○ ○ ○	105	○ ○ ○ ○		

Answer Sheet

UNIT IV
Review Test 8

With a pencil, blacken the circle in front of the option you have chosen for your correct answer.

	1 2 3 4		1 2 3 4		1 2 3 4		1 2 3 4
1	○ ○ ○ ○	16	○ ○ ○ ○	31	○ ○ ○ ○	46	○ ○ ○ ○
2	○ ○ ○ ○	17	○ ○ ○ ○	32	○ ○ ○ ○	47	○ ○ ○ ○
3	○ ○ ○ ○	18	○ ○ ○ ○	33	○ ○ ○ ○	48	○ ○ ○ ○
4	○ ○ ○ ○	19	○ ○ ○ ○	34	○ ○ ○ ○	49	○ ○ ○ ○
5	○ ○ ○ ○	20	○ ○ ○ ○	35	○ ○ ○ ○	50	○ ○ ○ ○
6	○ ○ ○ ○	21	○ ○ ○ ○	36	○ ○ ○ ○	51	○ ○ ○ ○
7	○ ○ ○ ○	22	○ ○ ○ ○	37	○ ○ ○ ○	52	○ ○ ○ ○
8	○ ○ ○ ○	23	○ ○ ○ ○	38	○ ○ ○ ○	53	○ ○ ○ ○
9	○ ○ ○ ○	24	○ ○ ○ ○	39	○ ○ ○ ○	54	○ ○ ○ ○
10	○ ○ ○ ○	25	○ ○ ○ ○	40	○ ○ ○ ○	55	○ ○ ○ ○
11	○ ○ ○ ○	26	○ ○ ○ ○	41	○ ○ ○ ○	56	○ ○ ○ ○
12	○ ○ ○ ○	27	○ ○ ○ ○	42	○ ○ ○ ○	57	○ ○ ○ ○
13	○ ○ ○ ○	28	○ ○ ○ ○	43	○ ○ ○ ○	58	○ ○ ○ ○
14	○ ○ ○ ○	29	○ ○ ○ ○	44	○ ○ ○ ○	59	○ ○ ○ ○
15	○ ○ ○ ○	30	○ ○ ○ ○	45	○ ○ ○ ○	60	○ ○ ○ ○

	1 2 3 4		1 2 3 4		1 2 3 4		1 2 3 4
61	○○○○	76	○○○○	91	○○○○	106	○○○○
62	○○○○	77	○○○○	92	○○○○	107	○○○○
63	○○○○	78	○○○○	93	○○○○	108	○○○○
64	○○○○	79	○○○○	94	○○○○	109	○○○○
65	○○○○	80	○○○○	95	○○○○	110	○○○○
66	○○○○	81	○○○○	96	○○○○	111	○○○○
67	○○○○	82	○○○○	97	○○○○	112	○○○○
68	○○○○	83	○○○○	98	○○○○	113	○○○○
69	○○○○	84	○○○○	99	○○○○	114	○○○○
70	○○○○	85	○○○○	100	○○○○		
71	○○○○	86	○○○○	101	○○○○		
72	○○○○	87	○○○○	102	○○○○		
73	○○○○	88	○○○○	103	○○○○		
74	○○○○	89	○○○○	104	○○○○		
75	○○○○	90	○○○○	105	○○○○		

Answer Sheet

UNIT IV
Review Test 9

With a pencil, blacken the circle in front of the option you have chosen for your correct answer.

	1 2 3 4		1 2 3 4		1 2 3 4		1 2 3 4
1	○○○○	16	○○○○	31	○○○○	46	○○○○
2	○○○○	17	○○○○	32	○○○○	47	○○○○
3	○○○○	18	○○○○	33	○○○○	48	○○○○
4	○○○○	19	○○○○	34	○○○○	49	○○○○
5	○○○○	20	○○○○	35	○○○○	50	○○○○
6	○○○○	21	○○○○	36	○○○○	51	○○○○
7	○○○○	22	○○○○	37	○○○○	52	○○○○
8	○○○○	23	○○○○	38	○○○○	53	○○○○
9	○○○○	24	○○○○	39	○○○○	54	○○○○
10	○○○○	25	○○○○	40	○○○○	55	○○○○
11	○○○○	26	○○○○	41	○○○○	56	○○○○
12	○○○○	27	○○○○	42	○○○○	57	○○○○
13	○○○○	28	○○○○	43	○○○○	58	○○○○
14	○○○○	29	○○○○	44	○○○○	59	○○○○
15	○○○○	30	○○○○	45	○○○○	60	○○○○

	1 2 3 4		1 2 3 4		1 2 3 4		1 2 3 4
61	○ ○ ○ ○	76	○ ○ ○ ○	91	○ ○ ○ ○	106	○ ○ ○ ○
62	○ ○ ○ ○	77	○ ○ ○ ○	92	○ ○ ○ ○	107	○ ○ ○ ○
63	○ ○ ○ ○	78	○ ○ ○ ○	93	○ ○ ○ ○	108	○ ○ ○ ○
64	○ ○ ○ ○	79	○ ○ ○ ○	94	○ ○ ○ ○	109	○ ○ ○ ○
65	○ ○ ○ ○	80	○ ○ ○ ○	95	○ ○ ○ ○	110	○ ○ ○ ○
66	○ ○ ○ ○	81	○ ○ ○ ○	96	○ ○ ○ ○	111	○ ○ ○ ○
67	○ ○ ○ ○	82	○ ○ ○ ○	97	○ ○ ○ ○		
68	○ ○ ○ ○	83	○ ○ ○ ○	98	○ ○ ○ ○		
69	○ ○ ○ ○	84	○ ○ ○ ○	99	○ ○ ○ ○		
70	○ ○ ○ ○	85	○ ○ ○ ○	100	○ ○ ○ ○		
71	○ ○ ○ ○	86	○ ○ ○ ○	101	○ ○ ○ ○		
72	○ ○ ○ ○	87	○ ○ ○ ○	102	○ ○ ○ ○		
73	○ ○ ○ ○	88	○ ○ ○ ○	103	○ ○ ○ ○		
74	○ ○ ○ ○	89	○ ○ ○ ○	104	○ ○ ○ ○		
75	○ ○ ○ ○	90	○ ○ ○ ○	105	○ ○ ○ ○		

Answer Sheet
UNIT IV
Review Test 10

With a pencil, blacken the circle in front of the option you have chosen for your correct answer.

	1 2 3 4		1 2 3 4		1 2 3 4		1 2 3 4
1	○○○○	16	○○○○	31	○○○○	46	○○○○
2	○○○○	17	○○○○	32	○○○○	47	○○○○
3	○○○○	18	○○○○	33	○○○○	48	○○○○
4	○○○○	19	○○○○	34	○○○○	49	○○○○
5	○○○○	20	○○○○	35	○○○○	50	○○○○
6	○○○○	21	○○○○	36	○○○○	51	○○○○
7	○○○○	22	○○○○	37	○○○○	52	○○○○
8	○○○○	23	○○○○	38	○○○○	53	○○○○
9	○○○○	24	○○○○	39	○○○○	54	○○○○
10	○○○○	25	○○○○	40	○○○○	55	○○○○
11	○○○○	26	○○○○	41	○○○○	56	○○○○
12	○○○○	27	○○○○	42	○○○○	57	○○○○
13	○○○○	28	○○○○	43	○○○○	58	○○○○
14	○○○○	29	○○○○	44	○○○○	59	○○○○
15	○○○○	30	○○○○	45	○○○○	60	○○○○

	1 2 3 4		1 2 3 4		1 2 3 4		1 2 3 4
61	○○○○	76	○○○○	91	○○○○	106	○○○○
62	○○○○	77	○○○○	92	○○○○	107	○○○○
63	○○○○	78	○○○○	93	○○○○	108	○○○○
64	○○○○	79	○○○○	94	○○○○	109	○○○○
65	○○○○	80	○○○○	95	○○○○	110	○○○○
66	○○○○	81	○○○○	96	○○○○	111	○○○○
67	○○○○	82	○○○○	97	○○○○	112	○○○○
68	○○○○	83	○○○○	98	○○○○		
69	○○○○	84	○○○○	99	○○○○		
70	○○○○	85	○○○○	100	○○○○		
71	○○○○	86	○○○○	101	○○○○		
72	○○○○	87	○○○○	102	○○○○		
73	○○○○	88	○○○○	103	○○○○		
74	○○○○	89	○○○○	104	○○○○		
75	○○○○	90	○○○○	105	○○○○		

Answer Sheet
UNIT IV
Review Test 11

With a pencil, blacken the circle in front of the option you have chosen for your correct answer.

	1 2 3 4		1 2 3 4		1 2 3 4		1 2 3 4
1	○ ○ ○ ○	16	○ ○ ○ ○	31	○ ○ ○ ○	46	○ ○ ○ ○
2	○ ○ ○ ○	17	○ ○ ○ ○	32	○ ○ ○ ○	47	○ ○ ○ ○
3	○ ○ ○ ○	18	○ ○ ○ ○	33	○ ○ ○ ○	48	○ ○ ○ ○
4	○ ○ ○ ○	19	○ ○ ○ ○	34	○ ○ ○ ○	49	○ ○ ○ ○
5	○ ○ ○ ○	20	○ ○ ○ ○	35	○ ○ ○ ○	50	○ ○ ○ ○
6	○ ○ ○ ○	21	○ ○ ○ ○	36	○ ○ ○ ○	51	○ ○ ○ ○
7	○ ○ ○ ○	22	○ ○ ○ ○	37	○ ○ ○ ○	52	○ ○ ○ ○
8	○ ○ ○ ○	23	○ ○ ○ ○	38	○ ○ ○ ○	53	○ ○ ○ ○
9	○ ○ ○ ○	24	○ ○ ○ ○	39	○ ○ ○ ○	54	○ ○ ○ ○
10	○ ○ ○ ○	25	○ ○ ○ ○	40	○ ○ ○ ○	55	○ ○ ○ ○
11	○ ○ ○ ○	26	○ ○ ○ ○	41	○ ○ ○ ○	56	○ ○ ○ ○
12	○ ○ ○ ○	27	○ ○ ○ ○	42	○ ○ ○ ○	57	○ ○ ○ ○
13	○ ○ ○ ○	28	○ ○ ○ ○	43	○ ○ ○ ○	58	○ ○ ○ ○
14	○ ○ ○ ○	29	○ ○ ○ ○	44	○ ○ ○ ○	59	○ ○ ○ ○
15	○ ○ ○ ○	30	○ ○ ○ ○	45	○ ○ ○ ○	60	○ ○ ○ ○

	1 2 3 4		1 2 3 4		1 2 3 4		1 2 3 4
61	○○○○	76	○○○○	91	○○○○	106	○○○○
62	○○○○	77	○○○○	92	○○○○	107	○○○○
63	○○○○	78	○○○○	93	○○○○	108	○○○○
64	○○○○	79	○○○○	94	○○○○	109	○○○○
65	○○○○	80	○○○○	95	○○○○	110	○○○○
66	○○○○	81	○○○○	96	○○○○	111	○○○○
67	○○○○	82	○○○○	97	○○○○	112	○○○○
68	○○○○	83	○○○○	98	○○○○	113	○○○○
69	○○○○	84	○○○○	99	○○○○		
70	○○○○	85	○○○○	100	○○○○		
71	○○○○	86	○○○○	101	○○○○		
72	○○○○	87	○○○○	102	○○○○		
73	○○○○	88	○○○○	103	○○○○		
74	○○○○	89	○○○○	104	○○○○		
75	○○○○	90	○○○○	105	○○○○		

Answer Sheet

UNIT IV
Review Test 12

With a pencil, blacken the circle in front of the option you have chosen for your correct answer.

	1 2 3 4		1 2 3 4		1 2 3 4		1 2 3 4
1	○○○○	16	○○○○	31	○○○○	46	○○○○
2	○○○○	17	○○○○	32	○○○○	47	○○○○
3	○○○○	18	○○○○	33	○○○○	48	○○○○
4	○○○○	19	○○○○	34	○○○○	49	○○○○
5	○○○○	20	○○○○	35	○○○○	50	○○○○
6	○○○○	21	○○○○	36	○○○○	51	○○○○
7	○○○○	22	○○○○	37	○○○○	52	○○○○
8	○○○○	23	○○○○	38	○○○○	53	○○○○
9	○○○○	24	○○○○	39	○○○○	54	○○○○
10	○○○○	25	○○○○	40	○○○○	55	○○○○
11	○○○○	26	○○○○	41	○○○○	56	○○○○
12	○○○○	27	○○○○	42	○○○○	57	○○○○
13	○○○○	28	○○○○	43	○○○○	58	○○○○
14	○○○○	29	○○○○	44	○○○○	59	○○○○
15	○○○○	30	○○○○	45	○○○○	60	○○○○

	1 2 3 4		1 2 3 4		1 2 3 4		1 2 3 4
61	○○○○	76	○○○○	91	○○○○	106	○○○○
62	○○○○	77	○○○○	92	○○○○	107	○○○○
63	○○○○	78	○○○○	93	○○○○	108	○○○○
64	○○○○	79	○○○○	94	○○○○	109	○○○○
65	○○○○	80	○○○○	95	○○○○	110	○○○○
66	○○○○	81	○○○○	96	○○○○	111	○○○○
67	○○○○	82	○○○○	97	○○○○	112	○○○○
68	○○○○	83	○○○○	98	○○○○	113	○○○○
69	○○○○	84	○○○○	99	○○○○	114	○○○○
70	○○○○	85	○○○○	100	○○○○	115	○○○○
71	○○○○	86	○○○○	101	○○○○	116	○○○○
72	○○○○	87	○○○○	102	○○○○		
73	○○○○	88	○○○○	103	○○○○		
74	○○○○	89	○○○○	104	○○○○		
75	○○○○	90	○○○○	105	○○○○		

Answer Sheet
UNIT IV
Review Test 13

With a pencil, blacken the circle in front of the option you have chosen for your correct answer.

	1 2 3 4		1 2 3 4		1 2 3 4		1 2 3 4
1	○○○○	16	○○○○	31	○○○○	46	○○○○
2	○○○○	17	○○○○	32	○○○○	47	○○○○
3	○○○○	18	○○○○	33	○○○○	48	○○○○
4	○○○○	19	○○○○	34	○○○○	49	○○○○
5	○○○○	20	○○○○	35	○○○○	50	○○○○
6	○○○○	21	○○○○	36	○○○○	51	○○○○
7	○○○○	22	○○○○	37	○○○○	52	○○○○
8	○○○○	23	○○○○	38	○○○○	53	○○○○
9	○○○○	24	○○○○	39	○○○○	54	○○○○
10	○○○○	25	○○○○	40	○○○○	55	○○○○
11	○○○○	26	○○○○	41	○○○○	56	○○○○
12	○○○○	27	○○○○	42	○○○○	57	○○○○
13	○○○○	28	○○○○	43	○○○○	58	○○○○
14	○○○○	29	○○○○	44	○○○○	59	○○○○
15	○○○○	30	○○○○	45	○○○○	60	○○○○

	1 2 3 4		1 2 3 4		1 2 3 4		1 2 3 4
61	○○○○	76	○○○○	91	○○○○	106	○○○○
62	○○○○	77	○○○○	92	○○○○	107	○○○○
63	○○○○	78	○○○○	93	○○○○	108	○○○○
64	○○○○	79	○○○○	94	○○○○	109	○○○○
65	○○○○	80	○○○○	95	○○○○	110	○○○○
66	○○○○	81	○○○○	96	○○○○	111	○○○○
67	○○○○	82	○○○○	97	○○○○	112	○○○○
68	○○○○	83	○○○○	98	○○○○	113	○○○○
69	○○○○	84	○○○○	99	○○○○		
70	○○○○	85	○○○○	100	○○○○		
71	○○○○	86	○○○○	101	○○○○		
72	○○○○	87	○○○○	102	○○○○		
73	○○○○	88	○○○○	103	○○○○		
74	○○○○	89	○○○○	104	○○○○		
75	○○○○	90	○○○○	105	○○○○		

Answer Sheet

UNIT IV
Review Test 14

With a pencil, blacken the circle in front of the option you have chosen for your correct answer.

	1 2 3 4		1 2 3 4		1 2 3 4		1 2 3 4
1	○○○○	16	○○○○	31	○○○○	46	○○○○
2	○○○○	17	○○○○	32	○○○○	47	○○○○
3	○○○○	18	○○○○	33	○○○○	48	○○○○
4	○○○○	19	○○○○	34	○○○○	49	○○○○
5	○○○○	20	○○○○	35	○○○○	50	○○○○
6	○○○○	21	○○○○	36	○○○○	51	○○○○
7	○○○○	22	○○○○	37	○○○○	52	○○○○
8	○○○○	23	○○○○	38	○○○○	53	○○○○
9	○○○○	24	○○○○	39	○○○○	54	○○○○
10	○○○○	25	○○○○	40	○○○○	55	○○○○
11	○○○○	26	○○○○	41	○○○○	56	○○○○
12	○○○○	27	○○○○	42	○○○○	57	○○○○
13	○○○○	28	○○○○	43	○○○○	58	○○○○
14	○○○○	29	○○○○	44	○○○○	59	○○○○
15	○○○○	30	○○○○	45	○○○○	60	○○○○

	1 2 3 4		1 2 3 4		1 2 3 4		1 2 3 4
61	○○○○	76	○○○○	91	○○○○	106	○○○○
62	○○○○	77	○○○○	92	○○○○	107	○○○○
63	○○○○	78	○○○○	93	○○○○	108	○○○○
64	○○○○	79	○○○○	94	○○○○	109	○○○○
65	○○○○	80	○○○○	95	○○○○	110	○○○○
66	○○○○	81	○○○○	96	○○○○		
67	○○○○	82	○○○○	97	○○○○		
68	○○○○	83	○○○○	98	○○○○		
69	○○○○	84	○○○○	99	○○○○		
70	○○○○	85	○○○○	100	○○○○		
71	○○○○	86	○○○○	101	○○○○		
72	○○○○	87	○○○○	102	○○○○		
73	○○○○	88	○○○○	103	○○○○		
74	○○○○	89	○○○○	104	○○○○		
75	○○○○	90	○○○○	105	○○○○		

Comprehensive Examination
Part I

With a pencil, blacken the circle in front of the option you have chosen for your correct answer.

	1 2 3 4		1 2 3 4		1 2 3 4		1 2 3 4
1	○○○○	16	○○○○	31	○○○○	46	○○○○
2	○○○○	17	○○○○	32	○○○○	47	○○○○
3	○○○○	18	○○○○	33	○○○○	48	○○○○
4	○○○○	19	○○○○	34	○○○○	49	○○○○
5	○○○○	20	○○○○	35	○○○○	50	○○○○
6	○○○○	21	○○○○	36	○○○○	51	○○○○
7	○○○○	22	○○○○	37	○○○○	52	○○○○
8	○○○○	23	○○○○	38	○○○○	53	○○○○
9	○○○○	24	○○○○	39	○○○○	54	○○○○
10	○○○○	25	○○○○	40	○○○○	55	○○○○
11	○○○○	26	○○○○	41	○○○○	56	○○○○
12	○○○○	27	○○○○	42	○○○○	57	○○○○
13	○○○○	28	○○○○	43	○○○○	58	○○○○
14	○○○○	29	○○○○	44	○○○○	59	○○○○
15	○○○○	30	○○○○	45	○○○○	60	○○○○

	1 2 3 4		1 2 3 4		1 2 3 4		1 2 3 4
61	○○○○	76	○○○○	91	○○○○	106	○○○○
62	○○○○	77	○○○○	92	○○○○	107	○○○○
63	○○○○	78	○○○○	93	○○○○	108	○○○○
64	○○○○	79	○○○○	94	○○○○	109	○○○○
65	○○○○	80	○○○○	95	○○○○	110	○○○○
66	○○○○	81	○○○○	96	○○○○	111	○○○○
67	○○○○	82	○○○○	97	○○○○	112	○○○○
68	○○○○	83	○○○○	98	○○○○	113	○○○○
69	○○○○	84	○○○○	99	○○○○	114	○○○○
70	○○○○	85	○○○○	100	○○○○	115	○○○○
71	○○○○	86	○○○○	101	○○○○	116	○○○○
72	○○○○	87	○○○○	102	○○○○	117	○○○○
73	○○○○	88	○○○○	103	○○○○	118	○○○○
74	○○○○	89	○○○○	104	○○○○	119	○○○○
75	○○○○	90	○○○○	105	○○○○	120	○○○○

Comprehensive Examination
Part II

With a pencil, blacken the circle in front of the option you have chosen for your correct answer.

	1 2 3 4		1 2 3 4		1 2 3 4		1 2 3 4
1	○○○○	16	○○○○	31	○○○○	46	○○○○
2	○○○○	17	○○○○	32	○○○○	47	○○○○
3	○○○○	18	○○○○	33	○○○○	48	○○○○
4	○○○○	19	○○○○	34	○○○○	49	○○○○
5	○○○○	20	○○○○	35	○○○○	50	○○○○
6	○○○○	21	○○○○	36	○○○○	51	○○○○
7	○○○○	22	○○○○	37	○○○○	52	○○○○
8	○○○○	23	○○○○	38	○○○○	53	○○○○
9	○○○○	24	○○○○	39	○○○○	54	○○○○
10	○○○○	25	○○○○	40	○○○○	55	○○○○
11	○○○○	26	○○○○	41	○○○○	56	○○○○
12	○○○○	27	○○○○	42	○○○○	57	○○○○
13	○○○○	28	○○○○	43	○○○○	58	○○○○
14	○○○○	29	○○○○	44	○○○○	59	○○○○
15	○○○○	30	○○○○	45	○○○○	60	○○○○

	1 2 3 4		1 2 3 4		1 2 3 4		1 2 3 4
61	○○○○	76	○○○○	91	○○○○	106	○○○○
62	○○○○	77	○○○○	92	○○○○	107	○○○○
63	○○○○	78	○○○○	93	○○○○	108	○○○○
64	○○○○	79	○○○○	94	○○○○	109	○○○○
65	○○○○	80	○○○○	95	○○○○	110	○○○○
66	○○○○	81	○○○○	96	○○○○	111	○○○○
67	○○○○	82	○○○○	97	○○○○	112	○○○○
68	○○○○	83	○○○○	98	○○○○	113	○○○○
69	○○○○	84	○○○○	99	○○○○	114	○○○○
70	○○○○	85	○○○○	100	○○○○	115	○○○○
71	○○○○	86	○○○○	101	○○○○		
72	○○○○	87	○○○○	102	○○○○		
73	○○○○	88	○○○○	103	○○○○		
74	○○○○	89	○○○○	104	○○○○		
75	○○○○	90	○○○○	105	○○○○		